BSCS PUBLICATIONS

BSCS VERSIONS

Biological Science: An Ecological Approach
    Rand McNally & Co., Chicago

Biological Science: An Inquiry into Life
    Harcourt, Brace Jovanovich, Inc., New York

Biological Science: Molecules to Man
    Houghton Mifflin Co., Boston

BSCS SECOND COURSE

Biological Science: Interaction of Experiments and Ideas
    Prentice-Hall, Inc., Englewood Cliffs, N.J.

BSCS PATTERNS OF LIFE SERIES (12 titles)

    Educational Programs Improvement Corporation,
    Boulder, Colo.

BSCS SPECIAL MATERIALS

Biological Science: Patterns and Processes
    Holt, Rinehart & Winston, Inc., New York

BSCS SPECIAL EDUCATION PROGRAM

ME NOW–Life Sciences: A Special Education Program
    Hubbard Scientific Company, Northbrook, Ill.

BSCS LABORATORY BLOCK AND TEACHER'S SUPPLEMENTS (12 titles)

    D. C. Heath & Co., Boston

Innovations in Equipment and Techniques for the Biology Teaching Laboratory
    D. C. Heath & Co., Boston

Radiation and Its Use in Biology and Teacher's Supplement (A BSCS Laboratory Block)
    Educational Programs Improvement Corporation,
    Boulder, Colo.

BSCS PAMPHLET SERIES (24 titles)

    Educational Programs Improvement Corporation,
    Boulder, Colo.

BSCS RESEARCH PROBLEMS

Research Problems in Biology: Investigations for Students (in press)
    Educational Programs Improvement Corporation,
    Boulder, Colo.

BSCS BULLETIN SERIES (1, 2, 3)

    Biological Sciences Curriculum Study

The Changing Classroom: The Role of the Biological Sciences Curriculum Study (BSCS Bulletin 4)
    Educational Programs Improvement Corporation,
    Boulder, Colo.

BSCS SPECIAL PUBLICATIONS (4 titles)

    Biological Sciences Curriculum Study

BSCS RESOURCE BOOK FOR TEACHERS

Biology Teachers' Handbook
    John Wiley & Sons, Inc., New York

BSCS SELF-INSTRUCTIONAL PROGRAMS

Population Genetics: A Self-Instructional Program
(other titles in preparation)
    General Learning Corp., Silver Burdett Co. Division,
    Morristown, N.J.

BSCS SINGLE TOPIC INQUIRY FILMS (40 titles)

    Harcourt, Brace Jovanovich, Inc., New York
    Houghton Mifflin Co., Boston
    Rand McNally & Co., Chicago

BSCS SELF-INSTRUCTIONAL GUIDES TO INDEPENDENT INQUIRY
(for each of the 40 Single Topic Inquiry Films)

    Hubbard Scientific Company, Northbrook, Ill.

BSCS INQUIRY SLIDES (20 titles)

    Harcourt, Brace Jovanovich, Inc., New York

BSCS ISSUE-ORIENTED INQUIRY FILMS

The Tragedy of the Commons

An Interview with Garrett Hardin
    King Screen Productions, Seattle, Wash.

BSCS INQUIRY FILM

Elephant Seals
    King Screen Productions, Seattle, Wash.

BSCS INFORMATION FILM

The Story of BSCS
    Biological Sciences Curriculum Study

BSCS NEWSLETTER

    Biological Sciences Curriculum Study

BSCS INTERNATIONAL NEWS NOTES

    Biological Sciences Curriculum Study

BSCS SCIENCE AND SOCIETY SERIES

Birth Control, *by Garrett Hardin*

Human Heredity and Birth Defects, *by E. Peter Volpe*

Man and Birds: Evolution and Behavior, *by Andrew J. Meyerriecks*

Science, the Brain, and Our Future, *by W. R. Klemm*

Sex and the Single Cell, *by Dolores Elaine Keller*

Cancer: The Misguided Cell, *by David M. Prescott*

Use and Misuse of Drugs Subject to Abuse, *by Melvin H. Weinswig*

    Bobbs-Merrill Co., Inc., Indianapolis

BSCS TOPICS IN BIOLOGICAL SCIENCE SERIES

Symbiosis, *by Thomas Cheng*

Hormones: A Delicate Balance, *by Ruthann LeBaron*

Metabolism, *by Ingrith D. Olsen*

    Bobbs-Merrill Co., Inc., Indianapolis

BIOLOGICAL SCIENCES CURRICULUM STUDY • P. O. Box 930
Boulder, Colorado

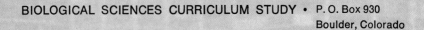

Revision Team:
   HAVEN KOLB, Hereford High School, Parkton, Maryland, *Supervisor*
   ROBERT DeWITT IVEY, Sandia High School, Albuquerque, New Mexico
   EDWARD J. KORMONDY, Evergreen State College, Olympia, Washington
   VICTOR LARSEN, Adelphi University, Garden City, New York
   ELRA M. PALMER, Baltimore City Public Schools, Baltimore, Maryland
   BRUCE WALLACE, Cornell University, Ithaca, New York

Editor: NANCY LEHMANN HAYNES, Rand McNally & Company, Chicago, Illinois

BIOLOGICAL SCIENCE

an ecological approach

 BSCS Green Version   THIRD EDITION

RAND MᶜNALLY & COMPANY   Chicago · London · New York · San Francisco
Printed in the United States of America

Cover photograph by Cindy Rymer from Van Cleve photography

Title page photograph by George Mars Cassidy from Van Cleve photography

Published by Rand McNally & Company

WRITERS

More than one hundred high school and university teachers participated in writing the experimental forms of this book in 1960 and 1961. Their names are listed in the first commercial edition (1963). The writers responsible for the first two commercial editions were:

NORRIS ANDERSON, Burlingame High School, Burlingame, California (1968)
RICHARD G. BEIDLEMAN, Colorado College, Colorado Springs, Colorado (1968)
HAROLD DURST, Southeast High School, Wichita, Kansas (1963)
DONALD S. FARNER, University of Washington, Seattle, Washington (1968)
HAVEN KOLB, Hereford High School, Parkton, Maryland (1963, 1968)
VICTOR LARSEN, Adelphi College, Garden City, New York (1963, 1968)
WILLIAM V. MAYER, Biological Sciences Curriculum Study, Boulder, Colorado (1968)
WILLIAM B. MILLER, Rand McNally & Company, Chicago, Illinois (1963)
ELRA M. PALMER, Baltimore City Public Schools, Baltimore, Maryland (1963, 1968)
PAUL G. PEARSON, Rutgers, The State University, New Brunswick, New Jersey (1968)
ELIZABETH PERROTT, University of Stirling, Stirling, Scotland (1968)
JONATHAN WESTFALL, University of Georgia, Athens, Georgia (1963)

The members of the revision team for the 1973 edition are listed on the title page.

BSCS STAFF

ADDISON E. LEE, Chairman
WILLIAM V. MAYER, Director
MANERT H. KENNEDY, Associate Director
GEORGE M. CLARK, Assistant Director
KEITH L. BUMSTED, Business Manager
JAY E. ANDERSON, Consultant
DOROTHY S. CURTIS, Consultant
JAMES S. ECKENROD, Consultant
ROY O. GROMME, Consultant
FAITH M. HICKMAN, Consultant
JILL R. NAGRODSKY, Consultant
PAUL F. PREUSS, Consultant
FRED A. RASMUSSEN, Consultant
KARIN RHINES, Consultant
JAMES T. ROBINSON, Consultant
NORRIS ROSS, Consultant
HAROLD A. RUPERT, JR., Consultant
JOE M. STEELE, Consultant
RICHARD R. TOLMAN, Consultant

ROBERT F. WILSON, Art Director, BSCS
LAWRENCE A. STRAND, Assistant Art Director
JOHN B. THORNTON, JR., Assistant Art Director
JUDY BUCHER, Artist
CAROLE JENCKS, Artist
GLORIA KROEGER, Artist
ARNE LUDVIGSEN, Artist
ANN MANNERING, Artist
TAY McCLELLAN, Artist
WAYNE E. MEINEKE, Artist
ROY UDO, Artist

RAND McNALLY

WILLIAM B. MILLER, Director of Science
NANCY L. HAYNES, Project Editor
ROBERTA McALLISTER, Copy Editor
GORDON HARTSHORNE, Art Director
MILI THOMPSON, Designer
JULIE LUNDQUIST, Picture Editor

A FOREWORD

Of all the disciplines, science is most relevant to the continuation of life on planet Earth. And of all the sciences, biology is most relevant to our daily lives on this planet because it touches our almost every action. Because of its preoccupation with life, biology examines all aspects of man: his evolutionary history, structure, function, behavior, relationship to the environment, and capacities. And in attempting to understand these aspects, biology must take note of man's social systems as well. Technological solutions for many of the biological problems today are available: Man could, for example, use his knowledge concerning control of the birth rate to prevent overpopulation. But often such solutions are not implemented because of their social implications—be they economic, political, psychological, moral, or ethical. A complete understanding of mankind, therefore, cannot be attained from the study of a single discipline. The study of biology can no longer be restricted to biological knowledge itself. Biology needs to be understood in a social context so that its great potential in benefiting mankind is considered along with its necessary limitations and, therefore, its interdependence with other disciplines.

This edition of the Green Version, *Biological Science: An Ecological Approach,* includes not only biological information but the social context of that information. It addresses itself to the social consequences of our actions in attempting to solve the biological problems we face in living harmoniously on and with the planet Earth.

Since its founding in 1958, the Biological Sciences Curriculum Study has been dedicated to the improvement of biological education. Its initial parent group, the Education Committee of the American Institute of Biological Sciences, had expressed concern over the state of biological education in the United States. With support from the National Science Foundation, it established the Biological Sciences Curriculum Study, composed of distinguished biologists and educators, and with consultative help from a wide variety of disciplines, in an attempt to restructure the discipline in such a way as to prepare students to cope with the biological problems they face by the simple fact of being living organisms. The first "experimental" edition of this course appeared in 1960; both it and the second edition, which appeared the following year, were truly experimental in nature. They were essentially devices to test the effectiveness of a new approach to biological science. In all, over a thousand teachers and 150,000 students in 35 states and the District of Columbia worked with these experimental materials to determine if their emphasis was relevant and if they could be comprehended by the average American 10th-grade student. These studies provided evidence that the materials were readily accepted and comprehended by average students. While the material was geared to provide a background in science for students pursuing other careers, subsequent studies have shown that in May of 1970, 47 percent of the students who took the College Board Achievement Test in Biology had taken a BSCS course, whereas only 22 percent categorically could state they had not been exposed to BSCS materials. So the program, designed primarily to provide biological information to the average citizen, was demonstrated to be an excellent college-preparatory course as well.

After almost four years of experiment, feedback, and rewriting, the first edition of this volume appeared in 1963. This third edition incorporates suggestions from teachers and students alike concerning its content and interpretation of biology. It is to this large number of students and teachers who have used and commented upon past editions that the present edition owes its structure. Their comments— fed back to writing teams of college biologists on the frontiers of research and high school teachers and others on the frontiers of education—produced this synthesis of biological information within a social framework.

Coherence of concepts is achieved by structuring the materials around a series of major themes: science as investigation and inquiry; the history of biological concepts; complementarity of structure and function; diversity of type and unity of pattern; change of organisms through time; genetic continuity; the complementarity of the organism in its environment; regulation and homeostasis; and the biological basis of behavior. This thematic material is illuminated by the use of microorganisms, plants, and animals to emphasize the pervasiveness of the concepts of biology. All levels of biological organization are depicted—from the molecule through cells, tissues, organs, individuals, populations, species, communities, and the world biome. Interweaving these unifying themes with the variety of organisms and the various levels of organization gives biology the structure of a science and enables its concepts to be applied to social problems. Recognition of this pattern by both student and teacher makes possible a variety of areas of emphasis that increase the effectiveness of instruction.

Each BSCS program includes materials selected for their applicability in the latter half of the 20th century and for their ability to illuminate the principles and concepts that underlie biological science. In addition to this volume, the BSCS has produced a wide variety of materials that supplement, complement, and augment the capacity of the teacher and the individual student to vary the educational process. These materials used in concert offer the teacher maximal flexibility in programming and the student optimal use of his talents.

The BSCS actively solicits the opinions of teachers and students who have used its materials; these aid in the realization of our goal to improve biological education at all levels. Such comments may be sent to the Director at the address below.

Addison E. Lee
Chairman of the Steering Committee
Biological Sciences Curriculum Study
The University of Texas at Austin
Austin, Texas 78712

William V. Mayer, Director
Biological Sciences Curriculum Study
Post Office Box 930
Boulder, Colorado 80302

PREFACE FOR STUDENTS

There are two major aims in studying any natural science.

One aim is to become acquainted with scientific facts and with the general ideas that are built upon them. These ideas have greatly changed our views of man's place in nature. They have greatly enlarged human abilities to use the forces and resources of nature. They have made our lives today very different from those of our ancestors.

The second aim in studying a natural science is even more important. It is to understand what science *is*—to feel its spirit, to appreciate its methods, and to recognize its limitations. Upon this understanding depends your ability to participate intelligently in the life of our scientific age.

If most citizens in a democracy think of science as a kind of magic, our scientific civilization will certainly not endure. For science is not magic. Science is a complex process by which we can arrive at reliable knowledge of our surroundings. It is compounded of curiosity, observation, and thought. It has no *necessary* connection with efforts to improve the circumstances of human life, although it brings about such results more frequently than does any other human enterprise. It is a social undertaking, depending upon accurate and free communication. It is a progressive activity, each generation building on the accumulated knowledge of the past.

Science, then, is a human activity, without any element of magic about it. If science is to flourish, every person must understand to some degree its aims, its methods, and its consequences. Thus all of us—not just those of us who are scientists or who wish to become scientists—must understand what science is.

It might be possible, by using textbooks only, to achieve the first aim of science study. But to pursue the second aim—the more important aim—requires experience in scientific work. Such experience cannot be gained by reading; it cannot be gained by listening—even listening to the most accomplished scientists; it can be gained only by doing the kind of things scientists do in their laboratories.

A laboratory, in the broadest sense, is a place where the work of a scientist is carried on. It may be either outdoors or indoors, but it is always a place where scientists are asking questions of nature. No scientist, however, locks himself alone in a laboratory. He needs

libraries, so that he can view his own work in relation to the whole of science; he needs conversation with fellow scientists, so that he can obtain the stimulation of many viewpoints; he needs skill in writing, so that he can report his work for checking and verification. Locked in a laboratory, you might become skilled in handling laboratory apparatus, but you could never gain the experience of science.

The book that lies before you, then, is but a fragment of a biology course. It contains part of what you will need. In addition, you will need materials and equipment. And you will need many kinds of living things. But most important, your biology course requires *you*. Without your eyes, your ears—all of your senses—your hands, your brain, there can be no biology course for you.

Haven Kolb
Supervisor, Green Version

Parkton, Maryland
21120
February 1, 1973

Contents

ABOUT MARGINAL NOTES

Even a well-read person finds the English language—like most other languages—full of surprises. And biology—like all the sciences—has its share of unfamiliar words, meanings, and usages.

The margins of this book contain notes to assist you in reading and understanding the text, and questions to encourage your further inquiry in certain areas. The notes do *not* contain basic information. Use them only as you need them for pronunciations, definitions, derivations, and reference to helpful materials in the text or elsewhere—or when your curiosity is aroused.

A Key to Pronunciation

All pronunciations given in this text are developed from the system used in *The American College Dictionary,* edited by C. L. Barnhart (New York: Random House, Inc., 1961), which follows:

ă act, bat
ā able, cape
â air, dare
ä art, calm

b back, rub
ch chief, beach
d do, bed

ĕ ebb, set
ē equal, bee

f fit, puff
g give, beg
h hit, hear

ĭ if, big
ī ice, bite

j just, edge
k kept, make
l low, all
m my, him
n now, on
ng sing, England

ŏ box, hot
ō over, no
ô order, ball
oi oil, joy
o͝o book, put

o͞o ooze, rule
ou out, loud

p page, stop
r read, cry
s see, miss
sh shoe, push
t ten, bit
th thin, path
th̶ that, other

ŭ up, love
ū use, cute
û urge, burn

v voice, live
w west, away
y yes, young
z zeal, lazy, those
zh vision, measure
ə occurs only in un- accented syllables and indicates the sound of
a *in* alone
e *in* system
i *in* easily
o *in* gallop
u *in* circus

Foreign Sounds

à as in French *ami* [a vowel intermediate in quality between the ă of *cat* and ä of *calm*, but closer to the former]

KH as in German *ach;* Scottish *loch* [a consonant made by bringing the tongue into the position for *k,* as in *key, coo,* while pronouncing a strong *h*]

N [a symbol used to indicate nasalized vowels, as in *bon.* There are four such vowels in French, found in *un bon vin blanc* (oeN bōN văN blăN)]

œ as in French *feu;* German *schön* [a vowel made with the lips rounded in position for ō, as in *over,* while trying to say ā, as in *able*]

Y as in French *tu;* German *über* [a vowel made with the lips rounded in position for o͞o, as in *ooze,* while trying to say ē, as in *easy*]

The symbol ('), as in moth · er (mŭth'ər), is used to mark primary stress; the syllable preceding it is pronounced with greater prominence than the other syllables in the word. The symbol ('), as in grand · moth · er (grănd'mŭth'ər), is used to mark secondary stress; a syllable marked for secondary stress is pronounced with less prominence than the one marked (') but with more prominence than one bearing no stress mark at all.

THE WORLD OF LIFE: THE BIOSPHERE

Dennis Brokaw

THE WORLD OF LIFE: THE BIOSPHERE

How shall we start to study biology—the science of life?

We might begin grandly with the universe, work down to the solar system, to the planet Earth, to a pond somewhere, and then look at the teeming life that finds a home there. We might start by looking into some living thing to find the smallest parts visible under our microscopes, study the ways in which these parts are put together to make up individuals, and then discuss the many kinds of relations among different individuals. Or we might start with chemistry—with electrons, atoms, and molecules—because all living things are composed of atoms, and we find chemical processes wherever we find living things. We might even take a historical approach, searching for clues to the beginning of life and then examining the evidence in the fossil record to trace the development of living things to the present.

There are many ways to start a biology course. Perhaps the best approach is one that will immediately permit us to examine some living things. And each one of us is alive. So let us begin with ourselves and with the familiar living things around us.

The Web of Life

Investigation 1.1

LOOK AT LIFE

INTRODUCTION

To be alive is to face problems of living. Just as do all other living things, we human beings face biological problems. But unlike other living things, we can recognize problems and use our minds to cope with them.

On the following pages are some pictures that present biological problems. Some of the scenes may be familiar to you, some unfamiliar. Some may be scenes you have read about but not seen. Whether familiar or strange, the pictures should help you to begin thinking biologically.

PROCEDURE

Part A. Each of the pictures below has an accompanying set of questions. The questions have no definite answers—no rights or wrongs. You are to think out answers that seem good to you. Write them in your data book. Your teacher will arrange a time for you to present your ideas in a class discussion.

Grant Heilman

Figure 1 • 1

The air of a city.
• Does all this blue haze (smog) come from sources such as that shown at the bottom of the picture? If you do not think so, what other sources can you name?(1)
• In what ways could this air affect the people living in the apartment buildings in the lower left corner?(2)
• Do you think the smog might affect plants? If so, how?(3) • Buildings and cars? If so, how?(4)

3

Figure 1 • 2

A strip mine.
• What advantages and disadvantages does this kind of mining have compared with tunnel mining?(5)
• What do you think will happen to this land after the mining is finished?(6)   • Do you think it is possible to have both a beautiful country and one that has plenty of coal for its industry?(7)

Figure 1 • 3

Dusting a potato field with an insect poison.
• Some poisoned insects may be eaten by other animals, such as birds, which then die. Would this be of any importance to you if you were growing crops?(8)
• Do you think that some insects might benefit us? If so, might they be killed by the crop dusting?(9)
• Some of the poisons used in crop dusting make their way into human foods. Do you think that this is a sufficient reason for asking that such crop dusting be stopped?(10)

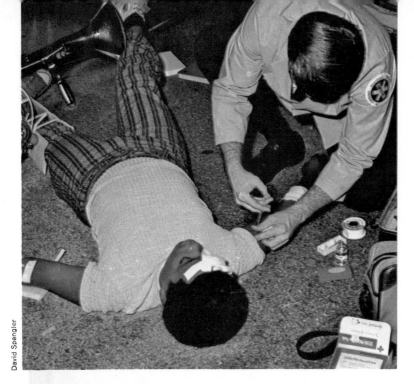

David Spengler

Figure 1 • 4

Morphine, a strong drug, relieves the injured person's pain.
• How does this use of morphine differ from its use by people who have no pain? (11)   • Aspirin also relieves pain. Do you think it too is a drug?(12)   • What do you think might happen to your body if you take any kind of pain reliever for a long time?(13)

Figure 1 • 5

Blood from a slaughter house.
• Where does this waste go? Is this good or bad? Why?(14)   • Cities and towns empty wastes from homes (sewage) into streams and lakes. What effect do you think this has?(15)   • Some wastes from factories, homes, and farms make streams and lakes more productive. What do you think this means?(16)

G. R. Roberts

Figure 1 • 6

This Alaska brown bear has just caught a salmon.
• Because they kill salmon, do you think we should get rid of bears?(17) • If we got rid of all animals that kill things we find useful, would human life be better? Why or why not?(18) • We kill cattle, sheep, and pigs for food. Is this different? If so, how?(19)

Figure 1 • 7

People.
• Do you think that living in these crowded conditions has any effects on the health of these people? If so, what effects?(20) • How much food do you think one person needs to live and do his work?(21) • How much land do you think would be needed to feed these people?(22). • Many of the world's people do not have enough food. How do you think this problem might be solved?(23)

Dan Morrill

Figure 1 • 8

What we leave behind.
• How long do you think we will have enough raw materials to continue to throw away manufactured things? (24) • When there is no longer enough land on which to dump such things, where do you think we might put them?(25)

Black Star

Figure 1 • 9

The surgeon is replacing a defective heart.
• Organ transplants and artificial organs might extend life indefinitely. Do you think this is a good idea? Why or why not?(26) • Do you think experiments should be performed on humans? Why or why not?(27)

Part B. Scenes that arouse biological questions are found not only in pictures. No matter where you may live, you see such scenes every day. Look for some on your way home from school and while you are at home tonight. In your data book record at least 3 of them as follows:

1. Describe the scene in a sentence or two. (For example, "While my dog was sleeping, his legs twitched." Or "My little brother and his sister were playing with dolls. Some other boys teased him.")

2. List biological questions that the scene brings to your mind. (For example, "Is my dog dreaming?" Or "Why is a person's sex associated with doing certain kinds of things?")

DISCUSSION

Part A. After the members of your class have had an opportunity to exchange ideas about the pictures, summarize the discussion by considering the following: • On what questions was there greatest agreement?(28) • On what questions was there least agreement?(29) • What kinds of information would be needed to increase agreement?(30)

Part B. List the scenes reported by students in your class. • Are there any that you do not consider to be biological? If so, why not?(31)

Keeping in mind the available time, the class should select questions that it thinks most interesting. For each such question consider: • Can a satisfactory answer be obtained with the information you already have? If not, what additional information is needed? (32) • Do you think biologists already have the additional information? If not, how might a biologist get such information?(33) • If all the imaginable biological information were obtained, would the question be answered? If not, what else would be needed to answer the question?(34)

A SCIENTIST'S VIEWPOINT

philosopher [fĭ lŏs'ə fər; Greek: *philos*, friend, + *sophia*, wisdom]

organism [ôr'gə nĭz'əm; Greek: *organon*, tool; also, the product made with a tool]

You have been looking at living things. Many people do. An artist might look at living things for their beauty of color and form. An engineer or agriculturist, for ways to manage them. A philosopher, to find a meaning for the universe. You have been looking at living things as a step in your study of biology. A biologist looks at living things (*organisms*) scientifically. What does that mean?

Your present ideas about this question may be clear or hazy, but instead of attempting to define what science is, let us discuss what scientists do. When we say that a scientist *looks* at organisms, we must think of the word broadly—here it can include hearing, smelling, tasting. The whole process of gaining information about our surroundings through the use of our senses is best termed *observation*. In the first investigation you observed organisms, thought about them, and asked questions about them. This is basically what a scientist does.

Which was harder for you, making observations or asking good questions—that is, seeing problems? Probably the latter. Although each of us has curiosity, some persons are able to raise questions faster and in greater number than others. We don't really know why this is so, but, in general, scientists are such questioning persons.

With his curiosity aroused by observing the twitching of a sleeping dog's leg, a scientist might ask, "What makes the dog's leg twitch?" This is a problem for investigation. Usually a scientist then tries to find out what is already known about the problem. He does this principally by library research—by reading. Or it may immediately occur to him, "When the sleeping dog's leg twitches, the dog is dreaming." This may seem to be a statement of fact, but a scientist does not think of it that way. It is a *hypothesis*—a guess stated in such a way that evidence can be gathered either in support of it or against it.

Can you think of other possible explanations?

hypothesis [hī pŏth'ə sĭs]; plural, hypotheses [hī pŏth'ə sēs]

An *experiment* is one way to obtain evidence. On the basis of his hypothesis a scientist makes a prediction and then sets up a situation that tests the prediction. He might say, "*If* I move the twitching leg, *then* the dreaming dog will growl." He tries this out (does the experiment), and each time he does it the dog growls. This supports his hypothesis. Or the dog does not growl. This fails to support his hypothesis. Such observations are called *data.*

experiment [ĭk spĕr'ə mənt; Latin: *ex*, out, + *periri*, to try]

prediction [prĭ dĭk'shən; Latin: *prae*, before, + *dicere*, to say]

data [dāt'ə; Latin: *datum*, thing that is given]; singular, datum

Modern science is usually said to have begun with Galileo, who first realized the importance of *measurement* for a clear understanding of the universe. Measurement results in data expressed with numbers. Only with numbers can exact descriptions and meaningful comparisons be made.

Galileo Galilei [găl'ə lē'ō găl'ə lā'ĭ]: 1564–1642. Italian scientist

Often observations must be made indirectly by means of *instruments.* Some of the instruments used by scientists are quite simple

Photos by Nathan W. Cohen

Figure 1 • 10

Which activities of a scientist are illustrated in these photographs?

complex [Latin: *cum*, with, together, + *plectere*, to twist]

microscope [Greek: *mikros*, small, + *skopein*, to look]

Try to think of some examples.

and have been used for a long time. Others are complex and have been developed only recently. All enable a scientist to extend his senses. A microscope, for example, lets him see things smaller than he can see with his unaided eye. Other instruments make measurements or record observations—data—faster and more accurately than can be done with unaided senses and hands.

All of these activities are in the daily work of a scientist—but they do not add up to science. Observations that other scientists cannot make, experiments that they cannot repeat, have no standing in science. A person may work on a problem in secret, but such work does not contribute to science. Only when observations and experiments are checked—confirmed—by others can an investigator be said to contribute to science. This **verification** can be obtained only when others know about his work. Therefore, a scientist must be able to report accurately what he has done and what he has observed.

confirmed [Latin: *cum*, together, + *firmare*, to make firm]

verification [vĕr′ə fə kā′shən; Latin: *verus*, true, + *facere*, to make]

Observing, experimenting, measuring, reporting—these are some of the activities of a scientist. But you cannot understand a scientist's viewpoint merely by reading about the work of scientists. You can understand only by *doing* the things scientists do.

Investigation 1.2

A BIOLOGICAL EXPERIMENT

BACKGROUND INFORMATION

The yeast that you buy in a store contains living organisms—invisibly small ones, *microorganisms.* As long as they are kept cool and dry, they are not active. But when they are given food, moisture, and warmth, they become active and do many of the things larger organisms do.

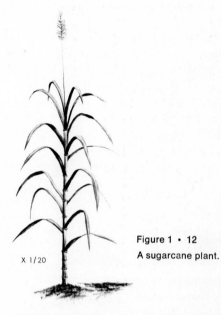

X 1/20

Figure 1 • 12
A sugarcane plant.

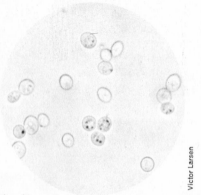

Victor Larsen

Figure 1 • 11
Yeast organisms as seen under a microscope.

Molasses, which you can also buy in a store, is a mixture of substances that are obtained from a kind of giant grass plant, sugarcane. Though the substances are not alive, they were made by living organisms, the cane plants. Therefore, they are called **organic** substances. Organic substances as well as organisms themselves are important to the work of biologists. The organic substances in molasses can be used to feed yeasts.

INTRODUCTION

When we observe the results of feeding molasses to yeasts, we may raise many biological problems. One of these has to do with the relationship between the amount of food provided and the rate of yeast activity. We might hypothesize that the less the amount of food, the less active yeast would be, or, in the form needed for an experiment, *If* we reduce the amount of food given to yeasts, *then* they will be less active.

To test this hypothesis we need to set up a number of yeast **cultures**—groups of yeasts growing under conditions that are known to be favorable for them. The cultures must all be set up in the same way except for one thing— a **variable.** Our hypothesis tells us what the variable must be: We must vary the amount of food.

But how are we to make meaningful observations on yeast activity? We must have some way to measure it. Among the activities that all organisms carry on is the giving off of wastes. In yeasts, one of these wastes is a gas that can easily be collected. By measuring the amounts of gaseous waste, a biologist can determine how rapidly the invisible organisms are carrying on their activities.

MATERIALS AND EQUIPMENT

(for each team)
test tubes, 18 x 150 mm, 5
test-tube rack
glass-marking crayon
graduated cylinder, 50-ml
molasses solution
beaker, 400-ml
container of water
medicine dropper
yeast suspension
test tubes, 10 x 75 mm, 5
aluminum foil, each piece about
    4 x 4 cm, 5
ruler marked in millimeters
graph paper, 1 sheet per student

PROCEDURE

With a glass-marking crayon, number the large test tubes from *1* to *5,* and add your team symbol.

Using a graduated cylinder, measure 15 ml of molasses solution. Pour the solution into Tube 1. Then measure 25 ml of molasses solution and add to it 25 ml of water. Mix the 50 ml of diluted molasses solution thoroughly by holding the palm of your hand over the top of the cylinder and shaking it. Pour 15 ml of this 1st diluted solution into Tube 2. Pour some of the remaining diluted solution into the beaker until 25 ml is left in the graduated cylinder. Add 25 ml of water to the cylinder and mix as before. Pour 15 ml of this 2nd dilution into Tube 3. Again discard some of the remaining solution until 25 ml is left in the graduated cylinder. In the same way as before, make a 3rd dilution for Tube 4 and then a 4th dilution for Tube 5.

Using a medicine dropper, add 10 drops of a yeast suspension to each of the 5 tubes. *Caution:* Be sure to shake the yeast suspension thoroughly before you take out each dropperful. After you have added the yeast suspension, shake each tube, holding your thumb over the mouth of the tube. Into each tube place one of the small tubes *upside down.* Remove bubbles of air from the small tubes by tilting the large tubes (Figure 1 • 13). Cover each tube with a small piece of aluminum foil. Place all the tubes in a warm place, as directed by your teacher.

The next day examine the small tubes for presence of gas. Using a ruler, measure the length of the column of gas in each small tube. In your data book record the amounts, identifying each by the number on the large tube.

STUDYING THE DATA

The molasses solution you used in Tube 1 was made by mixing 25 ml of molasses with

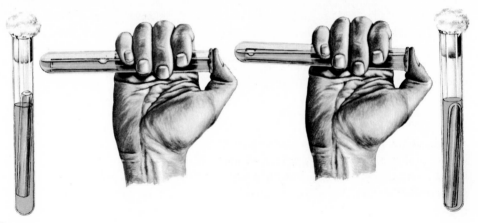

Figure 1 • 13
How to remove bubbles from the small tube.

75 ml of water—that is, it was a 25% solution of molasses. • Recalling the way you made your dilutions, what was the percentage of molasses in each of your tubes?(1) • Why do you think it is important to shake the yeast suspension just before you add some to the tubes?(2)

Millimeters are units of length, but a gas occupies a volume. • Why are millimeters acceptable in this case to measure amounts of gas?(3)

Scientists often put their numerical data into the form of a graph. On a grid, mark off a millimeter scale on the vertical axis and a percentage scale on the horizontal axis. Plot your data on the grid and connect the points. On the chalkboard, gather the data of all the teams in your class. Average all the Tube 1 data, all the Tube 2 data, and so on. Plot these averages on the same grid with your team data, but use a different color of pen or pencil to connect the points.

CONCLUSIONS

Data from an experiment can either (1) support the hypothesis, (2) fail to support the hypothesis, or (3) do neither very clearly. • Which best describes your data from this experiment?(4) • How could you obtain verification for your data?(5)

• If you were reporting this experiment to other scientists, what information would you include?(6)

FOR FURTHER INVESTIGATION

Using this method of measurement, you can investigate the effects of other variables on yeast activity. Suggest such a variable, state a hypothesis, design a procedure for testing it, and carry out the experiment.

INTERRELATIONSHIPS

interrelationships
[ĭn'tər rĭ lā'shən shĭpz'; Latin: inter, among, + relatus, carried back]

In Investigation 1.1 you probably noticed some ways in which different organisms affected each other. In Investigation 1.2 you saw that substances from one organism (sugarcane) affected the activity of another organism (yeast). Now let us look at a further example of *interrelationships*—how organisms affect each other.

We begin with you, a human being, and diagram an interrelationship with another organism:

The arrow indicates that corn is eaten by you—an interrelationship between corn and you. You know, of course, that some other organisms might eat the corn too. And you eat other foods. So we can add to the diagram:

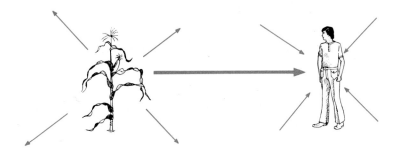

Among the other organisms that eat corn are chickens. And chickens are also eaten by you. We can put these relationships in the diagram:

relationships. The prefix "inter-" is frequently dropped from "interrelationships" when the connections referred to are few.

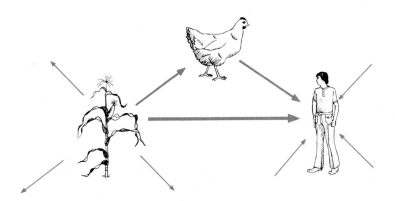

In this case, corn comes to you by way of the chicken.

Pigs eat corn and many humans eat pigs—in the form of pork chops, bacon, and so on:

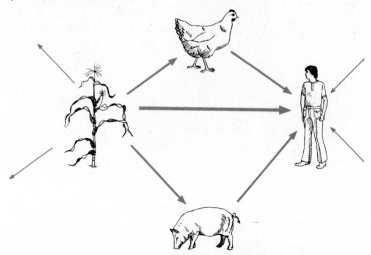

Now we have three pathways from corn to you: one is direct— you eat corn; and two are indirect—you eat either pigs or chickens that ate corn. One more step: weevils (small insects) burrow into corn grains, eating as they go. A chicken may eat both corn grain and weevil:

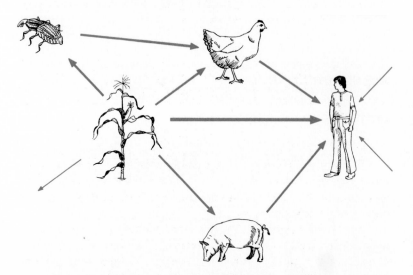

You can easily make more connections: for example, rats eat corn and pigs occasionally eat rats. Continuing in this way, we could construct a large diagram of interrelationships.

Such a diagram has been compared with a spider's web (Figure 1 · 14). Starting at any point on the web, you can follow threads to any other point. Sometimes you can go directly to another point;

Rue from Annan Photo Features

Figure 1 • 14
A spider's web.

sometimes you must turn at the intersections of the threads. Each thread is separate, but, by way of the intersections, each connects with all the other threads.

Because our diagram is based on eating, it can be called a *food web*. And any particular route through the web (for example, corn→ weevil→chicken→you) is called a *food chain*. There are, of course, other kinds of relationships between organisms besides eating and being eaten. Humans do not ordinarily eat rats, but we may kill them for various reasons. In a cornfield weeds may hinder the growth of the corn. Observing all kinds of interrelationships, biologists have come to the conclusion that all organisms affect each other directly or in-directly—that is, there is a web of life.

How would you define the word "weed"?

THE FOUNDATIONS OF LIFE

Where shall we take hold of this web of life? There are two handles: energy and matter.

energy [Greek: *en*, in, + *ergon*, work]

matter [Latin: *materia*, material, stuff]

ENERGY

In every living organism you can observe activity. Most of the time this is easy: look around at your classmates. And as still as you may try to be, you can observe your own breathing. Even a living corn plant is active: it grows.

Activity always requires energy. Whenever anything *happens,* energy is involved. A long time ago scientists developed an important principle called the Conservation of Energy: "Energy can be neither created nor destroyed." Therefore, whenever you see some biological activity, you can ask, "Where does the energy come from?"

Sources of energy. Where does *your* energy come from? No doubt you have heard that it comes from food. You have been urged to eat in order to play or to work—in other words, to be active.

It may require some imagination to look at a potato chip and see energy in it—or even at a hamburger and see in it the winning touch-

But you may have heard that matter can change to energy, and vice versa. Why is this not important here?

down of the big game. But energy is there. Energy is not only present when activity is occurring; it may be present when there is merely the possibility of activity. An automobile runs. There is activity; there is obvious energy. Gasoline sits in a tank; it is not active. But the activity of a running car can come from it. Therefore we can say that gasoline sitting in a tank contains energy, *chemical energy*. Such energy is found in bonds that hold together the atoms within the molecules of a substance. A potato and a hamburger also contain chemical energy in the bonds of their molecules. It is this energy that you and other organisms use in life activities.

Where does the chemical energy in the things you eat come from? Remember: We are operating under the principle that energy cannot be created in living things. So the question "Where from?" is inescapable. By this question we are led from one part of the web to another.

Consider a hamburger. It is made of meat that was once part of a cow. But where does a cow get energy? A cow, too, must take in substances that already contain chemical energy—substances from other organisms. Nothing in its animal body allows for any other form of energy-capture. In this respect animals—humans, cows, lions—are all alike. But a cow differs from a lion in one important way: A cow does not eat another animal; it eats plants—grass or grain, such as corn.

A grass plant does not eat any other organism—nor does a corn plant, a potato plant, or any other green plant. Then where does a green plant's energy come from? It comes from light. Light is a form of energy, and it supplies the energy for most plants. The source of light energy is, of course, the sun.

Capturing light energy. Not all the *radiant energy* that comes from the sun is visible light (Figure 1 · 15). Only the portion that eyes can detect is called visible light. It happens, however, that this is about the same portion of the sun's radiation as green plants capture.

No animal can use light directly for its activities. You may find a sunbath pleasant, but it supplies no energy to your muscular activities. Only green plants and a few other green organisms can change light energy to chemical energy in the process called *photosynthesis*. Such chemical energy can then be used by the plants themselves or by other organisms that eat them.

Later we shall look at some of the details of photosynthesis. Now we only need to point out that this process makes use of two materials: water and carbon dioxide. During photosynthesis these substances are combined to form complex molecules. Captured light energy is changed to chemical energy that holds together the atoms in these molecules. After this, the chemical energy can be shifted around among many kinds of substances. All organisms can accomplish many of these shifts, but only green plants can accomplish the first step—changing light energy to chemical energy.

The emphasis on *green* comes about because photosynthesis requires the presence of a green substance, *chlorophyll*. Not all

"What is the source of the sun's energy?" This is not a biological question, but you may want to turn to other books to investigate it.

radiant [Latin: *radiare*, to send out rays]

visible: what can be seen

photosynthesis [fō′tə sǐn′thə sǐs; Greek: *photos*, light, + *syn*, together, + *thesis*, putting in order, arranging]

chlorophyll [klōr′ə fǐl; Greek: *chloros*, green, + *phyllon*, leaf]

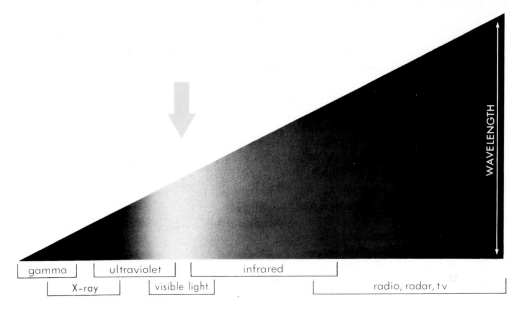

gamma | ultraviolet | infrared
X-ray | visible light | radio, radar, tv

plants contain chlorophyll, so not all plants are capable of photosynthesis. And some living things that you might not think of as plants do contain chlorophyll and can photosynthesize. Furthermore, a very few microorganisms obtain their energy in a way that does not directly involve light energy.

Energy pathways. Photosynthesizing organisms are called *producers* because they produce the energy-containing substances on which all other organisms depend. All non-photosynthesizing organisms are called *consumers.* A grass plant, as it grows, takes light energy and puts it into its own substance as chemical energy. A cow eats the grass; you eat the cow (or part of it). The energy is passed along from a producer to a consumer and then to another consumer.

Consumers that eat producers directly are called *herbivores;* those that feed on herbivores or on each other are called *carnivores.* a cow is a herbivore. You are a carnivore when you eat a hamburger. And a lion, another carnivore, might eat either the cow or you.

Figure 1 • 15
Radiations from the sun form a continuous series, from those of very short wavelengths to those of very long wavelengths. Bands within the series have been given names. The band that organisms can detect with their eyes—visible light—is roughly the band used by producers.

herbivore [hûr′bə vōr′; Latin: *herba,* grass, green crops, + *vorare,* to eat]

carnivore [kär′nə vōr′; Latin: *carnis,* flesh, + *vorare*]

But what are you when you eat corn?

Figure 1 • 16
Lion, giraffe, and acacia tree in East Africa. Describe the feeding relationships among these organisms.

Figure 1 • 17
What kind of consumer is this toadstool?

decompose [dē´kəm pōz´;
Latin: *dis-*, apart; + *compositus*,
put together]

In addition to growing, a producer carries on other activities that require energy. So not all of the energy that a grass plant gets from sunlight goes to a cow—even if the cow were to eat the whole plant, including the roots. Likewise, the cow has activities that use energy—from ambling about the pasture to flicking flies with its tail. In fact, you, as a carnivore, get from the cow only a little of the original light energy.

We have used the term "consumer" as equal to "eater." But many consumers do not "eat" in the sense that you and other familiar animals are said to eat. A toadstool that grows on a dead tree has no mouth; yet it uses the energy stored in the chemicals of the wood. Even though a toadstool does not take in the substance of the wood in the same way that the cow takes in the grass, it is still a consumer. It does not kill the tree (though some of its relatives may have done so); it attacks the wood after the tree has died. Consumers that break down or decompose the substance of already-dead organisms are called **decomposers.**

Figure 1 • 18 shows that energy is constantly being lost from living things. Eventually *all* the energy that is captured by producers

Figure 1 • 18
Every living organism carries on activities that result in the release of energy. Therefore, each following consumer level obtains a smaller percentage of the energy that was trapped by the producer.

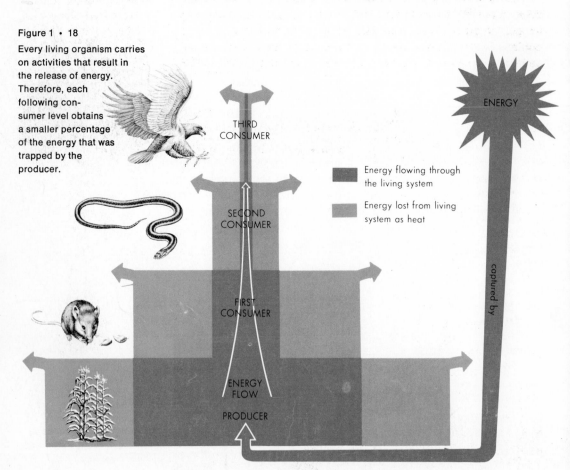

THIRD
CONSUMER

SECOND
CONSUMER

FIRST
CONSUMER

ENERGY
FLOW

PRODUCER

ENERGY

captured by

Energy flowing through
the living system

Energy lost from living
system as heat

is returned to the nonliving world. But it is not returned in the same form (light) in which it entered (with very unimportant exceptions, such as the light from fireflies). Instead, most of it is returned in the form of heat. Since heat cannot be used in photosynthesis, it follows that energy is on a one-way street through the web of life.

MATTER

Directly or indirectly, organisms get their energy from the sun. But they get their *matter* from Earth. You probably already know something about matter—chemical elements and compounds. In your classroom there may be a chart of the elements arranged in a manner found useful by chemists. For a long time scientists have searched in living things for some special elements that would be clearly different from those in nonliving things. They have never found any. Now biologists are convinced that all the elements in living things are also found in the nonliving world. The differences between living and nonliving things must be not in their elements but in the ways the elements are combined and react with each other.

Of the approximately 100 elements, only about 30 are used by living things as materials for building their substance. And in living things, the proportions of the elements are different from their proportions in the nonliving world. In other words, organisms use only certain elements from the nonliving world, and not the most abundant ones, either.

Figure 1 • 19

Some of the elements that occur in living organisms (mostly as compounds). Compare the percentages in man with the percentages in corn. Then compare both of these with the percentages in Earth's crust.

ELEMENT	SYMBOL	APPROXIMATE % (BY WEIGHT) OF A MAN	APPROXIMATE % (BY WEIGHT) OF A CORN PLANT	APPROXIMATE % (BY WEIGHT) OF EARTH'S CRUST
Oxygen	O	65.	75.	49.
Carbon	C	18.	13.	0.09
Hydrogen	H	10.	10.	0.88
Nitrogen	N	3.3	0.45	0.03
Calcium	Ca	1.5	0.07	3.4
Phosphorus	P	1.0	0.06	0.12
Potassium	K	0.35	0.28	2.4
Sulfur	S	0.25	0.05	0.05
Sodium	Na	0.24	trace	2.6
Chlorine	Cl	0.19	0.04	0.19
Magnesium	Mg	0.05	0.06	1.9
Iron	Fe	0.005	0.03	4.7
Manganese	Mn	0.0003	0.01	0.08
Silicon	Si	trace	0.36	25.

Energy has to be continuously supplied from outside of Earth, and it flows on a one-way street through the living world. In contrast, all of the matter in living things is Earth matter; the supply is limited to the quantity of matter present in Earth. Therefore, it must be used

circulate [sûr'kyə lāt'; Latin: *circulus*, circle]

cycle [sī'kəl; Greek: *kyklos*, circle]

reservoir [rĕz'ər vôr'; Latin: *re-*, back, + *servare*, to save]: a place where something is saved

over and over again. The elements that occur in living things circulate; that is, they move from nonliving things into living things, back to nonliving, again into living, and so on, over and over. Such a circulation is known as a *cycle.* How a cycle operates can best be understood by looking at some examples.

The carbon cycle. Like the rim of a wheel, a cycle has no beginning or end. It is, however, convenient to start a description of the carbon cycle with the carbon dioxide (CO_2) that is in the air or dissolved in water (Figure 1 • 20). In the process of photosynthesis, producers build carbon dioxide and water into the organic compounds that make up their bodies. These carbon-bearing organic compounds are passed in the eating process from producers to consumers. Whenever any organism removes energy from organic compounds, carbon dioxide is released either into air or into water, depending upon where the organism lives.

When an organism dies, its body is a reservoir of energy-bearing organic compounds. The dead body decays—decomposers remove the energy from the dead substances for use in their own life activities and in the process release the carbon in the form of carbon dioxide.

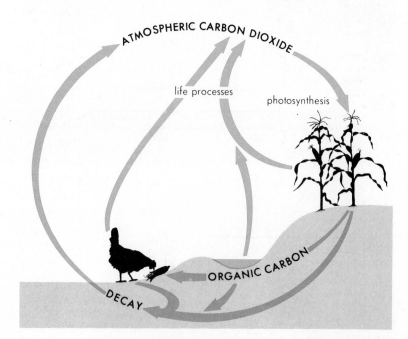

Figure 1 • 20
The carbon cycle. Use the text to explain the diagram. Where is man in this cycle?

Sometimes decay is extremely slow. Over millions of years large masses of carbon compounds have accumulated in the earth. These are found as peat, coal, and petroleum or in the form of rocks made from the shells of organisms such as clams and oysters. In these forms carbon may lie buried in the earth for ages. However, the main pathway in the carbon cycle is from Earth's atmosphere and waters into living things and then back again.

The water cycle. Life—at least as we know it on Earth—cannot exist without water (H_2O). Water leaves the atmosphere mostly as rain or snow. It may fall directly into the oceans, or it may fall onto the land, where it begins a downhill journey through streams, lakes, underground channels, and rivers, eventually reaching the ocean. In all these cases, some of it may go back into the atmosphere by evaporating. Thus there is a cycle of water movement, from the atmosphere to the lands and seas and then back to the atmosphere.

atmosphere [ăt'məs fîr'; Greek: *atmos*, vapor, + *sphaira*, sphere]

evaporating [ĭ văp'ə rāt'ĭng; Latin: *e*, from, + *vapor*]

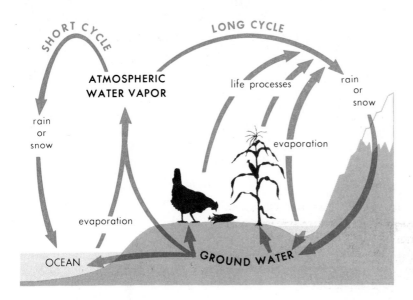

SHORT CYCLE

LONG CYCLE

ATMOSPHERIC WATER VAPOR

life processes

rain or snow

rain or snow

evaporation

evaporation

OCEAN

GROUND WATER

Figure 1 • 21

The water cycle. How would the absence of living things affect this cycle?

Land organisms may take in water at various points in this cycle. Land animals get most of their water by drinking, and land plants, by absorbing it from the soil. In all organisms—both those that live on land and those that live in water—some water becomes chemically combined with other substances, reappearing only when these substances are decomposed. Furthermore, most of the chemical activities of organisms, such as photosynthesis, require the presence of some water. Thus, water is involved in both the structure and the activities of living things.

Here is one of the few times we can use the word "all" in a general biological statement.

On land, organisms lose water directly to the atmosphere. In plants this loss is largely from the leaves; in animals, through breathing or evaporation from the skin. Land animals also lose water when they pass off waste. Eventually all water taken in by organisms returns to the nonliving world.

The calcium cycle. The cycles of oxygen, carbon, hydrogen, and nitrogen (see page 225) involve transfer of matter through the atmosphere. Other elements pass from organism to organism through water, soil, or rock. They all follow pathways similar to the pathway of calcium, which we will use as an example.

Calcium compounds are rather abundant in the rocks of Earth

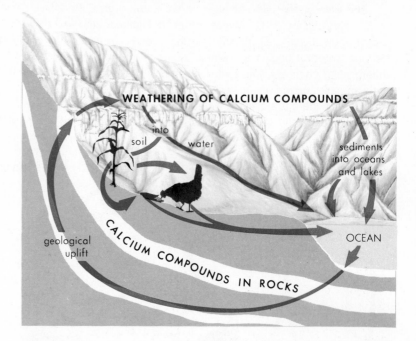

WEATHERING OF CALCIUM COMPOUNDS

into
soil   water

sediments
into oceans
and lakes

OCEAN

geological
uplift

CALCIUM COMPOUNDS IN ROCKS

Figure 1 • 22

The calcium cycle. Which other elements in living things follow similar cycles?

soluble [sŏl′yə bəl; Latin: *solvere*, to loosen]: ability to dissolve

(Figure 1 • 19). Several of these compounds are somewhat soluble, so they are also found in water. Organisms usually pick up dissolved calcium compounds with water they take in.

Land plants obtain calcium compounds from the soil. The calcium in the plants may be passed to a herbivore and then to a carnivore. At any stage the calcium may be returned to the soil or water by decomposers.

accumulate [ə kū′myə lāt′; Latin: *ad*, to, + *cumulare*, to heap]

Why do you think these are called *biogeochemical* cycles?

Many kinds of organisms use calcium compounds in building shells, such as those of clams and oysters, or bones, such as your own. When these organisms die, their shells or bones may accumulate on the bottoms of oceans, lakes, and ponds, eventually becoming rock. Later such rocks may be thrust upward to form hills and mountains. Then the calcium compounds, again dissolved from the rocks in the never-ending water cycle, move in the streams and rivers back toward the ocean.

Investigation 1.3

RELATIONSHIPS BETWEEN A PLANT AND AN ANIMAL

BACKGROUND INFORMATION

An *indicator* is a substance that shows the presence of another substance by changing color. Bromthymol blue is an indicator that becomes green or yellow in the presence of an acid. Carbon dioxide (CO_2) forms an acid when dissolved in water. Therefore, in this investigation, bromthymol blue is used to indicate, indirectly, the presence of CO_2.

MATERIALS AND EQUIPMENT

(for each team)

screw-cap culture tubes,
  20 x 150 mm, 8
glass-marking crayon
test-tube racks, 2
small water snails, 4
elodea, 4 pieces
bromthymol blue solution
container of melted paraffin
pond water, about 150 ml
light source
box, large enough to cover
  4 test tubes

PROCEDURE

Read through the whole procedure. Then try to think up a hypothesis that the procedure seems designed to test.

Prepare 2 sets of 4 culture tubes each and label them *A1, A2, A3, A4* and *B1, B2, B3, B4.*

Pour pond water into each tube until the water surface is approximately 20 mm from the top. Add 3 to 5 drops of bromthymol blue solution to each tube. To Tubes A1 and B1 add nothing more. To Tubes A2 and B2 add a snail; to Tubes A3 and B3 add a leafy stem of elodea; and to Tubes A4 and B4 add both a snail and a leafy stem of elodea (Figure 1 • 23).

Place a cap on each tube and tighten. Dip the capped end of each tube in melted paraffin. Allow the paraffin to cool; test the seal by turning the tubes upside down for about 5 minutes. There should be no leakage. When all tubes are watertight, place one set (A1–A4) in strong artificial light. Place the 2nd set (B1–B4) in a box, where it can be kept in the dark.

After 24 hours observe both sets of tubes. In your data book record changes in the color of the indicator and in the condition of the organisms. Record the letter and number of each tube for which you have an observation.

Then place the *A* series in the dark and the *B* series in the light. After another 24 hours repeat the observations. Switch the *A* series back to light and *B* back to dark. After several days observe the tubes again.

DISCUSSION

• In which tube did organisms die first? (1) Snails and elodea usually live well in an aquarium or a pond. We might, therefore, hypothesize that being cut off from air had something to do with their death. • What substance in air may have been needed?(2) Another possibility is that death may have resulted from the accumulation of a poisonous material in the water. • What does the indicator show?(3) Recall what you have read about photosynthesis and the carbon cycle. • Using this information and your answers to the previous questions, explain your data.(4) • Did the indicator change color in the tubes labeled *A1* and *B1?* If so, how might you explain this (keeping in mind the source of the water)?(5) • In the design of this experiment what would you call Tubes A1 and B1?(6) • What results might you expect if all tubes were kept in total darkness?(7)

CONCLUSION

• Do the data support your hypothesis? Explain.(8) • If not, try to devise a hypothesis that is consistent with (agrees with) all your observations.(9)

Figure 1 • 23

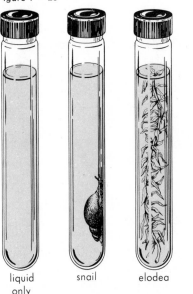

liquid   snail   elodea   snail
only   and
                                    elodea

FOOD

For knowledge to be verifiable, scientists need to be as exact as possible in communicating with each other. One result of this need has been the coining of new words to fit discoveries. Technical terms such as "photosynthesis" tend to make scientific reading difficult for the learner. Even greater difficulty comes from the use of a familiar word in a particular scientific sense. Such a word is *food.* There are many definitions of this word in the dictionary. But in this course, we shall always use it to mean a substance containing energy that organisms can use.

Food is what producers—photosynthetic organisms—produce. In producing it, they use the energy of sunlight. But they cannot produce food without matter; they must have raw materials. Such raw

Do the "plant foods" that you can buy to help lawn grasses and house plants grow fit this definition? Explain.

PRODUCERS   FIRST CONSUMERS   SECOND CONSUMERS   THIRD CONSUMERS

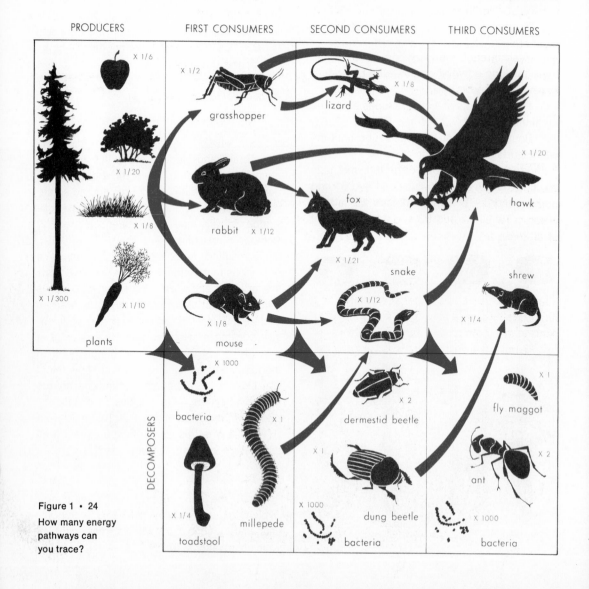

Figure 1 · 24
How many energy pathways can you trace?

materials, containing no usable energy, are *inorganic* substances. Water and calcium compounds are examples. For a consumer, food is not only the direct source of all energy; it is also the source of most of the matter needed to build up the consumer's body, though a few inorganic substances are needed, too.

Compare "inorganic" with "organism" (page 8) and "organic" (page 20).

Food, then, is involved in both the flow of energy and the flow of matter through the living world. And that is why we discussed a simple food web early in this chapter. Figure 1 • 24 shows a somewhat more complex food web. In this web not every kind of producer is eaten in the same quantity by every herbivore. Mice eat more of the fruits and seeds than other herbivores do; grasshoppers, more of the juicy leaves; and rabbits, more of the coarser stems of weedy and small woody plants. Any one herbivore prefers certain plants to others, but each may shift from one plant to another at different times. Similarly, there is considerable variation in the kinds of food eaten by carnivores. They tend to choose the kinds of food that are most easily captured, most preferred as to taste, and the best size for efficient eating. Notice that some carnivores are eaten by other carnivores, so there are three consumer steps in this food web—and sometimes there may be more. Notice, also, that decomposers are involved in all parts of the food web.

efficient: done with the least waste

How many consumer steps can you find in the last diagram on page 14?

A WORLD OF LIVING THINGS

We have emphasized eating and being eaten. But we have already noted (page 15 and Investigation 1.3) that there are other ways in which organisms may affect each other. How can we make sense out of all these interrelationships in the web of life?

BALANCE OF INTERRELATIONSHIPS

In a spider's web each strand pulls on other strands, but the other strands also pull back. There is a balance of pulls that keeps the web firmly stretched. In the web of life also, each organism seems to be in some kind of balance with other organisms. Let's consider an example.

Rabbits eat green plants, and many other organisms eat rabbits.

Figure 1 • 25

Why does a rabbit need to hide?

At first sight this seems rather hard on the rabbits. But rabbits breed fast. Start with a pair of rabbits, and presently a place may be overrun with them. If the rabbits multiplied without check, they would soon become numerous enough to eat all the plants—and then they would die of starvation. But foxes and other rabbit-eaters keep rabbits in check. This is one kind of balance among living things.

Balance? As you look about you, you can see that the living world is constantly changing. You see changes with the seasons: in most parts of the country, there are lots of houseflies in summer and none in winter. You see changes over the years: houseflies may be much more numerous in one summer than in another. And you know that changes have occurred over still longer periods of time: the dinosaurs and flying reptiles of the dim past have given way to the mammals and birds of the present. How, then, can we talk about balance?

dinosaurs [dī′nə sôrz′; Greek: *deino-*, terrible, + *sauros*, lizard]

Figure 1 • 26
What kind of evidence was used to construct this diagram of an ancient food web?

PRODUCERS	FIRST CONSUMERS	SECOND CONSUMERS	THIRD CONSUMERS

brontosaur

allosaur

X 1/800

X 1/500

frog

X 1/200

stegosaur

X 1/8

plants

X 1

stone fly

X 1/24

archaeopteryx

X 1/80

ornitholestid

DECOMPOSERS

If you look at one of your fellow students, he or she seems "balanced"; that is, muscles, brain, digestion, and breathing all work together smoothly. Yet there are changes during the day—with work, rest, eating, and sleeping. Consider breathing. While sitting in the classroom, you are probably breathing 14 to 17 times per minute. When you are working out in the gym, your breathing rate increases; when you are sleeping, it decreases. There are many changes in a person over long periods of time: from birth through childhood and adolescence to maturity, old age, and death. A healthy individual is in balance—but with time the balance changes.

In a similar way the whole living world tends toward balance at any given time. Yet it is subject to many changes, both short-term and long-term. Viewed in one way, the different parts fit together beautifully; viewed in another way, they are continually changing their relationships to each other. Like the balance of a seesaw, balance among living things is of a teetering kind. Scientists call this active and dynamic seesawing that allows for many kinds of adjustment to changing conditions a *steady state.*

THE BIOSPHERE

The webs of steady-state interrelationships we have been discussing can be extended in all directions. In studying these webs, biologists eventually came to the conclusion that *all* organisms are part of one worldwide web and all the organisms in the web are tied to the matter and energy of the nonliving world. We can think of this *biosphere* as a rather thin layer on the surface of Earth consisting of all living things and the air, soil, water, and other matter that surround them.

At any one time and place, we can observe directly only a small piece of the biosphere web. A great deal of research may be required to show very indirect relationships. But in using the term "biosphere," we express the idea that there are such relationships throughout the world, whether they are known at present or not. Such an idea, generalizing a great deal of observation, is called a *concept.* A concept is one of several kinds of ideas—a hypothesis is another kind—from which any body of scientific knowledge is built up.

MAN IN THE BIOSPHERE

Being a living thing, you yourself are a part of the biosphere. In a special sense, you have various kinds of relationships with your parents, your friends, and other human beings. But according to the biosphere concept, you also have relationships with all other organisms. The relationship between a corn plant and you is very direct: it is the producer-consumer relationship. The relationship between you and a smut (an organism that damages corn plants) is less direct; but clearly, damage to corn plants affects your food supply. Even less direct is your relationship to those weather conditions that favor the growth of smut that damages corn that reduces your food supply!

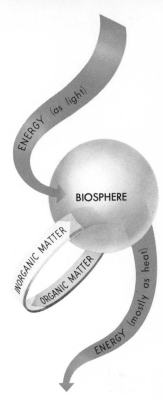

Figure 1 · 27

How does the flow of energy through the biosphere differ from the flow of matter?

biosphere [Greek: *bios*, life, + *sphaira*, sphere]

concept [kŏn′sĕpt; Latin: *cum*, together, + *capere*, to seize]

Department of Plant Pathology, University of Minnesota

Figure 1 • 28
A smut growing on corn.

fossils [Latin: *fossilis*, dug up]:
traces of organisms preserved
in the earth (see pages
310–312)

Man has also used energy
from food that he has not
himself eaten. Can you explain
this?

unique [ū nēk′; Latin: *unus*,
one]: without like or equal

tremendous [trĭ mĕn′dəs;
Latin: *tremere*, to tremble]:
fearfully or surprisingly great

You are a part of a group of organisms—mankind. All existing evidence indicates that mankind has been a thread in the web of life for only a little more than a million years. Yet evidence from fossils indicates that there has been a biosphere for at least three billion years. If the evidence is correct, man is a newcomer to the biosphere.

During most of his time in the biosphere, man apparently affected the web of life very much as any other organism did. But gradually he learned to use sources of energy other than food—first wood, then coal, and, much later, atomic energy. Today he controls enormous amounts of energy with which he changes the surface of Earth. In changing Earth, he affects many sections of the web of life. He has also brought about conditions favorable to increasing his own numbers. Today no other large organism is so numerous or widespread. And his numbers are still increasing.

The unique position of man in the biosphere presents problems that are of tremendous importance to the future of the whole planet Earth. In Investigation 1.1 you had a glimpse of some of these problems. They are problems that face every student who reads this book. They are problems that will not be completely solved tomorrow or next year or perhaps even in your lifetime. But you and all mankind must face them—there is no escape.

Investigation 1.4

STUDYING A PIECE OF THE BIOSPHERE

INTRODUCTION

In Investigation 1.1 you studied small pieces of the biosphere in pictures. In Investigations 1.2 and 1.3 you studied small pieces of the biosphere in your laboratory. Now you should study a piece of the biosphere out of doors. It need not be a very large piece

—just large enough to contain at least several kinds of organisms that show interrelationships with each other.

Different schools have different opportunities for out-of-doors studies. Therefore, procedures will have to be worked out by you, your classmates, and your teacher to fit the piece of biosphere that is most convenient to your school.

MATERIALS AND EQUIPMENT

These will depend upon the kind of place where you make your study and upon the procedures your class chooses.

GENERAL PROCEDURES

A. Selecting a study area. You may not have much choice, but let us examine some alternative possibilities.

A forest is complex and provides opportunities to collect abundant data, but it is most difficult to picture as a whole. A prairie is almost as complex and is somewhat easier to study. Cultivated areas—such as cornfields—and pastures are relatively simple and are easier to study than forests and prairies. Knowledge of them is important because they now make up such a large part of the land area of our country.

Pieces of the biosphere suitable for study can also be found in cities. Many city schools have lawns with planted trees and shrubs. Here the kinds of organisms may be fewer than in the country, but what is lost in complexity is usually gained in the thoroughness you can give your study. If there are no lawns, you can study vacant lots and spaces between buildings. Even cracks in paving, gutters, and the spaces around playground trees often contain a surprising number of organisms.

B. Organizing the work. Having decided on a place to make the study, your class must next decide what kinds of data to collect. (Suggestions are given below, under "Some Specific Procedures.") Then different teams should be assigned to gather the different kinds of data.

Each team must decide what materials and equipment it needs and arrange to obtain them. It may draw up a form on which its data can quickly be placed. And each team should have a leader to see that all parts of the work are completed and that each team member accomplishes some part of the task.

C. Collecting the data. It is easier to handle sheets of paper on a clipboard than to take data books into the field. The sheets can be pasted into data books when you return to the laboratory.

It is not necessary to identify every kind of organism found during your study. No biologist can identify every organism he sees. There are 2 ways to deal with this problem. One is to identify kinds only by general group names—for example, "trees," "spiders," "grass," "beetles," "turtles." These may be sufficient for developing many ideas about interrelationships. Another method is to collect a *specimen*—a sample individual or a characteristic part (a leaf, for example) of an individual. Assign the specimen a letter (A, B, C, etc.) and whenever you need to refer to that kind of organism, refer to its letter. Later you may show your specimen to an expert, or you may be able to look up its name after you have returned to the laboratory.

SOME SPECIFIC PROCEDURES

All of the following procedures can be greatly expanded, depending upon the wishes of your class. In many cases further procedures can be found in E. A. Phillips, *Field Ecology* (a BSCS Laboratory Block), (Boston: D. C. Heath, 1964) and in A. H. Benton and W. E. Werner, *Manual of Field Biology and Ecology,* 5th ed. (Minneapolis: Burgess Publishing Co., 1972).

A. Measuring a study area. In a forest, different organisms should be studied on sample areas of different sizes. These can be set up as in Figure 1 · 29. Square or rectangular study areas are called *quadrats.*

Materials needed by each team:

hammer or mallet
stakes, 8

plastic clothesline, 12 m, marked off
    at 0.5 m intervals
twine, about 60 m
right triangle, 60 x 80 x 100 cm, 2

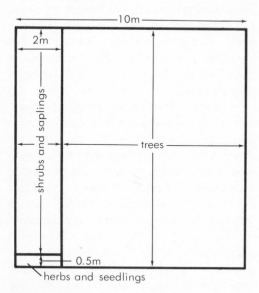

Figure 1 • 29

Plan of quadrats for use in the study of a forested
community.

Drive a stake into the ground. Measure
off 10 m in any direction from it, using the
marked clothesline, and drive another stake at
this point. Stretch twine from the 1st to the 2nd
stake, tying it to each. Place the triangle on the
ground with its right angle at the 2nd stake
and its short leg along the twine. Extend the
line along the long leg of the triangle. At 10 m
from the 2nd stake drive a 3rd stake and connect it with twine to the 2nd. Continue around
the square. Then use the line to mark off the
2 smaller quadrats inside the large one, driving
a stake at each corner and connecting them
with twine. If the forest is thick, the quadrat
may not be precisely square, because tree
trunks and bushes may stand in the way of the
line. Be as accurate as possible.

In unforested areas quadrats need not be
so large—perhaps 2 to 4 m on a side—and
need no internal divisions. In vacant city lots,
cultivated fields, and pastures, it is better to

have smaller teams and more of them, each
working on a quadrat 1 meter square (Figure
1 • 30). If the number of plants is small, the
frame may be replaced by a stiff wire bent into
a circle with a circumference of 345 cm. Laid
on the ground, this circle encloses an area
equal to 1 square meter (1 m²).

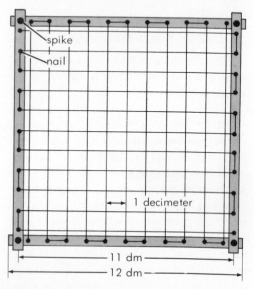

Figure 1 • 30

Frame for a quadrat in a nonforested community.

B. Gathering plant data. In a forest it is convenient to divide plants into three groups:
trees, shrubs, and herbs.

A tree is a tall woody plant with a single
stem (trunk). Trees over 5 cm in diameter
(about 16 cm in circumference) should be
studied in the main quadrat (Figure 1 • 29).
Note trees that form the **canopy** (the forest top,
which receives direct sunlight) separately from
those that do not reach the canopy. Make a
count of the trees, either by kinds or just as
"trees."

A **shrub** is a woody plant that branches
at or near the ground and therefore lacks a
trunk. A **sapling** is a young tree with a trunk
1–5 cm in diameter. Count both shrubs and
saplings in an area smaller than that used for
the trees.

An **herb** is a non-woody plant that dies

back at least to ground level in winter. A tree *seedling* is a very young tree with a stem less than 1 cm in diameter. Count both herbs and seedlings on small quadrats. In each small quadrat estimate the proportion that is covered by moss or other very small plants.

In non-forested places the directions given before can be adapted to the nature of the area. Special problems may arise, however. In a lawn, for example, there is no need to count blades of grass; but a count of the "weeds" might be of some value, especially if comparisons are made between a well-trodden area and a protected one. A frame (Figure 1 • 30) may be useful for this work.

C. Searching. In a forest study this activity should be carried out on the large quadrat after the studies of plants have been completed, preferably on a later day. Students can best work in pairs—one searching, the other recording. Turn over stones, dead logs, and other cover to find animals. These may be found on plants, too. Look in flowers, especially. Make notes of the kinds, numbers, and activities of animals you find. If it is permitted in the area where you are working, you should collect specimens of unknown kinds for identification, but all sheltering stones, logs, etc., should be returned to their original positions.

In non-forested areas searching can be carried on in much the same way.

D. Examining litter and soil. To study small organisms that live close to and in the soil, gather samples of the *litter* (loose organic material on the surface of the soil) and of the upper part of the soil. Each team will need:

plastic bags
rubber bands
glass-marking crayon
wire circle, 78.7 cm in circumference
     (enclosing 0.1 m²)
centimeter ruler
trowel

Before going into the field, label the plastic bags with your team number and date of collection. Use the wire circle to mark out an area. Scrape the loose litter from the inside

of the circle. Place each sample of litter in a separate plastic bag and tightly fasten the mouth of the bag by twisting a rubber band around it several times.

On the ground from which the litter was removed, mark out a square 10 cm on a side. Using a trowel, remove from the square a sample of soil to a depth of 10 cm. Place each sample in a separate plastic bag, and fasten with a rubber band.

At least 2 such pairs of samples (litter and soil) should be taken from different places in the large forest quadrats. On smaller quadrats in other kinds of areas, 1 soil sample per quadrat may be enough. If you are working in cracks in a paved area, there may be no possibility of a measured soil sample.

In the laboratory you will need the following materials and equipment:

ether or chloroform
medicine dropper
white-enameled pan or large sheet of
     white paper
light source
forceps
bottles or jars, with caps
alcohol or formalin, 50 ml per
     bottle
microscope
Berlese apparatus (Figure 1 • 31)
glass-marking crayon

Place a few drops of ether or chloroform in the bags containing the litter. Wait 5 minutes. Then empty the contents into a large, white-enameled pan or onto a table covered with white paper. Shine a strong light on the litter. Pick through the litter carefully with forceps and put all the organisms you find into a small jar of alcohol or formalin.

Loosen each soil sample and, if very dry, moisten—but you do not want mud! Then place the samples in the Berlese apparatus. The heat and light from the bulb cause small organisms to crawl downward and fall into the preservative. Label the vials with your team number and the date of collection. Leave the Berlese funnel in operation about 5 days.

Figure 1 · 31
Berlese funnel.

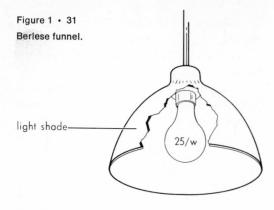

light shade

25/w

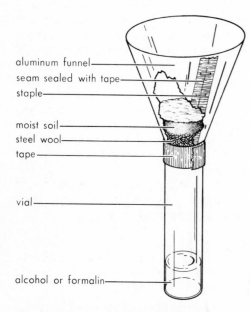

aluminum funnel
seam sealed with tape
staple

moist soil
steel wool
tape

vial

alcohol or formalin

E. Netting insects. In thick forest it is difficult to catch flying insects, but you can beat the shrubs and saplings with a stout net, holding the open end up. In open fields sweep your net through the plants. After beating or sweeping, place the net in a large plastic bag containing several drops of chloroform. Wait a few minutes, then pick out the organisms and place them in jars of alcohol or formalin, labeled with your team number and the date.

F. Studying the larger animals. The searching procedure (page 31) may uncover toads or snakes. To study reptiles, birds, and other large animals, it is usually necessary to cover much larger areas than the ones we have been considering and to observe for longer periods of time. Unless there is some good reason to keep the animals, they should be noted but not collected.

Birds may not be present or active when your class is collecting data. A few students may want to take on the special job of noting birds at different times over a period of several days.

Most wild animals cannot be observed as easily as birds. The most convenient way to begin a study of them is to trap them alive and unharmed. There are several good traps; but unless the area you study is fairly large, it will not be worthwhile to construct them. However, even if trapping is not attempted, do not overlook animal tracks. In cities keep in mind the possible presence of rats, mice, stray dogs, and alley cats. And don't forget to look for signs of man.

STUDYING THE DATA

When the field and laboratory work has been completed, place your team data on stencils from which copies can be made for all members of the class.

When you have all the data from your study area in front of you, consider carefully as many of the following questions as your information allows:

• What producers are in the area? This can be answered by using general terms like "trees," "shrubs," etc., or by naming some of the kinds of organisms that you were able to identify.(1)   • Are producers abundant or rare?(2)   • Do you have any evidence that there are seasonal changes in kinds and numbers of producers?(3)   • If there are different groups of producers, which one of them seems to contribute the most toward producing the food that is present on the area?(4)   • Are there layers of producers? If so, what relationships can you find between producers in different layers?(5)   • Does the area produce all its own food, or is food carried in from beyond its boundaries? What evidence do you have for your answer?(6)

• What consumers are in the community?

This, too, may be answered with such general terms as "insects," "spiders," "birds," etc., or with names of identified kinds.(7) • Which consumers are herbivores and which are carnivores? What evidence supports your answer?(8) • What relations can you find between the numbers of a particular organism and the numbers of another organism that eats it?(9)

• Do you have any evidence that any one kind of organism affects another in ways other than those involving food relationships? If so, what is the evidence and what is the relationship it shows?(10)

An investigation such as you have made should raise more questions than it answers. In studying the data, part of the job is to look for questions that need answering. • List as many questions about the organisms on your area as you can.(11)

GUIDE QUESTIONS

Use the guide questions to check your understanding of what you have studied.

1. What is the basic activity in scientific work? Why is it so important?
2. Describe the essential features of a scientific investigation.
3. Why must scientists be able to report their work accurately?
4. What is the meaning of the term "web of life"?
5. What is the source of energy for the living world?
6. By what process is light transformed to chemical energy?
7. How do consumer organisms differ from producer organisms?
8. Why are decomposers described as special kinds of consumers?
9. Why is there less energy at the top of an energy pyramid than at the bottom?
10. What is the source of the substances that make up the body of any organism?
11. How is the flow of matter through the living world basically different from the flow of energy?
12. What is the atmospheric source of the carbon in the substance of organisms?
13. How is water involved in both the structure and the activities of organisms?
14. How do calcium and most similar chemical elements enter the world of living things?
15. In the biological sense what is a food?
16. What does the biologist mean when he speaks of the biosphere?
17. How does a concept differ from a hypothesis?
18. Why can we think of mankind as having a special kind of place in the biosphere?

PROBLEMS

The following problems require thinking or research. Some involve applications of your understanding of the text and the laboratory. Others require further study.

1. Biology is the study of life. But what is life? You may have noticed that this question has not been discussed. That is left up to you. How do *you* define life?
2. How can the energy obtained from coal and oil be related to the activities of producer organisms? How are decomposers involved in the formation of coal and oil?
3. What might happen to the steady state of a pond if one of the kinds of organisms suddenly increased greatly in number? Is it likely that the increase would be permanent? Is your discussion affected by the kind of organism involved? For example: First suppose it is a producer; then suppose it is a consumer.
4. If all life on Earth ceased, what changes in the cycles of substances might you reasonably expect?
5. In making a journey into outer space, man must take along a part of the biosphere. Try to design an efficient "package" of the biosphere for such a journey.
6. Using the approach of a scientist, can you think of any way to prove that something (for example, an appearance of ghosts) can

not happen?

7. Collect magazine and newspaper articles that throw light upon the human biolog-

ical problems pictured in Investigation 1.1. Explain how each of the articles applies and to which problems it is most applicable.

SUGGESTED READINGS

KORMONDY, E. J. *Concepts of Ecology*. Englewood Cliffs, N.J.: Prentice-Hall, Inc., 1969. Pp. 35–54. (A rather detailed discussion of the cycles of matter. Fairly advanced.)

NACE, R. L. "Water of the World," *Natural History,* January, 1964. Pp. 10–19. (Details of the water cycle.)

ODUM, E. P. *Ecology*. New York: Holt, Rinehart & Winston, Inc., 1963. Pp. 37–64. (A good treatment of the material introduced in Chapter 1. Fairly advanced reading.)

PHILLIPSON, JOHN. *Ecological Energetics*. New York: St. Martin's Press, 1966. (A pamphlet that concentrates on the flow of energy through the biosphere. Advanced.)

Scientific American, EDITORS OF. *The Biosphere*. San Francisco: W. H. Freeman and Co., 1970. (A set of articles that closely parallel the topics in this chapter. Fairly advanced.)

SIMPSON, G. G., and W. S. BECK. *Life: An Introduction to Biology*. 2nd ed. New York: Harcourt, Brace & World, Inc., 1965. Pp. 3–12. (Closely parallels Chapter 1 but will deepen your understanding. Fairly advanced reading.) *In the same book:* Pp. 13–18. (Goes far beyond Chapter 1 in discussing the biologist's viewpoint and methods. Advanced.)

WEIGERT, R. *Energy Transfer in Ecological Systems*. Chicago: Rand McNally & Co., 1970. (A pamphlet about the flow of energy. Fairly easy.)

Individuals and Populations

INDIVIDUALS

In general, life processes occur in separate "packages." You are such a package; you carry on the processes of life within your own body, separate and distinct from the life processes in the bodies of your parents or brothers or sisters. Each person is an *individual.* So, too, is each cow in a herd, each bee in a hive, each tree in a forest.

individual [Latin: *individuus,* indivisible]

Sometimes individuals are so closely packed together that several appear to be one. From a distance, a flock of ducks may look like a single living mass. Of course, you have only to startle the flock into flight to see that it is composed of individuals. It is more difficult to untangle the individual grass plants in a lawn.

Look at Figure 2 · 1. You see a mass of stony material containing holes, and projecting from each hole is a small organism with waving tentacles. Each organism seems to be separate from the others—an individual. But if you examine the coral more closely, you find that all

tentacles [tĕn′tə kəlz; Latin: *tentare,* to touch, feel]

S. A. Reed

Figure 2 · 1

Coral. Is this one individual or many?

the tentacle-waving organisms are connected. Now, is each an individual, or is the whole mass an individual?

geranium [jĭ rā′nĭ əm]. See Figure 8·5.

originate [ə rĭj′ ə nāt′; Latin: *origo*, beginning, source]

X 1/10

Figure 2 • 2
From above ground how many iris plants do there seem to be? How many when the soil is removed?

There is still another difficulty. You can break off a piece of geranium, put it in soil, and see the piece grow and become a new individual. Or you can watch a chick hatch from an egg that was laid by a hen. In each case the new individual is clearly a piece of the old. Apparently, new individuals always originate from existing individuals; the living world is continuous in time. Yet, at any given moment it is also discontinuous—divided into separate individuals.

We may have difficulty deciding just what we mean by "individuals" in corals and irises or at just what moment an egg becomes an individual separate from the hen. But in the great majority of cases, we have little difficulty distinguishing individuals; we need not worry, then, about an exact definition. Science is based on observation. If we can fit all our observations into a definition, good. If we cannot, then we must get along with imperfect definitions.

POPULATIONS

A biologist is seldom interested in a single individual. Because he is concerned with verifiable observations, he must work with groups of individuals that are similar in one or more ways. He must work with *populations.* The term comes from a Latin word meaning "the group of people inhabiting a place." In ordinary conversation when we talk about the population of California, we are referring to the human beings in that state. Biologists, however, find the word useful in studies of other organisms.

Investigation 2.1

STUDY OF A YEAST POPULATION

INTRODUCTION

The yeast organisms that you worked with in Investigation 1.2 are useful for studying populations because they reproduce rather rapidly and are conveniently small—several million can be kept in a test tube. However, in this investigation you will use a broth *medium* (plural, media) in which to grow your cultures instead of molasses medium. And to prevent other organisms from growing with your yeast, the medium has been *sterilized;* that is, all the living things that may have been in it have been killed.

Read through the procedure for this investigation. • What is the variable?(1) • State a hypothesis that is appropriate for the procedure.(2)

MATERIALS AND EQUIPMENT
(per team of 10 students)

For Procedure A
glass-marking crayon
test tubes, each containing 10 ml
of sterile medium, 10
test-tube racks, 2

yeast culture
medicine dropper
formalin
aluminum foil, squares about
    4 x 4 cm, 10
For Procedure B
    cover-slip fragments, 30 to 40
    microscope slides, 10
    incubated culture tubes, 10
    medicine droppers, 10
    cover slips, 10
    microscopes, 5
    test tubes containing 9 ml of water,
        about 15

PROCEDURE

A. Growing the population. Using a glass-marking crayon, mark each tube of sterile medium with your team symbol. Then number the tubes from *0* to *9*. Assign one of the numbered tubes to each of the team members.

Using a medicine dropper, stir the yeast culture thoroughly. Immediately transfer 10 drops of the culture to Tube 0. Repeat for each of the other tubes.

Add 20 drops of formalin to Tube 0. Formalin kills the yeast organisms and preserves them until you can count them later.

Place a square of aluminum foil on each tube and bend the edges over the sides to form a cap. Place all the tubes except Tube 0 in a warm, dark place; in other words, *incubate* them. On each succeeding day take out the tube with the next higher number (Tubes 1, 2, 3, etc.) and add 20 drops of formalin to it.

B. Counting the population. After the last culture in the series (Tube 9) has been treated with the preservative, make counts of yeast organisms in all 10 tubes. To do this, members of each team will work in pairs. Each student will make a count from his own tube and a count from that of his partner.

First prepare in your data book a chart like that on page 38. Then carefully place 3 to 5 fragments of broken cover slip in the center of a microscope slide, positioning them to support an unbroken cover slip. Thoroughly shake the test tube to which you have been assigned until the yeast organisms are evenly distributed. *Immediately* place 2 drops of the culture on the slide between the cover-slip fragments. Place a clean cover slip on the fragments but avoid putting any pressure on it. Position the slide on your microscope stage. *Do not tilt the stage.* Focus with low power; then switch to high power.

Count the number of individual organisms in 5 different high-power fields, as indicated in Figure 2·3. (Note: Yeast organisms are difficult to see if the light is too

Figure 2 · 3

Approximate positions of
fields for counts.

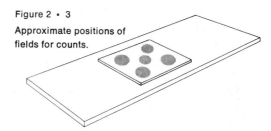

bright.) Refer to Figure 1·11 for the appearance of yeast organisms. They often stick together, but each individual in any clump is to be counted separately. Buds also count as individuals. Record your 5 counts on the chart in your data book (line A).

If the fields are too crowded for easy counting, you must make a dilution of the culture. To do this, obtain a test tube containing 9 ml of water; label this tube with your culture number and *D1* (for "dilution one"). Shake the yeast culture until the organisms are evenly distributed. Immediately transfer 20 drops of the culture into the dilution tube. Rinse the medicine dropper several times by running clean water in and out of it. Mix the contents of the dilution tube *thoroughly.* Immediately transfer 2 drops from the dilution tube to a slide as directed above and count the yeast organisms. If the field is still too crowded for easy counting, transfer 20 drops of the contents of Tube D1 to another test tube containing 9 ml of water. Mark this dilution *D2*. It may even be necessary to use a 3rd dilution (see Figure 2·4). In Tube D1 the culture is diluted 10 times; in Tube D2, 100 times; in Tube D3, 1000 times. If you make dilutions during counting, record the proper number (10 or 100 or 1000) after "Dilution Factor" on the data chart. If you make no dilutions, the dilution factor is 1.

Now have your partner make 5 counts of a sample taken from your culture, using the same procedure you used. Record his counts on the chart in your data book (line B).

As soon as you have finished recording the data, total the 5 counts in each line (adding across the line!). Then divide by 5 to get the average for the line. If your average (line A) and your partner's average (line B) differ by more than 10 organisms, prepare new slides and repeat the counts.

Repeat the entire procedure using samples from your partner's tube. He will enter his counts of his culture on line A of his data chart and your counts of his culture on line B of his chart.

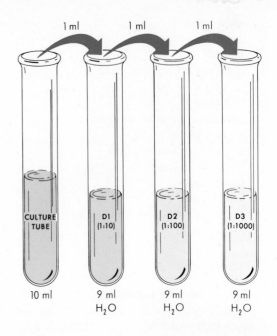

Figure 2 • 4
A dilution series.

Team _____						Culture No. _____		Dilution Factor _____	
MEMBER OF PAIR	FIELDS					TOTAL	AVERAGE	AVERAGE X DILUTION FACTOR	
	1	2	3	4	5				
A									
B									

Pair   Average _____

STUDYING THE DATA

You have already computed the figures for the "Total" and "Average" columns in your data chart. Now compute the last column by multiplying on each line the average number by the dilution factor. For example, if you made a count from Tube D2, the dilution factor is 100. If your average count was 15, then the number in the last column should be 1500. The "Pair Average" is obtained by averaging the 2 numbers in the last column. Record the "Pair Average" on the master chart on the chalkboard.

You have not counted the whole population in any of the tubes. You have obtained an estimate of the populations by a method called *sampling.* To increase the accuracy of your estimate, you have taken certain precautions. First, you shook each tube in an attempt to distribute the organisms evenly throughout it. Second, by using the cover-slip fragments, you made your counts in a constant volume of culture. Third, you counted the organisms in 5 different fields of view. By averaging these 5 fields, you tended to "smooth out" chance differences in the fields you counted. Fourth, 2 people made counts from the same tube, and you averaged their counts. Fifth, on the master chart you averaged the figures obtained by all the teams, which further tended to smooth out chance differences between the tubes. The count you finally have for the population at each period of incubation is the *average number of organisms per high-power field of view.*

On a sheet of graph paper, list the ages of the cultures (in days) on the horizontal axis and then list the numbers of organisms on the vertical axis. Plot the data from each team separately, using a different color for each team. Then use black to plot the averaged data of all teams.

CONCLUSIONS

• On the basis of the discussion in the preceding section, explain similarities and differences among the graph lines representing data from different teams.(3)

• Is there any general trend in the graph line representing the averaged data of all teams? If so, describe it.(4)   • Do the average data support your hypothesis? Explain.(5)

FOR FURTHER INVESTIGATION

Does temperature affect the growth of a yeast population? Repeat the whole procedure, but this time incubate the cultures at a constant temperature 15°C above or below the average temperature at which the tubes were incubated before.

CHARACTERISTICS OF POPULATIONS

The study of human population size has been going on for a long time. The ancient Romans and Chinese took censuses regularly, primarily for tax purposes. The beginning of population study in modern science can be dated from 1798, when Thomas Robert Malthus published *An Essay on the Principle of Population as It Affects the Future Improvement of Mankind.* Malthus was interested primarily in social problems, though he brought much biological information into later editions of his book. Basically, he presented evidence to show that all kinds of organisms, including man, tend to multiply up to the limit of their food supply and that the results are misery, sickness, and starvation for many individuals. Malthus' conclusion started arguments and investigations that are still continuing today.

censuses [sĕn′səs əz; Latin: *censere*, to enroll, tax]

Figure 2 • 5

Thomas Robert Malthus [măl′thəs]: 1766–1834. British economist.

In defining a set of individuals that make up a population, you need to identify the kind of individuals you are talking about and their limits in *time* and *space.* Thus you can refer to the population of pigeons during August, 1972, in New York City, or the population of apple trees during a given year in a particular orchard. Kind of individual, time, and place are always involved, though sometimes one or more of these may be implied. Usually you are also concerned with quantity; thus you say the human population of California in 1970 was 18,500,000.

implied: not directly stated but suggested by accompanying statements

Population changes. The size of any population continually changes. Whenever the amount of one thing varies with respect to units of another thing, we can express the change as a ***rate.*** How can we calculate the rate at which the size of a population varies during some period of time?

rate [Latin: *ratus,* fixed by calculation]

Suppose a biologist counted 1225 living white pines in a reforestation area in the year 1950 and 950 in 1960. The difference in time, $\triangle T$ (read "delta T"), is $1960 - 1950 = 10$ years. The difference

reforestation: process of planting trees to start a forest

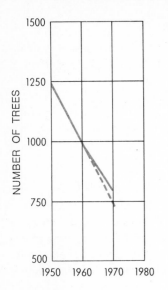

Figure 2 • 6

Changes in a white-pine population. The dotted line continues the 1950–1960 rate.

Such a slope as that in the graph above may become horizontal, but it can never become vertical. Why not?

mortality [Latin: *mortis*, of death]

Figure 2 • 7

Mortality graphs for three kinds of organisms.

in population size (the number of trees), $\triangle N$ (read "delta N"), is $950 - 1225 = -275$. (The population sizes must be written in the same order as the dates.) Now divide the difference in population size by the difference in time: $\dfrac{-275 \text{ trees}}{10 \text{ years}} = -27.5$ trees per year. The negative number tells us that the change was a decrease in population size; a positive number would indicate an increase.

This arithmetic can be summarized in the formula $R = \dfrac{\triangle N}{\triangle T}$. That is, the rate at which the size of a population changes is equal to the change in number of individuals divided by the change in time. Suppose that in 1970 in the reforestation area there are 770 living trees. Using the formula, we have: $R = \dfrac{770 - 950}{1970 - 1960} = \dfrac{-180}{10} = -18$ trees per year from 1960 to 1970.

Figure 2 • 6 shows the data for this white-pine forest in graph form. Our numbers show that the population decrease was less rapid in the decade 1960–1970 than it was in the decade 1950–1960. By the reduced slope of the second part of the line, the graph shows the same thing.

Increases and decreases. What happened to those 455 pines that were lost during the 20-year period? Since pines do not wander away, they must have died, by one means or another. We can thus speak of the decrease in the pine population per unit of time as the death rate or the **mortality.** Death rate is a characteristic of a population, never of an individual; an individual dies only once, so it cannot have a death rate.

Figure 2 • 7 shows that different kinds of organisms have different kinds of death rates. From a starting population of 1000 humans, about 800 individuals are still alive at an age about half that of the oldest humans. At half the **life-span** of European robins, only 20 are still alive from a starting population of 1000. This means that mortality is low among young humans but quite high among young European robins.

Mortality can change over time. The death rate of the human population of the United States has declined quite steadily during

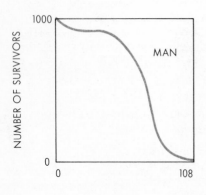
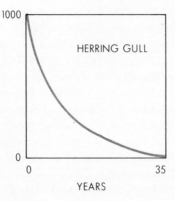
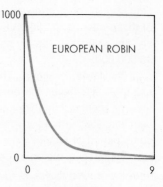

the 20th century. In 1900 the death rate per 1000 was 17.2—that is, out of every 1000 persons, 17.2 died that year. In 1925 the rate was down to 11.7, and since 1948 it has varied between 9.2 and 9.9.

What do you think might be responsible for this drop in death rate?

Our white-pine example may be too simple. While some individuals were being removed from the population others might have been added. Perhaps no new trees were planted, but the trees already there could have produced seeds that added to the population. As death tends to *decrease* a population, reproduction tends to increase it. Mammals are born, birds are hatched, seeds of plants germinate—we have a number of terms for the reproductive process. But it is customary to use as a general term for reproductive rate the word that is correctly applied to mammals—"birth." So the rate at which reproductive addition occurs is the birth rate, or **natality.** Again, note that this is a characteristic of a population, not of an individual.

natality [Latin: *natus,* born]

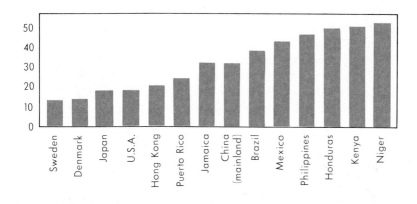

Figure 2 • 8

Natality (number of births per 1000 persons) in various countries in 1971.

As was the case for mortality, different kinds of organisms have different natalities. Even different populations of the same species may have different natalities: for example, among humans, the birth rate in 1971 was 4 times higher in certain African nations than in Sweden. Further, and again like mortality, natality changes with time. In the United States, for example, the birth rate in 1910 per 1000 was 30.1—that is, there were 30.1 live births for every 1000 persons. In 1930 the rate had dropped to 20.2; in 1970 the rate was 18.2.

What do you think might be responsible for this drop in birth rate?

Pine trees do not move about. However, for all *motile* organisms —those that can move about—we must take into account two other ways in which population size may be changed. A population of rats, for example, may be increased by *immigration* (individuals coming from other places), or it may be decreased by *emigration* (individuals going to other places).

motile [mōt′əl]

immigration [Latin: *in,* in, + *migrare,* to move from one place to another]

As mortality and natality change with time, so do movements into or out of a population. Human immigration to the United States, for example, was over 5,500,000 in the period 1911 to 1920, but just over 500,000 between 1931 and 1940. By contrast, human emigration from the United States amounted to 2,000,000 in the period 1911 to 1920 and just under 500,000 between 1931 and 1940.

emigration [Latin: *e-,* out, + *migrare*]

Interaction of rates. Suppose you are studying the pigeon population in a certain city. During some period of time—say, a year—some pigeons are hatched and some die. Further, some pigeons wander into the city and some wander out. All four causes of change in the density of the pigeon population can be calculated as rates. Two of these (natality and immigration) *increase* the population; two of them (mortality and emigration) *decrease* the population. Will the pigeon population in the city be greater or less at the end of a year? Clearly, this depends upon the interaction of the two sets of opposing rates. We can answer the question only when we have numerical values for all four rates.

Consider the student population of your classroom. Suppose that it is 35. You can assume that there is neither mortality nor natality. Suppose, further, that students come in (immigrate) at the rate of 5 every minute and leave (emigrate) at the rate of 5 every minute. What is the population size at the end of any one-minute period? Mathematically, we can express this as $35 + 5 - 5 = 35$. Thus, the population is the same at the end of a minute as it was at the beginning. The individuals in the room may not be the same individuals that were there before, but no change in population size has occurred. Now suppose that 5 enter and 10 leave every minute. What is the population size at the end of a minute? We have $35 + 5 - 10 = 30$. The population size has decreased.

What would be the density at the end of three minutes?

The mathematical method that we have just used can also be applied to natality and mortality. Like immigration and emigration, these factors work in opposite directions. So the size of any population at any given time is the result of the numerical relations among natality, mortality, immigration rate, and emigration rate. We may call these four rates the *determiners* of population size. In any study of population change, a biologist must consider these four rates. In any experimental study of populations, these determiners must be considered as possible variables.

Investigation 2.2

POPULATION CHANGES: A MODEL

INTRODUCTION

Just as we need physical tools such as microscopes to help us extend our powers of observation, so we need mental "tools" to help us extend our thinking. One such mental tool is called a *model.* Here the word does not mean an object; it is a mental image. This kind of model simplifies a complex real situation so that we can more easily understand it. Because the model is a simplification, it differs in some respects from the real situation. The simplifications we make are called **assumptions.** To simplify, we assume certain things that may be only approximately true. We must keep these assumptions in mind whenever we use the model to try to understand a real situation.

If the model gives results similar to the observations we make in some real situation, we can have confidence that the real·situation "works" in the same way the model does. Of course, the two never match exactly, but the degree of matching determines the extent of our confidence in the model.

MATERIALS

(per student)

graph paper (arithmetic), 4 sheets

graph paper (semilogarithmic), 1 sheet

PROCEDURE

Let us begin with real organisms—house sparrows. Now imagine an island. On that is-- land, in the spring of 1972, is an imaginary (hypothetical) population of 10 house sparrows —-5 male-female pairs.

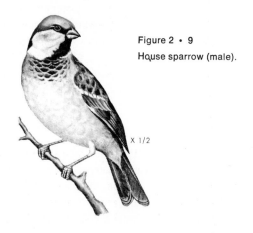

Figure 2 • 9
House sparrow (male).

X 1/2

Here are our assumptions:

Assumption 1: Each breeding season (spring), each pair of sparrows produces 10 off- spring, always 5 males and 5 females.

Assumption 2: Each year all the breeding (parent) birds die before the next spring.

Assumption 3: Each year all offspring live through the next breeding season. (In most real situations some parents would live and some offspring would die. But taken together, Assumptions 2 and 3 tend to balance each other, thus reducing the difference between the model and a real situation.)

Assumption 4: During the study no other spar- rows arrive on the island, and none leave.

How will the model work? You need to calculate the size of the hypothetical popula- tion at the beginning of each breeding season. According to Assumption 1, in the spring of 1972 there are 10 birds. Each of the 5 pairs produces 10 offspring, a total of 50 offspring. According to Assumption 2, the 10 breeding birds of 1972 die before the next spring. Ac- cording to Assumption 3, all of the 50 offspring live to the spring of 1973. Thus, at the start of the 1973 breeding season, there are 50 house sparrows on the island, and, again according to Assumption 1, there are 25 males and 25 females—25 pairs. Continue with this kind of reasoning to calculate the island's sparrow population at the *beginning* of the breeding season in 1974, 1975, 1976, and 1977.

You now have a series of numbers; you can get a clearer idea of the population change by plotting the numbers on a line graph. Con- struct the graph so that the years are shown along the horizontal axis and the number of birds along the vertical axis. Make the vertical scale large enough to show the 1972 popula- tion. Plot as many generations as you can.

No doubt you had difficulty plotting all the data on ordinary graph paper. This difficulty can be overcome with another tool—semi- logarithmic (usually called "semi-log") graph paper. It is not necessary to fully understand the mathematics of logarithms to use this tool. Your teacher will explain what you need to know to plot the data.

Construct your semi-log graph with the same data you used before. • What advan- tage(s) does the semi-log graph have over the ordinary (arithmetic) graph for plotting data on population growth?(1)

STUDYING THE DATA

Look first at the arithmetic graph. • How does the slope of the line connecting the plotted points change as you read from left to right (from year to year)?(2) • What does this mean in terms of rate of population change?(3) • Now compare the graphs. What kind of line shows the same thing on the semi- log graph?(4) • If you were to continue to use the same set of assumptions to calculate populations for an indefinite number of years and plot them on a graph, what would happen to the slope of the line on the arithmetic graph? (5)   • What would happen to the slope on the semi-log graph?(6)

SUMMARY

• In one or two sentences describe the change in a population that conforms to the assumptions stated in the model.(7)   • Do you think any real population might change in this way? Why or why not?(8)

FOR FURTHER INVESTIGATION

If a model gives results that are far from any real situation, changing the assumptions a few at a time and then comparing the new results with reality may reveal some of the ways a real situation works. Here are some suggestions. In each case calculate the populations, plot the resulting data on arithmetic graph paper, and compare with your original arithmetic graph. Then state the way in which the change of assumption has affected the hypothetical population.

1. Change Assumption 2 as follows: Each year 2/5 of the breeding birds (equally males and females) live to breed again a 2nd year and then die. All other assumptions remain unchanged.

2. Change Assumption 3 as follows: Each year 2/5 of the offspring (equally males and females) die before the beginning of the next breeding season. All other assumptions remain unchanged.

3. Change Assumption 4 as follows: Each year 20 new house sparrows (equally males and females) arrive on the island from elsewhere. None leave. All other assumptions remain unchanged.

4. Change Assumption 4 as follows: Each year 40 house sparrows (equally males and females) leave the island. None arrive. All other assumptions remain unchanged.

5. You can devise for yourself more complex problems by changing 2 or more assumptions simultaneously.

Density. Consider again the student population of your classroom. You might say there are 35 students per 150 square meters (abbreviated 150 m²)—this depends, of course, upon the size of your room. You might say 35 per 450 cubic meters (abbreviated 450 m³)—again dependent upon room size. In each case you are talking about population *density*—the number of individuals in relation to the amount of space they occupy at a given time.

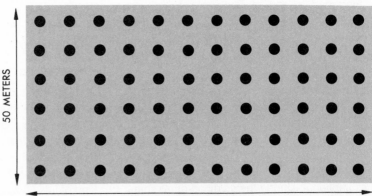

Figure 2 • 10

Plan of an orchard. Each dot represents one tree. What is the density of trees in the orchard?

50 METERS

100 METERS

Which space unit to choose depends upon your purpose. A biology teacher who is interested in setting up a laboratory activity may want to know the number of students per square meter. But the architect who designed the building had to allow for sufficient air, so he needed to know the number of students per cubic meter.

In working with land organisms, a biologist usually uses two-dimensional units of space, such as square meters; but if he is considering the fish population in a pond, he may use three-dimensional units of space, such as cubic meters. To find the density (D) of a particular population, you measure the space involved, count the number (N) of individuals of the population within the space, and divide the number of individuals by the number of units of space (S), or $D = \dfrac{N}{S}$.

The teacher would calculate $D = \dfrac{35 \text{ students}}{150 \text{ m}^2} = 0.23$, or a density of 0.23 student per m². For the architect: $D = \dfrac{35 \text{ students}}{450 \text{ m}^3} = 0.08$, or a density of 0.08 student per m³.

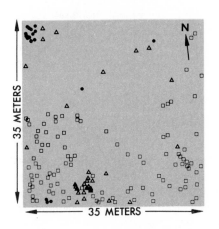

goldenrod   X 1/6

dusty clover   X 1/6

blazing star   X 1/3

Figure 2 • 11

Under natural conditions organisms are seldom distributed evenly. Calculate the density of dusty clover in the field as a whole and then only in the northwest quarter. Compare.

Biologists are usually more interested in population density than in mere population size. To learn that the human population of Rhode Island (in 1970) was 949,723 and that at the same time the population of Maine was 993,663 might cause you to think that the human populations in Rhode Island and Maine were rather similar—until you learn that Rhode Island occupies 2718 km² and Maine 80,102 km².

Calculate the densities of the human populations in the two states.

The determiners of population size are, of course, also determiners of population density. And a formula similar to the one you used to calculate the rate of change of population size can be used to calculate the rate of change of population density: $R = \dfrac{\Delta D}{\Delta T}$.

Obtain the 1960 and 1970 census figures and the area for your state. Calculate the rate of change per year in density of human population.

KINDS OF POPULATION CHANGES

If you measure the density of a population at intervals over a period of time, you seldom find that any two consecutive measurements are the same. Density increases or decreases from time to time. Biologists have made many such studies of population densities. From them they have been able to make some **generalizations** about ways in which populations change; that is, they have summarized many particular observations in a few general statements that hold true for most of the data.

generalizations
[jĕn'ər əl ə zā'shənz]

Closed and open populations. The yeasts in the tubes of Investigation 2.1 are *closed populations;* that is, they are subject to neither immigration nor emigration. In laboratories many such closed populations of small organisms have been set up to test various hypotheses about population changes.

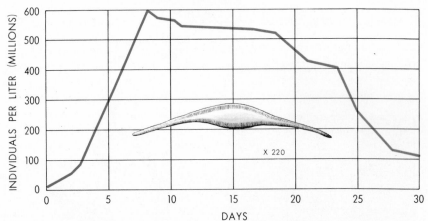

INDIVIDUALS PER LITER (MILLIONS)

X 220

DAYS

Figure 2 • 12

Changes in a laboratory population of a kind of diatom.

diatom [dī'ə təm]. See pages 167–168.

Figure 2 • 12 supplies data from an experiment involving a small photosynthetic organism. As in the case of your yeasts, a few diatoms were placed in a favorable medium and samples from the population were counted on succeeding days. Compare your yeast data with the diatom data. Many similar experiments with closed populations of other small organisms have produced data similar to these. Notice that the growth of the diatom population during the first eight days was similar to the growth of the hypothetical house-sparrow population (Investigation 2.2). The model agrees, then, with a real situation— up to a point. But no real population continues indefinitely to grow, as the model suggests.

Is the human population of Earth open or closed?

Closed populations are real, but they are found chiefly in laboratories. Most natural populations, on the other hand, are *open populations;* that is, individuals are free to enter or leave. Therefore, patterns represented by the diatom graph and by your yeast experiment cannot be assumed to apply to natural populations.

fluctuations [flŭk'chōō ā'shənz; Latin: *fluctuare*, to wave]

Population fluctuations. Figure 2 • 13 is a graph based on data collected by David E. Davis during population studies of Norway rats in Baltimore, Maryland. In 1942 the city health department conducted a poisoning campaign that apparently wiped out the rat population in

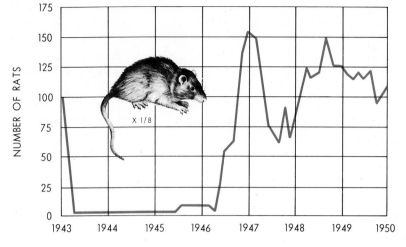

NUMBER OF RATS

X 1/8

175
150
125
100
75
50
25
0

1943   1944   1945   1946   1947   1948   1949   1950

Figure 2 • 13

Changes in the Norway-rat population of a city block.

the city block from which the data were collected. Of course it is difficult to count individuals in natural populations—even the United States census is not perfect—so there may have been one or two rats remaining or a few rats may have immigrated. In either case, a "new" rat population started early in 1945, much as you started "new" yeast populations in Investigation 2.1. You may, therefore, compare the part of Figure 2 • 13 from early 1945 to late 1946 with your graphs from Investigations 2.1 and 2.2 and with Figure 2 • 12.

From mid 1945 to the end of 1946 the line in the graph of the rat population is somewhat similar to the first part of the graph line of the diatom population. But look at the line for the later years of the rat study. As in the closed laboratory population of diatoms, a decrease in the population occurred (1947) after a peak density was reached (late 1946). But the decrease did not continue in the rat population. In open populations there is usually a turning point; the population increases again—as it did in this example (late 1947). But again a peak is reached, and again a decrease occurs. Natural populations characteristically show such population *fluctuations*—ups and downs —when the population counts are plotted on a graph. This is clearly an example of steady state, the "teetering balance" that was discussed in Chapter 1 (pages 25–27).

In the past, human populations have undoubtedly fluctuated like open populations of other organisms. Historical records make it clear that during the Middle Ages the population of western Europe decreased sharply several times as a result of such plagues as the black death and then rose again. Within the last few centuries, however, such fluctuations in human populations have tended to disappear in many countries. For the world as a whole, in fact, we have a population situation that begins to look rather like your graph of a hypothetical population in Investigation 2.2.

But the human population is real. So what prediction can you make about the future human population of Earth?

Population cycles. Sometimes population fluctuations are very regular, so that graph data show peaks at approximately equal dis-

Figure 2 • 14

Changes in the snowshoe-hare population (Canada) based on skins traded at Hudson's Bay Company posts.

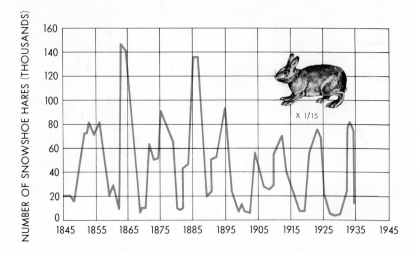

NUMBER OF SNOWSHOE HARES (THOUSANDS)

X 1/3

Figure 2 • 15

Lemming. These mouselike animals live in the northern parts of North America and Eurasia.

tances. Data gathered in Canada show that populations of snow-shoe hares there reach peaks about ten years apart. Similarly populations of lemmings reach peaks every three or four years. A number of other organisms have been shown to have such population *cycles*. Most such organisms are animals that live in the northern parts of Europe, Asia, and North America.

Although the data show very regular cycles when plotted on a graph, some biologists think that this regularity is misleading. They point out that a combination of purely chance events can produce apparently regular cycles. Gamblers have alternating winning and losing streaks. Therefore, the study of cycles may be no different from the study of irregular fluctuations.

Investigation 2.3

POPULATION CHANGES: FIELD DATA

INTRODUCTION

Gathering data on natural populations is difficult and time-consuming. You can observe some of the characteristics of population changes by using data that have already been obtained by biologists. Then you can compare these population data with the data from your hypothetical populations and from the laboratory population that you have investigated.

MATERIALS

(per student)
graph paper (arithmetic), 2 sheets
red pencil

PROCEDURE

Cotton mouse. The data in Figure 2•17 come from a study of cotton mice made by Paul G. Pearson near Gulf Hammock, Florida. Here the density is given as the number of

X 1/2

Figure 2 • 16
Cotton mouse.

DATE	NUMBER PER 100 TRAPS PER NIGHT
September 24, 1949	25
October 9	45
October 30	38
December 4	30
January 7, 1950	20
February 26	14
March 12	13
April 16	8
May 8	7
June 16	11
July 16	4
August 16	13

Figure 2 • 17

Data on density of cotton mice (Florida).

Figure 2 • 18

Heath hen (*left*) and ring-neck pheasant (*right*).

X 1/11

mice caught per 100 traps per night. As is often the case in studying natural populations, the actual number of animals present in the area is not known. Thus, even in this real situation, we have to make an assumption: that the number of mice caught was always in proportion to the actual density of the population.

Plot the data on a sheet of graph paper, using a vertical scale that will place the highest point for the population near the top. Compare the graph of the cotton-mouse population with the arithmetic graphs you made in Investigations 2.1 and 2.2. • What part of this mouse graph is similar to the other graphs?(1) • How does the mouse graph differ from your graph in Investigation 2.2?(2) • How do you explain the difference?(3) • How does the mouse graph differ from your graph of the yeast population?(4) • How do you explain the difference?(5) • Which (if any) of the 3 populations was an open population?(6) • In which season of the year do you think natality was highest?(7) • When do you think mortality and emigration were greatest?(8)

Ring-necked pheasant. A few ring-necked pheasants (native to Eurasia) were introduced on Protection Island, off the coast of Washington, in 1937. A. S. Einarsen made counts of

the population each spring and fall for the next 5 years. Figure 2 • 19 presents the data.

Plot the data on a sheet of graph paper and connect the points with a lead pencil. • How do you explain the regular fluctuations shown on your graph?(9)

Now, using a red pencil, connect all the points representing spring counts, skipping the fall counts. • What does this line tell you about the population?(10) • If spring counts

YEAR	SEASON	POPULATION SIZE
1937	Spring	8
	Fall	40
1938	Spring	30
	Fall	100
1939	Spring	90
	Fall	425
1940	Spring	300
	Fall	825
1941	Spring	600
	Fall	1520
1942	Spring	1325
	Fall	1900

Figure 2 • 19

Numbers of ring-neck pheasants (Washington).

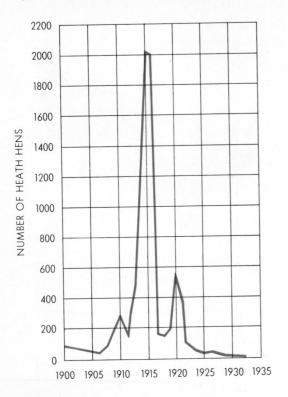

Figure 2 • 20

Numbers of heath hens (Martha's Vineyard, Massachusetts).

had been made after 1942, what do you think they might have shown? Remember that this is a natural population.(11)

Heath hen. Heath hens were once common birds along the Atlantic coast from New England to Virginia. By 1880 they had disappeared from all locations except Martha's Vineyard, an island off Cape Cod. Figure 2 • 20 shows the result of a careful study of this population by A. O. Gross. In accounting for the various changes in the heath-hen population, biologists point out several factors: hunting

pressure by man, then extreme efforts at preservation, disease, effects of forest fires, and an excessive number of males.

• What do you think happened about 1907?(12)   • How does the heath-hen graph between 1907 and 1916 compare with the pheasant graph?(13)   • How might an excess of males affect the determiners of density?(14) • What term is applied to a population that reaches the point attained by the heath hens in 1932?(15)

CONCLUSIONS

You should now be able to draw some general conclusions from your investigations of population change.   • Does the growth of a population tend to follow a basic pattern? If so, what are the characteristics of this pattern? (16)   • What is the chief difference between the graph for the hypothetical population (Investigation 2.2) and the graphs for the real populations (Investigations 2.1 and 2.3)?(17) • How do you account for the difference?(18) • Which of the graphs best illustrates a population in steady state?(19)

FOR FURTHER INVESTIGATION

Figure 2 • 21 presents data collected by F. S. Bodenheimer on a population of Italian bees. Plot the data on arithmetic graph paper. Does this graph most closely resemble the graph for the house-sparrow, the yeast, or the field-mouse population? On the bee graph what is beginning to happen toward the end of the graph line? If you know something about bees, you should be able to tell what probably happened soon after the collection of data was discontinued. Which of the population determiners mentioned in the text is involved in your prediction?

DAYS

0	7	14	21	28	35	42	49	56	63	70	77	84	91	98	105	112	119
1	1.5	2.5	4	8	16	22	32	40.5	50.3	55	62.5	72	72.5	71	82	78	81

POPULATION OF COLONY
(IN THOUSANDS)

Figure 2 • 21

Numbers of Italian bees in an experimental colony.

POPULATIONS AND ENVIRONMENT

We have been investigating ways in which population sizes and densities change. We have found that changes result from interactions of mortality, natality, emigration, and immigration. But we have said nothing about what factors may cause the numerical values of these four determiners to increase or decrease.

If we can discover what these factors are, we may be able to make some *predictions* about population growth and decline. Making predictions is an important part of scientific work. Predictions can result in hypotheses that lead to further discovery.

predictions |prĭ dĭk'shənz; Latin: *prae-*, before, + *dicere*, to tell|

SOME EXPERIMENTS

Let us first look at some experimental studies. Several biologists at the University of Wisconsin cooperated in studying populations of house mice. In one experiment they established a small population of mice in the basement of an old building. They provided the mice with 250 g of food during each day of the experiment. At first, this amount of food was not completely consumed each day. But the population grew, and eventually the mice were eating all the daily food supply. Soon after, the biologists began to capture mice on the upper floors of the building, where they had not previously been found. Evidently the population had increased until there was a shortage of food within the experimental space. Emigration was the determiner by which the population density in the basement area was maintained more or less at the level that the food supply could support. There was no evidence that either mortality or natality had changed.

Was this an open or a closed population?

Earlier, the same investigators had performed a similar experiment, but with one important difference: the mice were confined in pens. In this case, when the population grew to the point where a food shortage developed, emigration was impossible. Remembering Malthus (page 39), we might expect that there should have been famine and starvation—an increased mortality. Instead, when the daily food supply became insufficient to support the increased population, fewer young were born—a decreased natality. Thus a single factor (food shortage) may operate through different determiners (emigration or natality) to produce the same effect—a population steady state.

famine [făm'ĭn; Latin: *fames*, hunger]

In a third experiment the mice were again confined in pens, but *more than enough* food was always provided. As the population density increased, there was a decline in space per mouse, or we might say the population became crowded. This experiment was performed in different places, with different results.

At the University of Wisconsin, when the population became crowded, chasing and fighting increased greatly. Females ceased taking care of their nests and young. Though mice continued to be born, more and more died from neglect. Eventually mortality of the newborn approached 100 percent. Thus, further increase of the population was prevented by increased mortality in one part of the population—the young.

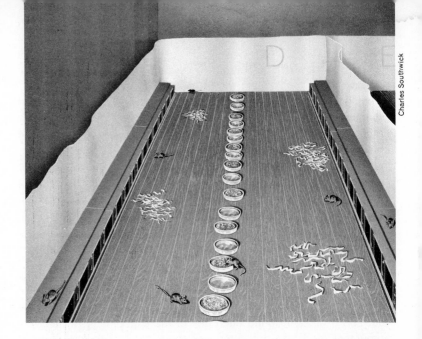

Charles Southwick

Figure 2 • 22

Part of one of the pens used in the Wisconsin experiment on crowding. Walls are of sheet metal; nest boxes line them.

An experiment with a similar aim (to test the effect of space shortage when food is abundant) was conducted in England. There the investigators found little of the chasing, fighting, and neglect of nests that had been so conspicuous at Wisconsin. And there was no mortality among the young. Instead, after the population had increased to the crowded point, natality declined almost to zero.

In both these experiments the populations reached a steady state. But at Wisconsin this came about through high mortality; in England it came about through low natality.

Apparently similar experiments produced different results. Could one or both groups of biologists be mistaken about their results? Here we see the self-corrective nature of science, which comes from the fact that science deals with verifiable observation. Close examination of the published descriptions of these experiments showed that the experiments were not really the same—there were differences in the construction of the pens and nesting boxes.

Biologists at Rutgers, the state university of New Jersey, then undertook tests of the two experimental designs. In both tests they used mice with the same ancestry to eliminate possible hereditary differences in behavior. The results of these additional experiments showed that with both the Wisconsin and the English designs the final population density came from a *combination* of increased mortality of the newborn and a decrease of natality.

EFFECTS OF ENVIRONMENT ON POPULATIONS

When we examine this group of experiments carefully, we see that all the factors influencing the determiners of population density came from outside the animals. Everything outside an organism is its *environment*. Therefore, we need to examine further the relation of

environment [ĕn vī′rən mənt]

environment to population density.

It is convenient to divide environment into two parts. The **biotic** environment is everything in an organism's surroundings that is alive or was recently alive. Thus all other organisms are a part of *your* biotic environment—your classmates, your dog, the fleas on your dog, the yeasts in your test tubes, the trees along the street, the polar bears of Greenland. Obviously, some of these are more closely connected to you in the web of life than others. The *abiotic* environment is everything in an organism's surroundings that is not alive. This includes such things as soil, solar radiation, rain, and waves on the seashore. And for you as a human being it includes a wide variety of man-made things—automobiles, houses, and electric lights, for example.

biotic [bī ŏt'ĭk; Greek: *bios*, life]

abiotic [ā'bī ŏt'ĭk; Greek: *a-*, without, + *bios*]

solar [sō'lər; Latin: *sol*, sun]

Nutrients. In the mouse experiments food was one of the important variables. For any consumer food is always important. Producers make their own food, but to do so they must have both radiant energy and various kinds of matter—mostly inorganic substances. All substances that an organism obtains from its environment—except oxygen, carbon dioxide, and water—are termed **nutrients.**

nutrient [nū'trĭ ənt; Latin: *nutrire*, to suckle, nurse]

What makes a nutrient important as a factor affecting population determiners is not its quantity, but its availability. When the amount of food remained constant in the mouse experiments, its availability also remained constant as long as mice were free to emigrate. But when the mice were confined and the amount of food remained constant, the availability of food per mouse decreased as the population density increased. When any nutrient is abundant in relation to the number of individuals, it is not a factor in regulating population density; when the nutrient becomes scarce, its importance increases.

availability: the extent to which a thing can be obtained

abundant [Latin: *ab*, from, + *undare*, to flow]: overflowing, more than enough

For producers the availability of nutrients depends upon the chemical nature of the soils or waters in which they grow. For example, when magnesium is abundant in a soil, a plant may not be able to take in sufficient calcium—even though calcium is also abundant—because of chemical interference between these two elements.

Space. Every individual requires living space. The amount of space required may be very small—so small that one individual may touch others, as do the plants in a cornfield. For motile organisms required space is usually greater than for nonmotile. In some cases it may be very large: pumas (mountain lions) usually remain several kilometers from each other.

X 1/26

Figure 2 · 23
Puma (also called cougar and mountain lion).

You might guess that the amount of space an organism requires is related to the availability of nutrients. This certainly is true to some extent. Consider the mouse experiments: Even when food was provided in abundance, a time came when the *space per mouse* became too small for normal activities of the mice to continue. Energy that normally would have gone into reproduction and care of young went instead into fighting, chasing, hiding—activities that tended to maintain space between mice.

How much space does a human being need?

Often, too, it can be shown that for a particular kind of organism a particular kind of space is needed. Consider raccoons: Two wood-

raccoon. See Figure 15 · 19.

precipitation [prĭ sĭp'ə tā'shən; Latin: *praeceps,* falling headlong]

humidity [hū mĭd'ə tĭ; Latin: *umere,* to be moist]. See Investigation 3.3.

mosquito. See Figure 7 · 7.

X 1/5

Figure 2 • 24
Barn swallow.

lands may have equal areas and equally good food supplies, but very different raccoon populations. The difference in density can be traced to a difference in the number of hollow trees, which are homes for raccoons.

Weather. The mouse experiments do not show the effects on organisms of those abiotic environmental factors that are usually grouped together as weather. These factors are *precipitation* (rainfall, snowfall, and the like); temperature; *humidity* (the amount of water vapor in the air); evaporation; and wind. Each may be measured separately, but they all affect each other.

In the northern part of the United States, the population of adult mosquitoes drops close to zero with the first heavy frost. In the autumn the swallow population drops also, though not as suddenly. Both these population changes are decreases, and both can be related to one weather factor—temperature. This factor changes the mosquito population through mortality, but it changes the swallow population through emigration.

Another example: In the deserts of southern Arizona, after one of the infrequent rains, blankets of small, bright flowering plants quickly appear on the formerly bare and baked desert soil. In a few days the density of visible flowering plants springs from zero to thousands. Again the population change is clearly related to a single weather factor—in this case, rainfall; and this factor operates through natality—the germination of seeds.

Josef Muench

Figure 2 • 25
Desert plants (*in the foreground*) that quickly germinate, flower, and wither after a rain.

Other organisms. The mouse experiments also fail to show another biotic factor that is often very important—the effects of other kinds of organisms. Under natural conditions consumers such as snakes, foxes, and hawks catch and eat mice. And microscopic organisms that live inside mice may weaken them so much that they die. Populations of producers as well as those of consumers are influenced by other kinds of organisms. We will not carry this topic any further at present, for it is part of the subject of Chapter 3.

Interaction of factors. When changes in the density of a population are thoroughly investigated, we usually find that they involve the interaction of many factors. Consider tomato plants in a southern New Jersey field in July. In some years the density of living plants may be nearly as high as when the plants were set out in April. In other years it may be much lower, almost zero. Four weather factors are involved: temperature, rainfall, wind, and humidity (which is itself a consequence of the other three). If temperature, rainfall, and humidity are high and wind is low, tomato plants usually grow very well. But there is a biotic factor in the tomatoes' environmental situation, too. A certain fungus also thrives in such weather. It may vigorously attack the tomato plants and greatly reduce their populations—a disaster for the tomato-grower.

fungus [fŭng′gəs]; plural, fungi [fŭn′jī]. A similar fungus is shown in Figure 7 · 3.

How does this disaster affect a city dweller?

Some environmental factors are difficult to place in any of the groups we have been discussing. For example, radiation from the sun is the driving force behind all weather factors. And for producers solar radiation is an environmental factor that controls the food supply, since it supplies the energy for photosynthesis. The amount of solar energy a particular producer receives depends upon still other factors. Consider a raspberry plant in the United States. It receives more solar radiation at noon than at eight o'clock in the morning; it receives more in June than in December; it receives more if it grows among grass plants than if it grows in a forest. If the plant is in northern Minnesota, the daily and seasonal variations in solar radiation cause the total annual energy received to be less than if the plant is in Tennessee. Time of day, season, shade, and latitude all influence the amount of solar radiation received by a plant.

Can you show that the amount of solar radiation received on any cm² of surface depends upon the angle of the sun's rays?

Thus far we have been discussing organisms that live on land—*terrestrial* organisms. Organisms that live in water—*aquatic* organisms—are affected by water conditions that correspond to the atmospheric conditions we call weather, but they do not vary as much. Aquatic producers get their nutrients from the water; for these organisms water corresponds not only to atmosphere but also to soil. The factors that influence aquatic populations are different from those on land, but the general principle—that environmental factors influence the four determiners of population density—applies to both land and water environments.

terrestrial [tə rĕs′trĭ əl; Latin: *terra*, earth, land]

aquatic [ə kwăt′ĭk; Latin: *aqua*, water]

Density itself a factor. If lightning strikes a pine tree in the woodlands of northern Arizona, the tree may be set afire and killed. But its neighbors are not likely to be damaged, because the trees are far apart there (a low population density). If, however, lightning strikes a pine tree in northern Idaho, a whole forest may be destroyed, because the trees grow very close together there (a high population density).

Photos by U. S. Forest Service

Figure 2 • 26

Two ponderosa-pine forests. What environmental factors might influence the difference in population density?

A single hard freeze in Vermont may not kill all adult mosquitoes; mortality depends upon how many, in relation to the total population, find shelter. If most find shelter, mortality is low; as the percentage of the population finding shelter decreases, the mortality increases. Thus the degree to which a certain factor affects the density of a population may be influenced by the density of the population itself.

Carrying capacity. All this discussion of environmental factors and population leads to an important conclusion. A particular combination of abiotic and biotic environmental factors determines the maximum population size of a particular kind of organism in any given amount of space. The number of individuals that an environment can support (or carry) is called its *carrying capacity*. When the carrying

Richard G. Beidleman

Figure 2 • 27
The scene is in Colorado, looking toward the east. Try to explain these effects of land slope on plant populations.

capacity of any given space has been reached, a population ceases to grow. Then individuals may emigrate, as did the mice in the first experiment described on page 51. Or mortality may increase or natality decrease as in the other mouse experiments. Lack of attention to carrying capacity was the principal defect in the population model of Investigation 2.2.

For the support of the human population the whole earth must be considered. What is the carrying capacity of Earth for the human population? At present scientists disagree among themselves. As far as food production is concerned some believe that as many as 30 billion might be supported while others believe 7 to 10 billion to be a more realistic estimate. In either case, more machinery, more fertilizers, and more energy would be required to raise more food; lack of these might act to limit carrying capacity. Still other scientists believe that crowding may be even more important than food and its production—as it was for the mice with unlimited food. But that Earth has a limited carrying capacity for the human population no scientist doubts.

Why must Earth as a whole be considered for man but not for house sparrows or pine trees?

POPULATION STEADY STATE

From your study of populations and interactions between populations and environment come three major generalizations. First, when a small number of organisms is introduced into a favorable environment, a characteristic pattern of growth follows. Second, after the initial growth period a population in a closed system develops differently from a population in an open system. Third, populations

initial [ĭ nĭsh′əl; Latin: *in*, in, + *ire*, to go]: beginning analogy [ə năl′ə jĭ: Greek: *ana*, on, + *logos*, reason]: explanation of one thing by comparison with another

stimulus [stĭm′yə ləs]; plural, stimuli [stĭm′yə lī′]

thermostat [thûr′mə stăt′; Greek: *therme*, heat, + *statikos*, causing to stand]

regulator [rĕg′yə lā′tər; Latin: *regere*, to guide, rule]

effector [ĭ fĕk′tər; Latin: *ex*, out, + *facere*, to make]

homeostasis [hō′mĭ ō stā′sĭs; Greek: *homoios*, like, same, + *stasis*, condition]

in open systems fluctuate at some level below the carrying capacity of the environment. We need to explore the third generalization somewhat further.

An analogy. In most classrooms temperature is in a steady state. When the heat supply is cut off, the room cools. At some preset temperature this cooling acts as a *stimulus* that causes a thermostat (the *regulator*) to "order" an input of heat. But before the furnace (*effector*) can deliver the heat, cooling has continued and the room temperature has dropped below the preset temperature. After the heat arrives, the rising temperature again reaches the preset point and this causes the regulator to shut off the heat. But before the heating system can be shut off, the temperature has passed the preset point. Thus there is an average room temperature, but the actual temperature reaches periodic highs ("overshoots") and lows ("undershoots"). A process of *homeostasis,* involving a stimulus, a regulator, and an effector, keeps the temperature more or less even.

Most natural populations are also in a steady state. Fluctuations of population size are like the ups and downs of room temperatures, and there is a homeostatic process that keeps the population density more or less even. But population homeostasis is more complex. The stimulus can be a shortage of nutrients, a shortage of space—or any other of the environmental factors we have discussed or any combination of them. The regulator is the ability of each individual in a population to sense environmental changes: for example, there is for a particular kind of organism some level of food shortage that causes individuals to die or to emigrate. The effector is the set of population determiners: natality, mortality, emigration, and immigration. Acting together they increase or decrease the population density.

Like most analogies this one is useful if not carried too far. One most important difference between the two situations involves the regulator. A thermostat operates on a simple "off-on" basis—it either turns on the heat or it does not. But we have seen that the amount of influence from an environmental factor may depend upon the density of the population: the greater the density of mice, the more severe the effect of space shortage. To improve the analogy the thermostat would have to continuously change the strength of its "order" for more or less heat. This emphasizes the major point: Population control is vastly more complex than heat control.

An example. Suppose that in a certain area a deer population is increasing. After a time the kinds of plants that deer eat become scarce as more and more deer consume them. A few deer may begin to look elsewhere for food—they may emigrate (if they can). Those that remain will not be as well nourished as they were before and will be more easily caught by the carnivores—such as pumas—that eat deer. As the population continues to increase, more and more deer emigrate and more and more deer are killed. But since emigration and mortality tend to reduce populations, the deer population begins to decline. This results in fewer plants being eaten. As the plants con-

X 1/30

Figure 2 · 28
Black-tailed deer.

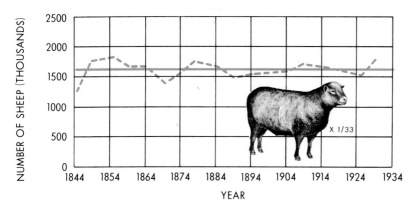

Figure 2 • 29
Changes in the domestic-sheep population, Tasmania (*dotted line*). The solid line shows an average around which fluctuations occurred. Try to explain how man was involved in this homeostasis.

tinue to grow, more food is available for the remaining deer. Deer may stop emigrating; in fact, attracted by food within the area, deer may immigrate from elsewhere. With more food the deer are better nourished and are not killed so easily by carnivores. Some carnivores may even stop trying to catch deer and look for other sources of food. Thus immigration and a reduction in mortality tend to start the deer population increasing again. And this is where we started.

A theory. What we have described in this example can be stated in a general form: Changes in environmental factors tend to prevent populations either from becoming very large, on the one hand, or from disappearing, on the other. This is a *theory*—an attempt to explain a set of observations. There may be natural populations to which this theory of population control does not apply. If so, the theory must be changed. But it is useful, at least for the present, for guiding investigations into the mechanisms of population change.

theory [thē′ərĭ; Greek: *theorein*, to look at]: a general explanation of apparent relationships among verified observations. See pages 574–575.

Investigation 2.4

ENVIRONMENT AND NATALITY

BACKGROUND INFORMATION

Brine shrimps are small aquatic animals that live in such places as Great Salt Lake, Utah. Unlike the eggs of most other aquatic animals, those of brine shrimps can survive drying. Indeed, the dried eggs may still be able to hatch after a year or more. This fact has made the eggs useful to tropical-fish fans, for the eggs can be easily kept until needed.

A number of environmental factors influence the hatching rate (natality) of brine-shrimp eggs. • Read the following procedure and then state one or more hypotheses concerning the relation of environmental factors to brine-shrimp natality.(1)

MATERIALS AND EQUIPMENT

(for each team)
glass-marking crayon
petri dishes, 6
graduated cylinder
distilled (or deionized) water, 10 ml
sodium chloride solutions (1%, 2%, 4%, 8%, 16%), 10 ml of each
volume measure (piece of 6-mm glass tubing with a mark 5 mm from one end)
brine-shrimp eggs, about 1 cm^2
refrigerator
incubator
stereomicroscope
medicine dropper

PROCEDURE

Using a glass-marking crayon, number 6 petri dishes on the rims of the bottom halves. Also place your team symbol on each dish. Into Dish 1 pour 10 ml of distilled (or deionized) water. Into Dish 2 pour 10 ml of 1% sodium chloride (salt) solution. Into Dishes 3 through 5 pour 10 ml of 2%, 4%, 8%, and 16% sodium chloride solutions, respectively.

Using a volume measure made from glass tubing, measure about 0.1 cm² of dry brine-shrimp eggs. Scatter them on the surface of the water in Dish 1. Scatter the same volume on the surface of each of the solutions in the other dishes. Cover the dishes and stack them in the place designated by your teacher. Some dishes will be left at room temperature; some will be placed in a refrigerator and some in an incubator at temperatures 10° to 15°C above that of the room. Check the temperature at the place where your dishes are to be kept and record it in your data book. Recheck and record the temperatures on each of the following two days.

Two days (about 48 hours) after setting up the cultures use a stereomicroscope to count the hatchlings in each dish. You may find that a rough count will be satisfactory, or use a medicine dropper to remove each young brine shrimp as it is counted. Record each number (indicating whether an estimate or a count) in your data book.

STUDYING THE DATA

Assemble data from all teams on the chalkboard. For each of the 3 temperature conditions, total the data for each of the 6 dishes and calculate an average for each dish. Using a separate sheet of graph paper for each hatching medium, plot the points for the low-temperature dishes (using O), for the room-temperature dishes (using X), and for the high-temperature dishes (using +). Connect the O's with one line, the X's with a 2nd line, and the +'s with a 3rd line.

• What statement can you make concerning the effect of temperature on brine-shrimp natality?(2)   • What statement can you make concerning the effect of salt percentage on brine-shrimp natality?(3)   • Do your data indicate any interaction of temperature and salt percentage?(4)

GUIDE QUESTIONS

1. Why is it difficult to say exactly what is meant by the term "individual"?

2. How did the scientific study of populations begin?

3. To define a set of individuals as a population, what things must you say about it?

4. How does a biologist calculate the rate at which a given population is increasing or decreasing?

5. Why are the terms "mortality" and "natality"—as defined in this text—not applicable to individuals?

6. How has human mortality changed in the United States during the 20th century?

7. Distinguish between immigration and emigration.

8. Which rates tend to increase population size and which tend to decrease it?

9. Describe, in words, what this formula states in symbols: $D = \dfrac{N}{S}$.

10. Describe the characteristic form of a line graph that represents the growth of a closed population in a favorable environment.

11. Describe the characteristic form of a line graph that represents the changes that occur in a well-established population under natural conditions.

12. A cycling population is a special case of a fluctuating population. Explain.

13. How do the experiments on mouse populations described in this chapter show the characteristics of scientific investigation?

14. What is meant by the environment of an organism?

15. How are the terms "food" and "nutrient" related?

16. In what ways does space per individual act as an environmental factor affecting

population density?

17. What are the major groups of environmental factors that influence the determiners of population?

18. Give an example of the way in which environmental factors interact in producing effects on population determiners.

19. How can the density of a population affect the extent to which an environmental factor may change that density?

20. What is meant by the carrying capacity of any given amount of space?

21. How does the process of homeostasis act to maintain a steady state?

22. How do biologists explain population fluctuations?

23. For what purposes do scientists develop theories?

PROBLEMS

1. In a certain city an eight-block area contained 1056 human beings and an estimated population of 1400 rats. Then an urban-renewal commission tore down the old buildings in the area and replaced them with modern apartments. The area was then occupied by 2480 human beings and an estimated population of 160 rats. Calculate the change in population density of both organisms. What determiners probably were predominant in effecting the changes in density?

2. A biologist studied a population of box turtles in an Ohio woodlot for a period of ten years. He determined that the natality averaged 40 per year, the mortality 30 per year, immigration 3 per year, and emigration 8 per year. Was the population increasing or decreasing? Was the area supplying box turtles to other places, or vice versa? What was the average annual change due to immigration and emigration? If the initial population was 15 turtles, what was the population at the end of ten years?

3. From *The World Almanac* obtain the total human population of the United States according to each United States census, from the first one in 1790. Graph the data. (a)Which of the population graphs that you have studied does the graph of the United States population most resemble? (b)What hypothesis can you advance for the slight change in the slope of the graph during the decade 1930–1940? (c) What can you predict about the slope of the graph line in the future? Explain your prediction in terms of the four determiners of popula-

tion density. (d)What additional information would you need to convert the census figures to densities? (e)Obtain the necessary information, figure the densities for each decade, and plot a new graph. How is the new graph different from the one based on total population only? (f)Does this new view of the United States population change your predictions about the future? If so, why?

4. Obtain the census data for your state. Draw a graph of these data, beginning with the first census after your state entered the Union. Why is it unnecessary (except in the case of Virginia) to refigure these data for density? How does the form of this graph compare with that for the population of the United States as a whole? Try to explain any differences.

5. It is seldom possible to count all the individuals in a natural population. How can a biologist study population densities without such data?

6. What difficulties may be involved when we use the word "natality" in discussing the population of plants that reproduce by means of seeds?

7. Obtain some duckweed, an aquatic plant that grows on the surface of ponds. Tap the mass of plants with your finger to separate a single individual. Place the single duckweed plant in pond or aquarium water in a petri dish. At intervals of 2 to 4 days make counts of the numbers of individuals. Keep a record of dates and numbers. Construct a graph to show the growth of the duckweed population.

SUGGESTED READINGS

BENTON, A. H., and W. E. WERNER. *Principles of Field Biology and Ecology.* 2nd ed. New York: McGraw-Hill Book Co., Inc., 1965. Chapter 8.

(This describes some methods of population study. Fairly easy.)
CAIRNS, J. *Population Dynamics.* Chicago: Rand

McNally & Co., 1966. (An excellent pamphlet that goes into details but is easier than Odum or Kormondy.)

CURRY-LINDAHL, K. "New Theory on a Fabled Exodus," *Natural History,* August, September, 1963. Pp. 46–53.

FARB, P. *Ecology.* New York: Time Inc., 1963. Pp. 141–161. (A general discussion of rises and falls of populations, with many examples. Easy.)

KORMONDY, E. J. *Concepts of Ecology.* Englewood Cliffs, N.J.: Prentice-Hall, Inc., 1969. Chapter 4. (An excellent account of some modern principles of population. Advanced.)

LANGER, W. L. "Checks on Population Growth," *Scientific American,* February, 1972. Pp. 92–99.

ODUM, E. P. *Ecology.* New York: Holt, Rinehart & Winston, Inc., 1963. Pp. 89–109. (An excellent treatment of growth and fluctuations of populations. Advanced.)

SIMPSON, G. G., and W. S. BECK. *Life: An Introduction to Biology.* Shorter ed. New York: Harcourt, Brace & World, Inc., 1969. Pp. 418–425. (Fairly advanced.)

WYNNE-EDWARDS, V. C. "Population Control in Animals," *Scientific American,* August, 1964. Pp. 68–74.

Communities and Ecosystems

STUDYING ECOSYSTEMS

No population lives alone. Every population interacts with other populations—its biotic environment—in a complex web of relationships. Likewise, every population interacts with its abiotic environment. In discussing the interrelationships that tie population to population and organisms to environment, we are dealing with the part of biology called *ecology.*

ecology [ĭ kŏl'ə jĭ; Greek: *oikos,* house, + *logos,* speech, reason]

An ecologist is concerned with all aspects of the biosphere. But the biosphere is too big to study conveniently as a whole. So he studies a piece of the biosphere: a forest, a city, a pond, an aquarium. Although each is but a part of the biosphere, each is a system in which organisms interact with each other and with their abiotic environment —an *ecosystem.*

ecosystem [ē'kō sĭst'əm; Greek: *oikos,* + *syn-,* together, + *histanai,* to place]

Ecosystems may be large or small, simple or complex. In Investigation 1.4 you began a study of one in the field—that is, out of doors—putting most of your attention on the organisms rather than their abiotic environment. Now you need to take a closer look at a smaller ecosystem—and you can do this best in your laboratory.

Investigation 3.1

A LABORATORY ECOSYSTEM

INTRODUCTION

In this investigation you will study several variables at the same time. In designing such an investigation, care must be taken that separate setups are provided for each variable. This makes it possible to distinguish results determined by any one variable from results determined by the others.

• Read through Procedure A to find what variables are present. Then state a hypothesis for the effect of each variable.(1)

MATERIALS AND EQUIPMENT

For Procedure A

(per team of 10 students)
glass-marking crayon
jars, about 1000-ml, 5
pond water, filtered, 2000 ml
pond organisms, mixed, 300 ml
graduated cylinder, 100-ml
balance
fertilizer, 1 g

pesticide, 0.1 g

peptone, 0.3 g

glucose, 0.5 g

Saran Wrap, about 15 x 15 cm, 5

box, large enough to cover jar

For Procedure B

(per pair of students)

cultures (from Procedure A), 5

pipettes, 5-ml, 5

vials, about 10-ml, 7

medicine droppers, 2

formalin

glycerin

glass-marking crayon

lens paper, 7 pieces, each about
4 x 4 cm

rubber bands, 7

pond water, filtered

For Procedure C

(per pair of students)

medicine droppers, 2

culture samples (from Procedure B)

microscope slides, 4

broken cover slips

cover slips, 4

microscope

graph paper, 10 sheets

colored pencils

PROCEDURE

A. Setting up the cultures. Using a glass-marking crayon, label the jars from *A* to *E* and add to each your team symbol. Pour 400 ml of filtered pond water into each jar. Stir the mixture of pond organisms; then transfer 50 ml of it to each of the jars. Each jar now contains a culture consisting of several kinds of producers and consumers.

To Cultures A and B add nothing further; to Culture C add 1 g of fertilizer; to Culture D add 0.1 g of pesticide; to Culture E add 0.3 g of peptone and 0.5 g of glucose. Cover all cultures with Saran Wrap. Place Cultures A, C, D, and E where each will get the same amount of light. Cover Culture B with a box to keep it in darkness and place it with the other cultures.

B. Sampling the cultures. On the day the cultures are set up, remove a sample from Culture A. First, stir the culture; then, using a pipette, transfer 5 ml of the culture to a vial. Add to the vial about 20 drops of formalin and 20 drops of glycerin. Formalin kills the organisms, and glycerin preserves them after the water and formalin evaporate. On the vial place your team symbol, the letter of the culture, and the date of sampling. Cover the vial with a piece of lens paper held by a rubber band. Finally, to keep the volume of the culture constant, add to it 5 ml of filtered pond water.

Every 2 or 3 days for 2 weeks use this method to sample the culture to which you have been assigned.

C. Counting the organisms. The counting procedure is that used in Investigation 2.1: Count the organisms in each of 5 fields on a microscope slide, with 2 people making a count of each sample. In this investigation, however, more than one kind of organism is present. Your teacher will provide you with drawings by which you can identify the different kinds. Be sure to wash out the medicine droppers thoroughly before using them with each sample.

In your data book prepare a chart like the one opposite. In the chart, blocks have been divided into triangles; record your data in the upper triangle and your partner's data in the lower one. After each of you has obtained the average number of individuals from your counts, obtain the average of yours and your partner's. Finally you must take into account, by multiplying the average by $\frac{1}{5}$, the fact that you concentrated the sample by evaporating the water.

Transfer the data from the last column of your chart to the class chart that your teacher has prepared.

STUDYING THE DATA

Use the class data to construct graphs. Place on the horizontal axis the ages of the cultures in days; on the vertical axis list numbers to represent the densities of the populations. Using a different-colored pencil for each kind of organism, plot the average data from Culture A. Make similar graphs for each of the other cultures. When you are finished you should have 5 graphs, each with as many lines as you have organisms.

• What is the purpose of Culture A in the design of the experiment?(2)   • What changes if any occurred in the populations of the different organisms in Culture A during the 2-week period?(3)   • What changes if any occurred in each of the other cultures?(4)   • Compare the changes in each of the cultures with those in Culture A.(5)

CONCLUSIONS

• For each of your hypotheses state a conclusion.(6)   • Make a general statement about the effects of abiotic variables on population changes in ecosystems containing a mixture of aquatic producers and consumers.(7)

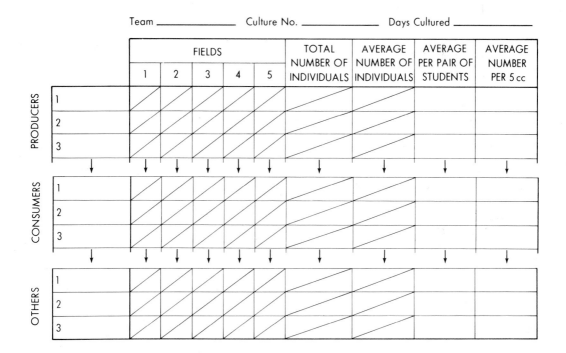

Team _____   Culture No. _____   Days Cultured _____

		FIELDS				TOTAL NUMBER OF INDIVIDUALS	AVERAGE NUMBER OF INDIVIDUALS	AVERAGE PER PAIR OF STUDENTS	AVERAGE NUMBER PER 5 cc
		1	2	3	4	5			
PRODUCERS	1								
	2								
	3								
CONSUMERS	1								
	2								
	3								
OTHERS	1								
	2								
	3								

BIOTIC COMMUNITIES

To understand an ecosystem as a whole, an ecologist must investigate both the organisms in it and their abiotic environment. It is not usually possible, however, to investigate all this at once. Often an ecologist may start his work by studying the set of interacting organisms—the *biotic community.*

Investigation 1.4 was a study of a biotic community. You found many kinds of organisms living together and affecting each other in various ways. However, different classes in different schools study different communities, find different organisms, and discover different relationships. So to provide a background to which all students can refer, a brief description of a particular biotic community follows. (The adjective "biotic" is used merely to show that we are not referring to exclusively human communities, and from here on it will usually be omitted.)

AN EXAMPLE

The sample community is located in the short rivers along the west coast of Florida. Since a community is a web of interactions, it is convenient to begin a description with one kind of organism—the river

Mary Root from Root Resources

Figure 3 · 1
A Florida river.

turtle—and let its relationships to other kinds lead into the community as a whole.

Adult river turtles are herbivores. They eat many of the kinds of plants that grow in the rivers, though they do not eat all kinds in equal amounts. Perhaps their favorite food is tape grass. Unlike the adults, young river turtles are not entirely herbivorous. They eat snails, which are themselves herbivorous; aquatic insects, many of which are carnivorous; and worms, some of which may be still farther along on a food chain.

And river turtles are food for other organisms. The highest mortality probably occurs in the egg stage. Turtle eggs are laid on land, in holes dug by the females. The nests are frequently discovered by

raccoons. See Figure 15 · 19.

skunks, raccoons, or snakes, all of which are fond of turtle eggs. The unhatched turtles are also killed by molds that live in the soil and grow

survive [sər vīv'; Latin: *super,* over, + *vivere,* to live]: to continue to live

through the thin shells of the eggs. If the eggs survive, the hatchlings may be picked up on the riverbank by snakes or raccoons. Once in the water, they may be eaten by some kinds of fish, by herons, or by a kind of snapping turtle.

When river turtles become larger, however, few organisms can

alligators. See page 113.

kill them directly. Adults could be attacked by alligators, but there is

leeches. See page 125.

little evidence of this. Leeches attach themselves to turtles and suck their blood but do not kill them. However, turtles do die in various ways. Then their bodies become food for decomposers, which finally return all of the substances in the turtle's body to the nonliving world.

Plants, besides serving as food, play another part in river-turtle life. The mats of half-floating vegetation, the tangled tree roots along the bank, the sunken logs—all these provide places for young turtles to hide from their enemies.

Each of the community relationships we have described so far is a *direct* relationship between a river turtle and another kind of orga-

Figure 3 • 2
Some animals that eat young river turtles.

skunk

great blue heron

alligator snapping turtle

nism. River turtles also have *indirect* relationships with other organisms. The snails are fond of tape grass. The tape-grass population varies greatly; sometimes it is plentiful and sometimes scarce. When tape grass becomes scarce, both turtles and snails may continue to eat it for a while. But eventually the snails turn to eating algae, which are tiny green plants that grow on the rocks. They can scrape these off the rocks in a manner that is impossible for the turtles. The turtles, on the other hand, are able to grasp mats of larger plants that have floated away from the land.

algae [ăl′jē]. For examples, see illustrations on page 168.

Humans trap skunks, kill snakes, and catch some of the fish that eat young river turtles. This indirectly reduces the mortality of river turtles. But humans also may dredge the rivers, destroying the tape grass.

Another kind of turtle, the musk turtle, eats nothing but snails. By reducing the number of snails, which eat tape grass, musk turtles have an indirect effect on the river turtles. The musk turtles never eat all the snails, because the snails are not easy to find among the beds of tape grass. Moreover, many animals that kill musk turtles also kill young river turtles. Thus the more musk turtles there are in the river, the less likely it is that young river turtles will be caught.

When tape grass is abundant, another kind of turtle, the pond turtle, which does not usually live in rivers, temporarily joins the community. Since the pond turtles leave as soon as the tape-grass supply

Figure 3 • 3

Tape grass, spiral-shelled snails, musk turtle (*left*), adult river turtle (*right, above*), and pond turtle (*right, below*).

Try to describe the community of organisms that you found during Investigation 1.4 in the way this river community has been described.

Figure 3 • 4

Black vulture.

X 1/10

predation [prǐ dā′shən; Latin: *praeda,* prey]

begins to decline, they have very little effect on river turtles.

We have been looking at the community as if through the eyes of a river turtle. If we had started with some other organism, we might have developed a somewhat different picture. To understand the community completely, we should have to look at all the relationships of all the organisms. Clearly, the study of a community—even a small one such as this—is not easy.

KINDS OF COMMUNITY RELATIONSHIPS

In the Florida river community you easily recognize some kinds of relationships that were discussed in Chapter 1. For example, tape grass, algae, and other green plants are producers; river turtles and snails are herbivores. But many other kinds of relationships help to form the community web of life.

Predation. Snapping turtles eat young river turtles; musk turtles eat snails; snakes swallow turtle eggs. In other communities, robins catch earthworms; house cats kill mice; you eat a chicken that someone has killed for you. A consumer that kills another living organism and eats it, regardless of whether it kills it before or during the eating process, is a *predator.* The organism that is eaten is called the *prey.*

However, these terms are not usually used for herbivores and the plants they eat. And sometimes organisms that are not usually predators kill their foods. In the southeastern states vultures may find an animal injured by an automobile and not wait for it to die before beginning to eat. On the other hand snapping turtles are predators most of the time, but if they find something edible that is already dead, they will not hesitate to eat it. So it is often difficult to decide whether or not to call a particular kind of organism a predator.

Parasitism. Leeches cling to a turtle's skin and suck blood, and microorganisms within the turtle absorb food directly from the blood. In other communities dogs have worms in their intestines, fish may be attacked by molds, and humans can be killed by tuberculosis microorganisms in their lungs. Plants may be inhabited by molds or microorganisms. And larger microorganisms may have smaller microorganisms within them. Organisms that live on or in other living organisms and obtain their food from them are called *parasites.* The organisms from which parasites obtain their food are called *hosts.*

edible [ĕd′ə bəl; Latin: *edere,* to eat]

Would you call yourself a predator when you eat a hamburger?

parasitism [păr′ə sī′tĭz əm; Greek: *para,* beside, + *sitos,* food]

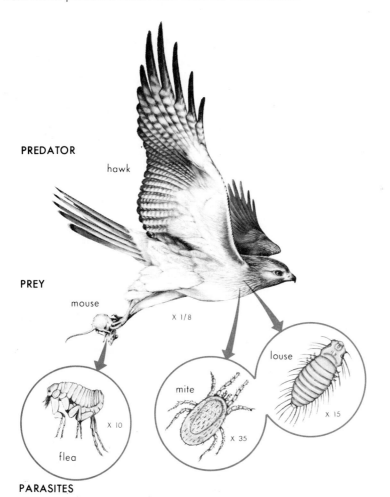

PREDATOR

hawk

PREY

mouse

X 1/8

louse

mite

X 15

flea

X 10

X 35

PARASITES

Figure 3 • 5

Some ecological relationships. Could the flea population have any effect on the hawk population?

Predators kill their prey; parasites *may* kill their hosts. But the death of its host is always a disadvantage and often a disaster for a parasite. When parasites kill, they usually kill indirectly, by producing substances that are in some way poisonous to their hosts. Of course

What happens to tuberculosis microorganisms when a tubercular person dies?

the host is just as dead when killed by a parasite's poison as it would be if it had been killed by a predator.

Difficulties. How long does an organism have to live on or in another before we call it a parasite? Once tuberculosis microorganisms get into the body of a human host, they stay, and they may multiply there through many generations. A leech may stay attached to its turtle host for weeks, but it does not spend its entire life there. Most biologists would agree to call a leech a parasite. But what about a mosquito? It consumes its victim's blood, just as the leech does, but it stays only long enough to obtain one meal—often a rather short one.

Further, we have seen that some consumers sometimes eat organisms that are already dead and sometimes act as predators.

precise [prĭ sīs'; Latin: *prae-*, before, + *cadere*, to cut]: sharply or exactly stated

Obviously the terms we have been using are not precise. This does not mean that they are useless; it merely means that their usefulness is limited to cases where their lack of precision does not matter. For example, it is quite safe to say that snapping turtles are predators on young river turtles, even though snapping turtles also eat dead flesh.

However, ecologists today are gaining more and more precise information about communities, and they need more precise terms with which to discuss their findings. So they are developing some new approaches to the description of community relationships.

benefit [bĕn'ə fĭt; Latin: *bene*, well, + *facere*, to do]

Benefit to one—harm to the other. One such approach is to consider the benefit or harm that a relationship brings to the organisms involved. The relationship between an individual predator and its prey seems to be beneficial to the predator and harmful to its prey. The relationship between herbivore and producer is of the same kind as that between predator and prey or parasite and host: beneficial to one, harmful to the other. As yet, however, ecologists do not have any one term to apply to this kind of relationship.

remora [rĕm'ə rə]

Commensalism. A remora is a fish that has a kind of suction disk on the top of its head. By means of this disk, it attaches itself to some large sea animal, most often a shark. The effect on the shark is probably neutral. But the remora benefits: first, it uses very little energy in moving about, because it is carried by the shark; second, it swallows

neutral [nū'trəl; Latin: *ne-*, not, + *uter*, one or the other]: here, neither benefit nor harm

Figure 3 • 6

Lion at its kill and vultures waiting. What ecological relationships are shown?

Figure 3 • 7
Shark with remora attached.

pieces of the shark's prey that float by. This kind of relationship—in which one organism is benefited and the other is unaffected—is called *commensalism.*

commensalism
[kə měn′səl ĭz′əm; Latin: *cum,* with, together, + *mensa,* table]

Commensalism does not necessarily involve a food relationship. For example, most of the holes used by bluebirds for nesting are chiseled out by woodpeckers. Bluebirds never use a woodpecker hole unless it has been abandoned. Thus, the presence of woodpeckers is beneficial to bluebirds. This is a commensal relationship, for, like that between a remora and a shark, it is neutral for one organism and beneficial for the other.

Figure 3 • 8
Mountain bluebird.

X 1/4

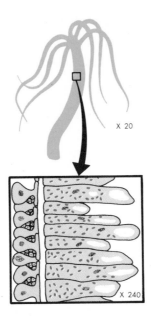

X 20

X 240

Figure 3 • 9
Green hydra. The green color in this small animal comes from hundreds of microscopic plants growing within it. What kind of ecological relationship might this be?

Mutualism. Clinging tightly to rocks or sometimes to the bark of trees can be found small plants that have no roots, stems, or leaves. Unlike mosses that are often found in the same places, they are never

lichens [lī′kənz]. See Figure
5 · 15.

bright green. Instead, they are a dull gray-green, or they may even appear yellow or orange. These organisms are called lichens. Actually, each lichen is composed of two different plants living in very close association. One is an alga, a producer that makes food by photosynthesis. The other is a fungus, a consumer that obtains its food from the alga. Without the fungus the producer probably could not long survive in the places where lichens grow; the consumer protects the tiny producer plants from drying out. Thus both organisms benefit. Such a relationship—one that is mutually helpful—is called **mutualism.**

mutualism [mū′chōō əl ĭz′əm;
Latin: *mutuus,* exchange]

Competition. Both snails and river turtles eat tape grass; the tape grass that a turtle eats is clearly not available for a snail to eat, and vice versa. Thus the presence of the turtle can be harmful to the snail, and the presence of the snail can be harmful to the turtle. This relationship is an example of **competition.** Whether snail and turtle actually do compete depends upon the amount of tape grass available and upon the amounts of the other plants that they eat. If both tape grass and other plants are scarce, competition for tape grass might be strong. Note that competition is always *for* something.

competition [kŏm′pə tǐsh′ən;
Latin: *cum,* with, together, +
petere, to seek]

Do pond turtles compete with river turtles for tape grass?

Competition does not necessarily involve food. Both bluebirds and starlings nest in holes in trees, poles, and fence posts. Neither species is able to dig holes for itself, so both are dependent upon holes already available. Thus the presence of bluebirds may be harmful to starlings and the presence of starlings harmful to bluebirds.

How many examples of competition between mankind and other organisms can you think of?

EVALUATING RELATIONSHIPS

The terms we have been discussing are based on the idea that some ecological relationships are beneficial, others harmful, still others neutral. Now what do·we mean by this? Clearly, when a musk turtle kills and eats a snail, that individual snail is harmed. But in the study of communities ecologists are not concerned with individuals; they are concerned with populations. The question is: Does the musk-turtle population harm the snail population?

X 1/5

Figure 3 · 10

Starling.

From what you have learned about the nature of science, why do you think scientists prefer numerical data?

To investigate this problem, an ecologist must define "harmful" in such a way that he can look for evidence concerning it. He might define "harmful" to mean that an increase in the musk-turtle population brings about a decrease in the snail population. "Beneficial" would then mean that an increase in one population brings about an increase in another population, and "neutral" that a change in one has no effect on another. Then the ecologist can obtain definite numerical data by measuring the sizes of the populations over a period of time. Because the preferred evidence in science is always quantitative (numerical data), these meanings of "harmful," "beneficial," and "neutral" are, in fact, the ones ecologists use.

lynxes [lǐngks′əz]

Here is an example of the kind of evidence required by these definitions: Lynxes undoubtedly eat snowshoe hares. But does the abundance of hares affect the abundance of lynxes? You have already seen graphed data for the Canadian snowshoe-hare population

(Figure 2 • 14); Figure 3 • 11 adds data on the Canadian lynx population. This allows us to consider the predator-prey relationship quantitatively. Because the graph shows that the population of the lynx goes
up and down, closely following the ups and downs in the population of
the hare, it provides evidence suggesting that the abundance of hares
is a factor in the abundance of lynxes. It is perfectly possible, however,
that some third factor was affecting both the hare and the lynx populations in the same way, so that even good quantitative data do not
necessarily lead to definite conclusions.

    The measurement of populations—particularly of animal popula-
tions—is difficult; as a result, knowledge of most community relationships is still very imperfect.

Often when human populations
become more dense, rat
populations do also. Explain.

For some methods by which
ecologists measure natural
populations, see the book by
Phillips (listed on page 29).

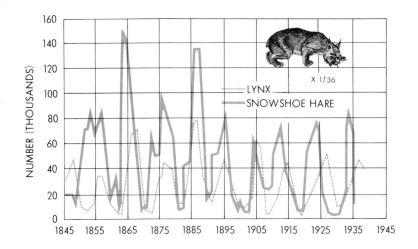

Figure 3 • 11

Population fluctuations of
lynx and snowshoe hare in
Canada, according to the
records of the Hudson's
Bay Company.

Investigation 3.2

RELATIONSHIPS BETWEEN TWO KINDS OF PLANTS

INTRODUCTION

    Many ecological problems are found in
biotic communities that have been formed by
human efforts. Plants that would never occur
together naturally are frequently found together
in gardens and cultivated fields. Understanding of the relationships among such plants is
an important contribution of scientists to agricultural practice.

MATERIALS AND SUPPLIES

        (for each team)
soil, enough to fill 3 boxes
trowel

pans, shallow, 3
oven
boxes, wooden, at least
        30 x 20 x 10 cm, 3
wood block, about 4 x 8 x 8 cm
sharp stick, pointed (or pencil)
tomato seeds, about 450
radish seeds, about 450
sheet glass, a little larger than
        the area of the boxes, 3
beaker, 1000-ml
paper towels
balance

PROCEDURE

Prepare the soil by removing stones and breaking all lumps. Place the soil in pans and bake it in an oven for 1 hour or more. Place the baked soil in the boxes and smooth to form a level surface. Use a block of wood to press the soil down firmly, but do not pack it tightly.

Add soil if necessary to obtain a firmed depth of at least 7 cm. Label the boxes *A, B,* and *C.* Water and allow to stand 24 hours.

Using a pointed stick or a pencil, draw furrows on the surface of the soil, parallel to the long side of each box, about 0.5 cm deep and 5 cm apart. In Box A place tomato seeds 1 cm apart along each row. In Box B place radish seeds 1 cm apart along each row. In Box C place tomato and radish seeds alternately 1 cm apart along each row. Each box should contain the same number of seeds. Use the wooden block to firm the soil again along the lines of planting. By doing this, you will barely cover the seeds with soil.

To reduce evaporation, cover each box with a sheet of glass. Put all the boxes in a place where they will receive strong light but even temperature. Remove the glass before the seedlings press against it. By this time the seedlings may be gently sprinkled with water without being disturbed. Keep all boxes equally moist. If they are kept on a windowsill, turn them daily so that seedlings on each side receive about the same amount of light each day.

When the plants are 10 to 15 cm high, harvest them. To do this, gently pull all the tomato plants in Box A. Rinse the soil from the roots and dry the plants on paper towels. Do the same with the radish plants from Box B. Remove, wash, and dry the tomato plants in Box C separately from the radish plants. Then weigh together all the plants from Box A, all the plants from Box B, all the tomato plants from Box C, and all the radish plants from Box C. Since there were only half as many radish seeds and tomato seeds in Box C as there were in Boxes A and B, it is necessary to divide the first and second weights by 2.

STUDYING THE DATA

Show the data in the form of a bar graph, with weight on the vertical axis. Arrange the 4 bars along the horizontal axis, left to right, in the order in which you obtained the weights.

• Is there a difference between the total weight of the tomato plants grown in Box A (divided by 2) and the total weight of those grown in Box C? If so, how do you account for the difference?(1) • Is there any difference between the total weight of the radish plants grown in Box B (divided by 2) and the total weight of those grown in Box C? If so, how do you account for the difference?(2)

CONCLUSIONS

• If you found a difference, does growing tomatoes and radishes together have more effect on the tomatoes or on the radishes? Or are the effects equal?(3) • Attempt to explain how any effect you noted may have occured. (4) • What term would you apply to the relationship between tomatoes and radishes shown in this experiment?(5)

• Did every seed germinate? If not, how could you correct for differences in germination?(6)

You judged the relationship by the weight of the plants. This is different from the measurements of community relationships discussed on pages 72–73. • Why can the weights of the plants be considered indirect evidence?(7)

ABIOTIC ENVIRONMENT

A biotic community cannot exist without an abiotic environment. Though an ecologist may choose to concentrate his investigation on a community, he can never understand it unless he considers factors of its abiotic environment too—in other words, the whole ecosystem.

ABIOTIC FACTORS

It is certainly important for the Florida river community that the water does not freeze; if it did, many of the kinds of organisms we have described could not exist. Temperature, sunlight, precipitation, and wind are among the physical factors that affect all ecosystems. Their effects differ, however, especially between aquatic and terrestrial ecosystems. Air temperature over a Florida river may change 10°C in 12 hours, but a few centimeters below the water surface it may change less than 1°C. Bright sunlight on the surface of the water becomes dimmer with depth, because water absorbs light; so most photosynthesis occurs near the surface. This effect is increased if heavy rainfall washes mud into the river.

If something happened to cut off the flow of water, the Florida river community would disappear. Water is a chemical substance—perhaps the basic chemical environmental factor.

Oxygen and carbon dioxide occur in both aquatic and terrestrial ecosystems, but the amount of each that can be held in water is considerably less than in air. The inorganic nutrients that producers require are likewise chemical abiotic factors that are not equally abundant in all ecosystems. And chemical substances that are injurious to organisms are found in some ecosystems. The kinds of substances present and their abundance determine whether or not a particular biotic community can exist in any given place.

injurious [ĭn jŏŏr′ĭ əs; Latin: *in-*, not, + *jus*, right, law]: capable of doing harm

What are some man-made chemical substances that may be injurious to organisms?

Haven Kolb

Figure 3 • 12

What abiotic environmental factor has produced the effect shown here?

Milton & Joan Mann

Figure 3 • 13
How has technology changed the abiotic environmental factors here?

EFFECTS OF ORGANISMS ON ABIOTIC ENVIRONMENTS

The current in Florida rivers—an abiotic factor—is not very strong; if it were, tape grass would not grow. But tape grass—especially when it is abundant—clogs the rivers and makes the current even slower than it would be otherwise. Thus the interaction between abiotic environment and community operates in both directions.

Give some other examples of ways in which organisms affect abiotic environmental conditions.

Of all organisms, mankind has by far the greatest ability to affect the abiotic environment. Very early in history, man covered himself with clothes and built houses that he warmed by fires; thus he extended a bit of tropical climate poleward. With the invention of agriculture, he had a much greater effect on the abiotic factors of ecosystems. He cleared and plowed the land. He spread the waters of rivers onto parched land. He added to ecosystems many chemical substances, some of which he himself invented. Since the invention of power machinery, man has become a force upon the landscape equal to earthquakes and hurricanes. And now, because of his ability to release atomic radiation in vast amounts, he is probably in a position to destroy the entire world ecosystem—the entire biosphere.

What other organisms did he permit to spread poleward by these activities?

Investigation 3.3

ABIOTIC ENVIRONMENT: A COMPARATIVE STUDY

BACKGROUND INFORMATION

The abiotic factors you will investigate are temperature and *relative humidity*. Relative humidity is a measure of the moistness of air. It is defined as the percent of water vapor actually in the air at any given temperature compared with the amount of water vapor that the air *could* hold at that temperature. In general, organisms lose water faster in an atmosphere with low relative humidity than in an atmosphere with high relative humidity. Therefore, this environmental factor is of special importance to land organisms.

MATERIALS AND EQUIPMENT

(per team of 6 students)

watches, 3

metersticks, 3

thermometers (0° to 100°C), 3

thermometers (of same range, with
cotton sleeves over the bulbs), 3

bottles (with screw tops) containing
30–50 ml of distilled water, 3

stiff pieces of cardboard for
fanning, 3

umbrellas for shading, 3

table of relative humidities

PROCEDURE

A team consists of 6 students working in 3 pairs. One member of each pair reads the instruments; the other fans the thermometer and records the data. Before starting, the 3 recorders synchronize their watches and agree on the time at which each measurement is to be made. These times should be recorded in a data form similar to this:

Location _____

	HEIGHT			
	0 cm	30 cm	90 cm	150 cm
TIME				
DRY-BULB TEMPERATURE				
WET-BULB TEMPERATURE				
RELATIVE HUMIDITY				

You will make measurements to compare 3 kinds of environment—3 *habitats.* One pair of students will make measurements in a dense cover of vegetation—a woods (preferably), a thicket, or a mass of shrubbery in a park. A 2nd pair will make measurements in a place that has a single layer of herbaceous vegetation—a meadow or a lawn (preferably not cut close to the ground). A 3rd pair will make measurements in a place that has no vegetation—bare ground or a tennis court. The 3 habitats should be as close together as possible. In each, you will make 4 sets of measurements: at ground level, at 30 cm above the ground, at 90 cm above, at 150 cm above.

Readings on both types of thermometers should be taken at the same time. Thermometers should be in their positions (see preceding paragraph) for at least 5 minutes before readings are taken. Thus, if the 1st reading is to be taken at 1:30 P.M., both thermometers should be in the 1st position at 1:25 P.M. The wet-bulb temperature is obtained by soaking the sleeve of a thermometer in water and fanning it vigorously for at least 2 minutes before making the reading. At least 8 minutes should be scheduled between readings so that there is time to move both thermometers to the next position and leave them there for 5 minutes. Use the umbrellas to shield the thermometers from the direct rays of the sun.

The reading from the dry-bulb thermometer is the air temperature. The relative humidity must be obtained from a table that will be supplied by your teacher. To find the relative humidity on the table, you need both dry-bulb and wet-bulb thermometer readings. When these 2 temperatures are known, it is possible to determine the amount of water vapor actually in the air compared with the amount that the air could hold. The necessary calculations were made when the table was constructed.

STUDYING THE DATA

• At ground level which habitat is coolest and most humid?(1)   • At ground level which is warmest and least humid?(2)   • How do these 2 habitats (Items 1 and 2) compare in temperature and humidity at higher levels above the ground?(3)   • At which level above the ground are all 3 habitats most alike in temperature and humidity?(4)   • How does the greatest temperature difference within the same habitat compare with the greatest temperature difference among the habitats?(5) • What differences among the 3 habitats may account for differences in temperatures and relative humidities?(6)   • How does this show interaction of biotic and abiotic factors in an ecosystem?(7)

You have been examining the differences among habitats. Now turn to differences within a habitat.   • How does the temperature in each habitat vary with respect to elevations?(8)   • Is the variation the same for each habitat? If not, in which is the variation greatest?(9)   • How does the humidity in each habitat vary with respect to elevation?(10)   • Is the variation the same for each habitat?(11)

DISCUSSION

In weather forecasts, temperatures predicted for the center of a city often differ from those predicted for the suburban areas.   • Relate this fact to the situations you have been observing.(12)   • What differences in temperature and humidity would be experienced by a beetle crawling on the ground in a meadow and a gnat hovering at 1.5 m above the meadow?(13)   In a general sense we may say the beetle and the gnat are in the same habitat, but small differences within a habitat are often important to the existence of some organisms. We can therefore distinguish small habitats within larger ones on the basis of measurements such as those you have made in this investigation.   • Would it be useful to measure such differences if you were studying the ecological relationships among cows in a meadow? Explain.(14)

ECOSYSTEM STRUCTURE

Study of an ecosystem involves measurement both of populations of organisms and of abiotic environmental factors. An ecologist who studies ecosystems must not only know organisms—biology; it is also necessary for him to know physics and chemistry. From such broad studies he tries to understand the structure of ecosystems and how they function.

STRUCTURE IN DEPTH

Your laboratory ecosystems obviously have length, breadth, and depth. The Florida river ecosystem likewise has structure in three dimensions: Some of its organisms are usually found floating near the surface; others swim deep in the water or crawl over the bottom. In water, it is easy to see that an ecosystem has volume.

On land, however, ecologists usually measure out study *areas,* as you probably did in Investigation 1.4. In some cases, it may be possible to overlook the third dimension—depth. But terrestrial ecosystems always have a volume, just as do aquatic ecosystems. In forests an ecosystem may be many meters in depth, stretching from the canopy of the trees down through shrubs, herbs, moss, and into the soil. Other ecosystems—a pasture, for example—may seem much more shallow than a forest ecosystem, but the air above the plants is an important part of it. The harmful effects on human health and comfort of many substances that man through his technology has put into the atmosphere have made mankind very much aware that every ecosystem exists in three dimensions.

How did Investigation 3.3 show this?

technology [těk nŏl′ə jǐ; Greek: *techne*, art or skill, + *logos*, speech, reason]: mankind's abilities to make and use tools and machinery. See page 78.

BIOTIC STRUCTURE AND ECOSYSTEM STABILITY

In describing the Florida river ecosystem, we named more than a dozen kinds of organisms and referred to many others in general terms. A careful biologist undoubtedly could find hundreds. The community that you studied in Investigation 1.4 surely had many more kinds than you were able to find.

Whatever the number of kinds of organisms may be within a given unit of space, some are always represented by many individuals and others by fewer. In any given volume of a Florida river there are many tape-grass plants, fewer snails, still fewer river turtles, and *very* few alligators.

In most ecosystems of middle latitudes, we find, when we study the macroscopic organisms, that the great majority of individuals belong to a rather small number of kinds. And when we consider the energy that passes through such an ecosystem—and this is a basic concern in any ecological study—we discover that most of it passes through this small number, or minority, of kinds. On the other hand, there is usually a rather large number of kinds that have so few individuals that specimens of them are seldom encountered. Only a small part of an ecosystem's energy passes through this large number, or majority, of kinds.

Into how many kinds of producers does a wheat farmer try to get solar energy to pass?

The biotic structure characteristic of most ecosystems in the middle latitudes does not occur elsewhere. In a given space in most tropical ecosystems, there are no large numbers of individuals of any one macroscopic kind, but there are a great many kinds. In contrast, in high latitudes—ecosystems of Antarctica, for example—and in other severe environments, only a few kinds of organisms can exist. These have the energy supply to themselves, and the number of individuals of each kind is comparatively large.

Most tropical ecosystems are rather stable, most middle-latitude ones are somewhat less so, and those of severe environments are characterized by wide fluctuations in population densities. It seems, then, that the greater the number of species—and the greater the number of links in food webs—the more effective is the homeostasis in an ecosystem.

The changes that man makes in ecosystems usually result in reducing the number of kinds of organisms. For example, man has changed forests and prairies, which contained a great many kinds of plants, into cultivated fields, in which he wants only one kind of plant, such as corn. Of course, he cannot succeed in reducing the community to just corn; but by simplifying the community, he produces an ecosystem that can have wide fluctuations in population densities. The corn density may be great; then he has a good crop. But he must spend much time and energy to prevent the smut population or the population of other plants, such as thistles, from overwhelming the corn. Thus an agricultural ecosystem is much like natural ecosystems in severe environments.

X 1/8

Figure 3 • 14
Thistle.

smut. See Figure 1 · 28.

Grant Heilman

Figure 3 • 15

A parasite can spread rapidly in a dense population of its host.

analyze [ăn'ə līz'; Greek: *ana,* up, + *lyein,* to loosen]: to separate a thing into its parts

niche [nĭch]

habitat [hăb'ə tăt'; Latin: *habitare,* to live in a place]

ECOLOGICAL NICHES

Some ecologists try to analyze the complexity of ecosystems by concentrating on the relationships of a single kind of organism. The sum of all relationships between any one kind of organism and its environment is its ecological *niche.* Most dictionary definitions of "niche" stress location; the ecological definition concerns a *way of living.* Of course, any particular way of living occurs in a suitable place—a habitat. But in describing the niche of an organism, an ecologist does not tell where it lives; he tells *how* it lives.

The habitat of river turtles, for example, is a rather warm, slow-moving river. In describing the niche of a river turtle, however, an ecologist must include all the relationships described on pages 66–68. He must also discover all the ways in which the abiotic environment affects river turtles—the temperature of the water, the flow of the current in the river, the clearness of the water, the nature of the soil in which the turtles dig their nests, and so on. Further, he must include all the ways in which river turtles affect both their biotic and their abiotic environments.

River turtles exist in one habitat. Some other kinds of organisms exist in several habitats and may have different niches in each. A human population that lives by hunting seals and whales has a niche different from the niche of a human population that lives by raising rice. Much of the study of human geography is the study of human ecological niches.

Seals and whales. See page 106.

CONTINUITY OF ECOSYSTEMS

What are the limits of an ecosystem? In our Florida example we would have clear boundaries for the ecosystem if it could be limited to the water. But turtles crawl onto the banks to lay their eggs, which then serve as food for land animals. Herons get almost all their food from the river but nest in tall trees. Frogs spend much time in the river, where they are food for snapping turtles, but, while on the banks, frogs may also be caught and eaten by raccoons, which are land animals. Frogs eat insects, which they catch outside the river, and the insects, in many cases, spend their early lives in the river.

This example is not a special case. All ecosystems have relationships, both biotic and abiotic, with others around them. Ecologists set boundaries primarily for convenience of study. Of course, some boundaries make more ecological sense than others. There are probably more relationships *among* the organisms that spend most of their time in the river and more *among* the organisms that spend most of their time on land than there are *between* the set of "land organisms" and the set of "river organisms." Therefore, the edge of the river makes a boundary that is both convenient for study and reasonable.

Is the political boundary of a city a reasonable ecological boundary? Explain.

Nevertheless, all ecosystems are linked to other ecosystems around them. A forest ecosystem connects with a river ecosystem; a river ecosystem blends gradually into a saltwater ecosystem of the sea —all ecosystems on Earth are connected to one another, forming one great world ecosystem, the biosphere.

Ecosystems also have continuity in time. We can recognize producers among the traces of early organisms preserved in ancient rocks. We can find fossils of extinct organisms that, from their structure, must have been herbivores; and we can find others that were clearly predators on these. These ancient organisms undoubtedly received energy from the sun; were affected by temperatures, winds, tides, and precipitation; and otherwise responded to factors in their abiotic environment.

Kinds of organisms have changed. Climates and landscapes have changed. But the system of interactions among organisms and environment seems to have remained much the same.

MANKIND IN ECOSYSTEMS

When mankind lived in small groups and had few tools, he was clearly a part of a local ecosystem. He had a niche in his ecosystem, and his effects upon it were not much more noticeable than those of other organisms. Today such small and primitive human groups have almost disappeared.

Now man is so numerous and the effects of his technology are so great that his activities greatly influence organisms and abiotic environments far beyond the places where the activities occur. Corn plants growing in Kansas, tomatoes growing in New Jersey, sugarcane growing in Hawaii, potatoes growing in Maine—all are producer organisms for humans living in all parts of the United States.

To grow his crops more effectively, man moves things from all parts of the world into his fields. He brings in some chemical substances to increase plant growth and others to decrease populations of organisms that eat the plants. And water and wind carry these chemicals far away. He brings in machines made of metals gathered from many parts of Earth, and when they wear out he dumps them on junk piles. He brings in gasoline and oil, and the wastes from their burning are carried into the air. He dumps his own wastes and those of his animals into streams. In short, his activities tend to result in the *pollution* of his environment.

pollution [pə lōō′shən; Latin: *polluere*, to pour over]

Clearly mankind can now be understood ecologically only when we consider the whole biosphere. In a city it is easy to forget relationships to the world ecosystem. Here man · has smothered the land under streets and buildings. The producers are far away, and most of the decomposers are in a distant sewage system or garbage dump. Yet without them—somewhere—the city could not exist.

Figure 3 · 16

Two steps in supplying biotic energy for a city's human population: a wholesale market (*left*); a retail market (*right*). Suggest places where the energy in this food will go.

Photos by A. Devaney, Inc.

aggregation [ăg′rə gā′shən; Latin: *ad*, to, + *gregare*, to collect]: a group that has been brought together

urban [ûr′bən; Latin: *urbs*, city]

A city is mainly an aggregation of organisms of a single kind. Yet man is not alone in a city. An urban community contains a number of organisms that in one way or another have adapted to urban conditions. The chief requirement is the ability to get along with man. Some organisms—dogs, cats, even pigeons—are deliberately cared for.

Figure 3 • 17
Wild rock doves nesting in
the cornices of city buildings.
What is their source of
biological energy?

Others—rats, mice, starlings, cockroaches—manage quite well without encouragement. Certain trees and shrubs that can live in the
polluted urban atmosphere are planted along streets and in parks.
Hardy herbs spring up unwanted and untended in vacant lots and even
in the cracks of city sidewalks. And, of course, microorganisms are
everywhere.

Outward from the center of a city, man shares space more generously with other organisms. There is more vegetation in suburbia,
though most of it is deliberately planted. Rabbits and squirrels manage
to exist with householders' pets. Many kinds of birds survive with or
without the encouragement of feeding stations and free housing. In the
south, various kinds of lizards get along nicely in gardens and even in
houses.

There is a strange biological sameness in man-dominated communities. It is true that the palms of Los Angeles are missing from
Boston, and perhaps crickets do not chirp everywhere between Miami
and Seattle. But grass and a few trees, dogs, rats, pigeons, and houseflies—these are the visible companions of urban and suburban man.

And whether he be a bus driver in the middle of Manhattan or a

Figure 3 • 18
Cockroach.

sheepherder on the plains of Nevada, a human being exists just as does every other organism—in a web of interrelationships. Man has learned how to separate himself physically from Earth. But whenever he ventures out into the universe, he must carry with him in his spacecraft a fragment of the biosphere.

Figure 3 · 19

Man dominates ecosystems only through ceaseless effort. What is happening here?

M. Fredric Stein

GUIDE QUESTIONS

1. Explain the statement "No organism lives alone."

2. What ideas are included in the term "ecosystem"?

3. Draw a diagram to summarize the interrelationships in the Florida river community.

4. How does a predator differ from a parasite?

5. In what way is the ecological relationship between a herbivore and a producer like that between a predator and its prey?

6. Distinguish between commensalism and mutualism.

7. In ecological competition between two organisms, what is the effect on both?

8. How would you describe the ecological relationship between a decomposer and the organism it uses as food?

9. How might an ecologist determine whether the effect of one kind of organism on another is harmful, beneficial, or neither?

10. A predator is a factor in determining

the population density of the prey it eats, but a parasite may not be. Explain.

11. Distinguish between a biotic community and an ecosystem.

12. How is the number of kinds of organisms in an ecosystem related to the ecosystem's stability?

13. In general, how does man affect the stability of the ecosystems in which he plays a part?

14. How can organisms living in the same place be said to occupy different niches?

15. Why is it impossible to draw sharp boundaries between ecosystems?

16. Why can we conclude that ecosystems have continuity in time?

17. How has technology changed mankind's relationships with natural ecosystems?

18. What are some characteristics that organisms in an urban biotic community need?

PROBLEMS

1. Rivers that run underground through caves (as in Kentucky) are ecosystems consisting of few kinds of organisms, none of which are producers. Explain why producers are lacking and how an ecosystem can exist without them.

2. Ecologists usually describe ecological relationships that tend to increase a population as "positive" and those that tend to decrease a population as "negative." How might a negative ("harmful") effect on a population actually benefit the population in the long run?

3. Here are two parasite-host relationships: (a) A fungus is the parasite; a chestnut tree is the host. The effect on the host is called "chestnut blight." (b) A microorganism (a bacterium) is the parasite; man is the host. The effect on the host is called "whooping cough." Investigate these two parasite-host relationships—especially their history, the effects on the parasite and host populations, and man's efforts to control these relationships. Then compare the relationships and attempt to explain any differences.

4. In the *Scientific American* of September, 1962, two articles describe biotic communities in the Antarctic (R. C. Murphy, "The Oceanic Life of the Antarctic," pages 186–210, and G. A. Llano, "The Terrestrial Life of the Antarctic," pages 212–230). Read these ar-

ticles. Then contrast land and water communities in the Antarctic, accounting for the contrast by describing the environmental factors in the two ecosystems.

5. What terms do you think are most appropriate to describe the ecological relationships between (a) mankind and rats, (b) mankind and sheep, (c) mankind and horses, (d) mankind and dogs. Do you think any of these relationships have changed during history?

6. Investigate the biotic community in a city, gathering evidence to support tentative answers to such questions as these: (a) To what extent is the biological energy in this community derived directly from the photosynthetic activity of its producers? (b) How does the community obtain the rest of its biological energy? (c) Which organisms in the community obtain their energy through the first source? Which organisms obtain it through the second? (d) Which organisms are present because man is a member of the community? (e) Which organisms are encouraged by man? Which organisms exist in spite of man's activities? (f) Which organisms would there be whether man was present or not?

7. Compare the system of biological energy in a cave community both with that in a deep-sea community and with that in an urban community.

SUGGESTED READINGS

BATES, M. *The Forest and the Sea.* New York: Random House, Inc., 1960. Chapter 10. (As good a statement of characteristics of a biotic community as can be made in 13 pages. Rather easy.)

BOOLOOTIAN, R. A. *Biology of Coral Atolls.* (BSCS Pamphlet 10.) Boulder, Colo.: EPIC, 1963. (Excellent description of one kind of ecosystem. Rather easy.)

CHENG, T. C. *Symbiosis, Organisms Living Together.* New York: Pegasus, 1970. (A whole book devoted to various kinds of ecological relationships. Fairly easy.)

KORMONDY, E. J. *Concepts of Ecology.* Englewood Cliffs, N.J.: Prentice-Hall, Inc., 1969. Pp. 1–6 and 54–60. (Advanced.)

LESHAN, E., *et al.* "Sabino Grove Ecology Study," *Natural History,* May, 1965. Pp. 14–23. (Report of a study made by high school students in California.)

ODUM, E. P. *Ecology.* Holt, Rinehart and Winston, Inc., 1963. Chapter 2. (An excellent description of the ecosystem concept by an ecologist who has helped to develop it. Advanced.)

SIMPSON, G. G., and W. S. BECK. *Life: An Introduction to Biology.* 2nd ed. New York: Harcourt, Brace and World, Inc., 1965. Pp. 642–663. (Illustrates how ecological terms are used in slightly different ways by different biologists. Fairly advanced.)

DIVERSITY AMONG LIVING THINGS

DIVERSITY AMONG LIVING THINGS

Every day of the week, and especially on holidays, crowds of curious people throng to zoos. They come to watch lions and elephants, owls and eagles, snakes and turtles. Only a little less popular than zoos are aquariums, where hundreds of kinds of animals that live in water —sharks and whales, eels and starfish, crabs and clams—can be seen. Equally fascinating to many people are botanical gardens, where living plants from all parts of the world are grown—some in the open, others in greenhouses.

Of course, you don't have to live near a zoo, an aquarium, or a botanical garden to learn at first hand about many different kinds of living things. You may find it easier to visit a forest, a meadow, or a pond. Even in backyards of cities and suburbs, many different kinds of organisms can be found.

Wherever you observe living creatures, you are sure, sooner or later, to get an impression of overwhelming diversity. For the casual visitor to the zoo on a Sunday afternoon, this may be only an impression and nothing more. But for one who has caught the spark of science, this impression of diversity arouses questions.

Biologists know of greater diversity than can be seen in any zoo. They know that almost 1½ million kinds of living organisms have been described and that more are discovered every year. How can we keep track of such a tremendous assemblage? When the kinds of organisms far outnumber all the words in any language, how can we even find names for them all? And why are there so many kinds of living things?

These questions provide the framework for Section Two. We are not setting out to describe every kind of organism; that is, of course, impossible. But we can find out how biologists keep track of so many different kinds; we can discover ways to put some order into diversity; we can look into the way in which biologists name organisms. We may even *begin* to find clues to the way in which so many different kinds of living things have appeared on Earth.

Animals

PRINCIPLES OF CLASSIFICATION

How can we possibly keep track of the enormous number of different kinds of organisms?

This is not a new problem. Long before the beginning of agriculture, men roamed far and wide searching for game and for edible or medicinal plants. Their ability to distinguish useful kinds of organisms from those that were predatory, poisonous, or otherwise dangerous was necessary for their survival. By mentally grouping organisms as "good," or useful, and "bad," or harmful, primitive men took the first step toward solving the problem.

medicinal [mə dĭs'ə nəl; Latin: *medicus*, physician]

Curiosity about things for their own sake, rather than for the sake of what they do to people or of what people can do with them, marked the dawn of science. When people began to look beyond the useful and the harmful, they had to invent new ways of grouping organisms. Perhaps they began by recognizing the groups "animal" and "plant."

By the 5th century B.C. science had really begun to develop in the lands around the eastern end of the Mediterranean Sea. Perhaps the early scientists began to recognize second-level groups. For example, plants were often divided into trees, shrubs, and herbs. Animals that live in the sea were often all grouped as fish.

Trees, shrubs, and herbs are *still* useful groupings for some purposes.

Not long afterward, Aristotle and his pupils attempted to classify all the living things they knew of—about 1000 kinds. But they made few improvements in the groupings. After the time of Aristotle, knowledge of living things increased rather slowly in Europe, but by the beginning of the 18th century A.D., about 10,000 kinds of organisms were known. A century later the number had risen to more than 70,000, and since that time the total has increased more than twenty-fold. Older systems of classification became inadequate to cope with such large numbers.

Aristotle [ăr'ə stŏt'əl]: 384–322 B.C. Greek philosopher and naturalist. He made many investigations, but his reputation in science suffered because later men accepted his writings rather than his example.

From these data you can construct a graph to illustrate the increase in man's knowledge of the species of organisms.

TWO METHODS OF CLASSIFICATION

The basic idea of classification is not difficult to understand. We all do some informal classifying, and almost anything may be classified—stamps, rocks, clouds, even the kinds of weather. The words in

Figure 4 · 1

Can you find a possibly harmful animal in this forest scene?

a dictionary are classified. They are classified according to their spelling—that is, alphabetically.

In classifying objects we could use an alphabetical method, arranging them according to the alphabetical order of their names. Suppose a supermarket manager arranged his merchandise alphabetically. Think of the varied goods to be found under the letter *A:* abalones, almonds, apples, apricots, artichokes, and many more. These would be followed by bacon, baking powder, beans, beef, beets, bread. . . . Imagine the practical difficulties in such a system! Refrigerators for perishable groceries would have to be scattered throughout the store. Actually, in any supermarket we find that the merchandise has generally been grouped according to the nature of the product. In one section we find various kinds of canned goods; in another, fresh fruits and vegetables; in a third, meats. Moreover, each of these sections may be further divided. Familiarity with this system of classification enables the shopper to locate groceries easily and quickly.

Thus we can classify in either of two ways: according to likenesses in names or according to likenesses in objects themselves. For biological classification names of organisms are certainly of much less importance than characteristics, so the alphabetical method is not satisfactory.

A BASIS FOR BIOLOGICAL CLASSIFICATION

As we look about us at the great number of organisms, we are first impressed by the differences between them—by their **diversity.** But when we look at them more closely, we begin to see likenesses—many kinds of likenesses. What kind of likenesses shall we choose as a basis for classifying organisms?

diversity [dĭ vûr'sə tĭ; Latin: *dis-*, away, + *vergere*, to bend]

We might decide to look for likenesses in color. So we lump together organisms that are blue: bluebirds, bluegrass, bluefish, blue crabs, blue spruce. Or we might pick out likenesses in the number of legs and lump together all organisms with four legs: frogs, alligators, mice, lions. Or we might classify organisms according to where they live, lumping together those that are found in human households: dogs, geraniums, canaries, rats, fleas.

These and many of the other kinds of likenesses we might use have a basic disadvantage—they do not lead to a consistent series of subdivisions. For example, after we have grouped all blue organisms together, we have difficulty in continuing to use color for subdividing the group. We must turn to some other characteristic.

However, when we examine organisms carefully, we find that some are very similar in structure and others are less similar, just as the words "comb" and "come" are more similar than "comb" and "cost." Therefore, on the basis of structure we can sort organisms into groups according to various degrees of similarity in the structures we consider important. The structure of organisms provides a consistent basis for classification.

structure [strŭk'chər; Latin: *struere*, to heap together, arrange]

There is a further reason for a structural basis of classification. *Taxonomists,* the biologists who specialize in problems of classification, must often work with preserved specimens of organisms. The structures of these specimens can easily be studied, but behavior or other characteristics of *living* organisms cannot be determined from dead specimens. So taxonomists have come to rely upon structural characteristics as a basis for classification.

taxonomist [tăks ŏn'ə mĭst; Greek: *tassein*, to arrange, + *nomos*, law]

BIOLOGICAL CLASSIFICATION

THE FIRST STEP

How much structural similarity must a group of individuals have to be thought of as one of the approximately two million kinds of organisms? First we must decide what we mean by a "kind" of organism.

Kinds of organisms. You would probably agree that boys and girls are different kinds of people, that cauliflowers and cabbages are different kinds of vegetables, that caterpillars and moths are different kinds of animals. But in none of these examples are we using the word in the way it was used in the preceding pages. What, then, does a taxonomist mean by "kinds of organisms"?

This may seem a trivial question, but it has importance in all lines of biological research. Since science is concerned with verifiable knowledge, the organisms used in any biological investigation must be identifiable—otherwise there is no way to ensure a verifying investigation. But the question is also important to non-biologists. Would you rather have a baseball bat made of hickory or one of pine? These are different kinds of trees. If an insect buzzed into your room, would you react in the same way if it were a fly as if it were a bee? Suppose you wanted to plant a shade tree. To order "a shade tree" would be as indefinite—and as unsatisfactory—as to order "a meal" in a restaurant. The tree salesman might ask whether you wanted a silver maple, a red oak, or a eucalyptus. Your choice could not be merely a matter of preference. You would need to consider which kinds of trees would flourish and which would die in the environment outside your home.

trivial [trĭv'ĭ əl]: of little worth or importance

eucalyptus [ū'kə lĭp'təs]

horse

X 1/60

donkey

Figure 4 · 2

species [spē'shĭz; Latin: *specere*, to look at]: hence, a shape or appearance

mongrels [mŭng'grəlz]: animals of mixed parentage

So intelligent citizens as well as professional biologists need to distinguish between kinds of organisms.

Deceiving appearances. A donkey differs from a horse: it is smaller, has larger ears and shorter mane and tail, and brays rather than neighs. You and a biologist agree that donkeys and horses are different kinds of animals—but a biologist would say "different *species*."

All donkeys differ from all horses in many ways. And all donkeys are similar to each other in many ways, as are all horses. On the other hand, organisms may look very different from each other and still be recognized by both you and a biologist as the same species. A Great Dane, a greyhound, a bulldog, a Pekingese—each is different from the others; but we recognize that they are all dogs. Why do we not recognize these different breeds as being separate species? Evidently something more than structural similarity is required for grouping individuals into species.

Meaning of "species." If we look at all dogs—not just those that appear in kennel shows—we can easily see that there are many intermediate mongrels between such different breeds as Great Danes and greyhounds. This is so because different breeds of dogs can interbreed—mate with each other and produce vigorous offspring that differ in various ways from both parents. These offspring can also mate and produce offspring that may be even more different among themselves than their mongrel parents were. Even if the most extremely different breeds cannot do this, as would be true of the Great Dane and Pekingese, they nevertheless form a part of one related series because they can mate with intermediate breeds. Therefore, all dogs are grouped into a single species.

Figure 4 · 3
Some breeds of dogs (*inner circle*). Mongrel offspring are intermediate between the breeds.

X 1/10

Figure 4 • 4

Mallard (*left*) and pintail (*right*). Females of these two species are much more alike than these males.

On the other hand, two groups of individuals are considered separate species if they do not interbreed and produce vigorous, fertile offspring. This is still true even though the two groups may look much alike to us. If two groups of individuals—two populations—*did* freely interbreed, then the characteristics of the two (whether visible or not) would soon disappear, being bridged by offspring populations that would share the characteristics of the two original populations. Therefore, two populations remain distinct from each other only so long as they fail to interbreed enough to produce populations of intermediate individuals.

fertile [fûr′təl; Latin: *ferre*, to bear, produce]

This distinctness of species populations is maintained in several ways. In many cases, no offspring are produced at all. Clearly, an elephant and a crab cannot mate and produce offspring. In other cases, offspring are formed but die when young. If the eggs of a bullfrog are fertilized by a leopard frog, they develop for a short time, then die. Thus no intermediate population ever results. In still other cases, the offspring are vigorous but completely or partly *sterile*, that is, unable to reproduce. Mules, which result when horses and donkeys are crossed, are almost always sterile.

sterile [stĕr′ĭl; Latin: *sterilis*, barren]

Sometimes individuals of two different species are able to form vigorous and fertile offspring in captivity but seldom do so otherwise. In these cases, distinctness of the species is maintained not by lack of ability to interbreed, but by other means. For example, the two species of duck known as mallards and pintails are so different that every duck hunter can tell them apart. Though they are found in the same places in many parts of North America, birds intermediate between them are rare. Yet when they are put together in the same pen, they readily produce fertile offspring. Apparently wild mallards and wild pintails seldom mate because of differences in their behavior and nesting habits. Alaska brown bears and polar bears provide a somewhat different example. In the Washington Zoo these species have successfully mated and produced vigorous, fertile offspring. However, in the wild no such cross has ever been discovered. The reason? Brown bears live in forests, eating berries, small animals, and fish that they catch in streams. Polar bears live on snowfields and ice floes, catching seals for food. Thus brown bears and polar bears rarely, if ever, see each other—except in zoos.

X 1/75

Figure 4 • 5

Polar bear (*above*) and Alaska brown bear (*below*).

For a different viewpoint, see Raven and Mertens, *Plant Systematics* (reference on page 176).

Figure 4 · 6

Some common animals in the order Carnivora. Which two look most alike?

X 1/30

coyote

X 1/27

wolf

X 1/18

fox

X 1/10

weasel

X 1/36

bear

genus [jē′nəs; Greek: *genos*, race]

Canis [kā′nĭs; Latin: dog]

Vulpes [vŭl′pēz; Latin: fox]

Canidae [kăn′ə dē]

In summary, then, we can say that a species is a population of individuals that are more or less alike and that interbreed and produce fertile offspring under natural conditions.

Difficulties. This concept of species is far from perfect. First, it cannot be used for organisms in which only one individual is involved in reproduction. For example, many small organisms reproduce by simply dividing into two parts; in such cases the word "interbreed" is meaningless. Second, although the definition can be verified, it cannot really be tested in experiments, since it is dependent upon the behavior of the organisms under natural conditions. And third, for practical use in identifying organisms, the definition is cumbersome. To use it, we need detailed information about breeding under natural conditions, and we have such data for only a small percentage of known kinds of organisms.

Thus, deciding whether a particular population is a species or not remains to some degree a matter of the opinions of biologists who are experts in the study of the organisms involved. But whenever the biological definition of species can be applied, it is valuable.

FURTHER GROUPINGS

Having grouped individuals into species, taxonomists next look for similarities among species. Dogs, coyotes, and wolves are separate species, but they are similar in many ways. Some breeds of dogs closely resemble wolves, and many a person has mistaken a coyote for a dog. Species such as these, with many similar characteristics, are grouped into the same *genus.* Some people may think that foxes are also very doglike. But by placing the doglike animals in one genus, *Canis,* and foxes in a separate genus, *Vulpes,* taxonomists express their belief that there are more important structural similarities among dogs, wolves, and coyotes than between wolves and foxes. (Do not worry about the strangeness of some of these names. Get classification straight first; then you can tackle the problem of naming.)

Similar genera (plural of "genus") are grouped together in a *family.* All taxonomists agree in placing *Vulpes* with *Canis* and several other genera of less familiar animals in the family Canidae. In some ways weasels resemble dogs and wolves, but they are less like them than are foxes; taxonomists express this difference by placing them

adult male

immature male

X 1/2

indigo buntings

X 1/2

Acadian flycatcher

least flycatcher

Figure 4 • 7

Appearance may be unreliable as a guide to grouping individuals in species. *Above:* These dissimilar birds are both indigo buntings. *Below:* These dissimilar birds are both red-winged blackbirds. *Right:* These similar birds are from populations that do not interbreed.

male

female

X 1/2

red-winged

blackbirds

Mustelidae [mŭs tĕl'ə dē; Latin: *mustela*, weasel]

Ursidae [ûr'sə dē; Latin: *ursa*, bear]

Carnivora [kär nĭv'ə rə; Latin: *carnis*, flesh, + *vorare*, to devour, eat]

Mammalia [mă mā'lĭ ə; Latin: *mamma*, breast]

phylum [fī'ləm; Greek: *phylon*, tribe]

Chordata [kôr dā'tə; Greek: *chorde*, string of musical instrument]

Animalia [ăn ə mā'lĭ ə]

in a separate family, Mustelidae. And bears, though they are furry predators, as are the other animals that have been mentioned, are structurally different from them in several ways, so taxonomists place them in still another family, Ursidae. These three families (Canidae, Mustelidae, Ursĭdae) are grouped with other similar families into the *order* Carnivora.

Wolves, weasels, and bears have many differences, but they still share many likenesses. Certainly these animals have more likenesses among themselves than they have with, for example, monkeys. Monkeys, therefore, are placed in a different order, Primates. But monkeys —and rats, cows, horses, and many other organisms—do share some characteristics that are the basis for putting all of them together when taxonomists make the next larger grouping—at the *class* level— Mammalia.

Continuing with this method of grouping, most taxonomists place the classes containing birds, frogs, fish, and other organisms with the Mammalia in the *phylum* Chordata. And finally, snails, butterflies, and thousands of other organisms are grouped into the *kingdom* Animalia —all the living things we think of as animals.

As we go from species to kingdom, the organisms that are grouped together share fewer and fewer characteristics at each succeeding level. At the species level the individuals are so much alike they can interbreed. At the kingdom level there are very few characteristics that are shared among all the individuals.

The levels can also be viewed in the opposite direction—kingdom to species. Reading Figure 4 · 8 downward shows the levels in this way. When the chart is read in this direction, the organisms that are grouped together at any level share more characteristics than those at the level above.

A classification is not a fact. It results from the interpretation of facts; it shows what the facts mean to the classifier. That cats and eagles and alligators have claws is a verifiable fact. But whether or not these three kinds of organisms should therefore be grouped to-

Figure 4 · 8

Examples of biological classification. In addition to the seven principal levels, intermediate levels are often used. For example, a *subphylum* level may be placed between phylum and class. See also page 108.

LEVEL	DOG	WOLF	MAN	CRAYFISH	BUTTERCUP	PARAMECIUM
Kingdom	Animalia	Animalia	Animalia	Animalia	Plantae	Protista
Phylum	Chordata	Chordata	Chordata	Arthropoda	Tracheophyta	Ciliophora
Class	Mammalia	Mammalia	Mammalia	Crustacea	Angiospermae	Ciliata
Order	Carnivora	Carnivora	Primates	Decapoda	Ranales	Holotricha
Family	Canidae	Canidae	Hominidae	Astacidae	Ranunculaceae	Parameciidae
Genus	Canis	Canis	Homo	Cambarus	Ranunculus	Paramecium
Species	familiaris	lupus	sapiens	bartoni	acris	caudatum

gether and, if so, at which level—these are matters of opinion. Therefore, though all taxonomists base their classifications on a system of levels, there is no general agreement about the places at which particular organisms should be fitted into the scheme. The more a taxonomist knows about organisms and the methods of classification, the better his opinions will be. Nevertheless, taxonomists of equal knowledge and experience sometimes differ greatly in their views.

scheme [skēm; Gre_... _chema, shape]

Investigation 4.1

THE LEVELS OF CLASSIFICATION

INTRODUCTION

In this investigation you will discover some of the structural characteristics that taxonomists use in separating animal groups at different levels of classification. Because you will be using the observations of other persons (recorded as drawings), your conclusions can be no *more* valid than those drawings. How much *less* valid your conclusions will be depends upon your own thinking.

PROCEDURE

Prepare 4 forms like the one below.

Label the 1st form "Chart 1." In the spaces under "Animals" list "Man," "Chimpanzee," and "Gorilla." In the spaces under the heading "Characteristics," copy the italicized words in each of the following questions. These words should remind you of the full questions when you review the chart.

a. How does the *length of the arms* of the animal compare with the length of its legs?
b. Is there an *opposable 1st toe on the foot?* (An opposable toe is one that can be pressed against all the others, just as your thumb can press against your other fingers.)
c. Is the *brain case* of the skull relatively *large* or is it *small* as compared with the brain cases of the other organisms on the chart?
d. Are the *canine teeth* relatively *large* or are they *small* as compared with the other teeth of the same organism?
e. How many *incisor teeth* are present in the upper jaw?

Study Figure 4 · 9. For each of the animals, fill in the spaces in Chart 1 with your answer to each question. Then write the word "Family" in the space following "Classification level." From the information on pages 108–109 find the family into which each of these organisms has been placed. In the spaces at the bottom of the chart, write the information you have found.

Now fill in the 2nd form and label it "Chart 2." In the spaces under "Animals," list "Man," "Dog," "Cat." Under the heading "Characteristics," copy the italicized words in each of the following questions:

a. How many paired *appendages* (arms and legs) does the animal have?
b. Are *nails* present *or* are *claws* present on the toes of the foot?

Chart _____

CHARACTERISTICS	ANIMALS		
	1.	2.	3.
a.			
b.			
c.			
d.			
e.			
Classification level ___			

. To what extent do you find the *collarbone* developed?

d. How does the size of the *canine teeth* compare with that of others in the lower jaw?

e. How many *incisor teeth* are present in the lower jaw?

Study Figure 4 • 10. For each animal fill in the spaces in Chart 2 with your answers to the questions. Then write the word "Order" in the

blank space following "Classification level." From the information on pages 104–111 find the order into which each of these organisms has been placed. Write this information in the spaces at the bottom of the chart.

Use the same procedure to fill in the other 2 forms.

For Chart 3 use the information in Figure 4 • 11 and the following questions:

a. What kind of *body covering* (hair, feathers,

Figure 4 • 9

	MAN	CHIMPANZEE	GORILLA
BODY FORM			
TEETH			
SKULL			
FOOT			

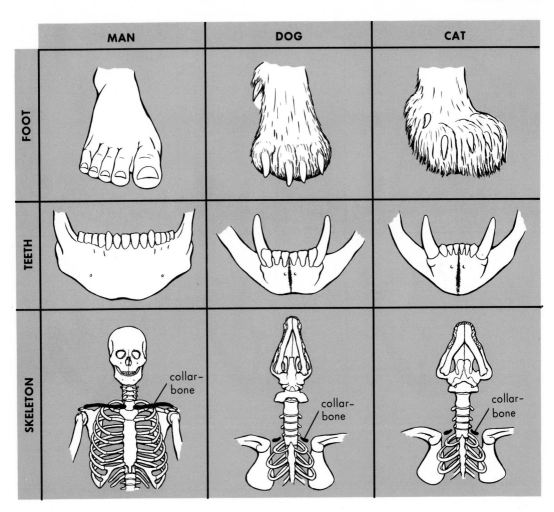

	MAN	DOG	CAT
FOOT			
TEETH			
SKELETON	collar-bone	collar-bone	collar-bone

Figure 4 · 10

scales, none) does the animal have?

b. How many paired *appendages* (arms and legs) does the animal have?

c. How many *ventricles* are *in the heart*?

d. Do the *ears* project from the surface of the head?

e. How stable is the *body temperature*? Is it similar to the temperature of the environment, or is it quite different?

Write the word "Class" in the space following "Classification level" and add the name of the class into which each organism in Figure 4 · 11 is placed.

For Chart 4 use the information in Figure

4 · 13 and the following questions:

a. What kind of *skeleton* (internal or external) does the animal have?

b. Is the *position of* the *nerve cord* along the back or along the belly?

c. Compared with the rest of the nervous system, is the *brain* large or small?

d. Are *paired appendages* present or absent?

e. Are there *grooves behind the head region* of the very young organism?

Write the word "Phylum" in the space following "Classification level" and add the name of the phylum into which each animal in Figure 4 · 13 is placed.

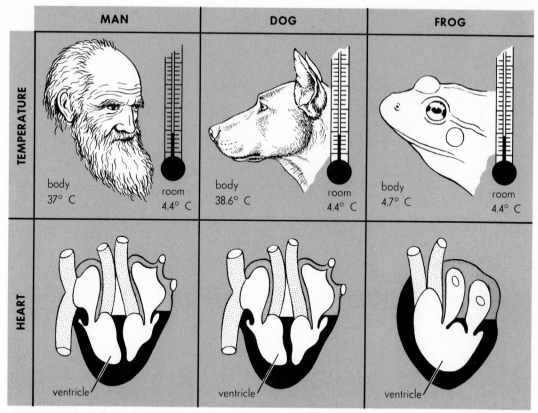

	MAN	DOG	FROG
TEMPERATURE	body 37° C room 4.4° C	body 38.6° C room 4.4° C	body 4.7° C room 4.4° C
HEART	ventricle	ventricle	ventricle

Figure 4 • 11

CONCLUSIONS

• How does the system of classification express the fact that there are more structural similarities:

a. between chimpanzee and gorilla than between chimpanzee and man?(1)

b. between dog and cat than between dog and man?(2)

c. between man and dog than between man and frog?(3)

d. between man and bird than between man and crayfish?(4)

e. between man and chimpanzee than between man and dog?(5)

• If you are told that Species A and B are classified in the same kingdom but different phyla and that Species C and D are classified in the same phylum but different classes, what general statement can you make about similarities among Species A, B, C, and D?(6)

Figure 4 • 12

Skeletons of horse and man. At what level of classification would you put these two organisms together?

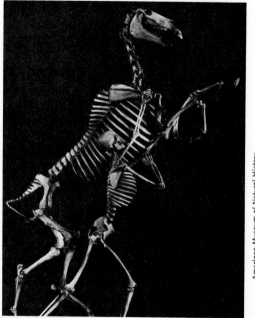

American Museum of Natural History

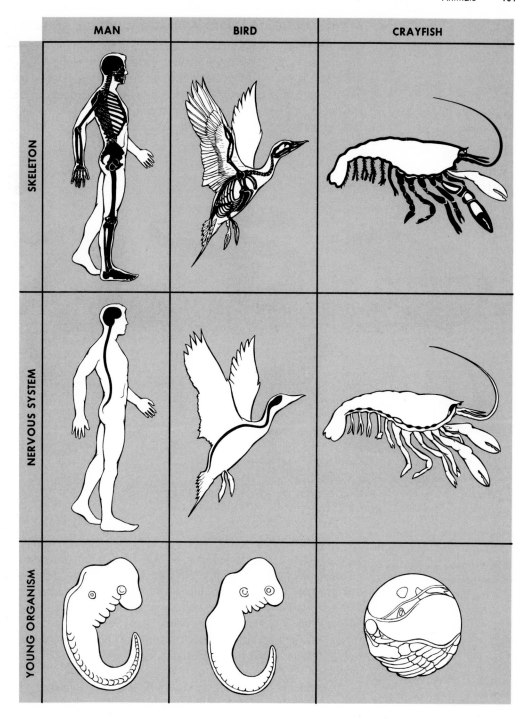

MAN   BIRD   CRAYFISH

SKELETON

NERVOUS SYSTEM

YOUNG ORGANISM

Figure 4 · 13

A CATALOGUE OF LIVING ANIMALS: KINGDOM ANIMALIA

Now let us see how classification can guide us through the diversity of organisms. In this chapter we shall consider only animals. All animals are motile at some part of their lives and are able to react to their environments rather quickly. They never carry on the process of photosynthesis. There is not much more that can be said, for at the kingdom level organisms share few characteristics.

For alternate classifications, see Appendix 3.

Figure 4 · 14
What characteristics do all these animals share?

X 1/18

X 1/2

X 1/3

rattlesnake

bat

frog

X 1/4

X 1/24

shark

robin

sunfish

X 1/4

PHYLUM CHORDATA
chordates; about 46,000 species

Look at a set of six selected animals: a sunfish, a frog, a bat, a robin, a rattlesnake, and a small shark (Figure 4 · 14). Can we unite these in one phylum? If so, we must find some structural likenesses among them. The bat and robin have paired wings; the shark and the sunfish have paired fins; the frog has paired legs. Perhaps we can group wings, fins, and legs as similar structures, calling them **appendages.** But on this structural basis the snake would obviously not belong to the group.

If we sought help from a **zoologist**—a biologist specializing in the study of animals—he would point out that all these animals have similar internal skeletons. Each has a backbone made up of pieces called **vertebrae**—some separate, others fused in groups, and enclosing a tubular nerve cord, a **spinal cord.**

Having helped this much, the zoologist might then show us a small, fishlike animal called a lancelet, stating that in his opinion it

appendage [ə pĕn′dĭj; Latin: ad, to, + pendere, to hang]

zoologist [zō ŏl′ə jĭst; Greek: zoion, animal, + logos, word, speech, reason]

vertebrae [vûr′tə brē; Latin: vertere, to turn]; singular, vertebra

lancelet [lăns′lĭt; Latin: lancea, spear]

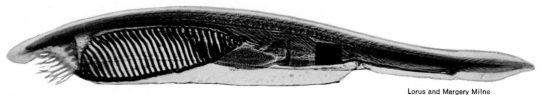

Figure 4 • 15

Lorus and Margery Milne

Lancelet. This animal lives partly buried in the sand of ocean shallows.

should be added to the group we already have. But close examination shows that the lancelet has no vertebrae. Instead, it has a kind of flexible rod, called a **notochord,** in nearly the same position as the backbone of the other animals. Just above this (closer to the surface of the back) is a nerve cord that seems much like the spinal cord in the other animals we have examined.

notochord [nō'tə kôrd'; Greek: *noton,* back, + *chorde,* string of musical instrument]

Then, after a bit of dissection, the zoologist might point out a set of paired slits located along both sides of the lancelet's body just behind its mouth. Further, he might show us some lancelet **embryos**— the early stages in development before hatching. In the embryos we could see a series of paired pouches that grow outward in the throat region and a corresponding series of paired grooves that push inward from the body surface. When these **pharyngeal** pouches and the grooves meet, in the fully developed lancelet, paired pharyngeal slits are formed.

embryo [ĕm'brĭ ō'; Greek: *en,* in, + *bryein,* to swell]

pharyngeal [fə rĭn'jĭ əl; Greek: *pharyngos,* of the throat]

Both the shark and the sunfish have similar slits. But what about the frog, bat, robin, and snake? The zoologist tells us that in the tadpole stage, such pharyngeal slits were present in the frog—but they disappeared before it became an adult. In the bat, robin, and snake, pharyngeal pouches and grooves were formed early in embryonic development; but they failed to meet, so no openings were ever formed. In all of these animals a notochord like that of the lancelet was also present in the embryo. As development proceeded, it was replaced by the vertebrae of the backbone.

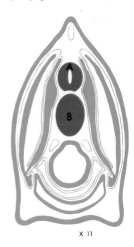

X 11

Figure 4 • 16
Diagram of a lancelet in cross section: *A,* nerve cord; *B,* notochord.

Here, then, is a new idea: To detect the basic structure of an organism, we may have to study not only its adult form but its embryonic stages as well. On the basis of such a study, zoologists group all the animals we have been studying into a single phylum, the chordates. Although they differ greatly, all the animals in this phylum share at some stage of their development (1) a notochord, (2) pharyngeal pouches, and (3) a **dorsal** nerve cord—that is, one that is near the upper side of the body.

dorsal [Latin: *dorsum,* back]

SUBPHYLUM VERTEBRATA
vertebrates; 45,000 species

All the animals in Figure 4 • 14—all we have been discussing except for the lancelet—are vertebrates. In these chordates the notochord is replaced during early development by a backbone of vertebrae. Also, at the **anterior** end, the end that usually is in front when the animal moves, the nerve cord is enlarged. This enlargement—a brain—is en-

Vertebrata [vûr'tə brāt'ə]; vertebrates [vûr'tə brāts']

anterior [ăn tĭr'ē ər; Latin: *ante,* in front of]

closed in a protective case—a skull. Probably most of the larger animals that you know fit this description of vertebrates.

Class Mammalia
mammals; about 5000 species

At present all zoologists probably agree on which vertebrate animals should be called mammals. From a tiny field mouse to a giant blue whale more than 30 meters long (the largest animal that has ever lived), all mammals share two characteristics. First, all have hair, although it is sometimes not very evident and in some whales it is completely absent after birth. Second, all species of mammals feed their young with milk, a fluid secreted from special glands in the skin called *mammary* glands. These glands function only in females, but they are present in males as well. Further, mammals are usually **warm-blooded** —able to maintain their bodies at a constant temperature regardless of the temperature of the environment. This characteristic they share with birds.

modifications [mŏd′ə fə kā′shənz]: changes in a basic plan

Although they have many characteristics in common, mammals show great diversity. Much of this diversity comes from modifications that enable organisms to function in particular ecological niches. Such modifications are called **structural adaptations.** For example, mammalian hair may be greatly modified—it appears as quills in porcupines; as horns in rhinoceroses; as odd, flattened plates in pangolins; as wool in sheep. Zoologists know that these are modifications of hair from studies of the way in which the structures are formed during embryonic development.

adaptations [ăd′əp tā′shənz; Latin: *ad,* to, + *aptare,* to fit]

Artiodactyla [ärt′ēə dăk′tĭl ə; Greek: *artios,* even, + *daktylos,* finger or toe]

Order Artiodactyla
even-toed hoofed mammals; about 170 species

These are primarily herbivorous mammals. Most have complex stomachs that allow them to digest rough grasses and leaves. They have 2 or 4 toes on each leg, and these toes are modified as hooves. Many of these mammals have horns or antlers. (Examples: hippopotamus and impala.)

X 1/60

X 1/36

impala

hippopotamus

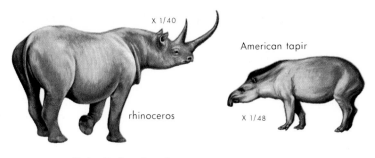

X 1/40

American tapir

rhinoceros

X 1/48

Order Perissodactyla
odd-toed hoofed mammals; about 15 species

These herbivorous mammals lack complex stomachs, but they have very well-developed grinding teeth (*molars*) in the back of their mouths. They have hooves, each of which consists of 1, 3, or 5 modified toes. (Examples: rhinoceros and American tapir.)

Order Sirenia
sirenians; 5 species

Sirenians are herbivorous mammals that are completely aquatic. They have no hind appendages, but their broad, flat tails are expanded and serve as fins. Adults have only a few hairs. (Example: manatee.)

Order Proboscidea
proboscideans; 2 species

In these large herbivorous mammals the upper front teeth—*incisors*—are modified as tusks. Molars are produced 2 to 4 at a time as older ones wear out. A proboscidean is easily recognized by its trunk, which is formed as a modification of the nose and upper lip. (Example: elephant.)

Perissodactyla
[pə rĭs′ō dăk′tĭl ə; Greek: *perissos*, uneven, + *daktylos*]

molar [Latin: *mola,* mill]

Sirenia [sī rē′nĭ ə; Latin: *siren,* a kind of mermaid]

X 1/60

manatee

Proboscidea [prō′bə sĭd′ĭ ə; Greek: *pro-,* in front of, + *boskein,* to graze]

incisor [ĭn sī′zər; Latin: *in,* in, + *caedere,* to cut]

X 1/90

elephant

X 1/12

hyrax

Order Hyracoidea
hyraxes; 5 species

Hyraxes are small herbivorous mammals with nails instead of hooves. They have skeletons that in some characteristics are similar to those of proboscideans. (Example: hyrax.)

Hyracoidea [hī′rə koi′dĭ ə; Greek: *hyrax,* small animal]

Carnivora [kär nĭv′ə rə; Latin: *carnis*, flesh, + *vorare*, to eat]

canine. Can *you* supply the derivation of this word?

Order Carnivora
carnivores; about 280 species

Most of these mammals are carnivorous, and many of their structural adaptations are related to a predatory life. Their *canine* teeth—the ones just behind the incisors—are large and pointed, and some of their molars have sharp shearing edges. The toes of carnivores end in claws rather than hooves or nails. (Examples: seal, striped hyena, and cheetah.)

seal

X 1/24

X 1/24

striped hyena

X 1/36

cheetah

Cetacea [sə tā′shē ə; Greek: *ketos*, whale]

Order Cetacea
cetaceans; about 80 species

These entirely aquatic mammals are almost all marine. Their front appendages are modified as flippers and hind ones are lacking. Their heads are very large without any external necks. Adults have no hair. (Example: blue whale.)

X 1/200

blue whale

Rodentia [rō dĕn′shĭ ə; Latin: *rodere*, to gnaw]

Order Rodentia
rodents; about 1700 species

Most rodents are rather small mammals. Their incisors are chisel-like and grow continually from the roots. Within the order there is great structural diversity, which is correlated with much ecological diversity; rodents run over the ground, live in trees, burrow in soil; some are even semiaquatic. (Examples: woodchuck and squirrel.)

woodchuck   squirrel

Order Lagomorpha
harelike mammals; about 60 species

These herbivorous mammals have incisors much like those of rodents, but there are 4 of them in the upper jaw instead of 2. Their tails are very short. (Examples: rabbit and pika.)

Lagomorpha [lăg'ə môr'fə; Greek: *lagos*, hare, + *morphe*, form]

rabbit   pika

Order Tubulidentata
aardvarks; 1 species

The embryos of these mammals have numerous teeth, but the adults have only a few. Adults have toes that end in structures that are intermediate between claws and hooves. (Example: aardvark.)

Tubulidentata [tū'byə lə dĕn tä'tə; Latin: *tubulus*, small tube, + *dens*, tooth]

aardvark

pangolin

Order Pholidota
pangolins; 8 species

These are ant- and termite-eating mammals that have no teeth. Their bodies are encased in scales formed from modified hairs. (Example: pangolin.)

Pholidota [fä'lə dōd'ə; Greek: *pholis*, scale]

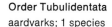

Edentata [ē děn'tăd ə; Latin:
ex, away, + *dens*, tooth]

Order Edentata
edentates; about 30 species

These mammals have no front teeth, and some have no teeth at all.
They have rather small brains. Many are ant and termite eaters. (Examples: sloth and armadillo.)

armadillo

X 1/20

X 1/15

sloth

Primates [prī mā'tēz; Latin:
primus, first]

Order Primates
primates; about 200 species

Below is a complete classification of this order, to show how complex classification can become.

Suborder Prosimii

   Infraorder Lemuriformes

      Superfamily Tupaioidea

         Family Tupaiidae: tree shrews

      Superfamily Lemuroidea

         Family Lemuridae: lemurs

         Family Indriidae: indris

      Superfamily Daubentonioidea

         Family Daubentoniidae: aye-ayes

   Infraorder Lorisiformes

         Family Lorisidae: lorises, pottos, galagos

   Infraorder Tarsiiformes

         Family Tarsiidae: tarsiers

Suborder Anthropoidea

      Superfamily Ceboidea

         Family Cebidae: New World monkeys

         Family Callithricidae: marmosets

      Superfamily Cercopithecoidea

         Family Cercopithecidae: Old World monkeys, baboons

      Superfamily Hominoidea

         Family Pongidae: apes

         Family Hominidae: man

Primates have well-developed incisor, canine, and molar teeth. At the ends of their toes most primates have flat nails instead of hooves or claws. Their eyes are usually directed forward, unlike those of most other mammals. (Examples below.)

tarsier

bush baby

X 1/12

marmoset

squirrel monkey

X 1/16

X 1/3

red howler

X 1/15

X 1/15

baboon

chimpanzee

X 1/2

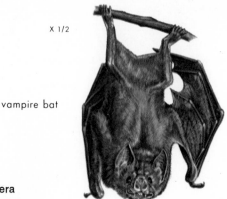

vampire bat

Chiroptera [kī′răp′tə rə; Greek: *cheir*, hand, + *pteron*, wing]

Order Chiroptera

bats; about 900 species

These are true flying mammals. They have wings formed of webs of skin between their fingers and between their front and hind appendages. (Example: vampire bat.)

Dermoptera [dər′măp′tə rə; Greek: *derma*, skin, + *pteron*]

Order Dermoptera

colugos; 2 species

These mammals have webs of skin between their front and hind appendages and their tails; when the appendages are spread, the webs form a surface that allows the animals to glide but not actually to fly. (Example: colugo.)

X 1/12

colugo

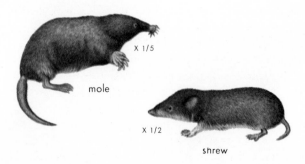

X 1/5

mole

X 1/2

shrew

Insectivora [ĭn′sĕk′tĭv′ə rə; Latin: *insectum*, insect, + *vorare*, to eat]

Order Insectivora

insectivores; about 400 species

The name of this order is somewhat misleading; insectivores eat almost anything they can find. They have many small teeth, incisors, canines, and molars. All the insectivores are rather small, and most are active chiefly at night. (Examples: mole and shrew.)

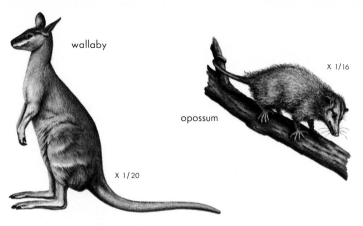

wallaby

opossum

X 1/16

X 1/20

Order Marsupialia
marsupials; about 250 species

Marsupialia [măr sōō′pĭ āl′yə; Greek: *marsypos*, pouch, bag]

In all the previously discussed orders an embryo develops within the body of the mother, nourished by a special structure. Marsupials lack this structure, so a young marsupial is born in a very undeveloped state. Then it is carried in a pouch on the underside of the mother, where it remains tightly attached to the nipples of the mammary glands during further development. (Examples: wallaby and opossum.)

Order Monotremata
monotremes; 5 species

X 1/8   platypus

These are the only mammals that lay eggs. Like all other mammals, however, they nourish their young with milk, though their mammary glands lack nipples. (Example: platypus.)

Monotremata [mŏn′ə trĕm′ət ə; Greek: *monos*, one, + *trema*, hole]

Class Aves
birds; about 8600 species

Aves [ā′vēz; Latin: *avis*, bird]

All birds have feathers, and all animals with feathers are birds. No other major group of animals is quite so easy to characterize. All birds have wings, too, though not all can fly. All birds hatch from eggs, which, unlike the eggs of the monotreme mammals, have hard shells. Like mammals, birds are warm-blooded; but unlike mammals, they have no mammary glands, and no living species of bird has teeth.

Many structural adaptations are found in both the feathers and the wings of birds. Feathers form the soft down of geese and ducks, the long ornamental plumes of ostriches, and the waterproof coat of penguins. Wings vary from the short, broad ones of chickens—which seldom fly, and then only for short distances—to the long, slim ones of albatrosses—which spend almost all their lives gliding on air currents. Yet diversity among birds is not so striking as it is among mammals. The difference between a hummingbird and a penguin is great, but hardly as startling as that between a bat and a whale. It is modification of details, such as those of feet and beaks, that has been important in the adaptation of birds to many kinds of ecosystems. (Examples on page 112.)

How are wings used by penguins?

albatross X 1/20

X 1/3

quetzal

man-of-war

X 1/5

X 1/2

hummingbird

X 1/10

flamingo

penguin   X 1/10

Class Reptilia
reptiles; about 7000 species

Reptilia [rĕp tĭl'ĭ ə; Latin: *repere*, to creep]

Turtles, snakes, lizards, alligators—all these are reptiles. But it is rather difficult to see just what a taxonomist means by a reptile. Reptiles have no obvious characteristics that immediately separate them from other vertebrates. They have skin outgrowths called scales (basically unlike the scales of fish), but so do birds and some mammals. They breathe by means of lungs all their lives; so do birds and mammals. Though a reptile's heart, like the heart of a mammal or bird, has 2 **ventricles,** in most species there is an opening in the wall between them. Their body temperatures vary with the environmental temperature—that is, like amphibians and fish, they are **cold-blooded.** By using a combination of these characteristics, we can obtain some idea of the reptile class without resorting to a study of skeletal characteristics, which taxonomists find very useful.

ventricle [vĕn'trə kəl]. See Figure 4·11.

None of the reptiles living today can really fly, though a lizard of the East Indies can glide by means of membranes stretched between its front and hind legs. Nevertheless, there is great diversity among reptiles. Contrast an alligator crawling through the mud with a chameleon far out on a limb in a tall tree, grasping a twig with its tail. Perhaps snakes are most extreme in structural adaptation; some are adapted to burrowing, some to climbing, and some to swimming—all without the use of appendages. (Examples below.)

chameleon [kə mēl'yən]

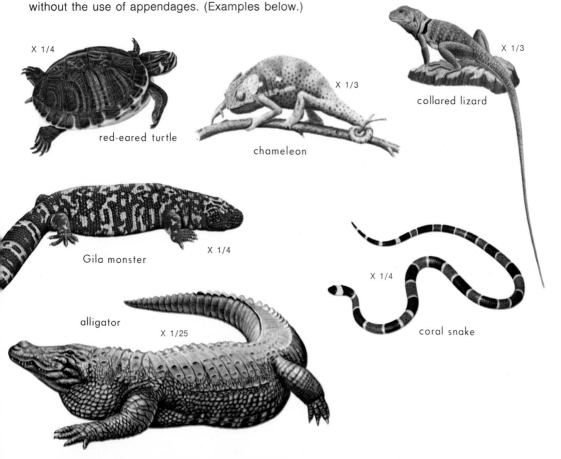

X 1/4

red-eared turtle

X 1/3

chameleon

X 1/3

collared lizard

Gila monster

X 1/4

X 1/4

coral snake

alligator

X 1/25

Amphibia [ăm fĭb′ĭ ə; Greek: *amphis*, on both sides of, + *bios*, life]

Class Amphibia
amphibians; about 2800 species

Although some amphibians are shaped like some lizards, there are many differences between amphibians and reptiles. Unlike most reptiles, very few amphibians have either claws or scales. Further, the eggs of amphibians never have shells, so they must be laid in water —or in places where moisture is available. Young amphibians, such as the tadpoles of most frogs and toads, may live in the water, but almost all adult amphibians are air breathers.

Although amphibians cannot live in very cold regions and none are marine, they show considerable diversity. Some amphibians climb by means of pads on their toes—structural adaptations that act like suction cups. On the other hand, many live in the loose upper layer of the soil or under rocks and dead logs. Some swim well and spend most of their lives in ponds or streams. A few have no appendages— an adaptation that favors burrowing. (Examples below.)

How might lack of appendages favor burrowing?

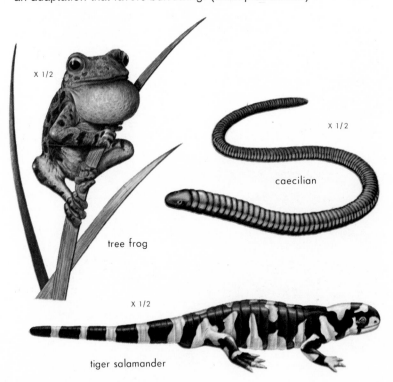

X 1/2

X 1/2

caecilian

tree frog

X 1/2

tiger salamander

Osteichthyes [ŏs′tē ĭk′thĭ ēz; Greek: *osteon*, bone, + *ichthyes*, fish]

Class Osteichthyes
bony fishes; about 20,000 species

Most people know more about catching or eating fish than about classifying them, so it may be surprising to learn that living fishes are usually placed in three separate classes. However, almost all the fishes you are likely to know, especially if you do not live near the ocean, are "bony fishes." This simply means that these fish have skeletons made of the hard substance we call bone. Unlike animals in the other classes we have been discussing, almost all fishes, both young and adult, obtain their oxygen supply through gills. In bony fishes these are in the pharyngeal slits, which are covered by flaps and are therefore not visible from the outside.

In number of species, this is the largest class of vertebrates. Among bony fishes there is great diversity that involves structural adaptation to many aquatic ecosystems. There are tiny minnows in cold freshwater brooks, and there are large tuna in warm seas. There are narrow, round sunfish and long, slim eels. There are flying fish, which can glide through the air on expanded fins, and toadfish, which lie half-buried in the muddy bottom of a bay. The bony fishes have invaded almost all the waters of the earth. (Examples below.)

How does the shape of a fish relate to the manner in which it swims? What structural adaptations do bottom-living fish have? You may be able to answer these questions by carefully observing fish in an aquarium.

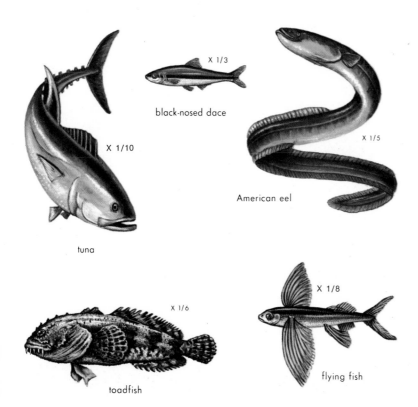

X 1/3

black-nosed dace

X 1/10

X 1/5

American eel

tuna

X 1/6

X 1/8

toadfish

flying fish

Class Chondrichthyes
cartilaginous fishes; about 600 species

Almost everyone knows something about sharks, but not many people know sharks at first hand—or wish to, perhaps. At first glance a shark seems to be as much a fish as a minnow is. Like other fish—and also like amphibians—a shark has a heart with but 1 ventricle and is cold-blooded. However, some basic structural differences have led biologists to place sharks in a separate class. This means that taxonomists think the differences between a minnow and a shark are just

Chondrichthyes [kŏn drĭk'thĭ ēz; Greek: *chondros,* cartilage, + *ichthyes*]; cartilaginous [kär'tə lǎj'ə nəs]

cartilage [kärt'əl ĭj]

as important as those between a snake (Reptilia) and a rabbit (Mammalia). The principal characteristic of this class is a skeleton made up entirely of **cartilage** rather than of bone. Cartilage is the substance that gives shape to your ears and nose; it is stiff enough to give support, but it is more flexible than bone. Also, nearly every cartilaginous fish has no flap over the pharyngeal slits. Besides sharks, the class contains rays, animals that have oddly flattened bodies, which perhaps adapt them to feeding on the bottom of the sea. (Examples: sawfish and stingray.)

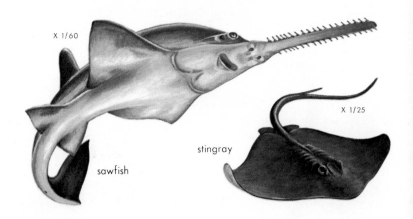

X 1/60

X 1/25

stingray

sawfish

Agnatha [ăg'nə thə; Greek: a-, without, + gnathos, jaw]

lamprey [lăm'prē; Latin: lambere, to lick, + petra, rock]: so called because many cling to rocks with their mouths

Class Agnatha
agnathans; 10 species

These fish lack paired fins. Their skeletons are poorly developed, and notochords are present in adults as well as in embryos. The best-known agnathans are the lampreys that greatly reduced the fish population of the Great Lakes a few years ago. A lamprey attaches itself to a fish, rasps a hole in the body, and sucks out the body fluids of its victim. This method of feeding by suction is necessary in agnathans, because unlike all other vertebrates they have no jaws. (Example: lamprey.)

X 1/8

lamprey

SUBPHYLUM CEPHALOCHORDATA

lancelets; about 28 species

Lancelets are small marine animals. A lancelet lacks a skull, jaws, heart, vertebrae, and paired appendages. But it does have a large number of gill slits, and, as shown in Figure 4 · 16, a supporting notochord that extends the length of the body and a hollow dorsal nerve cord. (Example: lancelet.)

Cephalochordata [sĕf'ə lō kôr dä'tə; Greek: *kephale*, head, + *chorde*, string of musical instrument]

X 1

lancelet

SUBPHYLUM UROCHORDATA

tunicates; about 700 species

It is hard to believe that adult tunicates are chordates. They do not even seem to be animals. They are soft, rounded masses that are found in seawater, firmly attached to solid objects such as piling, rocks, or wrecked ships. Each tunicate has a tube with 2 openings through which flows water bearing small organisms—the tunicate's food. Only in the *larvae*—young that are very different from the adults —is it possible to clearly detect their chordate characteristics. (Example: sea squirt.)

Urochordata [yōōr'ə kôr dä'tə; Greek: *oura*, tail, + *chorde*]; tunicates [tū'nə kĭtz]

larva [lär'və; Latin: *larva*, ghost]; plural, larvae

X 1/2

sea squirt

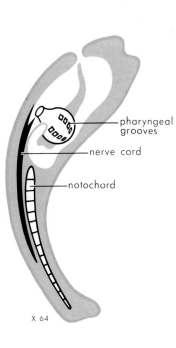

pharyngeal grooves

nerve cord

notochord

X 64

Figure 4 · 17

Diagram of a tunicate larva.

Hemichordata [hĕm′ĭ kôr dā′tə; Greek: *hemi-*, half, + *chorde*]

PHYLUM HEMICHORDATA
hemichordates; about 100 species

These are all small marine animals. Most are wormlike and burrow in mud and sand. A hemichordate has a short dorsal nerve cord, pharyngeal slits, and a structure that some zoologists call a notochord; but most zoologists do not agree and they therefore place these animals in a phylum separate from the chordates. (Example: acorn worm.)

X 1

acorn worm

Echinodermata [ĭ kī′nə dûr′mə tə; Greek: *echinos*, hedgehog, + *derma*, skin]

posterior [păs tîr′ē ər; Latin: *post*, behind]

bilateral symmetry [bī lăt′ər əl sĭm′ə trĭ; Latin: *bis*, twice, + *latus*, side; Greek: *syn*, together, + *metron*, measure]

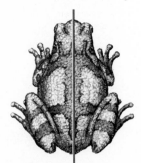

Figure 4 · 18
Bilateral symmetry.

crinoids [krī′noidz, krĭn′oidz; Greek: *krinon*, lily]

What examples of structural adaptation can you find here?

PHYLUM ECHINODERMATA
echinoderms; about 5000 species

In the phyla considered so far, each animal has a "front end," that is, an anterior end. The opposite end—the end that usually trails along behind—is the *posterior* end. If you divide such an animal as shown in Figure 4 · 18, you get right and left sides that are very much alike. This kind of body design is called *bilateral symmetry.*

In echinoderms the body has a different kind of symmetry. A starfish is a well-known echinoderm, and it shows this symmetry well (page 119). You immediately see that a starfish has no anterior and posterior ends and no definite left and right sides. There are many ways you could cut through the center of a starfish and get approximately equal halves. This kind of body design is termed *radial symmetry* because the parts radiate from a center as spokes radiate from the hub of a wheel.

Just beneath its skin, an adult starfish has a hard skeleton with many little bumps and projections. In some echinoderms these are long spines, but in sea cucumbers the skeleton is reduced to a few small, hard particles in the leathery skin.

No echinoderms are found on land or in fresh water. But echinoderms live in every part of the marine environment, from shallow shores to the greatest depths. We find delicate sea lilies (crinoids) and brittle stars in the still, dark waters far beneath the surface; we find sea cucumbers plowing through muddy bottoms of both deep and shallow waters; and we find sea urchins, with their long spines, on reefs and rocky coasts. (Examples on page 121).

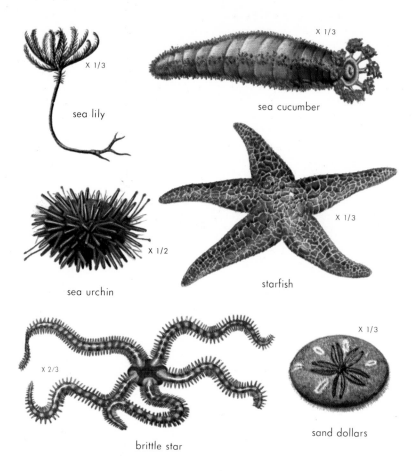

X 1/3

X 1/3

sea lily

sea cucumber

X 1/3

X 1/2

sea urchin

starfish

X 1/3

X 2/3

brittle star

sand dollars

PHYLUM ARTHROPODA

arthropods; about 750,000 species

The easiest way to understand basic arthropod structure is to compare it with basic chordate structure. From an arthropod's point of view, a chordate is upside down. An arthropod's main nerve cord is close to its *ventral* body surface—the lower surface, which is usually toward the pull of gravity. In a chordate the main nerve is close to the dorsal surface. Moreover, a chordate's nerve cord is a tube; an arthropod's nerve cord is solid and often double. We might also say, again from the arthropod's point of view, that chordates are inside out. In an arthropod the skeleton is outside the muscles—an *exoskeleton.* In a chordate the skeleton is inside the muscles—an *endoskeleton.* Further, the body of an arthropod is usually made up of a series of more or less similar *segments,* or sections, to which jointed appendages of various kinds—legs, paddles, mouthparts, wings—are usually attached. Segments can be detected in the bodies of young chordates, but they are not associated with appendages.

Arthropoda [är thrŏp'ə də; Greek: *arthron*, joint, + *pous*, foot]

ventral [Latin: *venter*, belly]

Although they are constructed on a pattern very unfamiliar to us (who are chordates), arthropods are at least as widespread in the world as chordates. And more than three-quarters of the species of living animals are arthropods. This means that arthropod structure has been adaptable to many kinds of environments.

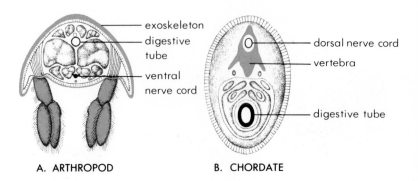

A. ARTHROPOD   B. CHORDATE

Figure 4 • 19
Comparison of arthropod
and chordate structure.

Insecta [ĭn sĕk'tə; Latin: *in*, into, + *secare*, to cut]

antenna [ăn tĕn'ə]
thorax [thŏr'ăks]
abdomen [ăb'də mən]

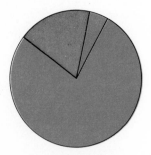

● INSECT ARTHROPODS
● NONINSECT ARTHROPODS
● NONARTHROPODS

Figure 4 • 20
Relative numbers of animal
species.

Class Insecta
insects; about 700,000 species

Besides having all the arthropod characteristics, insects have characteristics of their own. An insect's body is divided into three regions: a head, bearing a pair of **antennae,** "feelers"; a middle part, a **thorax,** bearing three pairs of legs; and a rear section, an **abdomen,** which is usually clearly segmented. Some insects, such as silverfish and lice, never develop wings, but in most adult insects one or two pairs are attached to the thorax. All young insects lack wings, and many are larvae that are quite wormlike, hardly seeming like insects at all.

You can find many species of insects if you look for small as well as large and showy ones. Even within a house you may find flies, ants, silverfish, and moths, not to mention the unpleasant possibility of fleas or lice. Many insects live close to man—some very close indeed! On plants, in the soil that supports them, and flying in the air about them, you may find grasshoppers, aphids, beetles, butterflies, wasps, and many more kinds. If fresh water is available (ponds, streams, or even a little water collected in a tin can), you may find in it many immature forms of such insects as dragonflies, mayflies, and mosquitoes. Insects walk, fly, burrow, and swim. Of all the major habitats on Earth, only the oceans, which support so much other life, almost completely lack insects. (Examples on page 121.)

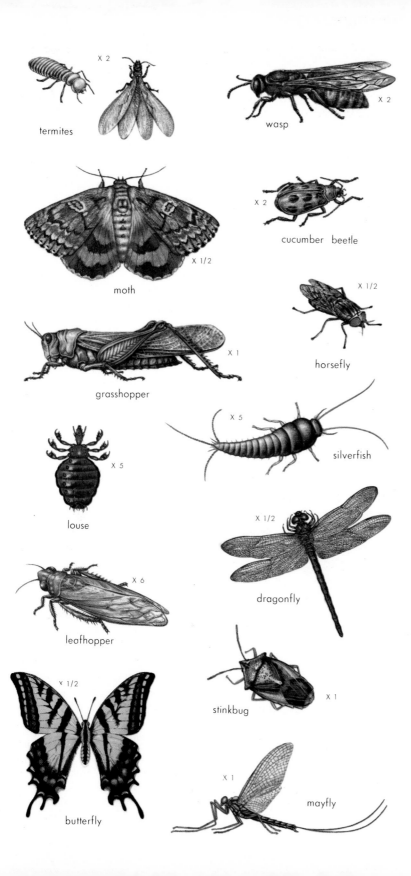

X 2

termites

X 2

wasp

X 1/2

moth

X 2

cucumber beetle

X 1/2

horsefly

X 1

grasshopper

X 5

silverfish

X 5

louse

X 1/2

dragonfly

X 6

leafhopper

X 1/2

butterfly

X 1

stinkbug

X 1

mayfly

Chilopoda [kī lăp'ə də; Greek: *cheilos*, lip, + *pous*, foot]; centipedes [sĕnt'ə pēdz; Latin: *centum*, hundred, + *pedes*, feet]

Class Chilopoda
centipedes; about 800 species

A centipede is an elongated, conspicuously segmented animal with a flattened body and one pair of legs on each segment. On its head it has a pair of long antennae and just behind its head a pair of poison glands. Centipedes are predators that prey mostly on insects. (Example: centipede.)

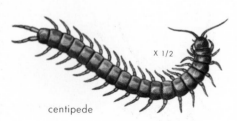

X 1/2

centipede

Diplopoda [də plăp'ə də; Greek: *diploos*, two, double, + *pous*]; millepedes [mĭl'ə pēdz; Latin: *mille*, thousand, + *pedes*]

Class Diplopoda
millepedes; about 6000 species

Like a centipede, a millepede is elongated and conspicuously segmented. Unlike a centipede, a millepede has a pair of short antennae and a body that is rounded in cross section, with two pairs of legs on each segment. Also millepedes lack poison glands; they eat dead plant material such as fallen leaves. In forest ecosystems millepedes are important decomposers. (Example: millepede.)

Some zoologists group centipedes and millepedes in one class. How might they support this classification?

X 1/2

millepede

Arachnida [ə răk'nəd ə; Greek: *arachne*, spider]

Class Arachnida
arachnids; about 15,000 species

Of all the arthropods, arachnids are most likely to be confused with insects. They differ from insects in having only two body regions, in having four pairs of legs, and in lacking antennae.

Spiders are the most familiar arachnids. The web-building activity of spiders is fascinating—even to persons who dislike the builders. Some spiders make no webs, but all have poison glands, which they use in capturing and killing their prey. Only a few spiders, however, are dangerous to man. Scorpions, which are fairly common arachnids

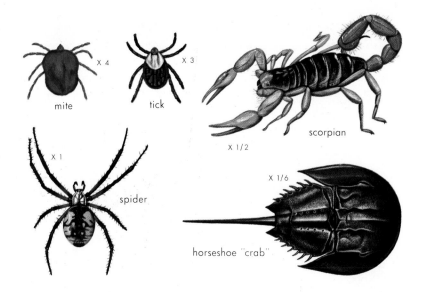

mite   X 4

tick   X 3

scorpion   X 1/2

X 1

spider

X 1/6

horseshoe "crab"

in the Southwest, are also poisonous, and a few are really dangerous, particularly to young children.

What kinds of dangerous arachnids live in the region of your home?

Some less familiar arachnids are actually much more dangerous than spiders and scorpions—mites, for example. In the United States they merely cause irritating skin rashes. But in parts of the Far East and in the South Pacific region, certain species of mites carry the germs of scrub typhus, a serious disease. Ticks, better known than mites because they are larger, also carry disease germs.

Most arachnids are terrestrial; horseshoe crabs, however, are marine animals. They are common along the eastern coast of the United States, where their hard shells adapt them to plowing through muddy or sandy bottoms of shallow waters. Such habitats have been available on Earth for a long time, and horseshoe crabs have changed only slightly in two hundred million years! Some zoologists do not consider them arachnids and place them in a separate class. (Examples above.)

Class Crustacea
crustaceans; about 25,000 species

Crustacea [krŭs tā′shē ə; Latin: *crusta*, rind]

The crustaceans form a very diverse group of arthropods. All have two pairs of antennae and breathe by means of gills. Most familiar are the large ones that are good to eat—lobsters, crabs, and shrimp. But most crustaceans are small, almost microscopic, animals that exist in huge numbers in ponds, lakes, and especially the oceans, where they are the basic food supply for animals ranging from tiny fishes to giant whales.

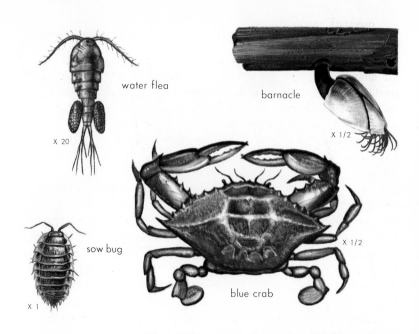

water flea

X 20

barnacle

X 1/2

sow bug

X 1

blue crab

X 1/2

These crabs breathe by gills. What adaptations might allow them to live on land?

Just as some species of mammals—a primarily terrestrial group —have adapted to life in the ocean, so a number of crustaceans—a primarily aquatic group—have adapted to a life on land. In the humid tropics of the Pacific, some crabs spend most of their lives on land, climbing coconut palm trees and breaking open the coconuts with their stout claws. They do, however, return to the sea to lay their eggs. In the United States sow bugs are crustaceans that lead an entirely terrestrial existence. Although they may be found far from water, they do live in damp places.

barnacle [bär′nǐ kəl]

sessile [sĕs′ĭl; Latin: *sedere,* to sit]

Barnacles have such extreme structural adaptations that they were once classified in a different phylum. Although the larvae are free-swimming, they soon become *sessile;* that is, they become permanently attached to some solid surface in the ocean—a wharf piling, a rock, or even the back of a sea turtle. There each develops a limy cup, into which it seals itself tightly at every low tide. (Examples above.)

X 1/2

Peripatus

Onychophora [ăn′ə kă′fə rə; Greek: *onyx,* nail, claw, + *-phoros,* carrying or bearing]

Class Onychophora

velvet worms; about 80 species

These are terrestrial animals that live in the tropics. They are worm-like creatures with paired legs and poorly developed segmentation. Because they have a combination of annelid and arthropod characteristics, they are classified by some zoologists in a phylum by themselves. (Example: *Peripatus.*)

PHYLUM ANNELIDA
annelids; about 6500 species

Annelida [ə nĕl′ə də; Latin: *anulus*, ring]

The biological name of this phylum refers to a conspicuous feature of the animals included in it. An annelid's body consists of a series of ringlike segments. We have already seen segmentation in arthropods, but in annelids it is developed much further: each external groove marks the location of an internal partition, so that an annelid consists of a series of compartments that are more or less similar. Many of the internal body organs are repeated in one compartment after another.

Annelids usually have appendages, but these are not jointed as in arthropods. They have nerve cords in a ventral position, solid, and often paired—just as in arthropods.

The most familiar annelids are terrestrial—earthworms—but the majority of annelids are aquatic. Some marine species reach a length of nearly a meter. Swimming around on the surface of the sea, annelids like this may have given rise to stories of sea serpents. But many marine annelids burrow in sand or mud. From their hiding places they reach out with their sharp jaws and seize small passing animals. Leeches show another kind of annelid diversity; they are parasites that suck blood. A leech has a flat body without appendages, but it has an obvious structural adaptation—a pair of suction disks, one at each end, with which it clings to its host. (Examples: clam worm, leech, and plume worm.)

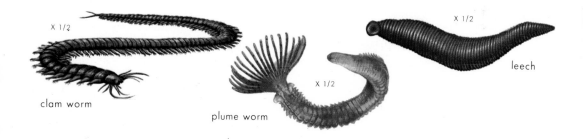

X 1/2

X 1/2

leech

clam worm

X 1/2

plume worm

PHYLUM MOLLUSCA
mollusks; about 70,000 species

Mollusca [mə lŭs′kə; Latin: *mollis*, soft]

Like members of the other phyla we have discussed, a mollusk has a nervous system, a heart that pumps blood, and a tubular digestive system—an **alimentary canal.** Unlike chordates and arthropods, mollusks are not segmented. Although some are bilaterally symmetrical, many show no symmetry at all. The most distinctive characteristic of a mollusk is an organ that, in most species, secretes a hard shell.

alimentary [âl′ə mĕn′tə rĭ; Latin: *alere*, to nourish]

Most mollusks are aquatic. They are abundant in the seas, where they have the greatest structural diversity, but many species live in fresh water. And many snails live completely terrestrial lives. Few ecosystems lack mollusks.

Cephalopoda [sĕf'ə lŏp'ə də; Greek: *kephale*, head, + *pous*, foot]

tentacles [tĕn'tə kəlz]

Class Cephalopoda
cephalopods; about 400 species

These are marine mollusks that swim by means of jets of water. They have long, muscular *tentacles,* which they use for capturing food and clinging to rocks. Most cephalopods have small shells buried within their bodies, but a few have coiled shells divided into a series of chambers. They are the largest mollusks, some growing to 20 m in length. (Examples: nautilus and octopus.)

X 1/5

nautilus

X 1/10

octopus

Pelecypoda [pĕl'ə sĭp'ə də; Greek: *pelekys*, hatchet, + *pous*]

Class Pelecypoda
bivalves; about 15,000 species

These are marine or freshwater mollusks. They have shells in 2 parts, which are movable on a hinge. Some are sessile most of their lives; others burrow in mud or sand. Many, such as clams, oysters, and scallops, are important as food for man. (Examples: clam and scallop.)

clam

X 1/3

scallop

Scaphopoda [skə făp'ə də; Greek: *skaphe*, boat, + *pous*]

tooth shell

X 1/2

Class Scaphopoda
tooth shells; about 200 species

These are marine mollusks. Their shells form tapering tubes from which food-catching tentacles protrude. (Example: tooth shell.)

Class Gastropoda
gastropods; about 55,000 species

Some gastropods are terrestrial, but many others are aquatic—either marine or freshwater. Some lack shells, but most have coiled shells with a single chamber. Most have distinct anterior ends with well-developed sense organs. (Examples: sea slug, banded tulip snail, and garden snail.)

Gastropoda [găs trŏp′ə də; Greek: *gastros*, stomach, + *pous*]

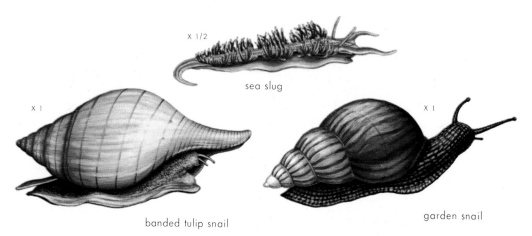

X 1/2

sea slug

X 1

banded tulip snail

X 1

garden snail

Class Monoplacophora
3 species

These are marine mollusks that live at great depths. Their shells are in 1 piece, each with a curved end. (Example: *Neopilina*.)

Monoplacophora [mŏn′ə plăk′ə fôr′ə; Greek: *monos*, solitary, + *plax*, tablet, flat plate, + *-phoros*, bearing, carrying]

X 2

Neopilina

Class Amphineura
about 630 species

These marine mollusks have shells each of which is composed of 8 overlapping plates. They cling to rocks along seacoasts, where they are often exposed to the air during low tide. (Example: chiton.)

Amphineura [ăm′fə nyŏo′rə; Greek: *amphis*, both sides of, + *neuron*, nerve]

chitons   X 1

Chaetognatha [kē tăg′nə thə; Greek: *chaite*, hair, + *gnathos*, jaw]

PHYLUM CHAETOGNATHA

arrowworms; about 30 species

Arrowworms are marine animals that either float about or actively swim. They are bilaterally symmetrical and have straight alimentary canals.

This is one of several small phyla containing animals that are seldom seen except by zoologists. These animals differ so greatly among themselves that zoologists have not been able to find enough similarities among them to put them together into any grouping below the phylum level. (Example: *Sagitta*.)

Sagitta

X 1

Phoronis

X 1/2

Phoronidea [fōr′ə nĭd′ē ə; Greek: *Phoronis*, name of a mythological character]

PHYLUM PHORONIDEA

about 15 species

These marine animals live in tubes in mud. Each has a pair of appendages that bear tentacles and an alimentary canal that is U-shaped. (Example: *Phoronis*.)

Brachiopoda [brā′kĭ ŏp′ə də; Greek: *brachion*, arm, + *pous*, foot]

PHYLUM BRACHIOPODA

brachiopods; about 120 species

Externally a brachiopod looks somewhat like a clam except that its 2-piece shell is bilaterally symmetrical. Internally a brachiopod is not at all clamlike; for example, it has a pair of appendages that bear tentacles. (Example: *Lingula*.)

Lingula

X 1

Electra

X 10

Bryozoa [brī′ə zō′ə; Greek: *bryon*, moss, + *zoion*, animal]

PHYLUM BRYOZOA

bryozoans; about 3000 species

Bryozoans are aquatic and mostly marine. They live in colonies that are attached to solid objects. They have U-shaped alimentary canals and mouths encircled by tentacles. (Example: *Electra*.)

PHYLUM ACANTHOCEPHALA
spiny-headed worms; about 100 species

This phylum consists entirely of parasitic species. Young spiny-headed worms are parasitic in arthropods; adults are parasitic in the alimentary canals of vertebrates. Neither young nor adults have alimentary canals themselves; they absorb food from their hosts. (Example: *Oncicola*.)

Acanthocephala [ə kǎn'thə sěf'ə lə; Greek: *akantha*, spine, + *kephale*, head]

X 1

Oncicola

PHYLUM ASCHELMINTHES
about 12,500 species

Many zoologists consider each of the following classes as separate phyla. Indeed, there is great diversity among them. However, all the animals in these classes share a number of characteristics. Each is bilaterally symmetrical, with internal organs in a body cavity that develops in a characteristic way in the embryos. Each has a body that is covered by a **cuticle,** which is a firm but flexible "skin." And each has a muscular feeding organ at the anterior end of its alimentary canal.

Aschelminthes [ǎsk'hěl'mǐn'thěz'; Greek: *ascos*, bag, bladder, + *helmins*, worm]

cuticle [kū'tə kəl]

Class Nematoda
roundworms; about 10,000 species

Many kinds of wormlike animals are round in cross section, but this is the only group actually named "roundworms." Unlike most of the animals we have discussed previously, roundworms have no **circulatory** system—no system of tubes through which blood is circulated. But they have a fluid that is squeezed about in their bodies as they wriggle. Roundworms vary from about 0.5 mm to more than 1 m in length, though most are nearer the first extreme. Many species of roundworms are decomposers. Many more species are parasitic, especially on roots of plants. About 30 species have been found living in man. (Examples: *Ascaris, Trichinella,* and hookworm.)

Nematoda [něm'ə tō'də; Greek: *nema*, thread]

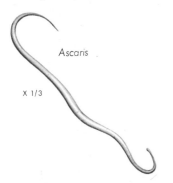

Ascaris

X 1/3

Trichinella

X 37

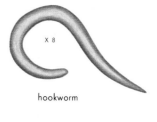

X 8

hookworm

Nematomorpha
[nĕm′ə tə môr′fə; Greek:
nema, thread, + *morphe*, form]

Class Nematomorpha

horsehair worms; about 200 species

Young horsehair worms are parasitic in arthropods, but the adults are free-living. They have very simple alimentary canals. (Example: *Gordius*.)

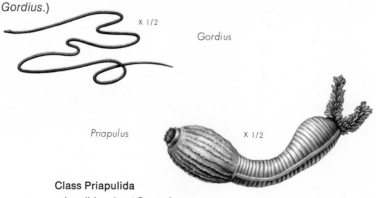

X 1/2

Gordius

Priapulus   X 1/2

Priapulida [prī′ə pyōō′lə də;
Greek: *Priapos*, god of gardens]

Class Priapulida

priapulids; about 5 species

These are free-living marine worms. They have spines in the mouth region, and their bodies are covered with rings of thickened cuticle, giving them a superficial resemblance to annelids. (Example: *Priapulus*.)

Echinoderella    X 19

Kinorhyncha [kĭn′ə rĭng′kə;
Greek: *kinein*, to set in motion,
+ *rhynchos*, beak]

Class Kinorhyncha

100 species

These are very tiny marine animals. At the anterior end each of these animals has a spiny snout that can be protruded or pulled back. The outer surface of the body is covered with rings of thickened cuticle. (Example: *Echinoderella*.)

Chaetonotus   X 22

Gastrotricha [găs trät′rə kə;
Greek: *gaster*, belly, + *thrix*,
hair]

cilia [sĭl′ĭ ə]; singular, cilium

Class Gastrotricha

gastrotrichs; about 140 species

These are microscopic or nearly microscopic animals that live mostly in fresh water. They move by means of tiny hairlike structures—*cilia*—on their ventral surfaces. A scalelike cuticle covers their bodies. (Example: *Chaetonotus*.)

Asplanchna

X 28

X 32

Philodina

Class Rotifera
rotifers; about 2000 species

These tiny animals are likely to be among the first organisms found by a curious student equipped with a microscope. At their anterior ends they have cilia that beat so rapidly they appear to be rotating like wheels. Hence, early observers named them rotifers. Like nematodes, they lack circulatory systems.

There are only a few marine species, but rotifers are abundant in all kinds of fresh water. Some even inhabit the drops of water that collect among mosses. This water may not last long, but before it dries, the rotifers produce eggs with thick shells that enable them to resist evaporation. These survive until the next rain wets the moss again. (Examples: *Asplanchna* and *Philodina*.)

Rotifera [rō tĭf'ə rə; Latin: *rota*, wheel, + *ferre*, to bear]

Cerebratulus

X 1/4

PHYLUM NEMERTINEA
ribbon worms; about 500 species

These animals are mostly marine, living along shores in sand or mud or under rocks. A ribbon worm is flat and shows no trace of segmentation. It has an alimentary canal, but no body cavity. (Example: *Cerebratulus*.)

Nemertinea [nĕm'ər tĭn'ē ə; Greek: *Nemertes*, name of mythological water nymph]

Pseudicyema

X 20

PHYLUM MESOZOA
about 45 species

These are tiny wormlike animals that are parasitic in marine mollusks and annelids. They have very simple structures internally, and cilia on their external surfaces. (Example: *Pseudicyema*.)

Mesozoa [mĕz'ə zō'ə; Greek: *mesos*, middle, + *zoion*, animal]

Platyhelminthes
[plăt'ĭ hĕl mĭn'thēz; Greek:
platys, flat, + *helmins*, worm]

PHYLUM PLATYHELMINTHES
flatworms; about 6000 species

One of the main characteristics of flatworms is indicated by the name. More important, a flatworm has no circulatory system nor even any space for a body fluid. Nor does it have an alimentary canal. Instead it has a hollow sac with but one opening, through which food enters and undigestible particles leave.

There are free-living flatworms in fresh water and in the ocean. There are flatworms that have either commensal or mutualistic relationships with other organisms. But most flatworms are parasitic. Some—tapeworms, for example—have a striking adaptation to the parasitic life. Living inside the alimentary canals of other animals, they completely lack digestive systems of their own. They simply absorb the digested food that surrounds them. (Examples: tapeworm, planarian, and liver fluke.)

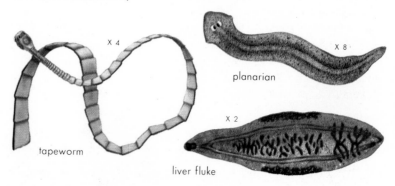

X 4

planarian

X 8

X 2

tapeworm

liver fluke

Ctenophora [tə năf'ə rə; Greek:
ktenos, comb, + *-phoros*,
carrying or bearing]

PHYLUM CTENOPHORA
comb jellies; about 100 species

Comb jellies are marine animals that move about near the surface of the water by means of 8 rows of cilia. They catch tiny organisms with their tentacles. They are jelly-like and made up largely of water. If one is stranded on the beach, there is little left of its body after the water evaporates. (Examples: sea walnut and Venus's-girdle.)

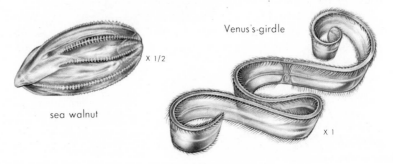

Venus's-girdle

X 1/2

sea walnut

X 1

PHYLUM COELENTERATA

coelenterates; about 9200 species

Coelenterata [sə lĕn'tə rād'ə; Greek: *koilos*, hollow, + *enteron*, intestine]

The body of a coelenterate is little more than a bag, and digestion occurs in the central cavity. Food is taken in and undigested particles are thrown out through the same opening. In this respect a coelenterate resembles a flatworm. But a coelenterate is radially instead of bilaterally symmetrical. Around the opening to its digestive cavity a coelenterate has tentacles that bear many small stingers; these can paralyze small organisms and, in some cases, quite large ones—even man. Stinger-bearing tentacles are the most distinctive characteristic of the phylum.

Coelenterates may be considered quite simple from the viewpoint of a chordate—that is, from *our* viewpoint. Nevertheless, there is considerable diversity in the details of the coelenterate body plan. Sessile coelenterates that live attached to each other—such as the corals— are fastened at the ends opposite their cavity openings, and their tentacles stretch upward. Other coelenterates—such as jellyfish—swim or float about in the water. These are—from the viewpoint of a coral— upside down. Their cavity openings are directed downward, and their tentacles hang beneath. (Examples: *Aurelia,* sea anemone, and *Obelia.*)

coral. See Figure 2·1.

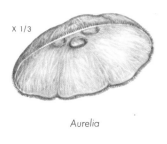

X 1/3

Aurelia

X 1/2

sea anemone

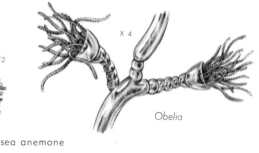

X 4

Obelia

PHYLUM PORIFERA

sponges; about 4200 species

Porifera [pə rĭf'ə rə; Latin: *porus*, pore, + *ferre*, to bear]

Sponges lack the structural systems we normally associate with animals. Of course, we have been pointing out that various animal phyla lack this or that system. Even a coelenterate can be said to have a nervous system and a digestive system of sorts. But not the sponges.

Basically the body of a sponge is a bag pierced by many pores. Through these pores water is pushed inward by the action of **flagella** —hairlike projections that are similar to cilia, but longer and less numerous. The water flows out of the body cavity through an opening that is misnamed a "mouth." The body wall is supported by interlocking particles of hard or tough material—a kind of skeleton.

flagella [flə jĕl'ə; Latin: *flagellum*, little whip]; singular, flagellum

Sponges as a group show a considerable range of diversity. Some are rather small, each with a single body cavity. Many others are large and massive, with complicated networks of body cavities. Some have

X 2   X 1/10

X 1/10

Scypha   bath sponge   fringed basket

skeletons of hard materials that are chemically similar either to glass
or to the substance in the shells of mollusks; others have skeletons of
a tough substance similar to that in a cow's horn. A few sponges have
radially symmetrical shapes; most are quite unsymmetrical. (Examples:
Scypha, bath sponge, and fringed basket.)

Investigation 4.2
_____

STRUCTURAL CHARACTERISTICS IN THE IDENTIFICATION OF ANIMALS

MATERIALS AND EQUIPMENT

animal specimens
hand lenses or stereomicroscopes

PROCEDURE

A. Observing animal specimens

Draw 2 charts in your data book similar to
the ones on page 135. Your teacher will tell
you how many columns you should draw on
the right side of each chart.

Several numbered stations are set up in
the classroom. At each station is an animal
species and a label giving its name. You may
find both living and preserved specimens at
some stations. Some of the preserved specimens may be partially dissected so that you
can make certain observations. Your teacher
will announce the total number of stations and
assign a starting station to each student. You
will be allowed a definite amount of time at
each station. When a signal is given, move to
the station with the next higher number. When
you reach the highest number, go to Station 1

and continue until you reach your starting
point.

At each station begin by deciding whether
the kind of animal you are studying has a
backbone and is, therefore, a vertebrate or
does not have a backbone and is, therefore,
an invertebrate. If it is a vertebrate, record its
common name on Chart 1 in one of the spaces
under the heading "Name of Animal." If it is
an invertebrate, follow the same procedure but
use Chart 2.

At the left side of each chart is a list of
characteristics to be observed. Each section
includes 2 or more characteristics. After studying the specimens, indicate the presence of
the characteristics you observed by placing a
check (√) in the appropriate box.

Suppose that the 1st specimen you study
is a cat. Because a cat has a backbone, you
write "Cat" in the space at the top of the 1st
vertical column in Chart 1. Now look at the 4
choices indicated in the section "Skin Struc-

tures." Only 1 of the choices applies to the cat: "Hair present." Therefore, you put a check in the box that is under "Cat" and to the right of "Hair present." Next look at the choices in the section "Appendages." Again there is only 1 choice that applies to the cat, so you check the box under "Cat" and to the right of "Legs present." Proceed down the column in this manner. When you think your observations are insufficient to make a decision on any point, leave the space blank.

B. Using a key

The process of identifying organisms is difficult because there are so many of them. One tool used is called a key. There are several different kinds; the kind you will use is called a *dichotomous key.* The word "dichotomous" (dī kŏt'ə məs) means "cut into two parts," and it describes the kind of choices you make in using such a key.

With the information you have recorded in Chart 1, use Key 1 (page 136) to determine

CHART 1

		NAME OF ANIMAL		
SKIN STRUCTURES	Hair present			
	Feathers present			
	Scales present			
	None of the above present			
APPENDAGES	Wings present			
	Legs present			
	Fins present			
	None of the above present			
SKELETON	Bony			
	Cartilaginous			
TEETH	Present			
	Absent			
JAWS	Present			
	Absent			
		Class	Class	Class

CHART 2

		NAME OF ANIMAL		
EXOSKELETON	Present			
	Absent			
BODY SYMMETRY	Radial			
	Bilateral			
	Part bilateral, part spiral			
JOINTED WALKING LEGS	3 pairs present			
	4 pairs present			
	More than 4 pairs present			
	Absent			
BODY SEGMENTATION	Present			
	Absent			
TENTACLES	More than 4 present			
	4 or fewer present			
	Absent			
ANTENNAE	2 or more pairs present			
	1 pair present			
	Absent			
		Phylum	Phylum	Phylum

KEY 1

Dichotomous Key to Classes of the Subphylum Vertebrata

1a. Hair present . . . .   Class Mammalia
1b. Hair absent . . . .   go to 2

2a. Feathers present . . . .   Class Aves
2b. Feathers absent . . . .   go to 3

3a. Jaws present . . . .   go to 4
3b. Jaws absent . . . .   Class Agnatha

4a. Paired fins present . . . .   go to 5
4b. Paired fins absent . . . .   go to 6

5a. Skeleton bony . . . .   Class Osteichthyes
5b. Skeleton cartilaginous . . . .   Class Chondrichthyes

6a. Skin scales present . . . .   Class Reptilia
6b. Skin scales absent . . . .   Class Amphibia

---

the class to which each of the animals you have studied belongs. Begin at the top of the key with Item 1, where you have choices 1a and 1b. If the animal you are considering has hair, your choice is 1a. Follow the 1a line to the right side of the key and you find that it belongs to the class Mammalia. If the animal does *not* have hair, follow the 1b line to the right and you find that you are to go to Item 2 in the key. There 2 more contrasting characteristics are indicated, 2a and 2b. By again making a choice and, if necessary, continuing down the key, you eventually arrive at the name of the class in which the animal is classified. Write the name of the class in Chart 1. Repeat the process for each vertebrate animal.

Now use Key 2 to determine the phylum for each invertebrate in Chart 2. Record the phyla in the columns at the bottom of Chart 2.

Finally, use Key 3 to determine the class in which each of your arthropod animals has been placed. Record this information in your

---

KEY 2

Dichotomous Key to Selected Invertebrate Phyla

1a. Body symmetry radial . . . .   go to 2
1b. Body symmetry not radial . . . . . .   go to 3

2a. Tentacles present, body soft . . . . .   Phylum Coelenterata
2b. Tentacles absent, body hard and rough . .   Phylum Echinodermata

3a. Exoskeleton present . . . .   go to 4
3b. Exoskeleton absent . . . .   go to 5

4a. Jointed legs present . . . .   Phylum Arthropoda
4b. Jointed legs absent . . . .   Phylum Mollusca

5a. Body segmented . . . .   Phylum Annelida
5b. Body not segmented . . . .   Phylum Platyhelminthes

---

KEY 3
Dichotomous Key to Selected Classes of the Phylum Arthropoda

1a. Walking legs, more than 5 pairs . . . . . .   go to 2
1b. Walking legs, 5 or fewer pairs   .   .   .   .   .   .   go to 3

2a. Legs, 1 pair for each body segment .   .   .   .   .   Class Chilopoda
2b. Legs, 2 pairs for each body segment .   .   .   .   .   Class Diplopoda

3a. Antennae present .   .   .   .   go to 4
3b. Antennae absent .   .   .   .   Class Arachnida

4a. Antennae, 1 pair .   .   .   .   Class Insecta
4b. Antennae, more than 1 pair .   .   .   .   Class Crustacea

---

data book following Chart 2.

Keys can be made to carry identifications all the way down to the species level.

You must not assume that the simplified keys in this investigation will indicate a correct classification for every animal. A key gives you a correct identification *only* if it is used with the group of organisms for which it was constructed. If, for example, you attempt to classify a squid or a slug by using Key 2, the key will indicate the phylum Platyhelminthes; but both are actually mollusks. Unless you use a key to unlock only the series of doors for which it was designed, you will almost certainly end up in the wrong house! Therefore, you should check the correctness of your identifications by using references such as those listed at the end of this chapter.

SUMMARY

Having classified all the animals of your laboratory study, refer again to Charts 1 and

2. Once you know that an animal is a vertebrate, you need only determine a single characteristic—possession of hair—to place it in the class Mammalia. • Is there any other *single* characteristic that enables you to place a vertebrate in its class at once? If so, state what that characteristic is and in which class a vertebrate having it should be placed.(1) • Is there any single characteristic that enables you to place an invertebrate you have studied in its phylum? If so, what is the characteristic and which phylum does it indicate?(2) • Is there any single characteristic that enables you to place an arthropod in its class? If so, what is the characteristic and which class does it indicate?(3)

FOR FURTHER INVESTIGATION

Select 10 students, including yourself. Construct a dichotomous key, using characteristics that will enable another person to identify each student in the group.

MEANING OF BIOLOGICAL CLASSIFICATION

By the middle of the 18th century, a scheme of classification levels had been generally adopted by biologists. Before the middle of the 19th century, many of the animal phyla were recognized. But the goal of taxonomists at that time was still the goal mentioned at the beginning of this chapter: to arrive at a convenient way to catalogue species —to keep track of them. Biological classification was not designed to *mean* anything. In this respect it was like the listing of words in a dictionary: "Burmese" and "burn" may be next to each other, but they are entirely unrelated otherwise.

A QUESTION

In classifying organisms, we arrange them at different levels according to their structural characteristics. When we look over the result of this classification, some questions arise. Isn't it strange that *every* animal with an exoskeleton and jointed appendages also has a ventral nerve cord? Isn't it strange that *no* animal with a saclike digestive system has a circulatory system? Why do animals with the annelid body plan *always* lack skeletons? Why do animals with the mollusk body plan *always* lack segmentation?

All of these questions add up to one big question: By arranging organisms into groups according to their structural likenesses have we revealed some meaning? At the beginning of the 19th century there was at least a hint of an answer to this question. And even though most biologists of that time failed to understand the hint, they probably sensed it unconsciously.

How does the use by 18th-century taxonomists of "Family" as a level in classification show this?

A POSSIBLE ANSWER

eye fold. See Figure 19·13.

Why do all the Wu children in Hong Kong have a fold in the upper eyelid and black hair? Why do all the Pedersen children in Copenhagen have blue eyes and wavy hair? Why do all the Perez children in Guatemala have dark eyes and straight, black hair? In all three cases, of course, the characteristics go together because they are family characteristics—they have "run in the family" for generations. They have been inherited together.

This is another analogy (see page 58)—useful for explanation if not carried too far. If all the families moved to, say, Chicago or Honolulu, the characteristics might get mixed up in a few generations.

Perhaps it is also reasonable to assume that patterns of likeness are shared by organisms in a phylum or other taxonomic grouping because the organisms are related—in the kinship, not the ecological, sense. On this assumption, we could say that all chordates have dorsal, tubular nerve cords, pharyngeal pouches, and notochords, because all are descended from ancestors that had these characteristics. All insects have three pairs of legs and one pair of antennae, because all are descended from ancestors with these characteristics.

This reasonable idea did not come directly from a study of classification, however. It arose as evidence accumulated from fossils and later from experimental studies of heredity. The early taxonomists had a hint of the idea, but like everyone else, scientists may be blinded to new thoughts by the ideas they have grown up with—ideas that have become fixed. Nevertheless, about a century ago most biologists accepted the theory that the species of organisms are related through ancestry. Ever since then, taxonomists have tried to express the evidence of relationship in classification.

WORK OF MODERN TAXONOMISTS

Evidence for relationships. A modern taxonomist does not look merely at structural characteristics in organisms he is classifying. He looks for *any evidence of relationship.* Such evidence may come from the way organisms develop during their early lives, from the chemical materials in their bodies, or even from their behavior. The job of a modern taxonomist is much more complicated than that of an 18th-century taxonomist.

However, two factors still make structural characteristics particularly important. The first we have already mentioned—a taxonomist can observe structural characteristics in preserved specimens, and his observations can easily be verified. Secondly, structural evidence is all we are ever likely to have for organisms known to us only from fossils. We can make some good guesses about the life activities of such organisms, but the evidence is still based primarily on structure. And these organisms of the past are important in figuring out the relationships of living ones, because they may be the ancestors of the living organisms.

Expressing relationships taxonomically. Now go back to the example of classification used in the first part of this chapter (page 96). You read, "As we go from species to kingdom, the organisms that are grouped together share fewer and fewer characteristics at each succeeding level." Now we can say, "As we go from species to kingdom, the organisms are less and less closely related at each succeeding level." Going on from this point without directly comparing statements, we can say that individual dogs are all so closely related that they form an interbreeding population, a species. Dogs and wolves do not ordinarily interbreed, but it is not impossible. From structural and behavioral evidence most zoologists believe that dogs and wolves had a common ancestry not so long ago—in other words, that they are closely related. Taxonomists express this belief by putting them

common. Here the word means "shared by two or more individuals or groups," as we speak in mathematics of a "common denominator."

Field Museum of Natural History

Figure 4 · 21
A taxonomist at work.

together in one genus (*Canis*), as Figure 4 • 8 shows. By adding coyotes to this genus, taxonomists show that they believe dogs, coyotes, and wolves to be equally related. By placing foxes in a separate genus (*Vulpes*), they show that they believe foxes to be less closely related to dogs, coyotes, and wolves than these are to each other. And by placing the genera *Canis* and *Vulpes* in the same family, they show that dogs are related to foxes—but less closely than to wolves.

This is somewhat similar to saying that you are closely related to your sister (you and your sister have the same mother and father), but you are less closely related to your first cousin (you and your first cousin have only one pair of grandparents in common). By placing the dog family (Canidae) and the bear family (Ursidae) and the weasel family (Mustelidae) together in the order Carnivora, taxonomists imply that all of these animals descended from a common ancestral group —but probably long, long ago. As we continue up the list of levels, the relationships become less and less close. Thus, when a taxonomist places a dog and a goldfish in the same subphylum, he implies a very distant relationship indeed.

imply [ĭm plī′; Latin: *in,* into, + *plicare,* to fold]: to contain a meaning without directly stating it

Conflicting purposes. Have we abandoned the original purpose of classification—to catalogue organisms for convenient reference? Not at all. Modern taxonomists attempt to arrange organisms in a way that will both show relationships and allow convenient reference.

Of course, anyone who tries to do two things at once usually gets into trouble. The more evidence taxonomists obtain, the more complex the relationships of organisms appear to be. Moreover, taxonomists differ in how they interpret the evidence. Therefore, there are many existing schemes of classification, all designed within the same framework of levels. Classifications that are used to arrange specimens in museums often lean toward convenience and neglect relationships. In contrast, classifications in advanced and specialized textbooks usually lean toward relationships and neglect convenience. Classifications for general use—as in this book—are often compromises between the two aims.

Refer to pages 96–97.

Investigation 4.3

DIVERSITY IN THE ANIMAL KINGDOM: A COMPARATIVE STUDY

MATERIALS AND EQUIPMENT

Station 1
   hydras, living, 6 to 12
   stereomicroscopes or hand lenses, 3
   watch glasses, Syracuse, 3
   Daphnia, small culture
   medicine droppers, 3
   monocular microscopes, 3
   camel-hair brushes, 3

   hydras, prepared slides of longitudinal
      sections, 3
Station 2
   planarians, living, 6 to 12
   stereomicroscopes or hand lenses, 6
   watch glasses, Syracuse, 3
   liver (raw), small pieces, 6 to 12
   camel-hair brushes, 3

monocular microscopes, 3

planarians, prepared slides of cross
     sections, 3; whole mounts, 3

Station 3

earthworms, living, 6 to 12

hand lenses, 3

paper towels, moistened

boxes containing damp soil, 3

monocular microscopes, 3

earthworms, prepared slides of cross
     sections, 3

Station 4

crayfish, living, 3

aquarium

camel-hair brushes, 3

finger bowls, 3

liver (raw), small pieces, 6 to 10

crayfish, preserved, 2

dissecting needles, 3

Station 5

frog, prepared skeleton

frogs, live, 3

battery jars, 3

frog, freshly dissected

medicine droppers, 2

dissecting needles, 3

aquarium

PROCEDURE

A. General directions

Make an enlarged copy of the chart shown below. It should extend across 2 facing pages in your data book; each of the 13 spaces should allow for several lines of writing. Copy the following questions—each in a separate space—in the column headed "Characteris-

tics." (If more than 1 question follows a number, copy only the 1st.) The 13th space is for any additional observations you may make.

1. What is the habitat of the animal? Does it live in water, on land, or both in water and on land?
2. Is the symmetry of the body radial or bilateral?
3. Does the animal have a skeleton? If it has, is it an endoskeleton or an exoskeleton?
4. Is the animal's body segmented or un-segmented?
5. Which does the animal have—an alimentary canal or a digestive sac?
6. Does it have paired appendages?
7. How does the animal obtain oxygen? (Through lungs, gills, skin, or a combination of these?)
8. Are there any sense organs visible? If so, what kinds are they, and where are they located?
9. How does the animal move from one place to another?
10. What kinds of movement does it make while it remains more or less in one spot?
11. How does the animal capture and take in food?
12. How does it react when touched lightly with a dissecting needle or camel-hair brush?

All the specimens of 1 species of animal and the materials and equipment needed for observing them are arranged at 1 station. Each team will have a turn at each station.

Following are directions for observing

CHARACTERISTICS	HYDRA	PLANARIA	EARTHWORM	CRAYFISH	FROG
1					
2					
3					
↕	↕	↕	↕	↕	↕
13					

each species. Some will help you make the observations needed to answer the questions; some will direct your attention to additional observations that you should record in the 13th space of your chart. You may find some observations impossible to make; therefore, you may have blank spaces on your chart. Do the best you can. Remember that you are recording your *observations,* not what you have read or heard about the organism.

B. Observing hydras

1. You may observe food capture and feeding in hydras under a stereomicroscope or hand lens. Place a single hydra in a small watch glass that contains some of the same water in which it has been living. Wait until the animal attaches itself to the dish and expands its tentacles. Then slowly add a few drops of a culture of *Daphnia.*

2. Try to determine the presence or absence of a skeleton and of an alimentary canal by using a monocular microscope to examine a prepared slide of a longitudinal section.

3. Using a hand lens or stereomicroscope, observe a hydra's reactions when it is gently touched with a camel-hair brush.

C. Observing planarians

1. Feeding may be studied under a stereomicroscope or hand lens. Place 1 or 2 planarians in a small watch glass that contains pond or aquarium water. Add a small piece of freshly cut raw liver.

2. Presence or absence of a skeleton and alimentary canal may be determined by using a monocular microscope to examine cross sections and a stereomicroscope to examine whole mounts.

D. Observing earthworms

1. Pick up a live earthworm and hold it gently between your thumb and forefinger. Observe its movements as it attempts to escape. Are there any regions on the body surface that feel rough? If so, examine them with a hand lens and record your observations.

2. Watch a worm crawl about on the slightly moistened tabletop until you determine which is its anterior end. Using a hand lens,

examine both ends of the animal. How do its anterior and posterior ends differ in structure?

3. Place an earthworm on the surface of some loose soil and observe its movements as it burrows.

4. Using a monocular microscope, examine cross sections of the body under low power and high power. Try to determine whether it has a skeleton.

E. Observing crayfish

1. Observe the movements of the appendages and the pattern of locomotion of a live crayfish in an aquarium. Observe the movements of the antennae. Touch them gently with the tip of a camel-hair brush and note the animal's reaction.

2. Put a small piece of liver in a dish and observe how the crayfish eats.

F. Observing frogs

1. Examine a prepared skeleton of a frog. Compare it with a dissected, preserved specimen to determine the position of muscles and other soft tissues in relation to the bones.

2. Study the breathing movements of a live frog that is not moving about. To do this, observe from the side, with your eyes at the level of the animal.

3. If a hungry frog is available, your teacher may be able to show you how it captures food.

4. Observe the movements of a frog swimming in an aquarium. How do these movements compare with those of a frog hopping and moving about on a laboratory table? Your teacher will show you how to catch and hold a frog so it will not be injured.

SUMMARY

When you have completed your observations and recorded the data, review what you have learned about each of the items in the chart. By reading across the chart, you should be able to compare and contrast the characteristics of the 5 animals you have studied.

For each animal, select 5 functions that it performs as part of its way of life and describe how, in each case, its structure enables it to perform these functions.

GUIDE QUESTIONS

1. Why is it necessary for people to classify organisms?

2. What is the basis for biological classification? What advantages does it have over other possible bases?

3. Why is it necessary for both biologists and non-biologists to be able to distinguish different kinds of organisms?

4. What are some of the means by which members of one species are kept from interbreeding with members of other species?

5. Why is the biological definition of "species" inadequate?

6. How does the number of characteristics shared by all members of a classification level change as you progress from species to kingdom?

7. Why is it possible for equally experienced taxonomists to differ from each other about the classification of a particular species?

8. The vertebrates were once grouped as a phylum. Why are they now classified with such animals as lancelets and tunicates?

9. At what level of classification have we placed man, dog, and cat together? What are some characteristics that they share at this level?

10. Give some examples of structural adaptations within the orders of mammals.

11. What characteristics allow many birds and mammals but few reptiles and amphibians to live on land at high latitudes?

12. How does radial symmetry differ from bilateral symmetry?

13. How can arthropod structure be considered "upside down" and "inside out" from the chordate viewpoint?

14. What structural adaptations make it possible for insects to function in so many different niches?

15. In how many phyla can you find sessile animals?

16. List some examples of diversity among mollusks.

17. Compare and contrast flatworms with roundworms and with coelenterates.

18. Which animal phyla would most probably be represented in a small-stream ecosystem? In a desert ecosystem? In a shallow-sea ecosystem?

19. The more kinds of structures an animal has, the more complex it is said to be. From this viewpoint what phylum of animals do you consider the simplest?

20. How does a classification system reflect a taxonomist's ideas about kinship relationships among organisms?

21. Give the two aims of a taxonomist.

PROBLEMS

1. Suppose that by 1985 every kind of living organism on Earth will have been discovered, described, and classified. Do you think the development of taxonomy would then end? Explain.

2. Obtain several college zoology textbooks. Compare and contrast the classification schemes they present.

3. How can you explain the fact that many sessile or slow-moving animals are radially symmetrical, but unattached, fast-moving animals are bilaterally symmetrical?

4. Disregarding relationships but still using structure as a basis, devise a new classification of all the vertebrates you know.

5. Some apparently similar vertebrates are placed in separate classes by taxonomists. What characteristics would enable you to distinguish between the following: (a) An eel and a lamprey? (b) An eel and a snake? (c) A lizard and a salamander? (d) A turtle and an armadillo? (e) A bat and a bird? (f) A shark and a whale?

6. In this book Onychophora is listed as a class, but the group is sometimes placed at the phylum level—a good example of a difference of opinion among taxonomists. Collect evidence supporting each opinion.

7. Twenty years ago all living species of mollusks were placed in four classes. In 1957 a deep-sea dredge brought up some mollusks so different that taxonomists had to place them in a separate class. Look up the story of this discovery. During the last century what other major changes in classification have resulted from finding previously unknown organisms?

8. The word "worm" is used as a common name for a large number of animals that

are taxonomically very diverse. What do *you* have in mind when you use the word? Ask your English teacher to help you investigate the history of the word.

9. Observe the kinds of animals that live without human encouragement in a city. Try to discover the characteristics that enable them to live successfully in an urban ecosystem.

10. Some biologists have been studying three populations of frogs. Population A interbreeds with Population B under natural conditions. Similarly, Population B interbreeds with Population C. But Population A does not interbreed with Population C. How many species of frogs are involved in this study? How many species would there be if Population A became extinct? How many if Population B became extinct?

SUGGESTED READINGS

FLEAY, D. "Strange Animals of Australia," *National Geographic,* September, 1963. Pp. 388–411.

HANSON, E. D. *Animal Diversity.* 3rd ed. Englewood Cliffs, N.J.: Prentice-Hall, Inc., 1972. (Stresses aims of the modern taxonomist. Rather difficult.)

Larousse Encyclopedia of Animal Life. London: Paul Hamlyn Limited, 1967. (A well-illustrated book that has a worldwide viewpoint; combines some technical taxonomic details with short discussions of how various animals live in their environments.)

SIMPSON, G. G., and W. S. BECK. *Life: An Introduction to Biology.* Shorter ed. New York: Harcourt, Brace & World, Inc., 1969. Chapters 15 and 17. (Good short discussion of the principles of taxonomy and the major groups in the animal kingdom.)

STORER, T. I., R. C. STEBBINS, R. L. USINGER, and J. W. NYBAKKEN. *General Zoology.* 5th ed. New York: McGraw-Hill Book Co., Inc., 1972. (College textbook that emphasizes zoological classification.)

YAPP, W. B. *Vertebrates: Their Structure and Life.* New York: Oxford University Press, Inc., 1965. (Good general account of animals with back-bones. Rather difficult.)

ZAHL, P. A. "What's So Special about Spiders?" *National Geographic,* August, 1971. Pp. 190–219.

Each of the following is a series of books that treat the classification and identification of certain parts of the animal kingdom.

"Golden Nature Series." Edited by H. S. ZIM. New York: Western Publishing Co. Includes volumes on reptiles and amphibians, fishes, mammals, birds, spiders, insects. (Simple; many colored pictures.)

"Peterson Field Guide Series." Edited by R. T. PETERSON. Boston: Houghton, Mifflin Co. (Volumes on birds, mollusks, butterflies, mammals, reptiles, amphibians, insects. These books do not use keys but are copiously illustrated. Most are quite complete for the area and taxonomic group covered.)

"Pictured Key to Nature Series." Edited by H. E. JAQUES. Dubuque, Iowa: Wm. C. Brown Co., Publishers. (Volumes on flatworms, land snails, insects, spiders, freshwater fishes, birds, mammals. These books make extensive use of keys for identification.)

Plants

PLANT CLASSIFICATION

To a person who has no interest in automobiles, the flow of traffic along a highway is monotonous. But traffic holds great interest for many young men, whose ability to recognize the various models of cars is often remarkable. Most girls have similar ability with clothes and hair styles. Interest in automobiles or fashions, in birds or plants, is, in part, a measure of the extent to which a person has developed his powers of observation. The more closely anyone observes differences in the things around him, the less he finds monotonous.

monotonous [mə nät'ən əs; Greek: *monos*, single, + *tonos*, tone]: tiresomely the same

Many people do not observe plants carefully and therefore tend to take for granted their presence in the landscape. Most people do recognize some large plants as trees, or take a certain amount of pride in the grass of their lawns and parks, or, perhaps, know a rose when they see one. But being acquainted with trees, grass, and a few flowers is only the beginning, for there are approximately 350,000 species of plants!

For many centuries plant classification was based on the groupings made by the Greeks: tree, shrub, and herb. However, as *botanists* (biologists who study plants) increased their knowledge, they found that such a simple system of classification was neither convenient nor a good indicator of relationships. It was inconvenient because the same kind of plant might have the form of a tree in one climate and that of a shrub in another. It was not a good expression of relationship because in many cases a tree shared more characteristics with some groups of herbs than with other groups of trees.

Bettmann

Figure 5 • 1

Carolus Linnaeus [kär'ə ləs lĭ nē'əs]: 1707–1778. As a young man Linnaeus journeyed to the north to study the plants of Lapland. He is shown here holding a plant of a genus named after him —*Linnaea*.

What structures in plants should be used as the basis for classification? Early in the 18th century, part of the answer to this question came from a young Swedish botanist named Carolus Linnaeus. His idea was to use the reproductive parts—flowers, in the more familiar plants—as a basis.

Simple ideas can become complicated as new information is obtained. So it was with Linnaeus' idea. Today plant taxonomists still consider reproductive structures important for classification, but they

herb [ûrb]

botanists [Greek: *botane*, plant]

145

do not neglect other structures. And, like animal taxonomists, they take into consideration characteristics other than structure, such as the kinds of chemical substances found in plants. Further, their task today is, of course, more difficult than formerly, for their system of classification must express relationships as well as be convenient.

A TAXONOMIC PROBLEM

nomenclature [nŏ'mən klā'chər; Latin: *nomen,* name, + *calare,* to call]

We have already discussed a number of problems that taxonomists face. So far, however, we have ignored the problem of **nomenclature** —the problem of giving names to the kinds of organisms.

DEVELOPMENT OF NAMES

Sequoia sempervirens [sǐ kwoi'ə sĕm'pər vī'rənz]

But do you think a request for "redwood posts" would work well in Mexico—or France?

As long as there have been languages men have had names for the organisms that werę important to them. These so-called common names are still very useful. If you go into a lumberyard and ask for some *Sequoia sempervirens* fence posts, you are not likely to get what you want—a request for redwood posts works much better. Why, then, do biologists need any other names than the ones in common use? Where do these biological names come from? Why do they seem so strange to us?

The first attempts to give names to *all* known organisms, and not just to those of special interest to farmers and hunters, were probably made by the Greeks. These names became incorporated into Latin, which endured in western Europe for over a thousand years as the language of communication between educated men. Only such men —scholars, clergymen, physicians—were interested in all organisms. Thus the names they used were necessarily Latin.

2 *Caryophyllus ſylueſtris ſimplex, ſuaue rubens.* Single red Pinks.

During the Middle Ages, efforts were made to fit the names used by the Greeks and Romans to the plants and animals of the rest of Europe. But this did not work. The plants and animals of England, Germany, and other northern lands were often different from those of Greece and Italy. The differences had to be recognized. This was usually done by simply attaching a new adjective to the old name of a similar plant or animal.

Then came the Age of Exploration. Year after year, explorers sent back to European scientists strange new organisms—from Africa, South America, North America, the East Indies. Year after year, the scientists added words to names to indicate differences between the newly discovered organisms and those already known. By the beginning of the 18th century, names had become unmanageable. Here is the name that was used at that time for the carnation plant: *dianthus floribus solitariis, squamis calycinis subovatis brevissimis, corollis crenatis*—"the pink (a general name for the carnation and its relatives) with solitary flowers, the scales of the calyx somewhat egg-shaped and very short, the petals scalloped."

Victor Larsen

Figure 5 · 2

Woodcut from the *Herball* of John Gerard (1545–1612). This was an early English book on botany. Note the length of the biological name.

Imagine writing about organisms when you had to refer to them in such a cumbersome way! But at that time there was no other way to be exact. Europeans had no common names for foreign organisms. And names from the native languages of Africa, the Americas, and India were meaningless to Europeans.

For many years both botanists and zoologists fumbled toward a more workable system of nomenclature. The solution to the problem was developed by the same Linnaeus who had done such remarkable things for botanical classification a few years before. His system, at first designed as a shortcut in especially difficult cases, was well developed by 1753. With this date modern biological nomenclature begins.

However, some of these names were later adopted into European languages—for example, "skunk" and "opossum" into English. Can you find other examples?

Victor Larsen

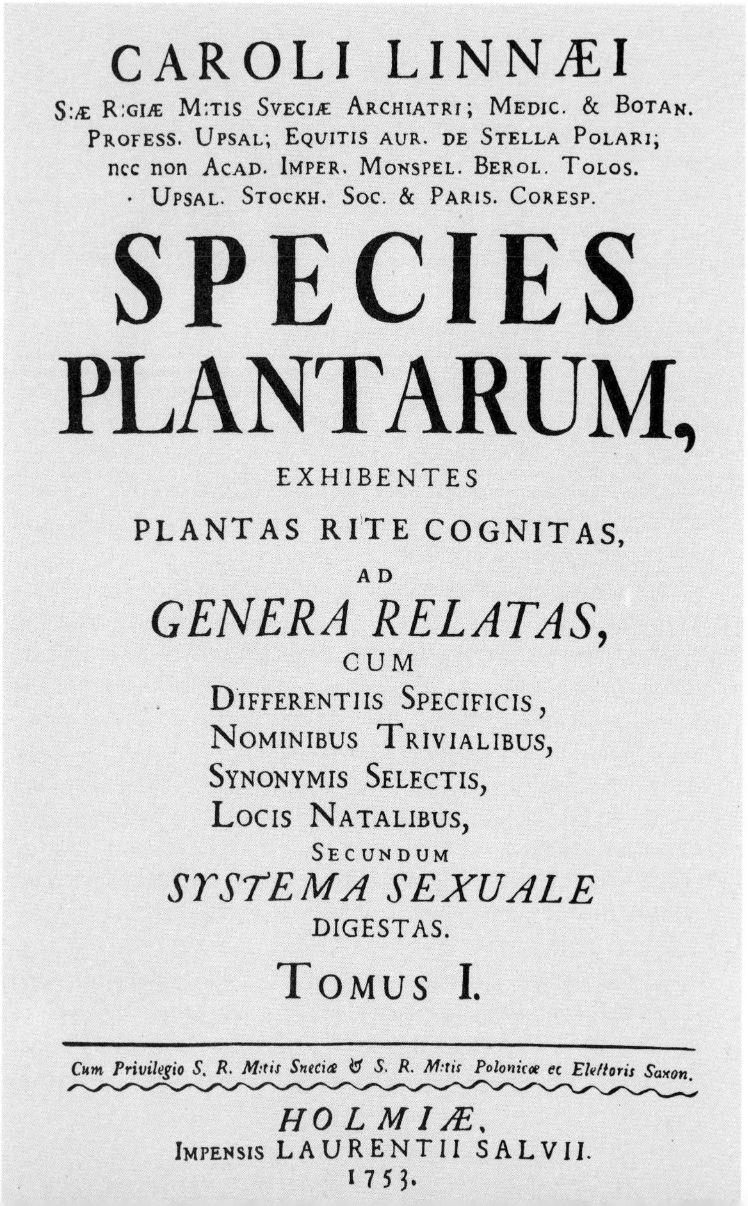

CAROLI LINNÆI

S:æ R:giæ M:tis Sveciæ Archiatri; Medic. & Botan. Profess. Upsal; Equitis aur. de Stella Polari; nec non Acad. Imper. Monspel. Berol. Tolos. · Upsal. Stockh. Soc. & Paris. Coresp.

SPECIES PLANTARUM,

EXHIBENTES

PLANTAS RITE COGNITAS,

AD

GENERA RELATAS,

CUM

DIFFERENTIIS SPECIFICIS, NOMINIBUS TRIVIALIBUS, SYNONYMIS SELECTIS, LOCIS NATALIBUS, SECUNDUM SYSTEMA SEXUALE DIGESTAS.

TOMUS I.

Cum Privilegio S. R. M:tis Sneciæ & S. R. M:tis Polonicæ et Electoris Saxon.

HOLMIÆ, Impensis LAURENTII SALVII. 1753.

Figure 5 · 3

Title page of Linnaeus' *Species Plantarum* (1753), the first book in which binominal nomenclature was consistently used. With it, modern plant nomenclature began.

binomial [bī nō′mĭ əl; Latin: *bis*, twice, + *nomen*, name]

Dianthus [dī ăn′thəs]

caryophyllus [kăr′ĭ ō fĭl′əs]

THE BINOMIAL SYSTEM

Linnaeus' system was simple. He restricted the name of each group that he thought of as a species to just two words. The first word indicated a group of similar species. Linnaeus called this larger group a genus—one of the levels in the scheme of classification we discussed in Chapter 4. Thus all species of pinks were called *Dianthus*. (The first letter of a genus word is always capitalized.) The second word of the name was usually an adjective. For the common carnation, formerly referred to by the long name given on page 146, Linnaeus picked the word *caryophyllus*.

The first rule of the system decreed that *Dianthus* could never be used for any other genus—only for pinks. The second rule of the system decreed that *caryophyllus* could never be used for any other species in the genus *Dianthus*. It might be used with some other generic word; this would not create duplication, since the scientific name of a species was always *two* words: neither word was, by itself, the name. Thus the carnation plant became *Dianthus caryophyllus;* as long as Linnaeus' rules are followed, no other species can have this name.

With these two rules a binomial (two-word) system of biological nomenclature was established. It has been used successfully for more than 200 years to name hundreds of thousands of newly discovered organisms. Though there have been many refinements, the two basic rules remain unchanged.

A few misunderstandings about biological ("scientific") names need to be cleared up. First, the words used may seem strange, but they are not necessarily long or difficult to pronounce (*Mus,* mice; *Poa,* blue grasses). Many words for genera have been absorbed into English. As common names they are properly spelled without initial capitalization—for example, iris, petunia, aster. The strangeness of words disappears as we use them.

How many other examples can you find?

Second, using biological names is not a way of showing off; it is necessary for scientific exactness. For one thing, there is no other single set of names available for all organisms. We have English names for the things we know; Malayans have Malay names for the things they know; no language includes names for all known organisms. Further, different languages have different names for the same organisms—as "carrot" in English, "zanahoria" in Spanish, and "Mohrrübe" in German. Even in the same language names may differ —for example, the plant that Americans call "corn" is termed "maize" in England and "mealies" in South Africa. Worse still, the same word may refer to different organisms: in Florida "gopher" refers to a turtle; in Kansas, to a rodent.

Third, the names are not a part of the Latin language. They started out as Latin simply because Linnaeus, like other scientists of his day, wrote in Latin. Although Latin and Greek word roots are frequently used in the names, the words may be from any language or be entirely manufactured. *Tsuga* (the hemlocks) comes from Japanese, and *Washingtonia* (a genus of palms) is obviously not Latin. The names must, however, be written in the Latin alphabet—"our" alphabet. Thus, in a Russian or Chinese biology book, biological names are printed in the Latin alphabet, though the rest of the printing is different.

Finally, there is nothing wrong with using common names when you do not need to be exact. Up to this point in our biology course, we have managed to get along without biological names. But sometimes it is better to say *"Pinus strobus"* instead of "white pine." There are several species of trees called white pines, and a biologist may need to state exactly *which* species he is referring to.

Pinus strobus [pī'nəs strō'bəs]

Investigation 5.1

DIVERSITY AMONG PLANTS: LEAVES

INTRODUCTION

Suppose a visitor to Earth from another planet were spending a weekend on a farm. Because he does not yet know the names of the animals he is encountering, you might give him the identification chart shown below.

You will probably recognize that the chart is a kind of dichotomous key. When such a key is made, a group of objects is repeatedly divided into smaller groups. Each division is based on sharply contrasting characteristics.

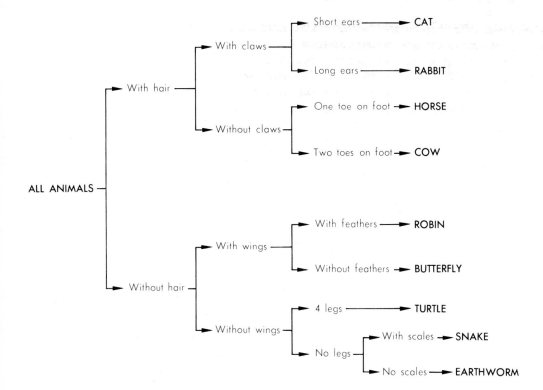

Wherever possible, the characteristics used at any point in the key lead to a division into 2 subgroups of approximately equal size. Eventually the repeated divisions result in each kind of object being separated from all the others.

MATERIALS AND EQUIPMENT

(for each student)

10 leaves (Set A): 1 each from 10 plant species, mounted on cards. The cards, numbered *1–10,* are labeled with the plant names.

10 leaves (Set B): 1 each from the same 10 species as Set A, mounted on cards. Each card has the same number as the card holding the corresponding leaf in Set A, but no name.

PROCEDURE

Construct a dichotomous identification chart for the leaves in Set A. Begin by spreading all the leaves on the table in front of you. Study each leaf. In what ways does it resemble the others in the set and in what ways does it differ? What kinds of characteristics should you look for? A few suggestions are listed below:

Are there 2 distinct regions in the leaf—a stemlike portion (*petiole*) and a flattened part (*blade*)?

Is the blade all in one piece or is it divided into separate *leaflets?*

Is the edge of the blade smooth or is it notched?

Is the blade uniformly green or are other colors present?

Is the blade heart-shaped, oval, or spear-shaped?

Now select 2 clearly contrasting characteristics, 1 of which is possessed by about half the leaves in the set and the other by the remaining half. Following the same arrangement as that used in the chart, draw a box at the left margin of a left-hand page in your data book and label it "All Leaves in Set." (You will probably need both the left-hand and the right-hand pages for the complete chart.) Draw 2 more boxes to the right of the 1st box and label them to indicate the characteristics used in making your 1st division into 2 groups. Draw lines that will show the division of 1 group into 2.

Next study 1 of the 2 subgroups. Again find a pair of contrasting characteristics that enables you to divide the group into 2 subgroups of approximately equal size. Using labeled boxes and lines, place these characteristics in the appropriate positions on your chart. Then do the same for the other group. Continue this process until you have completed a key in which there is a final branch for each of the 10 kinds of leaves. Label each of these branches with the name of the plant from which the leaf was obtained, but do *not* include the identifying number.

Next, turn to Set B and use your chart to identify each of the leaves included in it. Since no 2 leaves are exactly alike, it is possible that some characteristics used in your chart will need to be changed so that it will work with both sets of leaves.

Now exchange with another student the chart and Set B (but *not* Set A). Using his chart, identify the leaves in his set. Write the number of each leaf next to the name of the species indicated. When you have finished, obtain his Set A (which includes both names and numbers) and check your identifications. If you have not achieved complete success, the fault lies either in his key or in your use of it. Repeat the keying-out process. If differences still turn up, return his key, indicating where you think it needs correction.

FOR FURTHER INVESTIGATION

Go back to the dichotomous keys in Investigation 4.2 (pages 136–137). In these keys each pair of contrasting characteristics is identified by a number-letter combination. Determine the principle used in this arrangement, and then convert your leaf key from chart form to the number-and-letter system.

UNDERSTANDING PLANT DIVERSITY

Even before reading Chapter 4, you would probably have had little difficulty in deciding that a mosquito and a mouse should be placed in different groups of animals. The contrast between insect and mammal is obvious. To most people, however, contrasts among plants are not so clear.

In walking through a forest a botanist collects a clump of green plants that cover a fallen tree. He calls these "true mosses" (Figure 5 • 4A). A little later he picks up another mossy plant that is growing between fallen leaves on the forest floor (Figure 5 • 4B). This he calls a "club moss." Later he shows you another small, greenish plant that he collected in the Arctic (Figure 5 • 4C). He calls this "reindeer moss." Finally he points to a picture (Figure 5 • 4D) and refers to the mossy plant shown there as a "moss campion." Four "mosses" in both appearance and common name—surely they should be placed, if not in the same genus, at least in the same family of plants.

It turns out, however, that these four plants are usually classified in widely differing groups. Though they all share certain obvious characteristics—they are mossy—botanists evidently use characteristics that are not so obvious in working out taxonomic relationships among plants. Therefore, most people find an understanding of plant diversity more difficult than an understanding of animal diversity.

Figure 5 • 4

(A) True moss; (B) club moss;
(C) reindeer moss;
(D) moss campion.

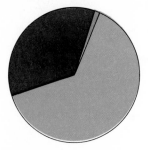

● FLOWERING TRACHEOPHYTES
● NONFLOWERING TRACHEOPHYTES
● NONTRACHEOPHYTES

Figure 5 • 5
Proportion of plant species
in various taxonomic groups.
Compare this graph with
Figure 4 • 20.

Phylum Tracheophyta
[trā′kē ǎf′ə tə; Greek: *tracheia,*
windpipe, + *phyton,* plant]

vascular [vǎs′kyə lər; Latin:
vasculum, little container]

Pteropsida [tə rǎp′sə də;
Greek: *pteron,* feather, + *opsis,*
appearance]

Angiospermae [ǎn jē′ō spər′mē;
Greek: *angeion,* container, +
sperma, seed]

sepals [sē′pəlz; Greek: *skepe,*
covering]

petals [pět′əlz; Greek: *petalos,*
outspread]

stamens [stā′mənz; Latin:
stare, to stand]

pistils [pǐst′əlz; Latin: *pistillus,*
pestle]

pollen [päl′ən; Latin: *pollen,*
dust]

A CATALOGUE OF LIVING PLANTS: KINGDOM PLANTAE

The organisms that taxonomists commonly group in the plant kingdom
lack ways to move themselves from place to place and, in general,
react rather slowly to their environment. In addition, they have a chemical characteristic: they contain *cellulose,* a substance that gives their
bodies more firmness.

PHYLUM TRACHEOPHYTA
vascular plants; about 211,900 species

The chances are very good that almost all the plants you can name
are tracheophytes. Every tracheophyte has a continuous system of
tubes (a *vascular system*) extending through its roots, stems, and
leaves. By means of this conducting system, water and substances
dissolved in it move rather easily from one place in the plant to another. For land plants, movement of water upward from the soil is
especially important. Any land plant that stands as much as a meter
high is almost certainly a tracheophyte.

SUBPHYLUM PTEROPSIDA
seed plants and ferns; about 210,700 species

The subphyla of tracheophytes are very unequal in number of species
included. This subphylum contains 99 percent of the species in the
phylum. It is distinguished from other tracheophyte subphyla by the
fact that the position of each leaf is marked by a gap in the vascular
tissue of the stem.

Class Angiospermae
flowering plants; about 200,000 species

Botanists think of a flower as a short branch bearing groups of leaves.
Some of these may resemble ordinary leaves, but others are so different in structure that it is hard to think of them as leaves at all. If you
examine the flower of a buttercup, for example, you see on the underside a number of green, leaflike structures—*sepals.* Before the bud
opened, the sepals enclosed the other parts of the flower. The most
conspicuous flower parts in a buttercup are the *petals,* which, like the
sepals, are more or less leaflike in shape but of a quite different color.
Attached just above the base of the petals are a number of *stamens,*
each having an enlarged tip. And grouped together in the center of
the flower are numerous small, rounded structures called *pistils,* each
with pointed tip. Despite their shape, both stamens and pistils are believed to be modified leaves.

A flower is a reproductive structure. Stamens produce *pollen*
grains; when these are transferred to the tips of the pistils, *seeds* may
develop. The sepals and petals are not directly involved in seed formation, so a flower can function without them. In fact, in a few plants
a flower may consist of only a single stamen or a single pistil.

Much of the diversity shown by angiosperms lies in their flowers.
There is no better way to appreciate this than to examine various kinds

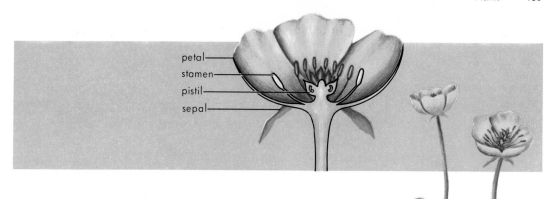

petal —
stamen —
pistil —
sepal —

of flowers you can find in a field, in a greenhouse, or even in vacant lots. Diversity in flower structure is usually related to the way flowers function. Flowers in which pollen is transferred from stamen to pistil by insects are often large and conspicuous. Many have brightly colored petals, and some have colored sepals as well. The petals, moreover, often have small glands that produce a sugar solution. These adaptations probably attract pollinating insects. On the other hand, flowers in which pollen is transferred by wind usually have small sepals and petals or none at all. They are often located high up on the plant and produce an abundance of pollen. Their pistils commonly have large, long, or feathery structures at the tips, which are covered with a sticky fluid. Such structural adaptations probably increase the likelihood of wind pollination.

X 1

Figure 5 • 6

Buttercup plant and diagram of its flower structure (*above*).

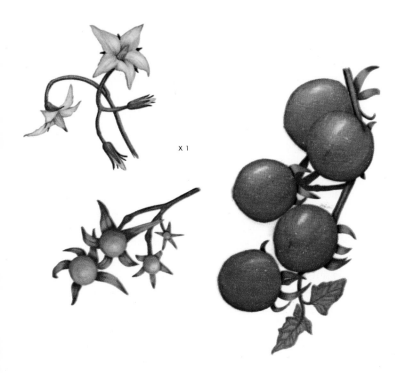

X 1

Figure 5 • 7

Stages in the development of tomato fruit from flowers (*left*).

As development proceeds, pistils are transformed into *fruits,* which contain seeds. Each seed contains a tiny new plant—an embryo. Part of an embryo consists of one or two modified leaves, called *cotyledons,* and part is a beginning of a root. Each seed also contains a supply of food that is used when the embryo starts to grow. The food may be stored in a special part of the seed called the **endosperm,** or it may be stored in the embryo itself, usually in the cotyledons.

cotyledons [kŏt′ə lē′dənz; Greek: *kotyle,* anything hollow]

endosperm [ĕn′dō spûrm′; Greek: *endon,* within, + *sperma,* seed]

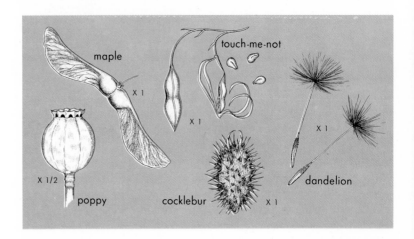

Figure 5 • 8
Diversity among fruits. How does each of the structural adaptations shown here provide for seed scattering?

Seeds and fruits show as much diversity as flowers. In many cases, part of the pistil becomes thick and fleshy, as in the fruits of peach, plum, and tomato. Other fleshy fruits, such as apples and pears, also include parts of the flower stalk. Fleshy fruits are often eaten by animals. The seeds in many such fruits have thick coats that permit them to pass through an animal's digestive tract unharmed, later to be dropped at some distance from the parent plant. Many fruits are not fleshy but have other adaptations that aid in scattering their seeds.

What kind of ecological relationship exists between plant and animal in this case?

In addition to the diversity in their flowers, there is great diversity in the size of angiosperms and in the life-span of their *shoots*—the parts that appear above ground. Many angiosperms are trees. A tree form enables a plant to bear its leaves well above the surface of the ground, where they are likely to receive more light than do those of shorter plants. Because of their size, trees can store large reserves of food in trunks and roots, allowing survival through a series of several bad years. Trees have relatively long life-spans; this increases the probability that a tree species will survive even though the entire seed crop of any one year may be destroyed. But most species of angiosperms are not trees. Some, such as roses and raspberries, are woody shrubs. Others, such as ivy, grapes, and hundreds of tropical species, are *lianas*—woody vines—which rely on rocks, walls, or other plants for support. Most, however, are neither shrubs nor vines, but non-woody plants—herbs.

lianas [lĭ ăn′əz]. See Figure 8 · 20.

Many of these herbaceous plants have roots or stems that year

herbaceous [hûr bā′shəs]

after year remain alive in the soil during winter and during each grow-ing season send up new shoots. These are **perennial** herbs, such as goldenrod, iris, and asparagus. Others are **annuals.** These (for exam-ple, garden beans, sunflowers, and corn) produce seeds and die after growing for only one season. Still others have life-spans intermediate between those of perennials and annuals.

perennial [pə rĕn′ĭ əl; Latin: *per,* through, + *annus,* year]

goldenrod. See Figure 2·11. Iris. See Figure 2·2.

Subclass Monocotyledoneae
monocots; about 34,000 species

Botanists divide angiosperms into two large groups. Figure 5·9 shows the characteristics on which these subclasses are based. In studying the figure, keep in mind that it is a summary and does not take all known angiosperms into consideration; for example, some monocots have netted-veined leaves. The basic characteristic, as the name of the group indicates, is that the embryo contains a single cotyledon.

Monocotyledoneae [mŏn′ə kŏt′ə lē′də nē; Greek: *monos,* one, single, + *kotyle*]

Many of the plants most economically important to man are mono-cots. All important grain-producing plants, such as wheat, rice, and corn, are monocots; these are a major source of biological energy for mankind. The pasture grasses that feed the cattle that are another source of human food are also monocots. It is safe to say that without the monocots the human population could never have reached its present size. (Examples below.)

In addition to grains, what other monocot plants are important for human food?

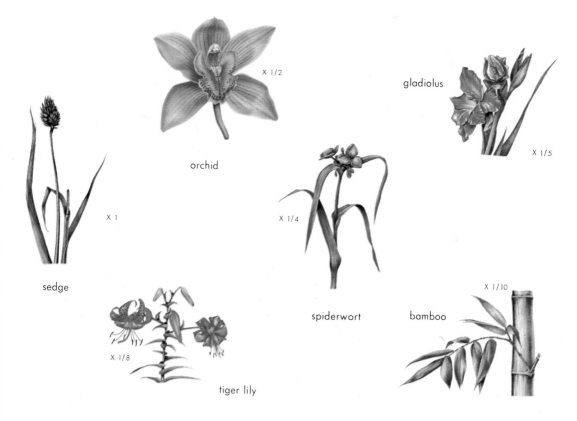

orchid

X 1/2

gladiolus

X 1/5

sedge

X 1

spiderwort

X 1/4

bamboo

X 1/10

tiger lily

X 1/8

Dicotyledoneae
[dī kŏt′ə lē′də nē; Greek:
dis-, two, double, + *kotyle*]

Subclass Dicotyledoneae
dicots; about 166,000 species

Most of the fruits and vegetables that serve as human food come from dicots. In addition, the so-called hardwoods used in furniture and flooring—and in hockey sticks and baseball bats—come from dicot trees. Almost all shade trees are dicots, also. (Examples below.)

X 1/3

oak

X 1/2

scarlet sage

columbine

X 1/2

X 1/2

wild rose

X 1/2

morning glory

X 1/2

dandelion

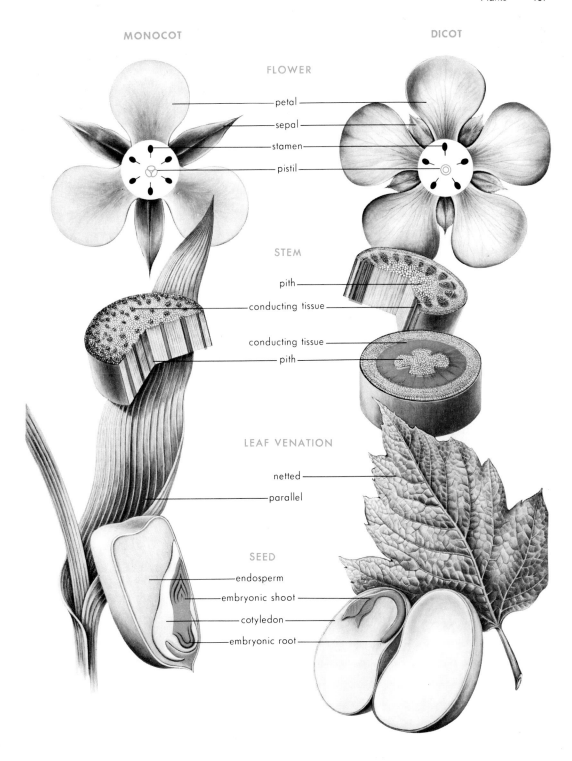

MONOCOT

DICOT

FLOWER

petal

sepal

stamen

pistil

STEM

pith

conducting tissue

conducting tissue

pith

LEAF VENATION

netted

parallel

SEED

endosperm

embryonic shoot

cotyledon

embryonic root

Figure 5 · 9

Comparison of monocot and dicot characteristics.

Gymnospermae
[jĭm′nə spûr′mē; Greek:
gymnos, naked, + *sperma*,
seed]

conifers [kō′nə fərz; Latin:
conus, cone, + *ferre*, to bear]

Class Gymnospermae

gymnosperms; about 700 species

Like angiosperms, gymnosperms produce seeds. But the seeds do not develop within pistils; instead, they are attached to the upper surfaces of scales. In the most familiar gymnosperms, the conifers, these seed-bearing scales are grouped together in cones. A seed developing in a cone may be covered by the scales, somewhat as a small

A

Field Museum of Natural History

B

Josef Muench

Figure 5 • 10

Three contrasting gymnosperms: (A) Cycad in Australia. Seed-bearing structures are in the center of the plant.
(B) A sequoia in California—one of the most bulky individual organisms that ever lived. (C) *Welwitschia mirabilis* in southwestern Africa. The plant has only two split leaves arising from a flat stem that bears small cones on its rim.

Field Museum of Natural History

C

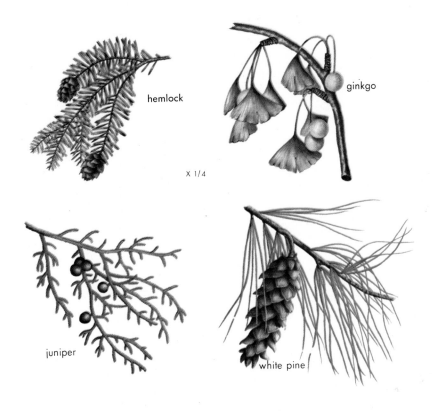

hemlock

ginkgo

X 1/4

juniper

white pine

coin may be concealed between the pages of a book; or other struc-tures may grow up around the seed before it matures. The term "gymnosperm" is therefore somewhat misleading.

So the term "gymnosperm" is somewhat misleading. Why?

Almost all gymnosperms are trees or shrubs, and all are at least somewhat woody. Though the number of species is small, the num-ber of individual gymnosperms is enormous; in some parts of the world, much of the vegetation is made up of such conifers as pines and spruces. From these trees comes the greater part of our North American lumber supply—the so-called softwoods. (Examples above.)

To what extent are the lumberman's terms "hardwood" and "softwood" justified?

Class Filicineae
ferns; about 10,000 species

Ferns lack seeds, but they have other reproductive structures. At cer-tain times of the year, small brown spots develop either on the under-sides of fern leaflets or on special leaves that are different from the others on the plants. Each spot consists of a group of knob-shaped cases containing large numbers of **spores,** which are almost micro-scopic in size. Spores are far simpler than seeds: a spore contains no embryo and only a small amount of food.

Filicineae [fĭl'ə sĭn'ē ē'; Latin: *filix*, fern]

spore [spōr; Greek: *spora*, that which is sown]

When a spore case is ripe, it opens and throws the spores out into the air. If a spore falls in a suitably moist place, it germinates and develops rapidly into a thin, green, heart-shaped plant that is rarely over 1 cm in diameter. This small plant is seldom noticed in the

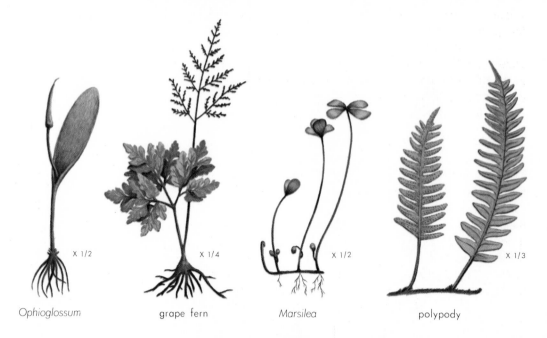

Ophioglossum   grape fern   Marsilea   polypody

X 1/2   X 1/4   X 1/2   X 1/3

Figure 5 · 11
Tree fern on the island of
Java.

woods, but from it eventually grows a conspicuous spore-bearing fern plant.

The ferns native to most of the United States are perennials with underground stems. From these stems new sets of leaves appear above ground each spring. But in the state of Hawaii and elsewhere in the tropics, many species of ferns have stems that grow upright —trees that may reach a height of 20 m. (Examples on facing page.)

SUBPHYLUM LYCOPSIDA
club mosses; about 1100 species

Club mosses are low-growing evergreen plants that seldom become more than 40 cm tall. They spread by means of branching horizontal stems that grow on the surface of the soil or just below it. The most noticeable part of a club-moss plant is an upright branch growing from one of these horizontal stems. Club mosses reproduce by spores, which are produced on modified leaves. In many species these leaves form club-shaped cones at the tips of short, straight stems. From this feature the name "club moss" is derived. Club mosses are rather common plants in much of the United States and are often used to make Christmas wreaths. (Example: *Lycopodium*.)

SUBPHYLUM SPHENOPSIDA
horsetails; 32 species

Horsetails have hollow, jointed, upright branches that grow from horizontal underground stems. Their small leaves are arranged in a circle around each stem joint. At the tips of some of the upright branches are cones. In these are produced the spores by which the plants reproduce. In middle latitudes horsetails rarely reach a height of 2 m, but in the American tropics one species may be as much as 12 m high.

Horsetails are harsh to the touch; their tissues contain silica, a compound present in sand. Pioneer women scrubbed pots and pans with them, and they are still sometimes called "scouring rushes." (Example: *Equisetum*.)

Lycopsida [lī kŏp′sə də; Greek: *lycos*, wolf, + *opsis*, appearance (because the roots were thought to resemble a wolf's claw)]

X 1/2

Lycopodium

Sphenopsida [sfī nŏp′sə də; Greek: *sphen*, wedge, + *opsis* (from the shape of the leaves)]

silica [sĭl′ə kə; Latin: *silex*, any hard stone]. This same glasslike substance forms the skeletons of some sponges (pages 133–134).

X 1/3

Equisetum

Psilopsida [sī lŏp′sĭ də; Greek: *psilos*, bare, + *opsis*]

primitive. See Investigation 5.2.

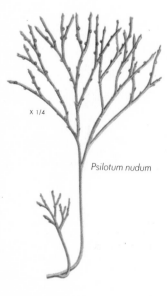

X 1/4

Psilotum nudum

Bryophyta [brī ăf′ə də; Greek: *bryon*, moss, + *phyton*, plant]

Musci [mə′sī′; Latin: *muscus*, moss]

rhizoids [rī′zoidz; Greek: *rhiza*, root, + *eidos*, shape]

SUBPHYLUM PSILOPSIDA
psilopsids; 3 species

Unless you live in Florida, Georgia, South Carolina, or Hawaii, you are not likely to encounter psilopsids. These small plants have forking stems without leaves. Spore cases are borne at the tips of short branches. There are only three species, all of which are found in warm parts of the world. They are the most primitive living tracheophytes. (Example: *Psilotum nudum.*)

PHYLUM BRYOPHYTA
bryophytes; about 24,000 species

All bryophytes are less than 70 cm tall, and very few are taller than 20 cm. Most bear structures resembling stems and leaves, but they lack vascular (conducting) tissue.

Class Musci
true mosses; about 15,000 species

The true mosses always grow in clumps (Figure 5 • 4A). If you use a hand lens to examine an individual moss plant from such a clump, you find that it consists of an upright stalk with threadlike structures **(rhizoids)** growing out of its base. The rhizoids absorb water and help to hold the plant in place. A large number of flat, green, leaflike structures are attached spirally along the stalk. Examining sections of a moss under a microscope, you find no vascular tissue. And so, although a moss plant may look somewhat like a tiny tracheophyte with roots, stems, and leaves, these terms are not used in describing mosses because they imply the presence of such tissue.

Mosses reproduce by spores: spores grow into masses of green threads from which the familiar moss plants arise. Most mosses grow in fairly damp places and a few in water, but some are able to withstand drought by becoming dormant. Many mosses are able to photosynthesize in weak light, so they are often found on the ground in forest ecosystems. (Examples: *Sphagnum* and *Polytrichum.*)

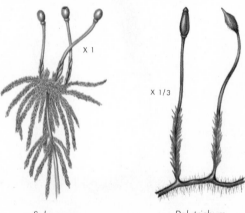

X 1

X 1/3

Sphagnum   *Polytrichum*

Class Anthocerotae
hornworts; about 50 species

Anthocerotae [ăn thäs'ə rō'tē; Greek: *anthos*, flower, + *keras*, horn]

The main body of a hornwort is flat, with rhizoids on the lower side. From this base rise spore-bearing structures, which, unlike those of true mosses, are capable of continuous growth. Hornworts are inconspicuous plants that are found in shaded places beside streams. (Example: *Anthoceros.*)

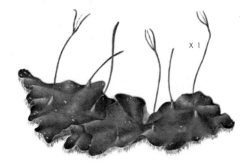

Anthoceros

Class Hepaticae
liverworts; about 8500 species

Hepaticae [hə păd'ə sē'; Greek: *hepatikos*, liver-like (from the shape of some species)]

Like the bodies of hornworts, those of liverworts are flat. In many species they are branching masses of green tissue, but in others they are stemlike, with flat, leaflike structures arranged in two rows. Liverworts reproduce by spores.

Many people who can recognize a moss have never noticed liverworts. This is not surprising, because liverworts are not nearly so common or widely distributed as mosses. Neither liverworts nor hornworts play very large roles in most ecosystems. (Examples: *Porella* and *Conocephalum.*)

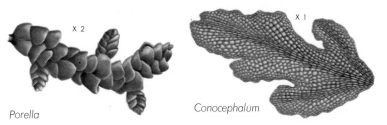

Porella

Conocephalum

PHYLUM MYCOPHYTA
fungi; about 75,000 species

Mycophyta [mī'kō fī'tə; Greek: *mykes*, mushroom, + *phyton*, plant]

fungus [fŭng'gəs]

Mushrooms—and plants called by such names as mold, mildew, rust, and smut—are collectively known as fungi (singular, "fungus"). All fungi have three characteristics: they have no vascular tissues; they reproduce, at least in part, by means of spores; they lack chlorophyll.

hyphae [hī′fē; singular, hypha;
Greek: *hyphe*, a web]

Most of a fungus plant is a mass of slender white threads called
hyphae. These grow in soil that contains large amounts of dead plant
and animal matter—food for the fungus.

The great majority of fungi are decomposers. You can often find
white hyphae growing among decaying leaves or pieces of rotten
wood in a forest. But it is only a short step from feeding on dead
organisms to attacking organisms that are not yet dead. You might,
therefore, expect some fungi to be parasites—and indeed many are.

Because the hyphae of most fungi look very much alike, classification of fungi is based primarily upon differences in reproductive
structures.

Basidiomycetes
[bə sǐd′ǐ ō mī sē′tēz; Greek:
basis, base, + *myketes*,
mushrooms]

How are commercial
mushrooms grown?

Class Basidiomycetes
club fungi; about 23,000 species

These fungi produce spores on the surfaces of clublike structures.
Many have rather large and conspicuous spore-bearing parts. Most
of the species of mushrooms, both edible and poisonous, are club
fungi. Many, however, are parasites of plants that are important to
man, such as wheat and corn. (Examples: *Coprinus* and *Puccinia.*)

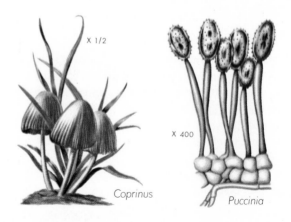

Figure 5 • 12

Reproductive structure of a
field mushroom, a basidiomy-
cete. Where are the spores?

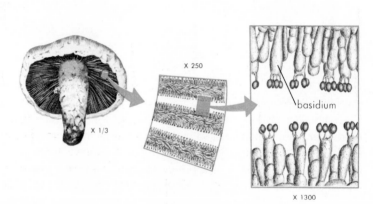

Class Ascomycetes
sac fungi; about 25,000 species

In these fungi, spores are produced in sacs. Some of the sac fungi are important in the manufacture of cheeses. The distinctive flavor and appearance of Roquefort cheese is, in part, the result of the growth of an ascomycete, *Penicillium roqueforti.* In Camembert cheese another fungus, *P. camemberti,* is similarly involved. Still another species, *P. notatum,* produces the drug penicillin. Yeasts also are included among the sac fungi, since, under unfavorable environmental conditions, many of them produce spores enclosed in a sac. Among the many parasitic ascomycetes is a species that has destroyed many of the elm trees in parks and along streets. (Examples: *Neurospora* and morel.)

Ascomycetes [ăs'kə mī sē'tēz; Greek: *askos,* bag, bladder, + *myketes*]

Penicillium roqueforti [pĕn'ə sĭl'ĭ əm rōk fôr'tĭ]

camemberti [kăm'əm bâr'tĭ]

notatum [nō tā'təm]

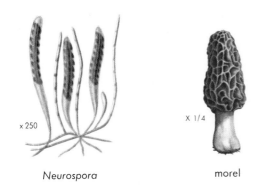

Neurospora   morel

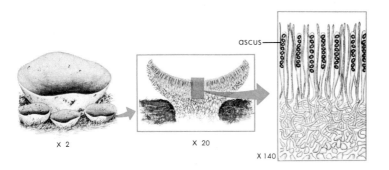

Figure 5 · 13
Reproductive structures of a sac fungus, an ascomycete. Where are the spores?

Class Phycomycetes
alga-like fungi; about 1500 species

Alga-like fungi are distinguished from other fungi by the lack of cross walls in the hyphae. Their spores are borne in various kinds of cases. Bread mold (genus *Rhizopus*) is the member of this class most familiar to many people. It is a decomposer that can be destructive to human foods—not only to bread but also to fruits such as grapes, plums, and strawberries. But many species are parasitic and some attack crop plants. For example, in 1845 and 1846 one species ruined the potato

Phycomycetes [fī'kō mī sē'tēz; Greek: *phykos,* seaweed, + *myketes*]. The term "alga" (plural, algae [ăl'jē]) often refers to a seaweed.

crop in Ireland, resulting in a disastrous famine there. (Examples: *Saprolegnia and Rhizopus.*)

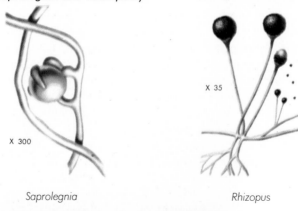

X 300

X 35

Saprolegnia

Rhizopus

Victor Larsen

Figure 5 • 14

A phycomycete (*Saprolegnia*) growing on a drowned fly in an aquarium. Only the hyphae, not the reproductive structures, appear here. × 8

Rhodophyta [rō′də fī′tə; Greek: *rhodon,* rose — hence reddish, + *phyton,* plant]

PHYLUM RHODOPHYTA
red algae; about 2500 species

All the red algae are aquatic and almost all are marine. The macroscopic kinds are among the plants commonly called seaweeds. All have chlorophyll, but it is usually masked by red pigments. Red algae have rather complex life histories by which botanists distinguish them from other plants. They also differ from most other plants in storing food not as starch but as a related chemical compound. (Examples: *Polysiphonia, Corallina,* and *Chondrus.*)

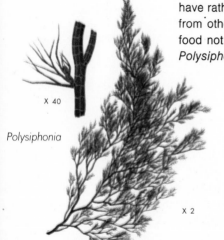

X 40

Polysiphonia

X 2

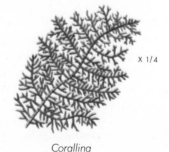

X 1/4

Corallina

X 1/2

Chondrus

PHYLUM PHAEOPHYTA
brown algae; about 1000 species

Phaeophyta [fē'ə fī'tə; Greek: *phaios*, brown, + *phyton*]

Like the red algae, the brown algae are all aquatic and most species live in the seas. Some are very large seaweeds, and most are at least macroscopic. They have chlorophyll that is usually masked by brownish pigments. They store food as compounds related to carbohydrates and as carbohydrates other than starch. In general, brown algae live in cold seas and red algae in warm. (Examples below.)

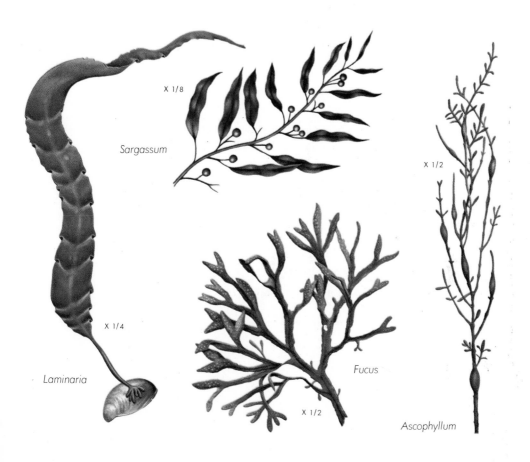

X 1/8

Sargassum

X 1/2

X 1/4

Laminaria

Fucus

X 1/2

Ascophyllum

PHYLUM CHRYSOPHYTA
golden algae; about 5700 species

Chrysophyta [krə säf'ət ə; Greek: *chrysos*, gold, + *phyton*]

The golden algae are mostly microscopic aquatic plants, though some may grow in damp places on land. They have chlorophyll, but it is usually masked by yellow pigments. Some are threadlike in form. These often grow in masses at the edges of ponds or streams, or on moist flowerpots in greenhouses. Within the phylum is a large group of plants commonly called diatoms. These have shells made of silica and store food in the form of oil. They are abundant in both fresh and

diatom [dī'ə təm]. For another example, see page 46.

marine waters, where they are the principal producer organisms of many food webs. (Example: diatoms.)

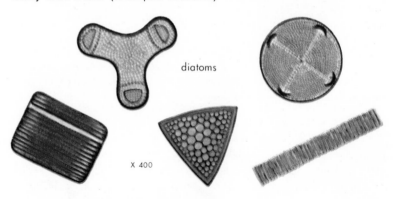

diatoms

X 400

Chlorophyta [klō räf'əd ə; Greek: *chloros*, green, + *phyton*]

PHYLUM CHLOROPHYTA
green algae; about 6000 species

Green algae are aquatic plants of both marine and fresh waters. Their chlorophyll is not usually masked by other pigments, so they appear bright green. They store food as starch, as do most plants. Some green algae are macroscopic though many are microscopic. Some are rather small seaweeds. The microscopic ones are sometimes so abundant that they color the water of ponds and lakes green. (Examples below.)

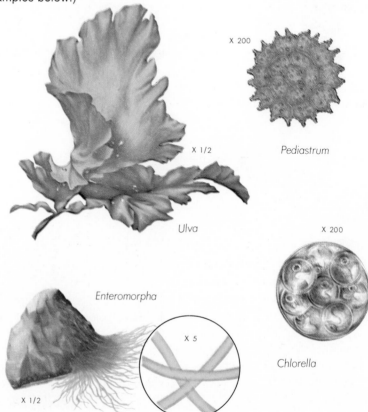

X 200

X 1/2

Pediastrum

Ulva

X 200

Enteromorpha

X 5

X 1/2

Chlorella

SOME PROBLEMS OF PLANT CLASSIFICATION

You have learned that the difficulties of a taxonomist are increased by his attempts to show kinship relationships and at the same time make his classification system convenient to use. Here are some examples of such difficulties in plant taxonomy.

See page 140.

ALGAE

In some biology textbooks you may find a chapter entitled "The Algae." This implies that there is a group of plants similar in enough characteristics to be grouped under one name. In our catalogue of living plants, however, there is no such group. But each of the last four phyla has the word "algae" as a part of its common name. The term is a convenient one and it is useful to many kinds of biologists, such as ecologists. But plant taxonomists have become convinced that many of the organisms that are so named have very little relationship to each other. For taxonomists to include all of these organisms in a single group would, therefore, be misleading.

The names that are used for the algal phyla are left over from a time when botanists did not know as much as they now do about plant relationships. Some plants that have all the other characteristics of "green algae" are actually reddish, some "brown algae" are yellow-green, and at least one of the "red algae" is a beautiful violet-green. Again, you have an example of how an apparently convenient way to classify organisms can be misleading.

LICHENS

lichen [lī'kən]. See page 257.

On the bark of a tropical tree, on a tombstone in New Hampshire, buried under arctic snow, on a rock in Arizona—in all these places you can find lichens. In Chapter 3 we discussed the mutualistic rela-

Dennis Brokaw

Nancy Haynes

Figure 5 • 15
Lichens. (See also Figures 5 • 4C and 8 • 38A.)

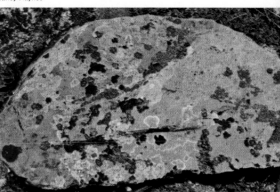

tionship between an alga and a fungus that make up a lichen. Yet, so definite are the form, color, and other characteristics of each of these partnerships that for several hundred years biologists described lichens as if they were single organisms.

The body of a lichen has a framework of fungal hyphae. In its upper layers are many groups of small algae. These algae can grow independently, and many can be recognized as species that are also known to live alone. The lichen fungi, on the other hand, do not grow well when separated from their partners. They can be placed in the known classes of fungi—mostly in the sac fungi—but they are unlike any of the species that live alone. None of this matters much when we view the world ecologically. But what can taxonomists do with lichens? They have described more than 15,000 "species," though each contains an alga that has its own specific name. But if taxonomists describe the partners separately, are not the species of fungi rather odd?

If you were classifying lichens as a group in the plant kingdom, at which taxonomic level would you place them?

"IMPERFECT" FUNGI

The classes of fungi are based on characteristics of their spore-bearing structures. But many fungi seldom produce such structures. Botanists have studied many species for years without discovering spore-bearing structures. What can taxonomists do with a species of fungus whose spore-bearing structures are unknown?

In some cases a species so closely resembles another species whose spore-bearing structures *are* known that it is a good assumption that the first should be placed in the same group with the second. For many species there are no such resemblances, and some of these are species important to man's interests—parasites that grow on crop plants and even on man's own skin. Something must be done with such important organisms. So for convenience only, taxonomists place these "imperfect" fungi together in a group called Deuteromycetes. Whenever a botanist discovers spore-bearing structures in one of these plants, it can then be shifted to one of the fungal classes. (Examples: *Alternaria, Fusarium,* and *Cordana.*)

Deuteromycetes [dū′tər ō mī sē′tēz; Greek: deuteros, secondary, + myketes, mushrooms]

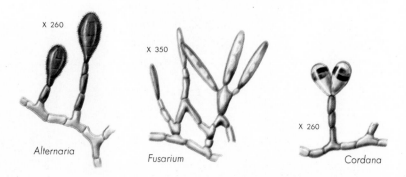

X 260

X 350

X 260

Alternaria

Fusarium

Cordana

Investigation 5.2

THE CONCEPT OF "PRIMITIVE CHARACTERISTICS"

BACKGROUND INFORMATION

Biologists sometimes use the term "primitive" (for example, on page 162) or "advanced" when discussing diversity among organisms. These terms are linked with the idea developed near the end of Chapter 4—that species existing today are related to each other through their ancestors. From this comes the further idea that some of the species living today retain more of their ancestors' characteristics than do other species. A species that has retained many of the older characteristics —in other words, one that has changed little from its ancestors—is said to be primitive. A species that has few of the characteristics of its ancestors is said to be advanced. Of course, there can be many degrees of advancement, so "primitive" and "advanced" are not absolute terms; they are useful only in making comparisons.

From the study of many kinds of evidence, but chiefly of fossils, botanists have reached fairly general agreement about which characteristics are very ancient in the history of plants and which characteristics have appeared more recently. Figure 5 · 16 is based on such studies.

MATERIALS AND EQUIPMENT

plants of various phyla,
    10 labeled specimens
monocular microscopes
hand lenses
stereomicroscopes
microscope slides
cover slips

PROCEDURE

You will be provided with labeled specimens of 10 different plants. Determine the "Advancement Score" for each of these as follows: Start at the left of Figure 5 · 16 (pages 172–173). Arrows from the starting point lead to 2 descriptions. Choose the 1 that fits the plant you are scoring. Proceed across the chart by following the arrows and choosing the descriptions that best fit the plant. At each description there is a number. In your data book record these numbers in the 2nd column of a chart like the following. Continue as far as the arrows go. The "Advancement Score" for the plant is the sum of all the numbers appearing after the descriptions you used in working through the chart. When you have the

NAME OF PLANT	NUMERICAL VALUES OF CHOICES MADE	TOTAL "ADVANCEMENT SCORE"	RANK
1.			
2.			
3.			
10.			

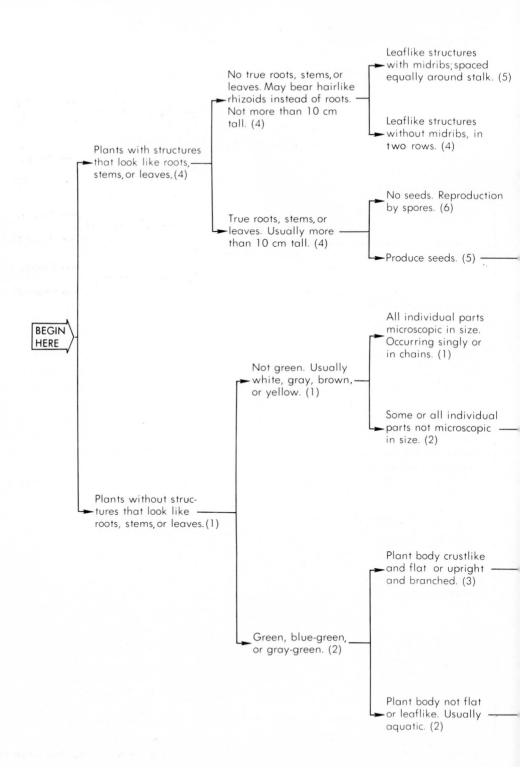

BEGIN HERE

Plants with structures that look like roots, stems, or leaves. (4)

No true roots, stems, or leaves. May bear hairlike rhizoids instead of roots. Not more than 10 cm tall. (4)

Leaflike structures with midribs; spaced equally around stalk. (5)

Leaflike structures without midribs, in two rows. (4)

True roots, stems, or leaves. Usually more than 10 cm tall. (4)

No seeds. Reproduction by spores. (6)

Produce seeds. (5)

Plants without structures that look like roots, stems, or leaves. (1)

Not green. Usually white, gray, brown, or yellow. (1)

All individual parts microscopic in size. Occurring singly or in chains. (1)

Some or all individual parts not microscopic in size. (2)

Green, blue-green, or gray-green. (2)

Plant body crustlike and flat or upright and branched. (3)

Plant body not flat or leaflike. Usually aquatic. (2)

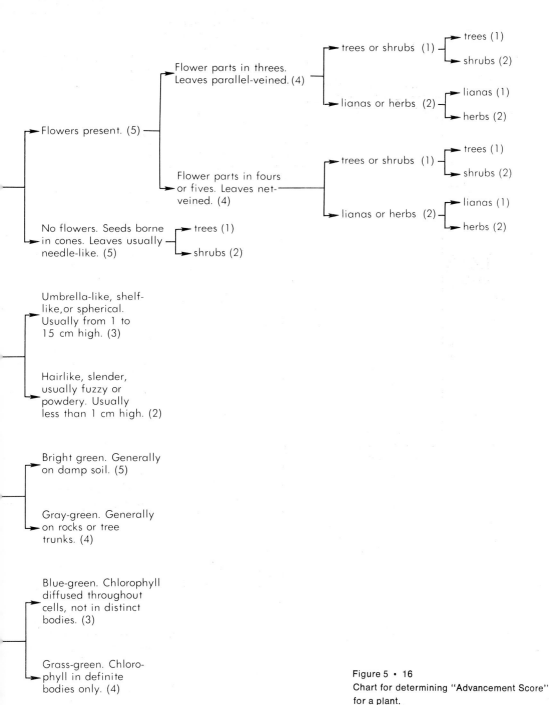

Figure 5 · 16
Chart for determining "Advancement Score"
for a plant.

"Advancement Score" for each of the plants studied, give the plant having the lowest score a rank of "1" and that having the highest score a rank of "10." Then rank all the others according to their individual scores. Record the rankings in the column at the right side of your chart.

The more alike two plants are, the more alike their scores will be. The greater the degree of difference between two plants, the greater the difference in their scores. Advanced plants will have high scores (maximum 26), and primitive plants will have low scores (minimum 3).

DISCUSSION

• Assuming that today's plants have developed from simpler, fewer, and older species, would you expect to find less diversity or greater diversity in the plant kingdom as time goes on? Explain.(1)

• Basing your conclusions upon the way the plant score chart was designed, list some of the most important differences among plants.(2) • What are some of the less important differences?(3) • On what basis do you distinguish between the important differences and those that are less important?(4)

• Using the information included in the chart, list the characteristics you would expect to find in a primitive plant.(5) • Do the same for a highly advanced plant.(6) • In what ways does the plant score chart resemble the dichotomous key constructed in Investigation 5.1?(7) • In what ways does it differ from the key?(8)

Photos by Haven Kolb

Nancy Haynes

Figure 5 • 17

Into which taxonomic group would you classify each of these plants?

GUIDE QUESTIONS

1. Why is a classification system that is based on the differences between trees, shrubs, and herbs a poor one?

2. Why did it become necessary for biologists to have a system of nomenclature?

3. What are the basic rules of the binomial system of nomenclature?

4. What were Linnaeus' major contributions to taxonomy?

5. Why is it incorrect to think of modern biological names as Latin?

6. Why is "moss" a rather indefinite term?

7. What is the chief structural characteristic of tracheophytes?

8. What does a botanist mean by the word "flower"?

9. How is diversity among flowers related to ways in which pollination occurs?

10. What structural characteristics of fruits seem to be adaptations that are related to seed dispersal?

11. In what ways do dicotyledons and monocotyledons differ?

12. What are gymnosperms?

13. What is a spore?

14. Why is it improper to use the terms "root" and "leaf" when you are referring to bryophytes?

15. How do fungi differ from most other plants with respect to ecological relationships?

16. What kinds of characteristics are used in classifying fungi?

17. Why do many taxonomists put the plants commonly called algae into separate phyla?

18. How do the characteristics of lichens cause a taxonomic problem?

19. What do botanists mean by the term "imperfect fungi"?

20. If a taxonomist refers to an organism as "primitive," what idea is he expressing?

PROBLEMS

1. How many of the taxonomic groups discussed in the catalogue section of Chapter 5 are represented in your locality? Consider wild and cultivated plants, indoor and outdoor plants, aquatic and terrestrial plants.

2. Choose one of the major taxonomic groups of plants and investigate (by library research) its relationships to mankind.

3. The classification of plants has been revised by several botanists in the last quarter century. Look up an old classification and a few recent ones in college botany textbooks. Compare these classifications with each other and with the one that is used in this book.

4. Criticize the following statement: "All plants that are producers are green, because they contain the green pigment chlorophyll."

5. What advantages and disadvantages does a seed-producing plant have compared with one that produces only spores? How do you interpret the words "advantage" and "disadvantage" here?

6. The plant parts that furnish the greatest amount of human food are either seeds, roots, or underground stems. Explain this.

7. Observe the kinds of plants that grow without human help in a city. Try to discover the characteristics that enable them to live successfully in an urban environment.

8. Choose some cultivated plants. Investigate the history of their domestication. Examples: wheat, apple, potato, cotton, corn, cabbage, sugarcane.

SUGGESTED READINGS

AHMADJIAN, V. "The Fungi of Lichens," *Scientific American,* February, 1963. Pp. 122–130+.

BENTON, A. H., and W. E. WERNER. *Principles of Field Biology and Ecology.* 2nd ed. New York: McGraw-Hill Book Co., Inc., 1965. Chapter 3. (An excellent, simple discussion of the problem of taxonomy—classification, nomenclature, and the concept of "species." Fairly easy.)

CHRISTENSEN, C. M. *Molds and Man; An Introduction to the Fungi.* Minneapolis: University of Minnesota Press, 1951. (A balanced account of the important relationships between fungi and man. Moderately difficult.)

MILNE, L. J., and M. MILNE. "Evergreen Review," *Natural History*, January, 1970. Pp. 80–91.

RAVEN, P. H., and T. R. MERTENS. *Plant Systematics*. (BSCS Pamphlet 23.) Boulder, Colo.: EPIC, 1965. (A clear statement of aims and methods of modern plant taxonomy.)

SIMPSON, G. G., and W. S. BECK. *Life: An Introduction to Biology*. Shorter ed. New York: Harcourt, Brace and World, 1969. Pp. 335–350. (Good short discussion of plant groupings. Fairly advanced.)

TIFFANY, L. H. *Algae: The Grass of Many Waters*. 2nd ed. Springfield, Ill.: Charles C. Thomas, Publishers, 1968. (An excellent introduction to this group of plants. Moderately difficult.)

WILSON, C. L., W. E. LOOMIS, and T. A. STEEVES. *Botany*. 5th ed. New York: Holt, Rinehart and Winston, 1971. (A good college-level reference book.)

YOUNG, P. "Mushrooms," *Natural History*, June-July, 1970. Pp. 66–71.

Each of the following is a series of books that treat the classification and identification of certain parts of the plant kingdom.

"Golden Nature Series." Edited by H. S. Zim. New York: Western Publishing Co. (Flowers, trees, orchids, non-flowering plants.)

"Peterson Field Guide Series." Edited by R. T. Peterson. Boston: Houghton, Mifflin Co. (Flowers, trees, shrubs, and ferns.)

"Pictured Key to Nature Series." Edited by H. E. Jaques. Dubuque, Iowa: W. C. Brown Co. (Flowers, plant families, seaweeds, freshwater algae, mosses, and liverworts.)

6

Protists

WHAT ARE PROTISTS?

The diversity of living things may be thought of as a continuous spectrum, like a section across a rainbow; but instead of colors, we observe species as we move across the spectrum of living things. At one end of the diversity spectrum, organisms are unmistakably animals—such as horses and elephants; at the other end they are just as obviously plants—such as grasses and roses. But what about the central zone? As we move from either end toward the center, we reach a place where the organisms—mostly microscopic—are neither clearly animals nor clearly plants. They possess some characteristics of both groups; yet they are different from either group.

More than a century ago Ernst Haeckel proposed a third kingdom, Protista, protists. For a long time his proposal received little support, but during the past few decades more and more taxonomists have adopted it. There is still, however, no agreement as to which organisms should be placed in a protist kingdom. Certainly size is not the only consideration. Though most organisms that have been considered protists are microscopic, some are *macroscopic.* And many microscopic organisms are undoubtedly animals (rotifers); others are undoubtedly plants (many algae). So the Protista are not just all the microorganisms.

The two aims in classification—convenience and the expression of relationships—often conflict. The protist kingdom is a grouping of convenience. There is little evidence of relationship among most of the protist phyla. But many organisms that have been placed in this kingdom have both animal and plant characteristics. If we do not place these puzzling organisms in a separate kingdom, we must place them in *both* animal and plant kingdoms. By assigning them to a third group, we can define the animal and plant kingdoms more clearly.

Figure 12·18 shows a section across a color spectrum.

Ernst Haeckel [hĕk′əl]: 1834–1919. German biologist

Protista [prō tĭs′tə; Greek: *protos,* first (here, most primitive)]

macroscopic [măk′rə skŏp′ĭk; Greek: *makros,* long, + *skopein,* to view]

For still other views of the taxonomy of organisms, see Appendix 3.

Investigation 6.1

A GARDEN OF PROTISTS

MATERIALS AND EQUIPMENT

(for each team)

glass-marking crayon
finger bowls, 8
fruit, very ripe
pond or river water with some bottom
    materials
hay or dried grass
beans, dried
cream cheese
bread
filter paper
garden soil
cornstarch
spatula
peppercorns
glass covers for finger bowls, 2 or 3

(for each pair of students)

hand lens or stereomicroscope
forceps
dissecting needles, 2
microscope slide
medicine dropper
cover slip
monocular microscope

PROCEDURE

A. Setting up the cultures. Mark each finger bowl with your team symbol and number the bowls *1* through *8*. Place materials in the bowls as follows:

Bowl 1—Fruit, cut to fit into bowl.

Bowl 2—Water from pond or river, containing bottom materials.

Bowl 3—Enough hay to cover the bottom of the bowl, and 200 ml of tap water.

Bowl 4—A few dried beans and 200 ml of tap water.

Bowl 5—Cream cheese, spread over bottom of bowl about 1 cm deep.

Bowl 6—Two pieces of stale bread, moistened (not soaked) with tap water. Expose to air for 24 hours before covering.

Bowl 7—Place a piece of filter paper on the bottom of the finger bowl. Mix 5 g of cornstarch with 95 g of rich soil. While mixing soil and starch, add enough water to give the mixture a doughlike consistency. Spread the mixture on the filter paper, using a spatula to make a smooth surface. Keep the soil mixture moist throughout the investigation.

Bowl 8—1 g of peppercorns and 200 ml of tap water.

Place the bowls in stacks of 3 or 4 and cover each stack with a piece of glass or an empty bowl. Do not place in direct sunlight. If any of the bowls fit very tightly together, place the flat end of a toothpick between them.

B. Observations. Examine the bowls each day. In your data book record (*a*) date of observation, (*b*) number of bowl, (*c*) macroscopic appearance of bowl's contents, (*d*) appearance under a hand lens or stereomicroscope, and (*e*) anything else that you can notice with any of your senses.

In describing organisms, consider color first, then size. Some of the following descriptive terms may be useful: fuzzy, cottony, powdery, smooth, rough, shiny, glistening, dull, compact, spreading, irregular. You should not, of course, limit yourself to these terms.

After good growth has been obtained, make observations with a monocular microscope as follows. From a solid medium, use forceps to transfer bits of the visible growth to a clean slide. From a liquid medium, draw up a drop or two with a medicine dropper and place on a slide. Then, for either kind of preparation, add a cover slip. Record your observations by making sketches. Using references provided by your teacher, attempt to place organisms in taxonomic groups.

DISCUSSION

• Is there any evidence that different groups of organisms grow better on one or another kind of food? If so, what is it?(1) • Which group of organisms was found in the largest number of dishes? What reason can you suggest for this?(2) • What happens to the food materials as the organisms grow? Explain.(3)

FOR FURTHER INVESTIGATION

1. You have seen what microorganisms do to their food substances, some of which are also foods for humans. Clearly it is desirable for us to try to prevent such effects.

Chemicals are often added to human foods to discourage use of them by microorganisms. Commercial bread and catsup usually contain such chemicals, which must be mentioned on the label of the product. By comparing the growth of microorganisms on homemade bread and catsup with growth on the commercial products, you can test the effectiveness of such chemicals.

2. Choose one food and investigate the growth of microorganisms on it at various temperatures.

THE DISCOVERY OF MICROORGANISMS

Behind words like "animal" and "plant" lies a long history. But when we turn from the familiar, visible world to the world revealed by the microscope, we encounter something comparatively new to human experience—so new that we can chart the history of its exploration.

LEEUWENHOEK AND HIS "LITTLE ANIMALS"

This world was discovered in the 1670's by Antony van Leeuwenhoek. The discovery resulted from the development of a technique: the grinding of lenses for magnification. It is somewhat strange that the discovery came so late in history. Eyeglasses had been known for several hundred years, but it was not until around 1600 that a few persons started to use lenses as telescopes, to look at distant things, and as microscopes, to enlarge things nearby. For many years, however, such lenses had low magnification and poor resolution.

Antony van Leeuwenhoek [lā'vən hook']: 1632–1723. Dutch lens-maker and naturalist

resolution. See Investigation A.1, Appendix 2.

Leeuwenhoek was a cloth merchant of Delft, Holland. His hobby was grinding lenses. He also did metalworking to construct tubes for holding his lenses. After a while he became interested in the things he could see with his instruments. Other men were examining the fine structure of easily visible plants and animals, but Leeuwenhoek alone had the idea of peering into drops of water from rain, wells, and other places. By 1675 he had observed in such water—apparently for the first time by any man—some of the living things that we now call protists. He called them *tierken,* Dutch for "little animals."

His instruments were made with simple lenses, but so carefully were they ground that he could obtain clear magnifications of 200X.

Fortunately for the fame of Leeuwenhoek, his observations were communicated in letters to the Royal Society for the Improvement of Natural Knowledge, London. In the Royal Society's *Philosophical Transactions,* the first scientific journal in the English language, a paper appeared (Vol. 11, 1677) with this title: "Observations communicated to the publisher by Mr. Antony van Leeuwenhoek in a Dutch Letter of the 9th of October, 1676, here English'd: Concerning little animals by him observed in Rain-Well-Sea-and Snow water; as

Philosophical Transactions [fĭl'ə sŏf'ə kəl trăns ăk'shənz]

180

Figure 6 • 1

Below is a replica of a
Leeuwenhoek microscope,
about natural size. The specimen was placed on the metal
point in front of the lens. The
turnscrews adjusted the
focus.

AIBS

natural philosophers: scientists.
The latter term did not replace
the former until the first half of
the 19th century.

spontaneous [spŏn tā'nĕ əs;
Latin: *sponte*, of one's own
accord]

Figure 6 • 2

Antony van Leeuwenhoek holding one of his microscopes in his left hand.

Bettmann

also in water wherein Pepper had lain infused." In 1680 Leeuwenhoek
also reported seeing the organisms now called yeasts, and in 1683
he observed bacteria—all "little animals" to him.

Such was the fame of the Royal Society—still flourishing today
—and so wide was the distribution of its *Transactions* that the news
soon spread among natural philosophers. But when we look back
now, progress in exploring the world of microorganisms seems to
have been remarkably slow. To scientists of the 18th century the study
of microorganisms seemed unimportant. These microscopic things
appeared suddenly in putrefying meat and meat broths. According to
the theory of **spontaneous generation,** they had no parents or ancestors, and when the conditions that brought them forth disappeared, they disappeared too. With so many beautiful and interesting
plants and animals being discovered all over the world, scientists did
not choose to spend time on things that were so hard to see and
that were here and then gone so quickly. In his great 18th-century
classification of all organisms, Linnaeus took little notice of the microscopic world.

THE BEGINNINGS OF MICROBIOLOGY

After 1800, following the Industrial Revolution, the manufacture
of microscopes improved rapidly and this led to an increased study

of *microbes,* as the organisms began to be called. But it was not until the middle of the 19th century that biologists focused their attention upon them. At that time a series of discoveries clearly showed the importance of these organisms to man's welfare.

microbes [mĭ'krōbz; Greek: *mikros*, small, + *bios*, life]

In this period the name of Louis Pasteur stands out because of the variety of subjects he studied, the ingenuity of his experiments, and the force of his personality. Pasteur showed the importance of microbes in the processes by which wine, beer, and cheeses are made. He thus linked the world of microscopic life to commercially important enterprises. He also furthered (though he did not originate) the idea that microbes are associated with diseases of larger organisms, including man. Thus biologists came to see that, despite their small size, microbes are important organisms and studying them became an important part of biology.

ingenuity [ĭn'jə nū'ə tĭ]: inventive talent

Pasteur was trained as a chemist, but his interests were many. Robert Koch was a physician, and he concentrated upon the relationship of microbes to disease. To study this relationship, he had to be able to grow and study the microbes. For nearly 40 years he and his colleagues invented methods, materials, and instruments for culturing, handling, and examining microbes. One of his students invented the petri dish, and the wife of another student suggested the use of agar, a substance derived from seaweed. These are still in use today. Koch himself set up the experimental procedure by which a particular microbe could be definitely associated with a particular disease, and he used the procedure to identify the microbe of tuberculosis. Building on the work of Pasteur, he founded the science of *microbiology.*

colleagues [kŏl'ēgz]: persons who work together

tuberculosis [tū bûr'kyə lō'sĭs]: disease in which tissues of the host—most often in the lungs—are destroyed

Figure 6 • 3

Louis Pasteur [lwē päs toer]: 1822–1895. French chemist and biologist.

Figure 6 • 4

Robert Koch [kôKH]: 1843–1910. The microbiologist is shown at work in his laboratory.

Photos by Bettmann

Investigation 6.2

EXPERIMENTS ON SPONTANEOUS GENERATION

INTRODUCTION

Throughout the 18th century most scientists believed in spontaneous generation. A few denied the theory.

Do microbes arise without parents from the nonliving materials in meat broths, or do they come from ancestors that have somehow got into the broths? At the time of the American Revolution, an Italian, Lazzaro Spallanzani (lä-tsä′rō späl′län-tsä′nē), conducted experiments in an attempt to settle the matter. His results cast doubt upon the theory, but he failed to convince those who believed it. Later, in the middle of the 19th century, Pasteur carried out more carefully designed experiments that led to general agreement.

In this investigation you will perform experiments similar to those of Spallanzani and Pasteur. You will use some techniques developed since their day, but the principles involved in your procedure will be the same.

MATERIALS AND EQUIPMENT

(per team)
glass tubing (pieces 30 cm long), 2
bunsen burner with wing top

triangular file
stoppers to fit flasks, 1-hole, 3
stoppers to fit flasks, without holes, 2
glass tubing (piece 8–10 cm long)
bouillon cube
beaker, 1000 ml
stirring rod
funnel
ring stand (to fit funnel)
filter paper
graduated cylinder
flasks, erlenmeyer, 250 ml, 7
heat source
autoclave or pressure cooker
paraffin
beaker
forceps and wad of cotton

PROCEDURE

Using a wing-top burner, bend one of the 30-cm lengths of glass tubing into a J shape, the other into an S shape (see Figure 6·5). Trim the tubes to the lengths of those in the illustration. Insert them into 1-hole stoppers. Insert the straight piece of glass tubing into the 3rd 1-hole stopper.

Dissolve 1 bouillon cube in 500 ml of

Figure 6 · 5

Completed setup for
Investigation 6.2.

1. unheated   2. boiled   3. boiled   4. autoclaved   5. autoclaved   6. autoclaved   7. autoclaved

warm water. When cool, filter. The broth must be clear. Pour 70 ml of the broth into each of 7 flasks. Using a lead pencil, number each flask on the small white area you will find on its side. Treat them as follows:

Flask 1: Plug with a solid stopper. Do not heat.

Flask 2: Add 10 ml of water to the broth. Boil gently for 15 minutes. About 10 ml of water will boil off, making the level approximately the same as in the other flasks. Leave open.

Flask 3: Add 10 ml of water to the broth. Boil gently for 15 minutes, with the solid stopper resting at an angle in the mouth of the flask. At the conclusion of boiling, plug immediately with the stopper. To seal, melt paraffin in a beaker; apply with a wad of cotton held in forceps.

Flask 4: Heat in an autoclave or a pressure cooker for 15 minutes at 15-lb pressure. Leave open.

Flask 5: Plug with the stopper through which a straight glass tube was inserted. Heat as for Flask 4. Then seal with paraffin around the neck of the flask and around the tube where it comes through the stopper.

Flask 6: Plug with the stopper through which the J-shaped glass tube was inserted. Heat as for Flask 4. Seal as for Flask 5.

Flask 7: Plug with the stopper through which the S-shaped glass tube was inserted. Heat as for Flask 4. Seal as for Flask 5.

Record the date on which the experiment is set up. Place all flasks on a laboratory table but not in direct sunlight or over a radiator.

Look for changes in the flasks each day for 1 week, then weekly for 5 weeks. Record any changes in the clearness of the broth, noting the number of the flask and the date. Other observed changes in the broth (appearance of scum, mold colonies, etc.) should also be recorded. At the end of the experiment, open the flasks and note the odor of the broth in each.

STUDYING THE DATA

Flasks 2 and 3 represent Spallanzani's experiment. • What differences did you observe in these flasks during the 5 weeks?(1) • How can you explain the differences?(2) In your experiment, Flask 3 may or may not have developed cloudiness. Spallanzani's sealed flask developed no cloudiness or putrid odor. But biologists of his day denied that this showed microbes had to get into the broth from outside; they clung to the theory of spontaneous generation. • How do you think they defended their point of view against Spallanzani's evidence?(3)

Flasks 4 to 7 represent some of Pasteur's work. • In the experimental setup, what is the function of Flask 4?(4) • Why did Pasteur provide openings in his flasks?(5) • How do you explain the result obtained in Flask 7?(6)

• What is the function of Flask 1 in this investigation?(7) Compare your observations of Flask 1 with those of Flasks 2 and 4. • Explain any likenesses and differences in these results.(8)

CONCLUSION

• In the light of the results of these experiments, discuss the question raised in the introduction to this investigation.(9)

A CATALOGUE OF LIVING PROTISTS: KINGDOM PROTISTA

PHYLUM MYXOMYCETES
slime molds; about 450 species

Myxomycetes [mĭk'sō mī sē'tēz Greek: myxa, slime, + myketes, mushrooms]

Although slime molds do not have a particularly attractive name, many are rather beautiful during certain stages in their life histories. They usually grow among damp, decaying leaves and other dead plant ma-

Victor Larsen

Figure 6 · 6

Slime-mold plasmodia crawling over a woodpile.

plasmodium [plăz mō'dē əm; Greek: *plassein,* to form, + *eidos,* like]

terial. If you search through a mass of such material soon after a heavy rain, you are likely to come across a slime-mold *plasmodium* —a glistening sheet or network that may be as much as several centimeters, or even a meter, across. A plasmodium is a living mass that crawls slowly from place to place.

After a period of feeding on small bits of dead organic matter, a plasmodium moves to a drier, more exposed location and slowly transforms into a number of spore cases. These stalked structures are usually not more than a few millimeters high, and many are brightly colored. Inside each case large numbers of spores are formed. When a case breaks, spores are released into the air. If they land in a suitable spot where water is available, the spores give rise to tiny, flagellated organisms. After swimming about for a brief period, these organisms lose their flagella and fuse in pairs. By feeding and growth, each pair develops into a new plasmodium.

Few other organisms have life histories that include such contrasting stages as slime molds have. In the plasmodium and flagellated stages slime molds move about like animals. Their spore cases and spores, however, are distinctly plantlike in structure. (Examples below.)

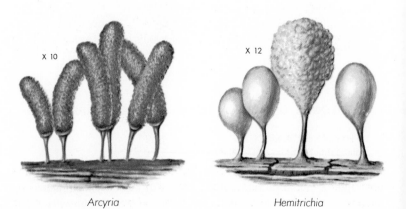

X 10

X 12

Arcyria

Hemitrichia

PHYLUM CILIOPHORA
ciliates; about 5000 species

Ciliophora [sǐl'ē ăf'ə rə; Latin: *cilium*, eyelash, + Greek: *-phoros*, bearing, carrying]

Ciliates are generally larger than other protists—excepting the slime molds. Some species are 0.25 mm long—visible to the unaided eye when seen in good light against a dark background. However, most species are microscopic.

If a ciliate requires one second to swim across the low-power field of your microscope, what is its speed in meters per hour?

The name of the phylum indicates its principal characteristic. Ciliates have a multitude of cilia extending from their outer surfaces. The cilia beat rhythmically, driving the organisms through the water. All ciliates have definite shapes. Some species that live attached to solid objects, such as twigs or dead leaves in a pond, tend toward radial symmetry. The many species that are active swimmers have definite anterior and posterior ends but are usually unsymmetrical.

Some ciliates are commensal or parasitic, but the majority are free-living. (Examples below.)

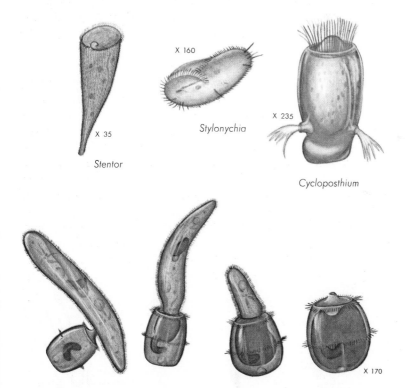

X 160

Stylonychia

X 235

X 35

Stentor

Cycloposthium

X 170

Figure 6 • 7

A predator that is smaller than its prey. From the left, four stages are shown as one ciliate (*Didinium*) consumes another (*Paramecium*).

PHYLUM SPOROZOA
sporozoans; about 2000 species

Sporozoa [spōr'ə zō'ə; Greek: *spora*, seed, + *zoion*, animal]

All sporozoans are microscopic. They have three characteristics in common. First, all are parasites; second, they have no means of loco-motion (at least, not as adults); third, a parent sporozoan reproduces by forming large numbers of tiny spores, which it releases into the environment.

Some species of sporozoans affect their hosts only slightly, if at all. Others have such a weakening effect that the hosts become ill. Still others frequently cause the death of their hosts. (Examples below.)

X 1000

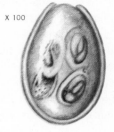

X 100

Plasmodium vivax

Eimeria

Sarcodina [sär'kō dī'nə; Greek: *sarx*, flesh, + *eidos*, form]

ameba [ə mē'bə; Greek: *ameibein*, to change]

pseudopods [sōō'də pŏdz'; Greek: *pseudes*, false, + *podion*, little foot]

PHYLUM SARCODINA
sarcodinans; about 8000 species

Probably the most famous microorganisms of pond water are amebas, which move around on the undersides of lily pads and similar surfaces. Amebas are barely visible to the unaided eye, but under the low power of a microscope they look like granular, grayish masses.

An ameba has no definite shape. It is constantly flowing into *pseudopods* (finger-like extensions), and often into more than one at a time. But one pseudopod outgrows the others, and the organism flows in the direction of that pseudopod. Pseudopods also serve in

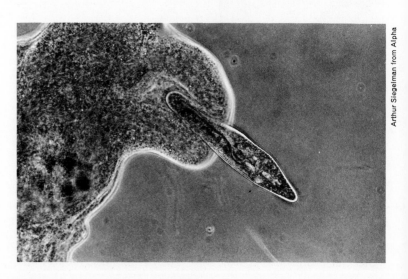

Arthur Siegelman from Alpha

Figure 6 · 8

Pseudopods of an ameba taking in food—a paramecium. × 160

obtaining food (Figure 6 • 8). Pseudopods are the characteristic structures of the phylum. In some sarcodinans, pseudopods are less numerous than in amebas; in others, they are more numerous and do not constantly change position.

One group of sarcodinans, the radiolarians, have shells of silica, a substance similar to sand. Many long, stiff pseudopods radiate from the shells. Another group, the foraminiferans, build shells of calcium carbonate—chemically the same as clam shells. Like their makers, most of these shells are very small. During past ages great numbers of such shells have accumulated in the seas and solidified into rock.

Many ameba-like sarcodinans live in ponds, puddles, and damp soil. Most of the shell-bearing kinds live in the seas. Other species live with larger organisms in various kinds of relationships—some as commensals, some as parasites. (Examples below.)

radiolarians [rā′dĭ ō lâr′ĭ ənz; Latin: *radius* (so named from the radiating pseudopods)]

foraminiferans [fō răm′ə nĭf′ər ənz; Latin: *foramen*, hole, + *ferre*, to bear]

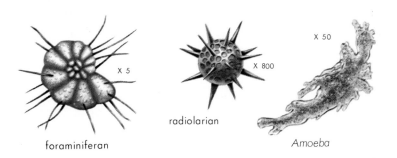

X 5

X 800

X 50

foraminiferan

radiolarian

Amoeba

PHYLUM MASTIGOPHORA
flagellates; about 2000 species

Flagellates are microscopic or very nearly so. They move about by means of flagella. Some contain chlorophyll and synthesize their own food when light is present. When light is not present, they may digest food particles in the surrounding water and absorb the products. Other species lack chlorophyll but capture smaller microorganisms and digest them internally.

Such a mixture of plant and animal characteristics has made the classification of flagellates puzzling. Some taxonomists who use a two-kingdom system group most flagellates together with sporozoans, ciliates, and sarcodinans as protozoa, and place them as a phylum in the animal kingdom. But then they must also place flagellates with algae in the plant kingdom!

Flagellates are abundant in soil, in fresh water, and in the ocean. Many live in close community relationships with other organisms. These relationships may be parasitic or mutualistic. For example, some live in the alimentary canals of termites. There they digest the wood eaten by the insects. Without the flagellates, the termites would

Mastigophora [măs′tĭ găf′ə rə; Greek: *mastigo*, whip, + -*phoros*, bearing]

protozoa [prō′tə zō′ə; Greek: *protos*, first, + *zoion*, animal]

Would you call this a mutualistic relationship? If so, what advantage do the flagellates gain?

starve to death, just as you would on a wood diet, for neither you nor the insects can digest this material. (Examples below.)

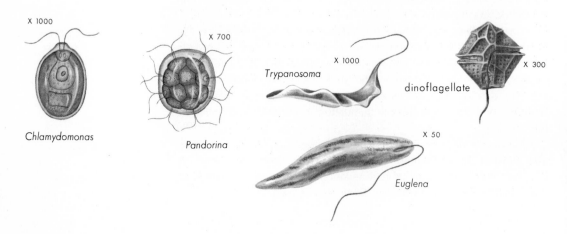

X 1000

Chlamydomonas

X 700

Pandorina

Trypanosoma

X 1000

dinoflagellate

X 300

X 50

Euglena

Cyanophyta [si'ə nä'fəd ə; Greek: *kyaneos*, dark blue, + *phyton*, a plant]

PHYLUM CYANOPHYTA
blue-green algae; about 1500 species

You may be surprised to find in the protist kingdom organisms called "algae." The name goes back to a time when biologists did not know as much about these organisms as they do now. Blue-green algae contain chlorophyll, but it is not organized into distinct structures as it is in plants. Moreover blue-green algae lack other plant characteristics and in some ways resemble bacteria. They are basically microscopic organisms, but many grow in colonies that are easily visible to the unaided eye and that have characteristic forms.

Blue-green algae are among the most hardy of organisms. They grow in almost any place that has a little liquid water: in ponds and streams, on moist soil and tree bark, and even in hot springs and on the surface of snowbanks. (Examples below.)

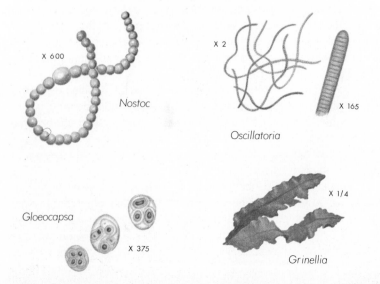

X 600

Nostoc

X 2

X 165

Oscillatoria

Gloeocapsa

X 375

X 1/4

Grinellia

PHYLUM SCHIZOMYCETES
bacteria; about 1600 species

Schizomycetes [skī̆z ō mī sĕt′ĕz; Greek: *schizein*, to split, + *myketes*, mushrooms]

All the organisms in this phylum are invisible to the unaided eye and some are the smallest things that can, with certainty, be called living. Most range from 0.001 to 0.005 mm (1 to 5μ) in size. Most species in this size range are called bacteria, and we can conveniently use the name for the phylum as a whole, except where noted otherwise.

As ordinarily prepared for microscopic study, bacteria have few visible characteristics besides shape. Early in the history of microbiology, however, it became clear that there are many more species than shapes of bacteria. Therefore, bacterial taxonomists were among the first to use characteristics other than structure for classification. The kinds of foods bacteria use, the kinds of waste materials they produce, their reactions to various stains and other chemicals, even the macroscopic appearance of colonies—all of these are used to identify species of bacteria.

The great majority of bacteria are consumers—they obtain their energy from foods produced by other organisms. Some are parasites, but many are decomposers. A few, however, possess pigments that are chemically similar to chlorophylls in plants. These bacteria carry on a kind of photosynthesis that produces food but differs in some details from plant photosynthesis. A few other bacteria obtain their energy from inorganic substances that contain iron, sulfur, or nitrogen. They are the only known organisms that do not depend, either directly or indirectly, upon radiant solar energy.

Besides the bacteria, some other organisms are usually classified as Schizomycetes. Among these are spirochetes, which, unlike most bacteria, are flexible and may reach a length of 0.5 mm—though they are invisible because they are very slender. Also included are actinomycetes, which form structures somewhat resembling fungal hyphae.

spirochetes [spī′rə kĕts′; Greek: *speira*, spiral, + *chaite*, hair]

actinomycetes [ăk′tə nō mī′sĕts; Greek: *aktinos*, ray, + *myketes*]

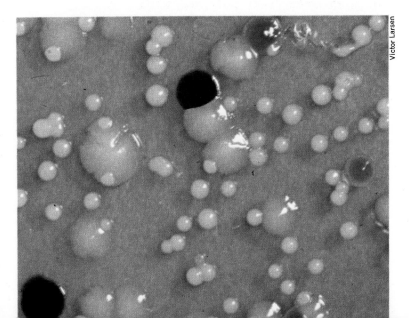

Victor Larsen

Figure 6 • 9

Colonies of four kinds of bacteria growing in a laboratory culture.   ×2

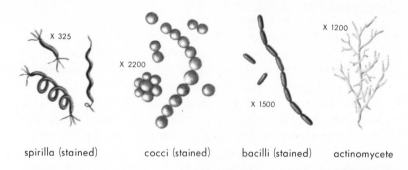

spirilla (stained)   cocci (stained)   bacilli (stained)   actinomycete

And there are organisms still smaller than most bacteria—rickettsias, among others.

Rickettsias measure about 0.35 by 0.25μ. They are, therefore, barely visible under a light microscope. However, they can be studied with an **electron microscope**—an instrument that uses rays of electrons rather than of light to produce an image on film or on a screen.

Electron micrographs show that a rickettsia has an internal structure much like that of a bacterium—in fact, some microbiologists think rickettsias may be very small bacteria that became parasitic in the past and can now live in no other way. With the exception of one known species, they can be grown only in living cells. (Examples of Schizomycetes: above and Figure 6 · 11 below.)

Figure 6 · 10

Compare this electron microscope with Leeuwenhoek's
microscope and with the
microscopes in your
laboratory.

Figure 6 · 11

Electron micrographs of (A) bacteria (× 4500) and (B) rickettsias (× 24,000).

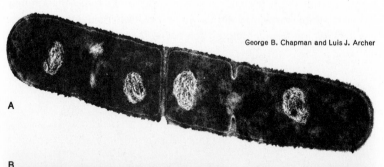

George B. Chapman and Luis J. Archer

A

B

Investigation 6.3

MICROBIAL TECHNIQUES: POPULATIONS

INTRODUCTION

If you have a mixed population of horses, cattle, and sheep in a pasture, it is easy to separate the 3 kinds of animals and determine the number of each. But if you have a mixed population of invisible microorganisms, how can you separate the kinds from each other to obtain a *pure culture* of each? And then how can you count the individuals?

There is a further difficulty: Occasionally horses and cattle may be dangerous, but at least you can see them coming. How can you protect yourself from dangerous kinds of microorganisms? Since the days of Koch, methods for safely studying microbes have been much improved, but a beginning microbiologist must still learn how to use basic microbial techniques.

MATERIALS AND EQUIPMENT

(per team)

culture tubes, containing 15 ml of sterile
    nutrient agar, 5
test-tube rack
beakers, 600-ml, 2
ring stand
bunsen burner or alcohol lamp
thermometer, −10°C to +110°C
petri dishes, sterile, 5
glass-marking crayon
inoculating loop
mixed culture of bacteria
paper towels

PROCEDURE

The following directions will be supplemented with demonstrations by your teacher.

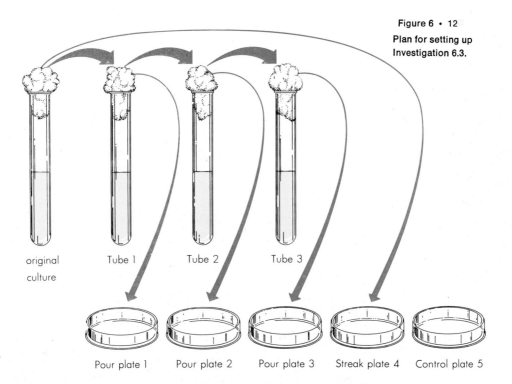

Figure 6 · 12
Plan for setting up
Investigation 6.3.

original culture   Tube 1   Tube 2   Tube 3

Pour plate 1   Pour plate 2   Pour plate 3   Streak plate 4   Control plate 5

A. Preparing the cultures. Place 5 tubes of nutrient agar in a 600-ml beaker and add water to fill the beaker until the level is above that of the agar in the tubes. Place the beaker on a ring stand and heat. When the agar has melted, transfer the tubes to a 2nd 600-ml beaker containing water at 44°C. Check the temperature of this water bath occasionally and whenever necessary heat gently to maintain approximately this temperature.

Wipe the top of the laboratory table with a wet paper towel. Place 5 sterile petri dishes on the table. Using a glass-marking crayon, number them *1* through *5;* write on the *bottom* of each dish, near the edge.

Sterilize an inoculating loop in the flame of a bunsen burner or alcohol lamp. Remove the plugs from the mixed culture of bacteria and from one of your tubes of melted agar. Using the sterilized loop, transfer a loopful of the culture to the tube of sterile medium. Replug both tubes immediately and reflame the loop. Mix the agar thoroughly by rolling the tube between your palms, being careful to keep the plugged end up so that the cotton remains dry. Using the crayon, label this tube with a *1.* Again flame the loop. Transfer a loopful of the mixture in Tube 1 to a 2nd tube of melted medium. Replug the tubes and reflame the loop. Mix in the same way you mixed Tube 1. Label this 2nd tube with a *2.* Return Tube 1 to the 44°C water bath.

Using the same technique, transfer a loopful of material from Tube 2 to a 3rd tube of melted medium. Replug the tubes, reflame the loop, and mix the contents of the tube. Label this tube with a *3.* Return Tubes 2 and 3 to the water bath.

Remove Tube 1 from the water bath, dry it with a paper towel, remove its plug, and flame the mouth of the tube. Pour its contents into Petri Dish 1. Do not allow the tube lip to touch the dish (see Figure 6 • 13). Cover the dish (called a "plate" once it is inoculated) and swirl it very gently, keeping it on the tabletop. This should distribute the medium in a uniform layer covering the bottom of the plate. Repeat for Plates (Dishes) 2 and 3.

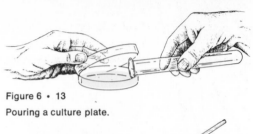

Figure 6 • 13
Pouring a culture plate.

Figure 6 • 14
Streaking a culture plate.

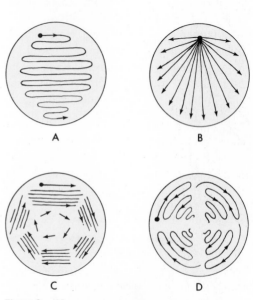

A   B

C   D

Figure 6 • 15
Four patterns for streaking culture plates.

Pour one of the remaining tubes of melted medium into Dish 4 and the other into Dish 5. Allow the medium to solidify. Flame the loop. Take a loopful of the original mixed culture and streak the surface of the medium in Plate 4, as shown in Figure 6 • 14. Use 1 of the patterns shown in Figure 6 • 15. Flame the loop. Record the pattern used. Dish 5 receives no treatment.

Set all the plates, upside down, in a place designated by your teacher. Observe daily until many bacterial colonies are clearly visible in at least 1 of the plates.

B. Counting the colonies. Ignoring differences in appearance, count the separate colonies of bacteria that have developed in each of the poured plates (1, 2, and 3) and record the counts.

In some cases the colonies may be very crowded. You can estimate the number by using the following sampling technique. First, using black ink draw a square 10 × 10 cm on a piece of white paper. Inside this square draw a series of straight lines parallel to its sides, forming a grid of 100 smaller squares —each 1 cm on a side. Second, position a plate on the paper so the colonies of bacteria can be seen against the background of the grid. Choose 5 to 10 of the small squares at random and count the number of colonies in each. Third, add all the counts and divide the total by the number of small squares counted. This will give an average count per small square. Fourth, calculate the total surface of the culture medium. To do this, square the radius (in cm) of the plate and multiply by π (= approximately 3.14). Finally, to obtain an estimate of the number of colonies on the whole plate, multiply the average number of colonies per square by the surface area (in cm^2) of the entire plate.

Examine Plate 5 (control). If there are colonies present in this plate, count them. • What correction in your original counts should be made if colonies are present in this control plate?(1)   Make such a correction, if necessary.

STUDYING THE DATA

When you have completed counts of Plates 1, 2, and 3, you are ready to estimate the population density of organisms (number per cubic centimeter) in the original mixed culture of bacteria. To do this, you need the following information:

The volume of liquid held in your inoculating loop was about 5 mm^3. One cm^3 contains 1000 mm^3. Therefore the loopful of material that was introduced into Plate 1 contained about 5/1000 (= 1/200) of the number of bacteria in each cubic centimeter of the original culture.

If we assume that each organism in Plate 1 produced a visible colony, the number of colonies in Plate 1 multiplied by 200 gives the number of organisms per cubic centimeter in the original culture.

Before Tube 1 was poured, a loopful of its contents was transferred to Tube 2. Since the volume of medium in Tube 1 was 15 cm^3 and that of the loopful of material was 1/200 cm^3, the loopful must have contained 1/15 × 1/200 (= 1/3000) of the number of organisms in Tube 1. But Tube 1 contained only 1/200 of the organisms in the original culture; thus Tube 2 must contain 1/200 × 1/3000 (= 1/600,000) of the number of organisms per cubic centimeter in the original culture. Thus, to obtain the number of organisms per cubic centimeter in the original culture, you multiply the number of colonies in Plate 2 by 600,000. • How many organisms per cubic centimeter of original culture does each colony in Plate 3 represent?(2)

From the counts in each of the pour plates, carry out the calculations necessary to estimate the density of the population in the original culture. If it was possible to make estimates for all plates, you now have 3 separate estimates of the number of organisms present per cubic centimeter in the original culture. • How closely do these compare with each other?(3)   It is thought that the best estimates can be made when the dilution results in a count of from 30 to 300 colonies per plate. • Do you have a plate that falls in this range? If so, circle the population estimate made from it.(4)

Next examine Plate 4—the streak plate. Compare the pattern of colonies with the pattern of streaking that you recorded. • Are the patterns different or similar?(5)   • How many kinds of colonies have developed? In what ways do they differ?(6)   • How many kinds of bacteria were in the original culture? (7)   • What seems to be the principal way in which the colonies of these bacteria differ macroscopically?(8)   Suppose you were to lift a part of *one* colony with a sterile inoculating loop and streak it on a plate of sterile medium.   • How many kinds of colonies would you expect to develop?(9)   • What would you call such a culture?(10)

SUMMARY

• Which steps in the procedure are concerned only with a determination of the population density of microorganisms?(11) • Which steps are concerned only with obtaining a pure culture?(12)   • Formulate a set of rules for working safely with microorganisms. (13)   • Suggest a method of disposing of the cultures after you have finished studying them.(14)

FOR FURTHER INVESTIGATION

1. You did not actually complete the procedure for producing a pure culture. Carry out the last step. How can you determine that you have been successful?

2. Use the methods of this investigation to determine the population density of microorganisms in a sample of stream or pond water. How might differences in kinds of culture medium and in incubation temperatures affect your results? The hypothesis that results from this question may be investigated by culturing samples from a single source in various kinds of media and at different incubation temperatures.

Investigation 6.4

MICROBIAL TECHNIQUES: MICROSCOPIC STUDY

MATERIALS AND EQUIPMENT

(for each student)

microscope slide
bunsen burner or alcohol lamp
inoculating loop
mixed culture of bacteria
beaker
glass-marking crayon
medicine dropper
crystal-violet solution
paper towels
glycerin
cover slip
monocular microscope

PROCEDURE

A. Staining bacteria. Gently heat a clean slide by passing it just above a burner flame 3 times. When the slide is cool, place a loopful of the mixed culture of bacteria on it. Use the loop to spread the liquid over an area the size of a nickel. Mark the slide, on the side having the bacteria on it, with a crayon. Let the slide dry in the air; an almost invisible film of bacteria will remain.

Quickly pass the slide *through* the flame 3 or 4 times, film side up. The slide should

feel just uncomfortably hot to the back of your hand. Let the slide cool to room temperature.

Into a beaker pour tap water until it is about 3 cm from the top. Place the slide across the top of the beaker with the film surface up, as shown in Figure 6 • 16A. Cover the film with 3 or 4 drops of crystal-violet solution. Allow the stain to remain on the film for 15 seconds. Then rinse off the stain by pulling the slide gently to one side until one end drops slowly into the water, as shown in Figure 6 • 16B.

Remove the slide. Empty the beaker and refill it with clean water. Gently dip the slide

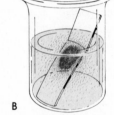

A   B

Figure 6 • 16
Staining procedure.

Figure 6 • 17
Blotting a stained slide.

organisms you can observe. Try to show accurately their shapes, the ways they are grouped, and their sizes in relation to the diameter of the field of view

Estimate the sizes (diameter of round organisms, length and width of others) of the smallest and largest bacteria on your slide. If you do not know how to estimate the diameter of the field of view, refer to page 707 in Appendix 2. • Record the dimensions in microns.(1) • Do all the bacteria appear to have reacted to the stain in the same way? If not, in what ways do they differ?(2)

FOR FURTHER INVESTIGATION

1. Observations at a magnification close to 1000X may be made if microscopes with oil-immersion objectives are available. Swing the high-power objective to one side. Put 1 drop of immersion oil directly on the stained bacterial film. Slowly swing the oil-immersion objective into place, watching the end of the objective from the side. The tip of the objective should dip into the drop of oil but should not be allowed to touch the slide. Using the *fine* adjustment, very carefully focus on the stained bacteria. Caution: Use only the fine adjustment, and turn it back and forth only a small fraction of a full turn at a time.

2. Because different species of bacteria react to staining procedures in characteristic ways, staining is useful for identification. Perhaps the most-used technique for this purpose involves Gram's stain. Your teacher can give you directions for it.

into the water several times. Drain the water from the slide by holding it vertically and pressing a lower corner against a paper towel. Remove the remaining water by blotting gently with a folded paper towel, as shown in Figure 6 • 17. Close the towel upon the slide as you would close a book. Do *not* wipe the slide. When the film is dry, add a drop of glycerin, then a cover slip.

B. Examining stained bacteria. Use the low-power objective of a microscope to focus on the stained bacteria on the slide. Many species of bacteria can barely be seen with low power. They may appear only as tiny colored specks. Move the slide around until a group of such specks is located near the center of the field of view. Swing the high-power objective into place and, if necessary, refocus with the fine adjustment.

In your data book draw a circle about 6 cm in diameter to represent the field of the microscope. In the circle carefully draw the

VIRUSES

After Koch showed the relationship between a species of bacterium and the disease tuberculosis, many biologists began to look for microbes in diseased organisms. In 1892 Dimitri Iwanowski was studying the mosaic disease of tobacco plants. He forced the juice of diseased plants through porcelain filters. When this filtered juice was injected into healthy plants, they developed the mosaic disease. This was puzzling because bacteria could not pass through such filters. Iwanowski concluded that some *toxin* (poisonous substance) pro-

viruses [vī′rəs əs; Latin: *virus*, slimy, poisonous liquid]

Dimitri Iwanowski [də mē′trĭ ē′və nŏf′skĭ]: 1864–1919. Russian microbiologist

Grant Heilman

Figure 6 • 18

Tobacco plant containing
mosaic virus.

Martinus W. Beijerinck
[bī′ə rĭngk]: 1851–1931.
Dutch microbiologist

duced by bacteria passed through and affected the tobacco plants. But he could not find the bacteria themselves.

Six years later M. W. Beijerinck, who was studying the same disease, verified Iwanowski's observations. Beijerinck repeated the experiment again and again—and always with the same result. In addition, he found that whatever was affecting the plants multiplied in them—that is, apparently reproduced. Toxins do not do this. Therefore, he concluded that the mosaic disease could not be bacterial but must result from what he called a "living fluid"—something that was able both to pass through porcelain filters and to reproduce. Today we call such substances *viruses.*

Scientists have learned much about viruses. They are not fluids but particles—particles that are too small to be seen with even the best light microscopes. With an electron microscope, however, we can obtain pictures of virus particles. They are of different sizes and shapes. Viruses are found not only in plant diseases but also in those of animals and even of bacteria. They occur in many familiar human diseases—for example, measles, mumps, smallpox, and colds.

Figure 6 • 19

Electron micrographs of
(*A*) a virus that attacks
bacteria, and (*B*) the virus of
human influenza.

A   × 13,000

B   × 130,000

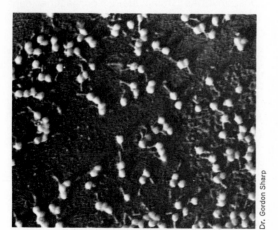

Dr. Gordon Sharp

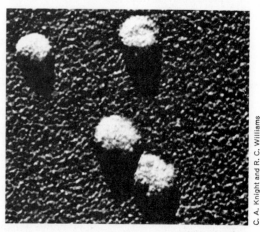

C. A. Knight and R. C. Williams

No virus has yet been grown in artificial culture media; viruses grow only within the substance of living things. Like the rickettsias, many viruses are most easily cultivated in developing chick embryos. Viruses, it seems, cannot "live" except in association with some other form of life.

But are viruses alive? They seem to possess two characteristics that we usually associate with living things: first, the ability to repro- duce, and second, the ability to undergo changes in hereditary char- acteristics. Yet what we call viral reproduction is quite different from reproduction of bacteria or other microbes. A virus cannot indepen- dently produce copies of itself; it can do so only in association with a living organism. For example, a particle of a bacteriophage virus attaches itself to a bacterium. Then part of the virus moves inside. Less than half an hour later the bacterium falls apart, releasing ap- proximately 200 new virus particles.

hereditary [hǐ rěd′ə těr′ĭ]: carried from parent to offspring

bacteriophage [băk tǐr′ĭ ə fāj′; Greek: *bakterion*, a little rod, + *phagein*, to eat]

While inside a living bacterium (or other organism), viruses be- have as though they were alive. But in 1935 W. M. Stanley crystallized tobacco mosaic virus much as you can crystallize salt or sugar from a solution. Crystallized virus can be stored on a laboratory shelf like a jar of salt; but, rubbed into a tobacco leaf, the virus particles mul- tiply. Thus viruses might seem to be a link between the living and nonliving worlds.

Wendell M. Stanley: 1904–1971. American biochemist

In classifying living things, we have seen cases in which orga- nisms do not fit neatly into our groupings. Viruses present a similar problem. Man likes to put things in order; he likes to have clear-cut answers to his questions. But the universe about him does not seem very neat; the answers to man's questions are often ambiguous.

ambiguous: having two or more possible meanings

Of course, it is not necessary to decide whether viruses are alive in order to study them. Many virologists have started as physicians, studying disease; others have started as biochemists. All, however, probably regard themselves as biologists of one kind or another. Per- haps this answers the question in one way. But you will notice that viruses have not been put into our catalogue of living things.

Haven Kolb

Figure 6 • 20

Effects of a kind of virus on a blackberry plant. Would you call this a disease?

GUIDE QUESTIONS

1. What are some reasons for a three- instead of a two-kingdom classification?

2. Why was progress in studying micro-organisms slow for a century and a half after Leeuwenhoek's discovery?

3. Why is the science of microbiology dated from Pasteur and Koch rather than from Leeuwenhoek?

4. What evidence led biologists to discard the theory of spontaneous generation?

5. Which characteristics of slime molds are animal-like and which are plant-like?

6. How do ciliates move about?

7. In what ways does an ameba use its pseudopods?

8. What are the taxonomic groups some biologists call protozoa?

9. Why are blue-green algae placed in the protist kingdom in our classification?

10. What are some characteristics used in distinguishing among the kinds of bacteria?

11. What are some differences between "true" bacteria and rickettsias?

12. What kinds of ecological relationships are found among protists?

13. What steps are necessary in preparing a pure culture of microorganisms?

14. How were viruses discovered?

15. Why might we consider viruses living things? Why might there be disagreement?

PROBLEMS

1. Under favorable environmental conditions an individual bacterium may divide once every 20 minutes. Suppose you begin with a single bacterium at noon on a certain.day. Assume that no bacteria die and that each divides every 20 minutes. How many bacteria would there be at noon on the next day?

2. In addition to rickettsias, other organisms in the size range between bacteria and viruses are now known. Investigate the characteristics of the pleuropneumonia organisms (PPO) and of the pleuropneumonia-like organisms (PPLO).

3. Pasteur, with the help of other early microbiologists, established the idea that mi-croorganisms and other forms of life arise only from similar living things. There is evidence, however, that at first the earth was without life. If life began once, why does it not begin again?

4. Some scientists have long speculated about the existence of life on Mars. If living things exist there, they are most likely to be organisms similar to protists. Find out what is known at present about conditions on Mars and what extremes of environment protists can endure.

5. Long before mankind knew that microbes exist, many people were making use of them. What are some of these uses? What are some industries that depend upon microbes?

SUGGESTED READINGS

ALEXOPOULOS, C. J., and J. KOEVENIG. Slime Molds and Research. (BSCS Pamphlet 13.) Boulder, Colo.: EPIC, 1964. (Results of experiments on these large protists. Fairly easy.)

ALLEN, R. D. "Amoeboid Movement." Scientific American, February, 1962. Pp. 112–120+.

BURNET, F. M. Viruses and Man. Baltimore: Penguin Books, Inc., 1953. (The viruses and their role in disease, written by the winner of the 1960 Nobel Prize in medicine.)

DOBELL, C. (ed.). Antony van Leeuwenhoek and His Little Animals. New York: Dover Publications, Inc., 1960. (Translations of the letters in which Leeuwenhoek described his discoveries. Fine description of his microscopes and his methods of work.)

ECHLIN, P. "The Blue-Green Algae," Scientific American, June, 1966. Pp. 74–81.

JAHN, T. L., and F. F. JAHN. How to Know the Pro-tozoa. Dubuque, Iowa: William C. Brown Co., 1949. Pp. 3–38. (The introduction contains excellent material on the biology of those protists often placed in the animal kingdom. Easy.)

MOROWITZ, H. J., and M. E. TOURTELLOTTE. "The Smallest Living Cells," Scientific American, March, 1962. Pp. 117–124.

PELCZAR, M. J., and R. D. REID. Microbiology. 2nd ed. New York: McGraw-Hill Book Co., 1965. (A standard college textbook on microorganisms. Advanced.)

POSTGATE, JOHN. Microbes and Man. Baltimore: Penguin Books, 1969. (Account of relationships between microbes and man. Fairly easy.)

WILSON, C. L., W. E. LOOMIS, and T. A. STEEVES. Botany. 5th ed. New York: Holt, Rinehart & Winston, Inc., 1971. Chapter 20. (Standard college-textbook account of bacteria and their relations with man. Somewhat advanced.)

PATTERNS IN THE BIOSPHERE

PATTERNS IN THE BIOSPHERE

We have seen how individual organisms may be grouped as populations. From an ecological viewpoint, populations may be studied as parts of communities and ecosystems. From a taxonomic viewpoint, species populations may be grouped to form a classification. Now we turn to another aspect of biology—to the distribution of organisms in the biosphere.

No species lives everywhere. Some are widespread, and some are found only in a few places; some are living on the earth today, and some have become extinct. Nor are species scattered helter-skelter over the earth. Different species live in different places and at different times. That whales do not live in Nebraska today, that echinoderms live only in the seas and apparently never lived elsewhere, that palms once lived in Greenland, that the bacterium of tuberculosis lives in man and cows but not in dogs—all these are facts of distribution. Some are obvious facts; some are facts that have been established only after much patient searching for evidence. But do these facts make any sense?

Cyril N. Hinshelwood, a British scientist, has said, "Science is not the mere collection of facts, which are infinitely numerous and mostly uninteresting, but the attempt of the human mind to order these facts into satisfying patterns." In Section Three we shall attempt to find some satisfying and meaningful patterns within the multitude of facts about the distribution of organisms in the biosphere.

Life in the Microscopic World

Investigation 7.1

MICROORGANISMS IN SCHOOL ENVIRONMENTS

MATERIALS AND EQUIPMENT

(per team)

petri dish containing sterile
nutrient agar

glass-marking crayon

PROCEDURE

Caution: Do not remove the cover from the petri dish until directed to do so!

Each team will trap a sample of microorganisms from the air. This is done by exposing to the air a sterile petri dish containing nutrient agar (a plate). Your teacher will assign your team to a location where you are to expose your plate. Some suggestions: laboratory, industrial-arts shop, English room, auditorium, gymnasium, lunchroom, corridor, washroom.

On the bottom half of your petri dish, write your team's number and assigned location. When you have put your plate in its location, remove the cover and expose the agar to the air for exactly 6 minutes. • Why must all teams expose their plates for the same length of time?(1) Replace the cover and return the dish to the laboratory. Turn it upside down (to prevent water that might con-

dense inside the cover from dripping on the growing colonies) and incubate it in a place designated by your teacher.

After 3 or 4 days count and record the number of colonies of microorganisms in your plate. You can distinguish mold colonies by their cottony or fuzzy appearance and their large size as compared with bacterial colonies. Place your count on a chart that includes counts from all teams.

STUDYING THE DATA

• According to the data collected by your class, which location had the largest population of microorganisms?(2) • Which location had the smallest population of microorganisms?(3) • Did the location with the largest population of microorganisms also have the largest number of different kinds, as indicated by macroscopic appearance of colonies?(4)

DISCUSSION

Coughing or sneezing may spread droplets of materials from the mouth and nose to a distance of 3 m or more. The water in these droplets evaporates rapidly, leaving bits of dry materials (dust particles) that contain bacteria. Microbes from many other sources may also be carried on dust particles. • How can you use this information to help interpret the class data?(5) • Where would you be more likely to pick up the microorganisms of disease—in an environment with large populations of a few kinds of microorganisms or in an environment with small populations of many different kinds? Explain.(6)

• How verifiable do you think the results of this experiment are?(7) • Depending upon your answer to the preceding question, suggest factors that may help or hinder verification of your results.(8) • Why is it especially important to use proper microbiological procedures when you are disposing of these plates?(9)

FOR FURTHER INVESTIGATION

Does the kind of medium used in the petri dishes affect the count obtained at any one location? Does the temperature at which the plates are incubated affect the count? Design and carry out experiments that test hypotheses based on these questions.

THE ECOLOGY OF MICROORGANISMS

Microorganisms can be found in all natural ecosystems. They grow on snowbanks in polar regions. They thrive in hot springs that would scald larger organisms. In the dark depths of lakes and seas, microorganisms live without free oxygen. They survive when carried high into the cold, thin atmosphere many kilometers above the surface of the seas.

When you study a biotic community, macroscopic plants and animals attract your attention, but you may easily forget the millions of microorganisms. From an ecosystem viewpoint it is misleading to separate the study of microorganisms from that of macroorganisms. However, when you are looking for patterns in the distribution of organisms, there is some convenience in doing so. The distribution of macroscopic organisms is linked closely to geography; the distribution of microorganisms is not. For example, pond fishes in any one region of the world tend to be different from those in other regions; pond microorganisms are likely to be much the same in all regions. Therefore ecologists often study patterns of distribution among microorganisms separately from those among organisms that are visible without the help of microscopes.

In the laboratory you have discovered some places where microorganisms live—habitats. Now we shall consider two sets of ecological relationships in which the niches of microorganisms are especially important—relationships in disease and relationships in soil.

MICROBES AND DISEASE

Dictionaries often state that *disease* is a departure from a state of health and that health is the absence of disease—which makes a nice circle. "Health" and "disease" are words like "hot" and "cold": each word in the pair has little meaning without reference to the other. If we could say what a completely healthy individual is, we could clearly define "disease." But is there any limit we can put on health? Many useful words are difficult to define, so we shall continue the discussion of disease without any further attempt at definition.

You are certainly acquainted with some human diseases. Anyone who has a pet dog or cat knows that animals also get diseases. And every person who has kept potted plants knows that they can become diseased. Diseases occur among protists, too. All diseases are of interest to biologists, and the principles of *pathology* (the science of disease) apply to all organisms.

Find in Chapter 6 a condition of bacteria that might be called a disease.

pathology [Greek: *pathein*, to suffer, + *logos*, speech, reason]

SOME HISTORY

An early and widespread idea was that human disease came from an evil spirit that had entered the body. Obviously, then, the cure for illness was to get the spirit out by frightening or coaxing it. This became the function of witch doctors, with their masks, rattles, and charms. Even ancient peoples, however, did not rely entirely upon magic. It was all right for the witch doctor to call upon the tooth-ache demon to depart; but in the meantime, an application of coca leaves was soothing.

Thus, primitive peoples discovered practical remedies for various kinds of illnesses. In fact, many of the drugs we use today have long histories—aspirin, for example. An extract of willow bark had long been used in folk medicine. The pain-relieving substance in

Josef Muench

Figure 7 · 1

Navajo healing ceremony. The medicine man (*right*) and his helper construct a design with colored powders. The young patient will sit in the middle of the design when it is finished.

Figure 7 • 2

Plants used in both ancient and modern medicine. *Datura metel* of India (*right*), used as a calming drug for asthma. *Erythrozylon coca* of South America (*below*), used for relieving pain.

John R. Clawson

Field Museum of Natural History

synthesized [sĭn'thə sīzd'; Greek: *syn*, together, + *thesis*, an arranging]: here, meaning to form a more complex chemical substance from simpler substances

salicylic [săl'ə sĭl'ĭk; Latin: *salix*, willow]

acetylsalicylic [ə sē'tō săl'ə sĭl'ĭk]

Do you remember what a theory is? See page 59.

willow bark was synthesized by a German chemist in 1835 and named salicylic acid. Later another German chemist discovered that salicylic acid is more effective in a chemical combination called acetylsalicylic acid, to which the trade name Aspirin was given. Today it is one of the most commonly used drugs, but not until 1972 did scientists begin to learn how it works.

Much folk medicine, however, was (and is) pure superstition. Scientific studies have been needed to sort the sense from the nonsense. The "evil spirit" theory of disease led to very little improvement in treatment.

Physicians of ancient Greece developed some theories that did lead to better treatment. For example, they developed the idea that health is related to the food we eat, and they investigated the effects of various diets in illness. But there was little progress in the centuries that followed. Two hundred years ago physicians were not much further along in understanding and treating human illnesses than they had been 15 centuries earlier.

That many diseases are "catching" has long been known, but for centuries no one guessed that the thing "caught" was a microorganism. Leeuwenhoek started writing to the Royal Society about his "little animals" in 1676, but the first clear evidence that disease might be the result of the activities of microorganisms did not come

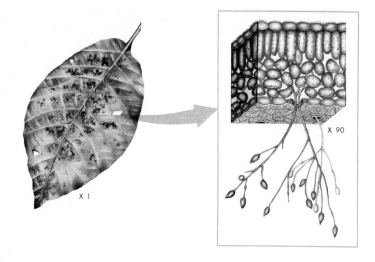

X 1

X 90

Figure 7 · 3
Late blight of potato.
Infected leaflet (*left*).
Section through the leaflet
with hyphae of the fungus
growing from it (*right*). The
hyphae bear spore cases.

until the 19th century.

The first evidence did not involve a human disease or even a disease of animals. It grew from the study of a plant disease. Late in the summer of 1845, potato plants throughout northern Europe were struck by a blight that almost overnight turned whole fields into black masses of rotting plants. In Ireland the consequences were disastrous, because most of the population depended on potatoes as the main source of food. During the next two years nearly half a million Irish died of famine, and two million emigrated to America.

Crop failures and famine had occurred many times in the past, but this time a scientific investigation could be made. It was soon found that the dying plants were full of fungal hyphae. But was the fungus present because the plant had died, or was the plant dead because the fungus was present?

Can you use terms from Chapter 3 to rephrase this question?

Early in the 19th century a French scientist had shown a close connection between another fungus and a disease of wheat. He had thought that the fungus brought about the disease, but his evidence was not strong, and few people knew of his work. The observations made on the potato blight, however, could not be ignored. By 1861 another scientist, Heinrich Anton De Bary, had gathered enough evidence to convince most biologists that the blight was a result of the fungus observed in the plants.

Heinrich Anton De Bary [hīn'rĭK ăn'tən dĕ bä rē']: 1831–1888. German botanist

By the end of the 19th century, largely through the work of Pasteur and Koch, the idea that microorganisms cause disease was thoroughly established. Just as it had once been thought that all disease was caused by evil spirits, so it seemed for a while that all disease might be caused by microorganisms. But disease is not so simple. Today pathologists recognize many kinds of diseases.

CLASSIFYING DISEASES

We still do not have any generally accepted classification of diseases, though a few broad groups are usually distinguished. First,

USDA Photo

Figure 7 • 4
A deficiency disease: lack of
iron affects the new leaves
of a soybean plant.

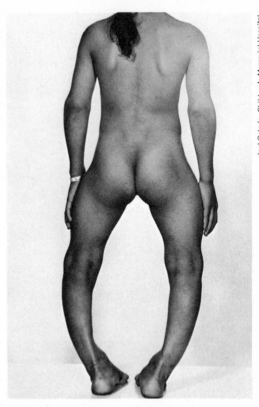

Joel Cole for Children's Memorial Hospital

Figure 7 • 5
Rickets, a disease resulting
from lack of vitamin D.

infectious [ĭn fĕk'shəs; Latin:
in, in, + *facere*, to make]

scurvy: characterized by
weakness, spongy gums, and
bleeding from mucous
membranes

allergies [ăl'ər jĭz; Greek: *allos*,
other, + *ergon*, work]

asthma [ăz'mə; Greek: *azein*,
to breathe hard]

hereditary [hĭ rĕd'ə tĕr'ĭ;
Latin: *heres*, heir]

degenerative [dĭ jĕn'ə rā'tĭv;
Latin: *de*, away, + *genus*,
race or kind]

arthritis [är thrī'tĭs; Greek:
arthron, joint, + *-itis*, (now)
inflammation of]

we have the diseases that involve microorganisms—*infectious* diseases. These are sometimes called germ diseases. By "germ" we
mean a living organism or at least a thing that can reproduce. Viruses
are certainly disease germs, whether we call them "living" or not.

In addition, there are many noninfectious kinds of diseases.
There are *deficiency* diseases, which develop when some substance
necessary for an organism is lacking in the organism's environment. Scurvy, for example, is a human disease caused by the lack
of vitamin C. *Vitamins* are complex organic substances that an organism must take in with its food because it cannot itself make
them.There are *allergies,* which are caused by environmental substances that irritate the skin or inner membranes of an organism. The
organism reacts in various ways, and disorders that range from skin
rashes to asthma result. There are *hereditary* diseases, which are
disorders passed by biological inheritance from generation to generation. Sickle-cell anemia, a condition in which blood does not carry
oxygen well, is an example. And there are *degenerative* diseases,
which involve disorders that develop in the functioning of an organism's body—usually as it becomes old. Arthritis is an example.

Most diseases are rather easy to classify, but others, such as
cancer, present difficulties. Some kinds of cancer are associated with

infection by viruses, some with factors in the abiotic environment, and some with heredity. One kind in mice arises from the combined actions of a virus, a hereditary factor, and a certain kind of body chemistry. Perhaps cancer should be considered not as a single disease but as a group of diseases.

INFECTIOUS DISEASES

In this chapter we are concerned with microorganisms, and it is primarily the infectious diseases that involve them. An infectious disease is an interaction of two organisms, a **pathogen**—usually a microorganism—and a host. It is a kind of ecological relationship. You might suspect that "pathogen" is a synonym for "parasite," but such is not the case. Not all parasites are pathogens. An organism may live at the expense of another without causing obvious damage—without producing **symptoms** (signs of illness). On the other hand, an organism that is not a parasite may be involved in a disease. The fungi that are associated with athlete's foot and ringworm are decomposers, living on the dead outer layers of skin. Yet athlete's foot is certainly an uncomfortable condition, a disease.

Transmission. Because an infectious disease is a condition—a relationship of pathogen and host—the disease itself cannot be transmitted (carried). The thing that actually is transmitted is the pathogen. The ways in which pathogens are transmitted are an important factor in understanding the control of infectious diseases.

Syphilis is a disease that results from infection of a human host by a corkscrew-shaped protist called *Treponema pallidum.* This organism dies in seconds when exposed to light and air, but within the human body it not only survives; it multiplies and eventually may inhabit every part of the host. The usual first symptom of the disease is a small open sore at the point of original infection. Treponemes from this sore are easily transmitted if the sore touches any moist membrane of another person. From two to six months after the appearance of the first sore, new symptoms appear—rashes, blotches, and more sores on the skin and mucous membranes. Symptoms may then disappear for a period of 10 to 20 years, while the treponemes attack internal body parts, especially nerves and brain. Eventually this leads to blindness, deafness, or insanity.

Human malaria is a disease that results from infection by protists of the genus *Plasmodium.* For infection to occur, the pathogenic organisms must enter the host's bloodstream. Through the bloodstream they travel to the liver and multiply. Their offspring move back into the blood, where they enter red blood cells, continue to multiply, and in doing so, destroy the cells. This destruction of blood cells takes place at definite intervals, depending upon the species of *Plasmodium.* At these times the host experiences alternating violent chills and high fever, the principal symptoms of the disease.

If an infected person happens to be bitten by a mosquito of the genus *Anopheles,* the pathogenic microorganisms may be picked up

pathogen [păth'ə jən; Greek: *pathein,* + *-genes,* born]

symptoms [sĭmp'təmz; Greek: *syn,* together, + *piptein,* to fall]

transmission [trăns mĭsh'ən; Latin: *trans,* across, + *mittere,* to send]

syphilis [sĭf'ə lĭs]

Treponema pallidum [trĕp'ə nē'mə păl'ə dŭm]

Figure 7 · 6

The spirochete of syphilis.
× 3000

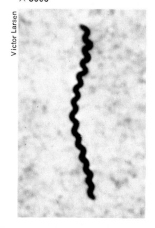

Victor Larsen

Plasmodium [plăz mō'dĭ əm]. See page 186.

Anopheles [ə nŏf'ə lēz']

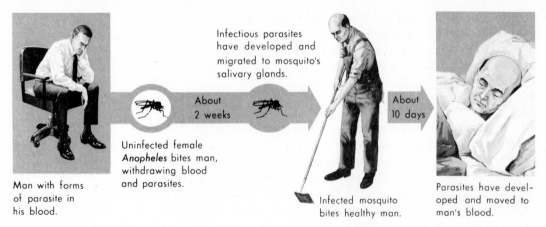

Infectious parasites have developed and migrated to mosquito's salivary glands.

About 2 weeks

About 10 days

Uninfected female *Anopheles* bites man, withdrawing blood and parasites.

Man with forms of parasite in his blood.

Infected mosquito bites healthy man.

Parasites have developed and moved to man's blood.

Figure 7 • 7

Transmission of malaria. What would be the best way to stop the spread of this disease?

salivary glands [săl'ə vĕr'ĭ glăndz]. Saliva produced by these glands prevents the blood of a mosquito's victim from clotting.

contagious [kən tā'jəs; Latin: *cum*, together, + *tangere*, to touch]

vector [Latin: carrier]

smallpox: disease in which the human host has a fever, develops sore spots on the skin, and often dies

tuberculosis: disease in which the host's tissues—most often in the lungs—are destroyed

typhoid fever: disease centered in the digestive system of the host

by the insect. In the mosquito's stomach they undergo some changes and then, in a new form, they squeeze through the stomach wall of the mosquito and eventually, after more changes, migrate through the mosquito's body to the salivary glands. When the mosquito bites, it injects saliva into the blood of its victim. If the mosquito has malarial parasites in its salivary glands, these are injected along with the saliva. Then the parasite has found a new human host.

Syphilis is a *contagious* disease. Because treponemes do not survive drying, they must be transmitted directly from a moist surface of one person to a moist surface of another. Normally such contacts occur only in the regions of the mouth and the sexual organs. Malaria, on the other hand, is strictly a *vector* disease; that is, the pathogen can get from one human host to another only when some other thing —in this case a living thing, a mosquito—carries it.

Few human diseases are strictly contagious. The germs of smallpox may be acquired by contact with a blanket used by a smallpox victim; the germs of tuberculosis may be acquired from breathing in dust particles that carry microbes coughed up by a person who has the disease. Even though the blanket and dust particles are vectors, smallpox and tuberculosis are often described as contagious. On the other hand, typhoid fever germs are carried in drinking water or on the feet of flies and then on food. Yet typhoid is usually described as a

Kenneth A. Wagner

Figure 7 • 8

A housefly walked over the nutrient medium in this petri dish before incubation. How do you explain the results?

vector disease even though the means of transmission are very differ-ent from the bite of a mosquito.

When a vector is a living thing that becomes a host for the para-site it transmits—as a mosquito is in malaria—the use of the word "vector" implies a point of view. For humans, mosquitoes are vectors of malaria parasites; but for mosquitoes, humans are the malarial vec-tors. From the biological point of view, it is preferable to think of such relationships as involving an *alternation of hosts.*

Alternation of hosts is far from unusual. The hosts for yellow fever are mosquitoes and humans (or monkeys); hosts of Rocky Mountain spotted fever are ticks and humans (or rodents); African sleeping sick-ness involves tsetse flies and humans (or cattle). Human diseases with alternate-host transmission are unfamiliar to us in the United States today, because it has been possible to control most of them through sanitary measures directed at the alternate hosts. Malaria, for example, has almost disappeared wherever *Anopheles* mosquito populations have been greatly reduced.

What other human diseases do you know that are considered contagious?

alternation [ôl'tər nā'shən; Latin: *alter,* other]

yellow fever: a chiefly tropical fever disease. See Figure 7 · 15.

Rocky Mountain spotted fever is actually most common in the Atlantic coastal states. It has caused many deaths.

African sleeping sickness affects the nervous system of the mammalian host.

tsetse [tsĕt'sĭ]

How have populations of these mosquitoes been reduced?

Merely transmitting pathogens from one host to another does not necessarily result in disease. For transmission to be effective, a path-ogen must enter the living substance of the host. Many potentially path-ogenic microbes exist at all times on human skin, but they are unable to get through the dead outer layers. However, any break in the skin may provide an entry for such germs. Though microbes cannot pene-trate skin, some—such as those of syphilis—can get through moist inner membranes.

Many microorganisms normally inhabit human digestive systems. Your intestine, for example, contains enormous numbers of bacteria, particularly the kind called *Escherichia coli.* These bacteria usually live without any harmful effects to you. But under some circumstances *E. coli* can infect you, producing symptoms of illness. Then a com-mensal has become a pathogen.

Virulence and resistance. Infection involves the interaction of a pathogen and a host. The severity of the symptoms—how serious the

Figure 7 · 9

Effects of a fungus on its two alternate hosts. On apple leaves (*left*) and on juniper (*right*).

What precautions should you take when a scratch or cut occurs in your skin?

Escherichia coli [ĕsh'ə rĭk'ē ə kō'lĭ']

Why is *E. coli* referred to here as a commensal?

virulence [vǐr′yə ləns; Latin: *virus*, a poison]

Corynebacterium diphtheriae [kôr ə nē′băk tǐr′ǐ əm dǐf thǐr′ǐ ē]

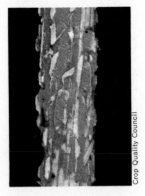

Figure 7 · 10

Stem rust of wheat. The pathogen, a fungus, has barberry as an alternate host. Some varieties of wheat have an inherited resistance to the disease.   × 1

immunity [ǐ mū′nə tǐ]

poliomyelitis [pō′lē ō′mī′ə lī′tǐs]: a disease in which a virus attacks nerves of its host, frequently leaving him crippled

illness is—depends upon characteristics of both. The extent to which a pathogen is capable of affecting its host is called its *virulence.* And the ability of a host to cope with a pathogen is termed *resistance.* A pathogen with high virulence may cause death in a host with low resistance, severe illness in a host with medium resistance, and perhaps only mild symptoms in a host with high resistance. A pathogen with low virulence is unlikely to cause severe illness even in a host with low resistance, and it may not even produce symptoms in a host with high resistance.

What determines the virulence of a pathogen? This is a complex problem, but consider some evidence. In the case of diphtheria, damage to the host is the result of a poison produced by the pathogen *Corynebacterium diphtheriae.* The ability of this bacterium to produce the poison can be determined by growing it in a petri dish and measuring the quantity of poison produced. But different pure cultures of *C. diphtheriae* obtained from different sources produce different amounts of poison even though. they are grown under identical conditions. In other words, different varieties have different virulences. Evidently virulence (at least in *C. diphtheriae*) is a characteristic that is inherited. This, of course, is only a first step in investigating the problem of virulence.

Immunity. Why do different individuals of the same host species have different degrees of resistance? This is another complex problem. We know that we can develop varieties or breeds of domestic plants and animals that are more resistant to particular diseases than are other breeds. And some human diseases seem to "run in families," though it is difficult to obtain convincing evidence of this. It seems, therefore, that resistance involves inherited characteristics.

On the other hand much resistance is not inherited, but acquired during the lifetime of an individual organism. When a human host is invaded by a pathogen, the host reacts by producing substances called *antibodies.* Antibodies combat the pathogen or the poisons produced by it. If the host survives the infection, its body retains the ability to produce these antibodies. Then, if a new infection by the same kind of pathogen occurs, the host's body can act immediately against it. Such resistance is called *immunity.*

Antibodies may be produced even though the virulence of a pathogen is too low to produce symptoms. Thus a person may be immune without knowing it. By the time they reach adulthood, many people have had some contact with the pathogens of poliomyelitis and tuberculosis and have acquired some immunity to these diseases.

Each kind of antibody is effective only against the kind of pathogen that brought about its production or occasionally against very similar pathogens. An antibody produced as the result of an infection by typhoid bacteria has no effect on diphtheria bacteria.

There is great variation in the length of time immunity lasts. Sometimes immunity is very short, as with the common cold. Sometimes it is lifelong, as with yellow fever. The strength of immunity to a disease may vary, too. Though an organism's immunity may be strong enough to ward off an attack by a weakly virulent variety of a pathogen, it may not be effective against a strongly virulent variety.

The immunity discussed so far occurs as a result of chance infection. Fortunately, we do not have to depend upon inherited resistance or upon natural immunity. We can artificially produce immunity in various ways.

artificially [är′tə físh′əl ē; Latin: *ars*, art, + *facere*, to make]

In the late 18th century Edward Jenner observed in England that milkmaids and other workers associated with cows seldom had smallpox—a common and often fatal disease at that time. However, such workers usually had been infected at one time or another by a mild disease of cattle, cowpox. From these observations Jenner concluded that a person might become immune to smallpox by being deliberately infected with cowpox. He developed this idea into a successful medical procedure—vaccination—more than half a century before the development of the germ theory of disease.

vaccination [văk′sə nā′shən; Latin: *vacca*, cow]. Why is it improper to use this term as a synonym for "immunization"?

Today several ways of bringing about artificial immunity are known. The kind of antibody formed in the body of a host depends upon the kind of pathogen rather than upon the kind of host. Therefore it is possible to inject a pathogen into a nonhuman host, where antibodies are then produced. These antibodies may then be removed from the blood of that host and injected into a person. Sometimes when the pathogens themselves, in a weakened or even dead state, are injected into a human being, they stimulate the production of antibodies without producing symptoms of disease. This method is used in immunizing against poliomyelitis. However, for some diseases —for example, syphilis—no effective artificial immunity has yet been developed.

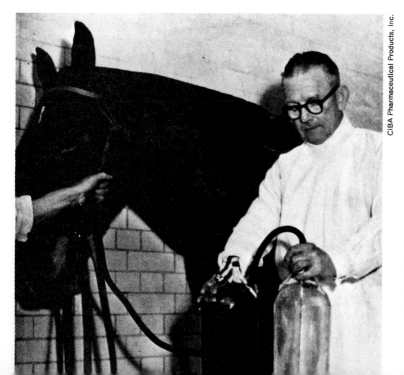

CIBA Pharmaceutical Products, Inc.

Figure 7 · 11
Drawing blood containing antibodies that will be used in treating a human disease. What advantage do horses have for this purpose?

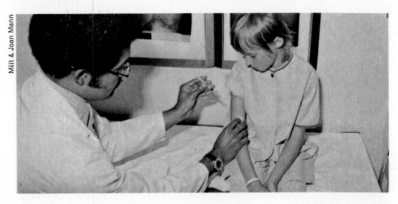

Figure 7 • 12

Injecting antibodies for treatment of a disease.

Environment and disease. During famines more people die from disease than from starvation. Lack of food—an environmental factor —lowers resistance so that even moderately virulent pathogens produce serious illness. This illustrates how important environment is in a biological consideration of disease.

Environmental factors may affect the host, the pathogen, or both. For example, if the environment is such that the host is vigorous and relatively free from other diseases, then the host is more able to resist infection than it would be otherwise. A host that is poorly nourished and already defending itself against other germs has much less resistance. The improved general health of the human population in the past half century has probably been an important factor in reducing cases of tuberculosis in the United States.

Environmental factors may also affect the ability of a pathogen to infect its host. For example, fungi that attack human skin are favored by a warm, moist atmosphere. In some parts of the tropics, these pathogens are very active in producing disease. In much of the United States, they usually find such favorable conditions only inside clothing—particularly shoes and stockings—where their growth results in athlete's foot.

It should now be evident that combating infectious disease involves much more than killing pathogens. It is a complex ecological problem involving three major factors: the nature of the pathogen, the nature of the host, and the nature of the environment in which pathogen and host interact.

POPULATIONS AND DISEASE

When you go to a physician for treatment of a disease, you hope that he is interested in your individual illness. He is. But modern physicians, recognizing that disease is an ecological problem, also devote much time and thought to disease in populations—to what is often called "public health." Today, indeed, some physicians never see individual patients; instead, they specialize in controlling the amount of disease. To do this they must study changes in the frequency of diseases in populations, the geographical distribution of diseases, and the ways in which diseases spread.

Epidemics. An *epidemic* is a severe outbreak of disease in a host population. The unusual, the epidemic, situation always attracts attention and often causes alarm and panic. But it cannot be understood except in relation to the usual, the **endemic,** situation. In the endemic situation a pathogenic species lives in a steady state with its host species. Many infectious diseases exist in the endemic state, often at a very low density but ready to break forth as epidemics, given the right conditions. "Right conditions" generally means increased chances for transmitting the pathogen from one host to another. Or it may mean lowered resistance in the host population or even increased virulence in the pathogen population.

An epidemic does not always affect an entire species population. Most adults have acquired immunity to measles, so measles epidemics—before the days of artificial immunization—occurred in the child population. Syphilis, gonorrhea, and other **venereal** diseases—those in which the pathogen is transmitted mainly by sexual contact between host individuals—have long been endemic. Within the past decade they have become epidemic—but mostly in the 15- to 25-year age group of urban and suburban populations. Immunity to these diseases either does not exist or is very short.

epidemics [ĕp'ə dĕm'ĭkz; Greek: *epi*, upon, + *demos*, the people]

endemic [ĕn dĕm'ĭk, Greek: *en*, in, + *demos*]

venereal [və nĭr'ĭ əl; Latin: *Venus*, goddess of love]

Why do you think this epidemic has occurred?

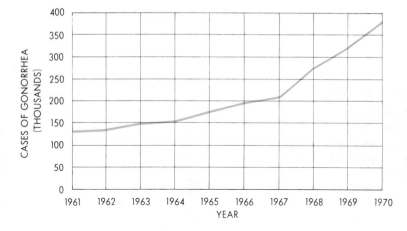

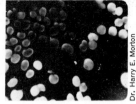

Figure 7 • 13
Number of cases of gonorrhea among people ages 15–24 in the United States. Try to explain this graph.

Figure 7 • 14
The bacterium of gonorrhea, *Neisseria gonorrhoeae.*
× 15,200

Dr. Harry E. Morton

Epidemics sometimes occur when control methods break down. Typhoid fever is infrequent in the United States, but we have no reason to think that *Salmonella typhi* is an extinct organism. Any relaxation in careful methods of treatment or sewage disposal could result in a major typhoid epidemic in any city.

Perhaps the most spectacular epidemics have occurred when diseases were introduced into populations that had no hereditary resistance. Measles, which seldom kills Europeans (except infants), was a deadly disease when introduced among island people in the Pacific.

Geography of disease. Many human infectious diseases—for example, colds and tuberculosis—are now almost worldwide. With modern transportation they have spread everywhere, and they persist

Salmonella typhi [săl'mə nĕl'ə ti'fi]: the pathogen of typhoid fever; not related to typhus fever, in which the pathogen is a rickettsia

Epidemics of noninfectious diseases can occur. Can you find any examples?

wherever the population is dense enough to support them.

Through history, however, the geographical patterns of human diseases have shifted greatly. We have just mentioned the introduction of measles into the Pacific islands. We know, too, that many infectious diseases of the Old World, such as smallpox, were absent from the New at the time of its discovery by Europeans. It is also possible that the New World contributed diseases to the Old. Syphilis suddenly became prominent in Europe about 1500 A.D., and some medical historians have supposed that it was brought back by Columbus' sailors, but this is by no means certain. Old descriptions of diseases and epidemics are usually incomplete and difficult to interpret.

Figure 7 • 15

Yellow fever in the American tropics. Forest mosquitoes (*shown on white*) transmit the pathogen from monkey to monkey. A man working in the forest may acquire the pathogen from these mosquitoes. In town this man may be the source of infection for other persons if *Aedes* mosquitoes (*on orange*) are not controlled.

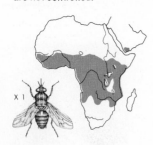

Figure 7 • 16

Distribution of tsetse flies in Africa. Into what parts of the world is African sleeping sickness most likely to spread?

Aedes aegypti [ā ē′dēz′ ē′jĭp′tī]

What kinds of immunizations must travelers obtain when they go from the United States to other countries?

Diseases that have limited infection periods of a few days or weeks and that leave the host temporarily or permanently immune to a second attack cannot persist among small or scattered human populations. To survive, the pathogens of such diseases need a steady supply of new hosts. The common cold is one of these diseases. Often when a ship visits a small Pacific island, everyone on the island will, within a few days, come down with a cold brought in by some visitor. When everyone has acquired temporary immunity, the colds disappear, and there will be no more until another ship arrives.

A pathogen that requires an alternation of hosts for survival can only occur in places where both hosts are present. African sleeping sickness, for instance, is transmitted to humans by tsetse flies, so the disease is found only where these flies live. It is thought that yellow fever also originated in Africa. The vector of this disease is a species of mosquito, *Aedes aegypti*. Breeding in the water kegs of sailing ships, these mosquitoes were carried from Africa to the New World. With modern air transportation it is easy to see how tsetse flies might be carried from Africa. Constant vigilance by public health specialists is necessary to prevent this.

Investigation 7.2

INVESTIGATING AN INFECTIOUS DISEASE

BACKGROUND INFORMATION

One of the first steps in controlling an infectious disease is to determine what pathogenic organism must be present in the host to produce the symptoms of the disease. Robert Koch (see page 181) was the first biologist to set forth a method for determining that a particular disease results from the presence of a particular microorganism. This method is embodied in the following set of tests:

1. The organism suspected of producing the disease symptoms must be found constantly associated with those symptoms.

2. The suspected organism must be grown in a pure culture outside the host.

3. When organisms from this pure culture are inoculated into a healthy individual of the host species, the symptoms of the disease in question must appear in the individual.

4. The suspected organism must then be taken from the experimental host, grown again in pure culture, and identified as the species present in the original culture.

Koch's procedure cannot be used to establish the cause of *every* type of infectious disease, because some microorganisms cannot be grown outside the body of the host (thus making the 2nd and 4th tests impossible). Nevertheless, this set of tests is still considered the basic procedure for determining the pathogen of an infectious disease.

MATERIALS AND EQUIPMENT

(for each team)
potted plants (bean, tomato, or
    sunflower), 2
dissecting needle
bunsen burner
culture of *Agrobacterium tumefaciens*
inoculating loop
microscope slides, 3
beaker, 5 to 7 cm in diameter
crystal-violet solution
medicine dropper

paper towels, 3
monocular microscope
glass-marking crayon
scalpel (or razor blade)
forceps
sodium hypochlorite solution, 1%
container for disposal of gall tissue
sterile distilled water in plugged test
    tubes
petri dish, sterile
tube of sterile dextrose agar

PROCEDURE

Caution: *Agrobacterium tumefaciens* does not infect man, but it is a dangerous plant pathogen. Be sure to maintain sterile laboratory conditions!

Choose 2 plants of approximately the same size and age, and with stems 4 to 6 mm in diameter. Using a lead pencil, label their pots *A* and *B;* then write your team's symbol on both pots.

Sterilize a dissecting needle by heating it in a flame. Allow the needle to cool. With the needle make several punctures (about 2 mm apart) on one side of the stem of Plant A, beginning about 1 cm above the soil.

Again sterilize the dissecting needle. *Allow it to cool.* Dip the tip of the needle into the culture of *Agrobacterium tumefaciens.* Using the needle, puncture the stem of Plant B just as you did that of Plant A. Sterilize the needle. Place the plants in a well-lighted part of the laboratory, and keep them well watered.

Prepare a stained microscope slide of *A. tumefaciens,* using the method given in Investigation 6.4. Examine under high power of a monocular microscope. Sketch a few of the bacteria, showing both their shapes and their arrangement. With a glass-marking crayon, label the slide *1* and store it for later use in this investigation.

Observe the potted plants every 2 or 3

days for a period of 4 or 5 weeks. Record all changes and the dates when they appear.

A knotlike growth, or gall, may appear on one of the plants. If this occurs, use a sharp scalpel to remove it. Wash the gall thoroughly. Using forceps, sterilize a clean microscope slide by dipping it into a 1% solution of sodium hypochlorite for about 20 seconds. Rinse in sterile distilled water. Place the slide on a paper towel on the laboratory table and cover with the top of a sterile petri dish. Do not touch the upper surface of the slide, and do not allow it to touch anything in the laboratory.

Again using forceps, dip the plant gall into the solution of sodium hypochlorite. Rinse in distilled water and place on the sterile microscope slide near one end. Using a sharp scalpel sterilized in a flame, cut the gall in half. Cut a small piece (about 2 mm in diameter) from the center of the gall and place it in the middle of the slide. (Important: Discard the remaining gall tissue into the container provided for this purpose.) Crush the small piece of tissue with the flat side of the scalpel blade. Sterilize the scalpel blade.

Using a sterile inoculating loop, transfer some of the juice from the crushed gall tissue to a sterile tube of dextrose agar. Label the tube and store it in a place designated by your teacher.

Examine the tube 4 or 5 days later. If colonies of microorganisms are present, take material from one of the colonies and prepare a slide as you did before. Label the slide 2.

Compare Slides 1 and 2 under high power of a monocular microscope. Draw a few of the organisms observed on Slide 2.

DISCUSSION

• Which of the two plants is the control?(1) • Why did you use a sterile needle to puncture Plant A?(2)   • Did either of the two plants develop a gall? If so, which one?(3)   • On the basis of your visual comparison of Slides 1 and 2, what conclusion can you draw about the identity of the organisms in Slide 2?(4)   • Why is similarity of appearance not sufficient evidence for concluding that the bacteria on the two slides are of the same species?(5)

• Do you believe that this experiment provides proof that *Agrobacterium tumefaciens* is the pathogen that produces gall growth? If so, explain how each step of Koch's procedure is fulfilled in the experiment. If not, what additional steps should you take?(6)

FOR FURTHER INVESTIGATION

The plants suggested for use in this experiment are dicots. Are monocots susceptible to infection by *A. tumefaciens*?

SOIL ECOSYSTEMS

What source of human food does *not* depend upon soil?

Farmers often pick up a handful of soil and let it trickle through their fingers. From its feel, odor, and appearance, they can tell a great deal about its condition and the kinds of crops for which it might be suitable. They know that they hold in their hands the source of their livelihood. The rest of us—nearly 95 percent of the human population of the United States—often forget that we, too, depend upon soil, even though our dependence is by way of the supermarket.

COMPONENTS OF SOIL

component [kəm pō′nənt; Latin: *cum*, together, + *ponere*, to put, place]: a substance that is part of a more complex substance

derived [dĭ rīvd′]: obtained from a source

A heap of builder's sand is not soil, nor is a lump of sticky clay in the brickworks. Soil is a complex mixture of substances derived from rocks and air, of substances derived from the dead bodies of living things, and of living things themselves. Soil is an ecosystem.

Inorganic components. Heating and cooling, freezing and thawing, wetting and drying—all these tend to weaken the structure of rocks. And minerals in rocks react chemically with water and air that enter through tiny cracks and crevices. Thus rocks break up, and the loose weathered material becomes the basic ingredient of soil.

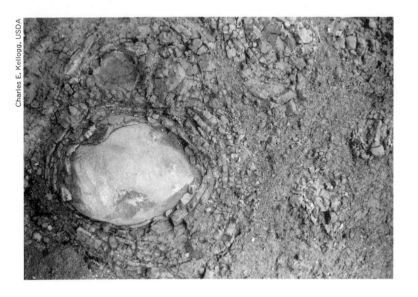

Charles E. Kellogg, USDA

Figure 7 • 17
Boulder weathering into
mineral soil particles.

Each rock particle holds a thin layer of moisture. In the spaces between particles are tiny pockets of gases, mostly the gases of the atmosphere. If the soil is very wet, many of the spaces between particles may be filled with water and the amount of air correspondingly reduced. Many substances that soil organisms need are dissolved in the soil water. Some of these substances are organic and some are inorganic. From rock particles come inorganic compounds containing sulfur, calcium, potassium, magnesium, and other elements mentioned in Chapter 1.

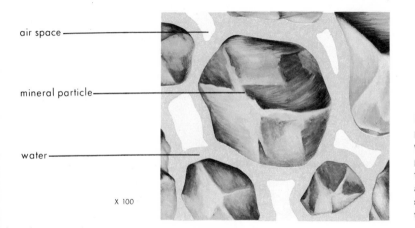

air space

mineral particle

water

X 100

Figure 7 • 18
Inorganic substances in soil.
Water clings to mineral
particles. Usually, the larger
the particles, the larger the
air spaces. Dissolved
substances are not visible at
this degree of magnification.

ions [ī'ənz]

Most of these inorganic compounds in soil water are not present as molecules. Magnesium sulfate, for example, is shown in symbols by the chemist as the molecule $MgSO_4$, but particles with this structure do not occur. Magnesium sulfate consists of the electrically charged particles Mg^{++} and SO_4^{--}. Such charged particles are called *ions*. An uncharged magnesium atom (Mg) is chemically very different from a magnesium ion (Mg^{++}).

hydroxyl [hī drŏk'sĭl]

Water, on the other hand, occurs chiefly as molecules, H_2O, also written HOH. But at any given moment a few water molecules in any sample ionize, each molecule forming a hydrogen ion ($H+$) and a *hydroxyl* ion ($OH-$). In pure water the two kinds of ions are equal in number. In soil water, however, ions from other substances are always present. Some of these substances also produce hydrogen ions. This results in a greater number of hydrogen ions than are present in chemically pure water. Water with more hydrogen ions than hydroxyl ions

acid [Latin: *acidus*, sour]

is said to be *acid*. Other substances in soil reduce the number of hydrogen ions. When hydroxyl ions are more numerous than hydrogen

alkaline [ăl'kə līn']

ions, the water is called *alkaline* (or basic). The acidity or alkalinity of the soil water is an important abiotic environmental factor in the distribution and growth of soil organisms.

humus [hū'məs; Latin: ground, soil]

Humus. Terrestrial organisms obtain the materials of their bodies directly or indirectly from soil. At death, their bodies return to the soil. Much of the activity of soil organisms is concerned with getting the remaining energy out of these dead substances. Through this activity, the substances are eventually returned to an inorganic form as minerals, gases, and water.

Figure 7 · 19

Sections through soils. A forest soil in North Carolina (*left*). A prairie soil in Nebraska (*right*). Which appears to have the larger proportion of humus?

Much of this decomposing activity is accomplished by microbes. Therefore, it occurs most rapidly under warm, moist conditions that

U. S. Forest Service

Conservation and Survey Division, Univ. of Nebraska

USDA-SCS Photo

Figure 7 · 20
Chopped leaves and twigs are being placed on these newly planted shrubs. What do you think is the purpose?

Haven Kolb

Figure 7 · 21
Fungi grow from humus of a forest soil.

favor their growth. However, in all climates some time is required, so organic substances in various stages of decomposition usually occur in soil. When decomposition has reached a point where the original organisms can no longer be distinguished, the organic substance is called *humus.*

In general, the darker a soil, the larger the proportion of humus it contains. Because humus is derived from dead matter that falls onto the surface, most of it occurs in the top layer of soil. The proportion of humus in the top layer varies from about 1 percent in desert soils to more than 70 percent in some bog soils.

Humus increases the water-holding ability of soil and, to some degree, the amount of air space. It also moderates extremes in soil temperature. These functions of humus tend to improve the soil as a habitat for living organisms. But there can be too much of a good thing —humus increases the acidity of soils. This makes many bog soils unfavorable to most organisms—including many of the decomposers themselves.

Soil organisms. Ground squirrels and other rather large animals dig into soil. Though they have few direct relationships with soil communities, they affect soil environments and so belong to soil ecosystems. Moles seldom go above ground, so they have more direct ties to soil communities. And earthworms are full-time members of soil communities.

The majority of soil organisms, however, are quite small. Arthropods are abundant in soil: centipedes, millepedes, mites, and many

bog: wet, spongy ground in marshes and swamps

Give some reasons why desert soils have low percentages of humus.

How does this help to explain the high percentage of humus in bog soils?

ground squirrels. See Figure 8 · 1.

small insects. And microscopic animals, such as rotifers and gastro-trichs, live in the soil water along with some of the more animal-like protists.

Bacteria are more widely distributed in the biosphere than are any other organisms. They are found in all soils but less abundantly in acid soils than in alkaline ones. Fungi, on the other hand, are most abundant in acid soils.

The importance of actinomycetes in soils was first pointed out in 1900 by Martinus Beijerinck, but it was not until the 1920's that soil microbiologists began to take much interest in them. Then they found that when they cultured soil samples, from 30 to 40 percent of the colonies that appeared were actinomycetes. Some of these decompose cellulose, one of the most abundant materials in the remains of plants. Less important, they are responsible for the pleasant, earthy smell of freshly turned soil.

cellulose [sĕl'yə lōs']

Did you find evidence of actinomycetes in Investigation 6.1?

More than 60 different species of algae have been found in soil samples. In wet soils algae sometimes develop on the surface as green, slimy growths. In paddy soils used for cultivation of rice, algae contribute to the nitrogen and oxygen content of the soil and so increase crop yields.

Investigation 7.3

A CHEMICAL CHARACTERISTIC OF SOILS

Part A: ACTION OF INDICATORS

BACKGROUND INFORMATION

The degree of acidity-alkalinity of a solution is indicated by a series of numbers from 0 to 14 called the *pH scale.* In chemically pure water there are equal numbers of hydrogen and hydroxyl ions; such water is neither acid nor alkaline. It is *neutral* and has a pH of 7. If the amount of liquid remains constant and the number of hydrogen ions is increased tenfold (that is, if the *concentration* of the hydrogen ions is multiplied by 10), the pH is 6. If the concentration of hydrogen ions is multiplied by 100, the pH is 5, and so forth. On the other hand, if the concentration of hydrogen ions is reduced to 1/10 of that in pure water, the pH is 8; if reduced to 1/100 of that in pure water, the pH is 9; and so on. The pH numbers below 7 indicate acid solutions (the smaller the number, the greater the acidity); pH numbers above 7 indicate alkaline solutions (the larger the

number, the greater the alkalinity).

The pH of a solution is measured most accurately by means of electrical instruments. It can also be measured by use of chemical indicators (pages 22–23). Many soluble *pigments* (colored substances) change chemically when there is an increase or decrease in the pH of the water in which they are dissolved. Often the chemical change in the pigment involves a loss of color or a shift to a different color.

For many such pigments the pH at which the color change occurs is known. Therefore, these pigments can be used as indicators to determine the pH of an unknown solution.

MATERIALS AND EQUIPMENT

(per team)

beakers, 50- or 100-ml, 6

glass-marking crayon

graduated cylinder, 25-ml

distilled water, 100 ml

glass stirring rods, 6

dropping bottles, 10-ml, 1 for each of
the following:

methyl red solution

bromthymol blue solution

phenolphthalein solution

hydrochloric acid

sodium hydroxide solution

PROCEDURE

Mark 6 beakers as follows: *1-A, 1-B, 2-A, 2-B, 3-A, 3-B.* Into each beaker pour 15 ml of distilled water and add a stirring rod. To each of Beakers 1-A and 1-B add a drop of methyl red solution; to each of Beakers 2-A and 2-B add a drop of bromthymol blue solution; to each of Beakers 3-A and 3-B add a drop of phenolphthalein solution. Record the color in each beaker.

To each of the three *A* beakers add a drop of hydrochloric acid and stir; to each of the *B* beakers add a drop of sodium hydroxide solution (an alkaline solution, or base) and stir. Keep each stirring rod in its own beaker If no color changes occur in either the *A* or *B* beakers of each set, add additional drops of acid or base. Continue in this way, alternating additions of acid to *A* beakers and base to *B* beakers until a color change occurs in one or the other in each set.

STUDYING THE DATA

• According to the background information given above, approximately what pH should distilled water have?(1) • As acid is added to the *A* beakers, what happens to the pH value?(2) • As base is added to the *B* beakers, what happens to the pH value?(3) • Keeping these ideas in mind and referring to your data, arrange the indicator colors in order of increasing pH.(4)   Your teacher will then give you the pH at which each indicator changes color. • What do you think is the principal inaccuracy in determining pH by this method?(5)

Part B: pH OF SOIL SAMPLES

BACKGROUND INFORMATION

With a large enough series of indicators, the approximate pH of solutions can be worked out. Often it is more convenient to use indicator paper than a pigment solution. Indicator paper is prepared by soaking porous paper in a pigment solution and then allowing it to dry. A number of pigments may be combined in the same paper so that different ones do not have to be tried separately. This part of the investigation makes use of such an indicator paper.

MATERIALS AND EQUIPMENT

(per team)

soil samples, 3 or more

mortar and pestle

graduated cylinder, 25-ml

distilled water

test tubes, 1 per soil sample

test-tube rack

glass-marking crayon

microscope slides, 1 per soil sample

pH test paper, wide-range, 1 cm per
soil sample

glass stirring rods, 1 per soil sample

PROCEDURE

Obtain soil samples from at least 3 different environments and number each for identification. Place about 10 g of soil in a mortar, add 10 ml of distilled water, and grind. Pour the mixture into a test tube labeled with the number of the soil sample. Wash the mortar and pestle and rinse with distilled water before preparing the next sample. Repeat this procedure for each sample. Let the tubes stand 10 minutes.

Place 1 microscope slide in front of each test tube. Place a small piece of pH test paper on each slide. Dip a glass stirring rod into the 1st sample and transfer a drop of the liquid to the test paper. Note the color of the test paper where the drop has been placed and compare it with the color scale that comes with the paper. Record the pH of the sample. Repeat this procedure for each sample, using a different stirring rod and slide in each case.

SUMMARY

• What are the pH ranges of your samples?
(6)   • From what kind of environment did your most acid soil come?(7)   • From what kind did your most alkaline soil come?(8)   • Suggest some reasons for the differences in soil pH.(9)
• This method provides a comparison of the pH of the samples, but it does not give the true pH. Why?(10)

COMMUNITY RELATIONSHIPS IN SOIL

Why would algae be unlikely to grow deep in soil?

Most soil organisms are consumers. The algae, which are producers, can live only at the surface and are rare in most soils. A soil ecosystem, therefore, is somewhat like a city: its food supply comes from outside. In soil some food comes into the roots of plants from their green parts, which are in the sunlight above the soil. But mostly the food supply of soil is in the form of dead organisms. Therefore, decomposers are important organisms in soil communities.

Decomposer relationships. In a dead leaf or twig lying on the soil surface, there are relatively large amounts of complex organic substances. Likewise, in a dead animal there are complex organic substances. Many of these—such as fats, starch, or proteins—can be used as food by beetles and other small animals that live in the upper parts of the soil or on its surface. But others—such as cellulose in plant bodies and chitin in insect bodies—can only be used by microorganisms such as bacteria and fungi. Often microorganisms leave as waste products simpler organic substances that still contain energy. Other species of bacteria and fungi then use these waste products. Even they may not extract all the energy but leave still simpler substances—such as sugars—that still other kinds of organisms may use. Thus, one decomposer organism depends upon another for its food supply. Such a food chain is like an assembly line in reverse. Instead of building step by step from simpler to more complex things, the food chain breaks down organic substances in steps until only inorganic substances—carbon dioxide, water, and mineral compounds —remain.

chitin [kī′tǐn]

Some of the intermediate organic substances affect the whole soil environment. For example, many organisms give off acids in their wastes. When these accumulate, as they do in many forest soils, the pH of the environment becomes unfavorable for many bacteria. But most fungi can grow in a low pH; thus they thrive in forest soils.

antibiotic [Greek: anti, against, + bios, life]

Some substances produced by soil organisms actively harm other organisms. Such an **antibiotic** substance, when accumulated in the soil around the organism that forms it, reduces growth of competing organisms. Some of these antibiotic substances have been found useful for combating bacterial infections in man; the drug Aureomycin, derived from an actinomycete, is an example.

Aureomycin [ô′rǐ ō mī′sǐn]. What other antibiotics that are used in medicine do you know?

On the other hand, a number of soil organisms produce substances that seem to promote the growth of other organisms in their environment. Some yeasts, for example, apparently increase the growth of certain neighboring bacteria. Other species of soil bacteria

promote [prə mōt′; Latin: pro, before, + movere, to move]: here, to further or to advance

Cornelius H. Muller

Figure 7 · 22

(A) A shrub, *Salvia leuco-phylla*. (B) A bare area about 2 m wide bordered by small herbs. (C) Grassland. Try to explain this interrelationship of plants.

are more abundant around the roots of plants than elsewhere in the soil. The latter pattern of distribution seems to be (at least in part) the result of substances given off by the roots.

What kind of ecological relationship would you call this?

If you trace fungal hyphae in loose soil, you often find that some of them lead to the roots of trees, shrubs, and other plants. There the fungi form feltlike sheaths around knobby branches of the roots. Microscopic examination shows that some of the fungal hyphae penetrate the outer parts of the roots and form complicated interweaving masses of tissue. These associations of fungi and roots are referred to as *mycorrhizae.*

mycorrhizae [mī′kə rī′zē′; Greek: *mykes*, fungus, + *rhiza*, root]

In a comparison of mycorrhizal pine seedlings with non-mycorrhizal seedlings of the same species growing in the same kind of soil, the mycorrhizal seedlings took up almost twice as much nitrogen and potassium and more than three times as much phosphorus. In this case and in many similar experiments, plants definitely benefited from the mycorrhizal relationship. Some plants—orchids, for example—either do not grow or show only limited growth if their mycorrhizal fungi are not present. On the other hand, mycorrhizal fungi probably absorb food from the roots.

What kind of ecological relationship occurs in mycorrhizae?

Figure 7 · 23

Pine roots without mycorrhizae (*left*). Pine roots with mycorrhizae (*right*). What differences do you see?

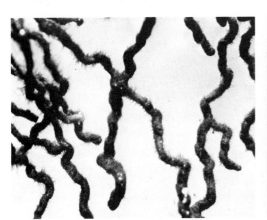

Photos by Edward Hacskaylo

Parasites and predators. It seems to be easy for a decomposer to shift from living on dead organisms to living on live organisms. Many kinds of soil fungi do this. So the parasite-host relationship is quite frequent in soil communities.

In agricultural soils nematodes are particularly important parasites, for many species attack the root systems of commercially important plants. On the other hand, some species of nematodes parasitize other animals that damage crops—for example, insects. In these cases the parasite-host relationships are similar; but from the viewpoint of man, one is good and the other is bad.

How are the words "good" and "bad" being used here? Would this statement be true if the insects attacked by the nematodes were honeybees?

Robert Bjork, USDA

Figure 7 • 24

Golden nematode infection of potato roots. Swollen females bear eggs, which can live in soil from year to year.

Predator-prey relationships also occur among soil organisms. Centipedes and many beetles prey on smaller animals. Rotifers prey on protists. Slime molds, amebas, and ciliates feed on bacteria. The predatory protists probably act as one of the chief biotic factors influencing populations of soil bacteria.

In soil ecosystems even plants act as predators. Several species of soil fungi form hyphae with stout lateral branches that curl in semicircular loops. The tips of the loops from adjacent hyphae intermesh, forming a network that produces a sticky fluid. Nematodes are caught, and despite violent struggles, they are held fast. Then other hyphae grow into the bodies of the captive nematodes and consume them.

adjacent [Latin: *ad*, toward, near, + *jacere*, to lie]

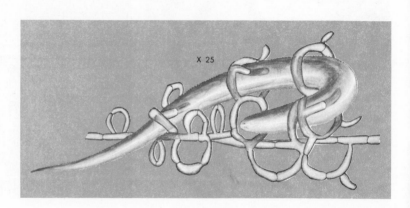

X 25

Figure 7 • 25

A nematode trapped in fungal hyphae.

THE NITROGEN CYCLE

Soil microorganisms are essential in the chemical cycles of the biosphere, and particularly in the nitrogen cycle.

Refer to pages 20–22.

Nitrogen gas (the uncombined element nitrogen, N_2) makes up about 78 percent of the atmosphere; yet the great majority of organisms cannot use it. We ourselves take it in at every breath and breathe it out unused. Likewise, elemental nitrogen in air or dissolved in water enters most other plants and animals and comes back out again without taking any part in their life processes. Yet nitrogen compounds occur in the substance of all organisms. Therefore a source of usable nitrogen is necessary for all organisms.

We humans—and all other consumers—get nitrogen-bearing compounds in the things we eat. All our food, of course, can be traced to producers. And producers get their nitrogen-bearing compounds from the soil (or the water) in which they grow. This brings us back to soil ecosystems.

Many soil organisms can decompose the complex nitrogen compounds in dead bodies, extracting most of the energy from them and

extracting [Latin: *ex*, out, + *trahere*, to draw]

Figure 7 • 26

Diagram of the nitrogen cycle.

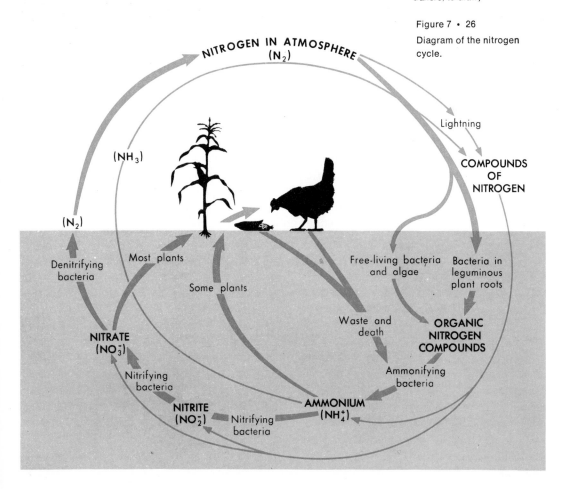

leaving simpler substances. Among these simpler substances, the chief one that contains nitrogen is ammonia (NH_3). Ammonia is a gas, but it dissolves readily in water. In soil water, ammonia reacts chemically with hydrogen ions to form ammonium ions ($NH_4{}^+$). In the form of ammonium ions, nitrogen may be absorbed by the roots of plants and built into living material again. When this occurs, there is a short pathway in the nitrogen cycle.

However, other things may happen. Two groups of bacteria in soil are called *nitrifying* bacteria. One group changes ammonium ions ($NH_4{}^+$) to nitrite ions ($NO_2{}^-$). Then another group rapidly converts the nitrite ions to nitrate ions ($NO_3{}^-$). In general, plants cannot use nitrites, but nitrates are the main source of nitrogen for most plants. Thus, there is a second, longer pathway in the nitrogen cycle.

nitrifying [nī'trə fī'ĭng]

nitrite [nī'trīt]

nitrate [nī'trāt]. Caution: Do not confuse these closely similar words.

aerobic [â rō'bĭk; Greek: *aer*, air, + *bios*]. In biology the term is applied specifically to oxygen, not to air in general.

Nitrifying bacteria operate only under *aerobic* environmental conditions—that is, with oxygen available in the soil water. Oxygen dissolves into soil water from the air spaces that normally occur in soil. But if all the spaces become filled with water, leaving no room for air, then the soil water has no source of oxygen—the soil environment is *anaerobic.*

anaerobic [Greek: *an*, without, + *aer*, + *bios*]

denitrifying [dē nī'trə fī'ĭng]

Under anaerobic conditions, nitrifying bacteria cannot carry on their activities. Even worse (from the viewpoint of the plants), *denitrifying* bacteria, which thrive in anaerobic environments, change remaining nitrates to nitrogen gas. The gas gradually escapes into the atmosphere, where it is lost to the great majority of organisms.

But, fortunately, it is not lost to all organisms. There is a long, third pathway of nitrogen through the biosphere. Although lightning changes a small amount of atmospheric nitrogen to nitrogen compounds, this process is of very little importance to living things. Much more important is the action of *nitrogen-fixing* organisms—organisms that can change elemental nitrogen (N_2) to nitrogen compounds.

Centuries ago man discovered that soils in which clover has been grown produce better crops of other kinds of plants than do soils in which clover has not been grown. Early in the 19th century, a French chemist showed that this is the result of an increase in the amount of nitrates in such soils. Not only clover but most plants of the family Leguminosae—beans, alfalfa, vetch, etc.—have this effect. Much later in the 19th century, the great Dutch microbiologist Martinus Beijerinck discovered that nitrogen-fixing is not performed by the legumes but by bacteria of the genus *Rhizobium* that live in the roots of these plants. There they form easily visible swellings called nodules. Under favorable conditions, root-nodule bacteria can fix as much as 225 kg of nitrogen per hectare (about 200 lb per acre) per year.

Leguminosae [lĕ gyü'mə nō'sē]

Rhizobium [rī zō'bē əm]

nodules [nŏj'ōōlz; Latin: *nodulus*, small knot]

During the 20th century, much more has been learned about nitrogen fixation. Microbiologists now know, for example, that different species of *Rhizobium* live in different kinds of legumes. And recently they have found that some actinomycetes have a similar relationship with roots of some shrubs and trees—alders, for example.

Further, nitrogen-fixing now is known to be carried on by a few

The Nitragin Co.

Figure 7 • 27

Soybean roots bearing abundant nodules formed with a species of *Rhizobium*. Why are these root outgrowths considered mutualistic, but those of Figure 7 • 24 infectious?

free-living bacteria. Even some of the blue-green algae are nitrogen-fixers. In forests, marshes, and natural grasslands, the relative importance of the various nitrogen-fixers is unknown. But for farmers, whose business it is to manage soil ecosystems, there is no question: about 95 percent of the nitrogen fixed in cultivated soil comes from *Rhizobium* bacteria.

Is this important to urban dwellers? If so, how?

Investigation 7.4

DECOMPOSING ACTION OF SOIL MICROBES

MATERIALS AND EQUIPMENT

(per team)

flowerpots, small, 4

washed sand, to fill 2 flowerpots

dead leaves, 2

dead insects, 2

dead twigs, 2

cotton string or twine, 2 pieces

rolled oats, about 4 cm³

nylon fabric, 2 x 2 cm, 2 pieces

deep dishes, 4

rich garden soil, to fill 2 flowerpots

petri-dish lids, 4

PROCEDURE

Cover the drainage holes in the flowerpots with small stones or pieces of broken pots. Fill 2 flowerpots with moist, washed sand. Press the sand down firmly to within 1.5 cm of the top. In both pots mark off the surface of the sand into 3 equal sectors. In the middle of one sector of the 1st pot, place a piece of dead leaf that has been soaked in water until it is pliable; in a 2nd sector place a dead insect; in the 3rd, place about 2 cm³ of rolled oats. In the middle of one sector of the 2nd pot, place a dead twig; in a 2nd sector, a piece of cotton string;

in the 3rd, a piece of nylon fabric.

Using a pencil, mark the rim of each pot with your team's symbol. Cover the materials with a petri-dish lid (open side downward), gently but firmly pressing the edge of the lid into the sand. Set the pots in deep dishes and fill each dish with water. The water will rise through each pot until its contents are moist.

Repeat this procedure with the 2 remaining pots, using rich garden soil instead of sand. Put all 4 pots in a warm, dark place. *Keep the soil moist at all times* by adding water to the dishes under the pots.

OBSERVATIONS

Make 2 copies of the chart shown below. The charts should extend across facing pages of your data book to allow wide columns under "Changes Observed." Label one chart *Sand* and the other *Garden Soil.* Make observations during the 2nd day and at weekly intervals after that.

Note any odors. Compare the appearances of the materials. Look for masses of mold hyphae. Test the strength of the twine by pulling it.

STUDYING THE DATA

• On the sand, which object decomposed most rapidly?(1) • Most slowly?(2) • On the garden soil, which object decomposed most rapidly?(3) • Most slowly?(4) • What kinds of organisms were you able to observe during the experiment?(5)

CONCLUSIONS

• What are the principal substances in each of the objects you tested? (Use clues in preceding text.)(6) • What statement can you make about the rate at which different substances are decomposed by soil organisms?(7) • Do your data show any general difference between rates of decomposition on sand and those on garden soil? If so, what hypothesis can you suggest to explain the difference?(8)

FOR FURTHER INVESTIGATION

1. In light of the results of this experiment, discuss problems involved in the preservation of fiber and wood products.

2. You can modify this procedure to investigate the effect of the warmth of a climate on the formation of humus.

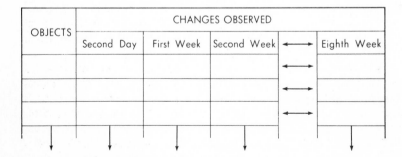

OBJECTS	CHANGES OBSERVED				
	Second Day	First Week	Second Week	← →	Eighth Week
				← →	
				← →	
				← →	

GUIDE QUESTIONS

1. How does study of ecological patterns of microorganisms differ from such study of macroorganisms?

2. With what is the study of pathology concerned?

3. What ideas about the causes and treatments of disease did man have before the 19th century?

4. What useful results have come from folk medicine?

5. How did biologists come to associate microorganisms with disease?

6. What are some of the major groups of diseases?

7. Contrast the ways in which the pathogens of syphilis and malaria are transmitted.

8. What is meant by an alternation of hosts?

9. The environment abounds in pathogens. What things must occur if any of these is to produce disease symptoms in a host?

10. Why do different host individuals react differently to infection by the same kind of pathogen?

11. In what ways may resistance to a specific infectious disease be acquired?

12. What are antibodies and how are they associated with immunity?

13. It is often said that a physician must know his patient. What other factors must a physician understand?

14. What relationships are there between endemic- and epidemic-disease situations?

15. Why are some human infectious diseases worldwide and others found only in certain geographic regions?

16. Why are problems concerning infectious disease considered ecological problems?

17. By what steps did Koch show that a specific disease resulted from infection by a specific microorganism?

18. Why is soil called an ecosystem?

19. What are the nonliving components of a soil?

20. In what chemical form do most dissolved minerals occur in soil?

21. What is humus?

22. What are the principal groups of organisms in a soil ecosystem?

23. How may pH be measured?

24. What is the principal part played by microorganisms in a soil ecosystem?

25. What kind of community relationship is represented by mycorrhizae? What evidence is there for this relationship?

26. Give some examples of predation and parasitism in a soil ecosystem.

27. List the principal nitrogen-bearing nutrients used by producers.

28. Some microorganisms grow best under anaerobic conditions. What does this mean?

29. How is nitrogen returned from organisms to the atmosphere?

30. What is nitrogen-fixing? Where do the principal nitrogen-fixers live?

PROBLEMS

1. Investigate an infectious disease, using the following outline of topics: history, symptoms, pathogen, vector (where appropriate), treatment, epidemiology. This outline is suitable for investigating diseases of plants as well as those of man and other animals. Suggested diseases: anthrax, bacterial meningitis, Dutch elm disease, filariasis, tsutsugamushi fever, hoof-and-mouth disease, black stem rust of wheat, brucellosis, fire blight of pears, diphtheria.

2. The following questions are about disease: (a) Why is it inaccurate (though customary) to say that a pathogen *causes* a disease? (b) Do vector-borne diseases necessarily involve pathogens that have alternate hosts? Why or why not? (c) Why is a disease—such as yellow fever—that occurs both in man and in other animals easier to study than one—such as leprosy—that occurs only in man?

3. In recent years epidemics of a virus disease usually referred to as "Asian flu" have periodically spread throughout the United States. How might you interpret these epidemics in the light of your understanding of pathogens, acquired immunity, and endemic diseases?

4. The transmission of cholera is favored by poor sanitation. Long ago cholera *almost* disappeared from countries where sanitation is good. In the fall of 1972, for example, cholera cases appeared in Israel and Australia, both of which have excellent public health systems. How can you explain this?

5. How do antibodies produce immunity? To investigate this problem thoroughly, you will need to consult books on human physiology.

6. Suppose that some catastrophe completely disrupted a large city's sanitation procedures—water purification, sewage disposal, trash and garbage collection, etc. Which diseases would become more frequent? Which less frequent?

7. Both infectious and noninfectious diseases have differences in their geographical

distributions. Investigate the geography of high blood pressure or stomach cancer.

8. The following questions are about soils: (a) How might the sizes of mineral particles in a soil affect its suitability as an environment for microorganisms? (b) In what ways may the acidity or alkalinity of soil water affect soil organisms? (c) Desert soils usually contain a relatively low percentage of humus and have a low density of soil microorganisms. Why are they often very productive of crops? (d) Wild plants are often difficult to transplant. List as many reasonable explanations as you can.

9. With sieves of different sizes you can separate the particles of a soil sample into size groups. Measure the groups either by volume or by weight and record their percentages by means of a bar graph. Use this method to contrast the soils in which a chosen species of plant is abundant, fairly frequent, and completely absent.

10. A farmer owned a field in which the soil seemed to be quite uniform in texture, mineral nutrients, microorganisms, and humus. He divided this field into halves, A and B. He planted rye in Plot A. When the rye was almost full-grown, he plowed it under; then he planted potatoes in both plots. More potatoes were produced in Plot B than in Plot A. Without further treating the soil, he planted potatoes in both fields the following year. In the second year, he harvested more potatoes from Plot A than from Plot B. Give an explanation for the differences in potato production in the two years.

11. Manufacture a complete artificial soil and grow a plant in it. Start by crushing rock with a hammer.

12. In this chapter some instances are discussed in which a practice developed before knowledge of how it worked—in other words, before theory. Though the sequence is usually the reverse today, the history of science contains many other examples of practice preceding theory. Find several and report on them.

SUGGESTED READINGS

ALVARADO, C. A., and L. J. BRUCE-CHWATT, "Malaria," *Scientific American,* May, 1962. Pp. 86–96.

BURNET, F. M. "The Mechanism of Immunity," *Scientific American,* January, 1961. Pp. 58–67.

DAUBENMIRE, R. *Plant Communities.* New York: Harper and Row, Publishers, 1968. Pp. 188–198. (Discusses relationships between plant communities and the soils in which they live. Advanced.)

DUBOS, R. *Man, Medicine, and Environment.* New York: New American Library, 1969. (A fine discussion of the ecology of disease. Fairly advanced.)

EDWARDS, C. A. "Soil Pollutants and Soil Animals," *Scientific American,* April, 1969. Pp. 88–92.

FARB, P. *Living Earth.* New York: Harper & Brothers, 1959. (Deals with the soil and organisms that live on it. Rather easy.)

FROBISHER, M. *Fundamentals of Microbiology.* 7th ed. Philadelphia: W. B. Saunders Co., 1962. Pp. 311–347. (A technical description of immunity. This book also contains materials on many other aspects of infectious diseases and on soil microorganisms. Advanced.)

GABRIEL, M. L., and S. FOGEL (eds.). *Great Experiments in Biology.* Englewood Cliffs, N.J.: Prentice-Hall, Inc., 1955. Pp. 119–126. (Original reports by Koch and Iwanowski on infectious diseases. Advanced.)

HARLEY, J. L. *Mycorrhiza.* London: Oxford University Press, 1971. (A well-illustrated pamphlet that describes experimental investigations of mycorrhizae.)

LANGER, W. L. "The Black Death," *Scientific American,* February, 1964. Pp. 114–118.

Life on Land

MEETING THE ENVIRONMENT

Consider all the species of organisms found within 50 miles of your school. Many you probably know by name. Many you know in a general way but cannot name. And many exist quite unknown to you. Whether you are well or poorly acquainted with the *biota* (all living things) of your region, you undoubtedly realize that some organisms do not "belong" there. In Kentucky, for example, you expect oaks and ferns, gray squirrels and woodpeckers—though you might see few of them in downtown Louisville. But on the plains of Wyoming, you find pronghorns, ground squirrels, and horned larks. The collection of species inhabiting a region generally has a recognizable character.

Palm trees are not a part of the biota of Kentucky; Kentucky is

biota [bī ō′tə; Greek: *bios*, life]

woodpecker. See Figure 18·22.

pronghorn. See Figure 8·28.

X 1/4

X 1/3

Figure 8 · 1
Thirteen-lined ground squirrel (*above*) and horned lark (*below*).

Haven Kolb

Figure 8 · 2
Coconut palms (Florida).

231

Jim Annan

not within the *geographic range* of any species of palm. Gray squirrels are a part of the biota of Kentucky. They are also a part of the biota of Kansas. But the geographic range of this species does not include Wyoming, so gray squirrels are not a part of the biota of that state. On the other hand, the geographic range of ground squirrels includes both Wyoming and Kansas but does not extend to Kentucky. Thus, with respect to squirrels, the biota of Kansas resembles that of both Wyoming and Kentucky. With respect to many other organisms, it is like the biota of neither. Why does a region tend to have a characteristic biota?

Figure 8 • 3
Gray squirrel burying a nut.

caimans [kǎ′mənz]

SURVIVAL

Are there dandelions in your lawn? Are rats a problem in your neighborhood? These organisms were immigrants to this continent in historical times, just as were European, African, and Asian men. Geographic ranges are not permanent; like everything else in the biosphere, they are constantly changing. That dandelions and rats exist here today is evidence that they—and man—are able to exist under the environmental conditions of this continent.

Every year visitors to Florida buy small caimans as souvenirs and carry them northward to New England and the Middle West. As the pets grow larger, they become bothersome and are then often dumped into the nearest river or pond. Although this has been going on for many years, the Ohio and Connecticut rivers are as free, of caimans today as they ever were.

X 1/2

Figure 8 • 4
Young caiman.

What determines the *survival* of a species in a particular ecosystem? Here "survival" does not mean mere existence in a dormant condition—a Michigan woodchuck in its January burrow or a lockjaw bacterium on a rusty nail. Here "survival" means active living—growing and reproducing. One or even several individuals may be able to exist in an environment, but this does not make the species a part of the ecosystem. Only continued reproduction accomplishes that.

tolerance [tŏl′ər əns; Latin:
tolerare, to endure]

TOLERANCE

If a household geranium is left outdoors during an Iowa winter, it dies. If a blacksnake is exposed in a shadeless cage to the July sun of Georgia, it dies. If a rancher in western Nebraska plants a hemlock tree in his upland pasture, he is probably wasting his time. Household geraniums do not tolerate long periods of freezing temperature; blacksnakes do not tolerate high temperatures; hemlocks do not tolerate low soil moisture. *Tolerance* is the ability—of either an individual or a species—to withstand particular environmental conditions.

Working with any one measurable environmental factor, we can, by experiment, determine an upper (*maximum*) limit and a lower (*minimum*) limit of tolerance in any one species. Likewise we can determine the range of conditions most favorable for growth and reproduction; these are called *optimum* conditions. This seems clearcut, but several complications arise.

First, the duration of the condition is important, especially in determining maximum and minimum limits. Geraniums can withstand short periods of freezing temperature but not long ones.

Second, there is variation within the same species between populations that come from different parts of the species' geographic range. The optimum temperature for swimming movements in the jellyfish, *Aurelia aurita,* is between 5° and 18°C in the population off Nova Scotia, but it is between 28° and 30°C in the population off the southern tip of Florida.

Third, there is variation among individuals. An experiment in which 25 domestic pigeons were kept at an environmental temperature of −40°C resulted after four days in 11 of them dying and 14 surviving.

Finally, there are complications due to the interaction of different factors. When relative humidity is near zero, man can withstand very high temperatures. But when it is close to 100 percent, man will die in a few minutes at a temperature between 48° and 50°C. At an intermediate humidity of 50 percent, the optimum temperature for clothed man is usually put at 20° to 22°C. For land animals the effects of humidity and temperature are so closely related that there is little point in measuring one without the other.

THE ENVIRONMENT AS A WHOLE

Consider now the interaction of tolerances in determining geographic range. Field sparrows *(Spizella pusilla)* of the eastern United States can survive northern winter temperatures if they have an adequate food supply. The food supply required for winter living is greater than that for summer living because heat loss in winter is greater. But sparrows can hunt food only during the day, and during the northern winter the day is short. Which, then, is the tolerance factor that sets the northern boundaries of the winter range of field sparrows—temperature, length of day, or food supply?

Abiotic conditions within a species' tolerance limits may allow it to survive, but they do not guarantee that the species will be part of a particular ecosystem. The species may fail because it has to compete with other organisms. For example, under natural conditions bald

X 1/4

Figure 8 • 5
Household geranium.

duration: here, length of time

Aurelia. See page 133.

relative humidity. See Investigation 3.3.

This refers to the temperature and humidity *outside* the clothing. Devise an investigation of within-clothing temperature and humidity under these outside conditions.

X 1/3

Figure 8 • 6
Field sparrow.

Figure 8 · 7
Bald cypress in an Arkansas
swamp.

Josef Muench

cypresses live in swampy areas. But when planted and tended by man, they also grow successfully on hilltops. Evidently they are tolerant of considerably less moisture than that found in swamps. Perhaps cypresses fail to grow naturally on hills because trees that are more tolerant of low moisture crowd them out. Or we may look at the matter from the opposite direction. Bald cypresses are tolerant of flooded ground, and few trees of other species are. Perhaps, then, cypresses grow in swamps not so much because they require a swamp environment as because they encounter weaker competition there.

Can you outline a plan for an experimental investigation of this hypothesis?

From these two examples, it is clear that the *whole* individual organism encounters the *whole* environment. But individuals can be observed to respond in certain ways when a particular environmental factor is changed experimentally. Therefore, ecologists can gain a partial understanding of the whole situation by studying environmental factors one at a time. This is an aspect of ecology that is best pursued in the laboratory.

Investigation 8.1

ENVIRONMENTAL TOLERANCE

MATERIALS AND EQUIPMENT

(for each team)
beakers, 50-ml, 4
seeds of radish, vetch, tomato, and
    lettuce, 50 each
fungicide, about 150 ml
petri dishes, 5
clear plastic bags, 5
rubber bands, 5
shallow cardboard boxes with covers, 2

pieces of paper toweling, cut to fit
    petri dishes, 20
cardboard dividers, cut to fit petri
    dishes, 20
forceps, 1
glass-marking crayon, 1
refrigerator, 1
incubator, 1
thermometers (−10° to +110°C), 2

PROCEDURE

Before beginning work, read through the procedure. • Then set up hypotheses on the basis of the experimental design.(1)

Label the beakers *tomato, radish, vetch,* and *lettuce*. In each, place 50 seeds of the species named. Add fungicide and allow to soak for the period of time recommended by your teacher.

Place 4 disks of paper toweling in each petri dish. Moisten the paper thoroughly. Divide each dish into quarter sections by inserting cardboard dividers, as shown below.

Figure 8 • 8

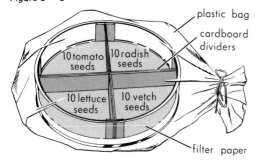

Pour the fungicide solution from the beakers. Rinse the seeds with water. Using forceps, place 40 seeds in each petri dish—10 of each kind in each quarter section. Label the dishes with the team symbol and number from *1* to *5*. Place each dish in a clear plastic bag and close the bag with a rubber band.

Place each dish in a different environment, as follows:

Dish 1: continuous light and cold
Dish 2: continuous dark and cold
Dish 3: continuous light and warm
Dish 4: continuous dark and warm
Dish 5: variable temperature and light

For Dish 1 use a refrigerator that has the light adjusted to remain on when the door is closed. Place Dish 2 in a lighttight box in the refrigerator. Try to maintain temperatures at 10° to 12°C. For Dish 3 use an incubator containing a light. Place Dish 4 in a lighttight box in the incubator. Try to maintain temperatures at 30° to 32°C. Place Dish 5 on a windowsill.

Each day count the number of seeds that have germinated. Record the counts in your data book. A suggested form:

Dish No. _____   Environment _____

KIND OF SEED	NUMBER GERMINATED		
	Day 1	Day 2 ←————→	Day 10
tomato			
radish			
vetch			
lettuce			

STUDYING THE DATA

Combine the data of all teams. • Why?(2)

First, consider the percentage of seeds that germinated. • In which environment did the greatest percentage of tomato seeds germinate?(3) • Of radish seeds?(4) • Of vetch seeds?(5) • Of lettuce seeds?(6)

Second, consider the speed of germination. • Is there any case in which the seeds of one species germinated more rapidly in one environment but germinated in larger proportion in another? If so, which species and which environments are involved?(7)

Finally, consider the environmental factors separately. • Which kind of seed has the greatest tolerance for continuous light?(8) • Which kind has the greatest tolerance for low temperature?(9) • Does any kind germinate similarly in all the experimental environments? If so, which?(10)

CONCLUSIONS

• Check results with your hypotheses.(11)

Recall that the establishment of a species in an ecosystem depends upon both its tolerances and its competition with other species. • Which do you think would give a species a greater advantage—ability to germinate rapidly or ability to germinate a large percentage of its seeds? Why?(12)

• On the basis of your experimental results, describe an ecosystem in which each species you studied in this investigation might have an advantage.(13)

FOR FURTHER INVESTIGATION

In markets it is possible to obtain seeds of plants that grow in many climates, such as avocados, dates, grapefruits, oranges, pomegranates, lentils, and many kinds of beans. These can be tested for germination in experimental environments, but in some cases the time allowed for germination may have to be greatly lengthened.

ECOLOGICAL DISTRIBUTION OF LIFE ON LAND

Environmental factors, operating through tolerances, sort out the kinds of organisms that are able to live in particular places. The result is a set of ecosystems. Though there are no sharp boundaries between ecosystems, biologists try to order them into meaningful patterns within the biosphere. One result has been a conceptual division of the biosphere on the basis of climate.

CLIMATES

Climate is a reasonable basis for large-scale ecosystems because it summarizes a number of biologically important abiotic factors. Solar radiation is the source of energy captured by producers and distributed as food in an ecosystem. It is also the source of heat energy, which results when radiant energy is absorbed by matter. This occurs chiefly at the surface of the earth, because there is relatively little matter in air.

The shape of the earth and its tilt with respect to its orbit around the sun result in an unequal reception of solar energy at different places on the earth's surface. But the circulation of the atmosphere —itself powered by solar energy—helps to distribute that part of the radiant energy that is converted to heat. At the same time, the circulating atmosphere carries water to land surfaces.

World maps showing the distribution of a number of climatic factors may be found in the 13th ed. of *Goode's World Atlas*, ed. Edward B. Espenshade, Jr. (Chicago: Rand McNally & Co., second revised printing, 1971—also available in paperback).

Climates occur in broad belts that encircle the earth. But the boundaries of these belts are disrupted by lands and oceans, and they are still further modified by mountains on land and currents in oceans. It is rather easy to map the distribution of a particular factor of climate—solar energy, wind, temperature, rainfall, humidity, or evaporation rate. However, it is difficult to map a climate as a whole, because the factors in the makeup of climate overlap and mix with one another in complex ways.

This also makes it difficult to describe climates quantitatively. To simplify, ecologists frequently use *climatograms,* which summarize monthly measurements of temperature and precipitation.

climatograms
[klī mǎ'tə grǎmz'; Greek: *klima*, latitude, + *gramma*, writing, record]

Figure 8 · 9 (*opposite*)

Climatograms. Average monthly temperatures in blue (degrees Celsius); average monthly precipitation in gray (centimeters).

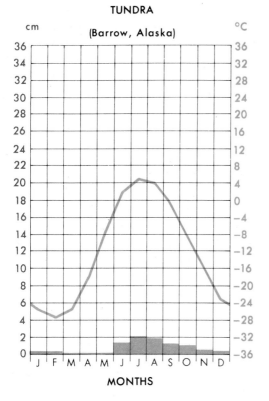

TUNDRA
(Barrow, Alaska)

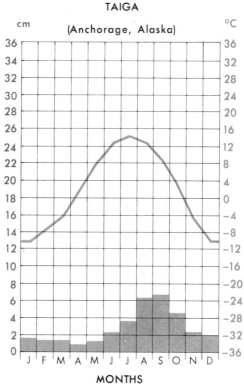

TAIGA
(Anchorage, Alaska)

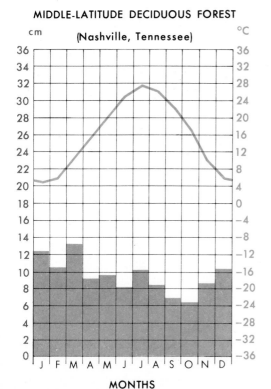

MIDDLE-LATITUDE DECIDUOUS FOREST
(Nashville, Tennessee)

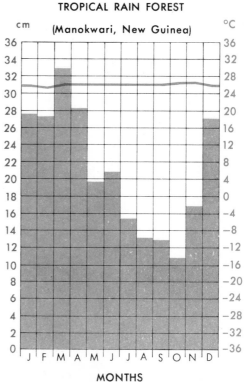

TROPICAL RAIN FOREST
(Manokwari, New Guinea)

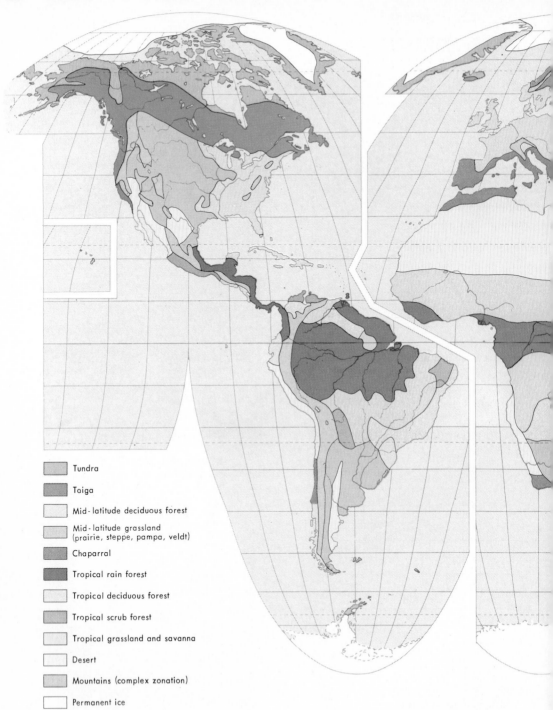

Tundra

Taiga

Mid-latitude deciduous forest

Mid-latitude grassland
(prairie, steppe, pampa, veldt)

Chaparral

Tropical rain forest

Tropical deciduous forest

Tropical scrub forest

Tropical grassland and savanna

Desert

Mountains (complex zonation)

Permanent ice

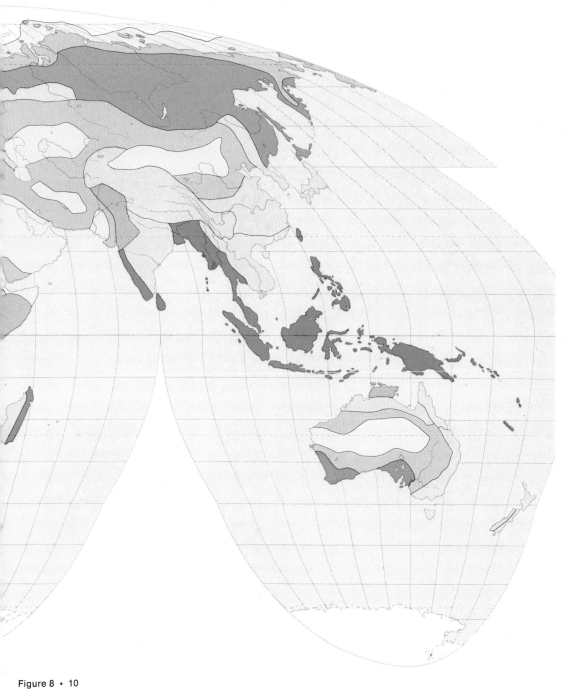

Figure 8 · 10
Major biomes. Many parts of
Earth have not been
thoroughly studied, and even
where observations are
plentiful ecologists sometimes disagree about their
interpretation.

BIOMES

In each major kind of climate, a characteristic vegetation tends to develop and then maintain itself. Warm, arid climates, for example, are associated with desert vegetation; semiarid climates, with grassland; moist climates, with forest. Such a recognizable kind of vegetation, together with the animal life adapted to it, is a *biome*—a major division of the biosphere characteristic of a major climate.

biome [bī′ōm; Greek: *bios*, life, + *oma*, group, mass]

Any one view over some area within a biome—as from an airplane—shows a landscape with a patchwork effect. Some parts of the landscape are ecosystems that do not seem to belong to the biome. They do belong, however, for a biome includes all the ecosystems that lead to the *climax*—the ecosystem that is determined by the climate. We might see bare rock or water surfaces or areas denuded by fire. Or we might see an area that recently (in terms of centuries) was in such condition but has not yet had time to develop the climax ecosystem. The process by which ecosystems in an area move toward the climax ecosystem—the one determined by climate—is called *succession.*

denuded: laid bare

succession [sək′sĕsh′ən; Latin: *sub*, under, after, + *cedere*, to go away]

BIOMES AND RADIANT ENERGY

You need not study all biomes in detail to gain some understanding of the ecological distribution of terrestrial life. In the following pages only selected biomes are described. The first series has sufficient water and an *increasing* total annual supply of radiant energy. This series begins near the poles and ends near the equator.

Tundra. The *tundra* biome is circumpolar in the Northern Hemisphere. It lies just south of the ice-covered polar seas. In the Southern Hemisphere a corresponding biome is not developed. There, north of the ice-covered Antarctic continent, in the latitudes where the climate would permit tundra, the earth is covered by ocean.

tundra [tŭn′drə]

circumpolar [sûr′kəm pō′lər; Latin: *circum*, around, about, + Greek: *polos*, a pivot]

Because the angle of the sun's rays is never high, tundra receives little radiant energy at any time. In summer, however, the long days somewhat make up for the low angle of the sun. Then the top layer of soil thaws, though the ground beneath always remains frozen— the *permafrost.* Melting snow cannot drain into permafrost, so water collects on the surface. For six to eight weeks tundra is a land of ponds and marshes, even though the yearly precipitation is small. In this short growing season, plants must synthesize a whole year's food supply.

permafrost [pər′mə frôst; Latin: *per*, through, + *manere*, to remain, + frost]

Grasses and sedges dominate tundra landscapes. Extensive areas are covered by low mats of lichens and mosses. The few woody plants, such as willows and birches, grow close to the ground, seldom reaching a height of more than a few centimeters. Leaves of most plants are small, and many are hairy or have margins rolled inward. Flowers appear rapidly and develop seeds quickly.

dominate [dŏm′ə nāt′; Latin: *dominus*, master, lord]

These are adaptations— structural and functional—to the abiotic environment. Try to explain them.

During summer, tundra teems with animal life. Hordes of waterfowl raise their young in the long days that allow around-the-clock food-gathering. Insects are few in species but great in number of in-

William Mayer

A

Haven Kolb

B

Elra M. Palmer

C

Figure 8 • 11
(*A*) Tundra (Alaska).
Tundra flowers: (*B*) Yellow
Geum and white *Arenaria*
(× ⅓), and (*C*) *Silene* (× 1).
Note the size of tundra
flowers in comparison with
the size of the rest of the
plant.

Rutherford Platt

Figure 8 · 12

A tundra willow. What environmental conditions limit the growth of this woody plant?

snowshoe hares. See Figure 2 · 14.

lemmings. See Figure 2 · 15.

polar bears. See Figure 4 · 5.

dividuals. Caribou graze on grasses and lichens. Ptarmigan, arctic foxes, and snowshoe hares are present in their brown summer coats. Lemmings scurry along runways among the plants. When the lemming population is high, predators such as snowy owls and weasels are numerous.

The change from summer to winter is rapid. Lakes and ponds freeze—the shallower ponds all the way to the bottom. Snowfall is light, and high winds sweep exposed areas free of snow. Daylight hours are few or lacking; photosynthesis ceases.

There are not merely cold and darkness but scarcity of food. The large numbers of waterfowl leave, flying far to the south. Among mammals the chief migrants are caribou, which return southward to the forests. Some animals, such as gulls and foxes, migrate to the seashores, where they become commensal with seal-hunting polar bears.

Almost all tundra plants are perennials; these are dormant in winter. The invertebrate animals also become dormant. Lemmings and other small animals avoid the windswept bare ground and burrow under the snow in sheltered spots. There they consume underground

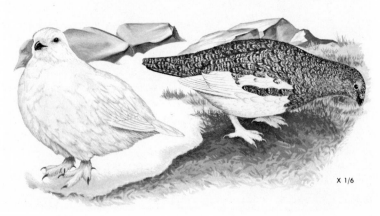

X 1/6

Figure 8 · 13

Ptarmigan in winter (*left*) and summer (*right*). How can you explain the difference in the coloration of the feathers?

Figure 8 • 14
Tundra mammals: musk oxen (*left*) and caribou (*right*).

parts of plants or supplies of seed that they stored during the summer. Ptarmigan burrow into the snow for protection during storms, but at other times they feed on buds of plants that protrude above the shallow snow. Only musk oxen face the tundra winter's full might. Living on lichens, they seek out bare areas or paw away the snow cover.

How does a snow cover provide protection?

protrude [prō trōōd'; Latin: *pro-*, in front of, + *trudere*, to thrust]

Taiga. As you travel southward in tundra, scattered clumps of dwarf trees appear in sheltered places, and presently tundra gives way to a great coniferous forest that extends in a broad zone across Eurasia and North America. This is the *taiga* biome. In the Southern Hemisphere the climates of the small land areas that exist at suitable latitudes are so strongly modified by the surrounding seas that taiga does not occur.

taiga [tī'gə]

Because it lies closer to the equator, taiga receives more radiant energy both annually and daily than does tundra. Summer days are not so long as those in tundra, but they are warmer and the ground thaws completely. Winters are not so long, and few places in taiga have winter days without sunlight. But snowfall is heavy.

Until 10 to 20 thousand years ago, most of the taiga region was covered by a great sheet of ice. Grinding its way slowly across the continents, it gouged out depressions. As it melted, it left masses of rubble that often formed dams across streams. The result is a multitude of ponds and lakes.

rubble: here, masses of loose earth and rock. "Rubble" is related to the word "rubbish."

Taiga forest is characterized by coniferous trees, most of which are evergreen. Throughout the year they keep out the sunlight, so there is little vegetation near the ground. Therefore, though the vegetation is deeper than in tundra, the production of food takes place mostly in the upper parts of the trees. Many insects attack the conifers, and a large number of small birds live on the insects. Porcupines eat the bark, and deer the needles. Beaver live near groves of willow and aspen, their favorite food plants. Moose wade into ponds and eat the aquatic vegetation.

Can you think of a coniferous tree that is not evergreen?

In winter, snow is deeper than in tundra and is kept from melting by the dense shade. The snow cover protects low vegetation from cold. Branches of conifers bend with the snow until it slips off. Many animals survive by *hibernation*—lengthy periods of dormancy. Many

hibernation [hī'bər nā'shən; Latin: *hibernus*, wintry]

Figure 8 • 15   Manert Kennedy

Taiga in Canada.

others migrate southward. Hares and lynxes spread their large feet and use them like snowshoes. Deer, moose, and the caribou that arrive in autumn from the north wade through the snow on their long legs and browse on buds and twigs of the trees.

Mid-latitude deciduous forest. As you go southward in taiga, you find more and more trees with broad leaves rather than needles. These trees usually shed their leaves in the fall. In eastern North America, by the time you reach Massachusetts, southern Michigan, or southern Wisconsin, such *deciduous* trees predominate. You are in *mid-latitude deciduous forest.*

deciduous [dǐ sǐj′oõ əs; Latin: *de,* from, + *cadere,* to cut]

Because Figure 8·10 is much simplified, you will find this biome mapped at two other Southern Hemisphere areas, but they are rather different from the biome described here.

This biome is not continuous. It is found in eastern North America, in western Europe, and in eastern Asia. In the Southern Hemisphere a small area of somewhat similar forest occurs in southern Chile. The following description applies in general to all of the biomes, but the specifically mentioned organisms are North American.

In summer the sun is high in the sky and days are rather long. This combination results in the reception of much radiant energy. In June, at the latitude of Philadelphia and Peking the daily supply of radiant energy is greater than it is in the tropics at any time of the year. But, of course, in December it becomes low, so the *annual* supply of radiant energy is much less than in the tropics. Precipitation is high enough and steady enough that droughts are infrequent and not severe. In winter, snow may be heavy, but it usually melts rapidly and the ground is seldom snow-covered throughout the season. In summer, heat and humidity may both be high; but at any time, cool, dry masses of air may push down from higher latitudes.

What effects might such conditions have on producers?

There are many species of deciduous trees. The tallest of these form a canopy, an upper layer of leaves that catch the full strength of solar radiation. But leaves of deciduous trees are rather thin, and much radiation filters through the canopy. Thus there is enough light

Photos by Murray F. Buell

Winter

Spring

Summer

Fall

Figure 8 · 16

Seasons in mid-latitude
deciduous forest (New
Jersey). All of these pictures
show the same area. What
effects do these changes
have on herbivores such
as deer?

X 1/4

Figure 8 · 17
Red-eyed vireo.

deer mice. See Figure 18·26.

Acadian flycatcher. See
Figure 4·7.

ovenbird. See Figure 4·1.

How does this paragraph
illustrate the concept of niches?

puma. See Figure 2·23.

raccoon. See Figure 15·19.

skunk. See Figure 3·2.

Figure 8 · 18
Section through tropical
rain forest.

to provide light energy for another layer of trees—*understory* trees. But even these do not use all the energy, so there is a layer of shrubs beneath. And finally, close to the ground, mosses and ferns are able to utilize the remaining light.

This large mass of producers supports a large number of consumers. Squirrels collect nuts and berries from trees. Deer mice climb in the shrubs for seeds or glean fallen ones from the ground. White-tailed deer browse on shrubs and the lower branches of trees. In summer, insects are abundant in all layers of the forest, from the canopy down into the soil, and insectivorous birds prey upon them. Red-eyed vireos specialize in consuming canopy insects. Acadian flycatchers catch insects flying through the understory. Ovenbirds search out insects on the ground. Woodpeckers extract boring insects from the bark of trees.

Large predators such as bears, wolves, and pumas are now gone from most of the biome, but during the hunting season man takes their place ecologically. Animals such as raccoons and skunks eat fruits, insects, small animals, and many other things.

There are four well-defined seasons. In autumn the leaves of the deciduous trees turn yellow or orange or scarlet and finally russet brown. Then they drift downward, covering the ground with a thick mass of organic matter. Nuts and acorns fall; berries cover the understory trees and shrubs. Many mammals fatten on the abundant food, and some store it. Woodchucks form thick layers of fat and then hibernate in burrows. Reptiles, much more abundant than in taiga, also hibernate. Many insectivorous birds migrate to the tropics.

Leafless deciduous trees lose little water during periods when soil water is frozen. Many mammals rest during cold spells and resume activity when warm masses of air push in from lower latitudes. Then gnats dance in swarms above brooks, and even a few butterflies may appear in the weak midday sun. Birds, much more abundant here than in the winter taiga, consume seeds and fruits and search out dormant insects and insect eggs from crevices in tree bark.

In spring, solar radiation becomes strong before air temperatures are high enough to bring the trees into leaf. A great number of herbaceous plants spring up on the forest floor. They put forth their leaves quickly and flower; and by the time the shade from the trees has closed over them, they have finished photosynthesis for the year. With food stored in roots or underground stems, they disperse their seeds and die back to the ground until the next spring. Few plants bloom in the deep-green summer shade.

Tropical rain forest. In three separate places along the equator there is a biome called *tropical rain forest*. The largest area is centered in the Amazon Basin of South America; the second, in the East Indies; the smallest, in the Congo Basin of Africa.

In tropical rain forest the noon sun is never more than 23½° north or south of the zenith; thus, the energy supply is both large and fairly constant. Rain falls almost every day, and the humidity is always

Ralph Buchsbaum

Figure 8 · 19
Within tropical rain forest.
How can you explain the pre-
dominant color of this scene?

How are such conditions
favorable to living things?

epiphytes [ĕp′ə fīts′; Greek:
epi, upon, + phyton, a plant]

high. Temperatures vary little from month to month. Beneath the upper layer of the canopy, there is not much change in temperature
even between day and night. No other terrestrial biome has such a
uniform climate.

Vegetation deeply covers the landscape. The canopy reaches an
average height of about 50 m, but some individual trees stretch above
it to 80 m or more. Thus the vegetation is much deeper than in mid-
latitude deciduous forest (averaging 30 m), taiga (15 m), or tundra
(0.1 m at most). Beneath taller trees are shorter ones that are tolerant
of shade, and beneath these are still others that are even more shade
tolerant. Weaving together the branches are many lianas.

The trunks and branches of the trees and the twisting stems of
the lianas serve as perches for many kinds of *epiphytes*. These plants
get no nourishment from the trees—they simply use them for support.
Since epiphytes have no connection with the ground, they must get
their water and minerals elsewhere. Some have roots that absorb
moisture from the damp atmosphere in the same way that blotting
paper absorbs water. Many obtain water by catching the daily rain in
the hollows of specially adapted leaves. Mosquitoes, water beetles,
many other aquatic insects, and even a species of frog live in such
treetop puddles.

The dense layers of the always-green trees absorb most of the
light, so few plants grow on the forest floor. The trunks of trees are
supported in the damp soil by massive buttresses (Figure 8 · 19).
Lianas coil upward into the dim green of the canopy overhead. But
the way through the forest—once you are in it—is uncluttered. Only
along rivers or at the edges of clearings does a thick wall of vegeta-

Walter Chandoha

Figure 8 · 20
Epiphytes in a tropical rain
forest. These plants are
relatives of pineapple plants.

buttresses [bŭt′rĭs əz]

X 1/25

Figure 8 • 21

Steps in the locomotion (brachiating) of a gibbon. What adaptations does this animal have for arboreal life?

Why does a "wall of vegetation" occur in such places?

What environmental factors are related to the rarity of large hoofed herbivores?

arboreal [är bōr'ĭ əl; Latin: arbor, tree]

forage [fôr'ĭj]: to search for food

sequence [sē'kwəns; Latin: sequi, to follow]: here, a series of connected things

tion extend down to the ground.

Overripe fruits drop to the forest floor, forming a food supply for some ground dwellers. Dead leaves also descend continuously, because the trees release worn-out leaves a few at a time. In the ever-warm, ever-moist environment a myriad of insects, molds, and bacteria attack this food supply rapidly. Therefore, organic remains do not accumulate on the ground. Large herbivores, such as hoofed mammals, are rare or live near riverbanks. Predators and parasites are abundant at all levels of the forest.

All forests have some animals that live in the treetops—*arboreal* animals. In the tropical rain forest, animal life in the canopy is abundant. In a study of rain-forest birds, Paul Slud, of the American Museum of Natural History, found that over 90 percent foraged primarily in the canopy. For winged animals such as birds, this may not be surprising. But in tropical rain forest, a large number of mammals also are arboreal—54 percent of the species in one South American study. Moreover, there are many tree snakes, tree lizards, tree frogs, and an untold number of arboreal insects.

BIOMES AND DECREASING PRECIPITATION

The principal variable in the preceding sequence of biomes was radiant energy. In each biome, precipitation during the growing season was sufficient for the needs of plants that could tolerate the temperatures. In many biomes, however, lack of water is a limiting factor.

Mid-latitude grassland. In mid-latitude deciduous forest, drought never kills off the trees. But as you go westward in the deciduous forest of North America, you eventually leave the trees behind.

In the great expanse of country stretching roughly from the Mississippi to the Rocky Mountains and from central Canada to the Gulf of Mexico, grasses are the predominant natural vegetation. The

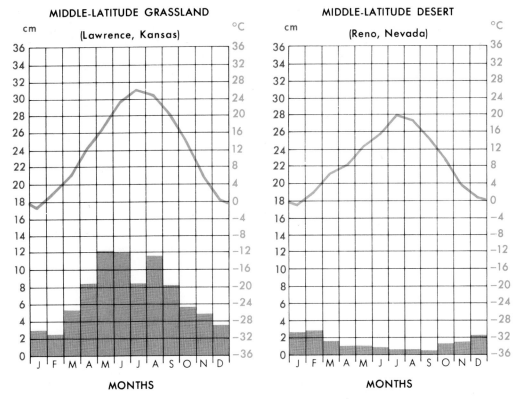

Figure 8 • 22

Compare these climatograms with those in Figure 8 • 9.

change to *mid-latitude grassland* occurs gradually; in Illinois much grassland lies east of the Mississippi, but in Missouri and Arkansas much deciduous forest extends far westward.

Because this biome stretches through the same latitudes as the deciduous forest to the east, the radiant-energy supply is similar. Temperature changes between day and night and between winter and summer are somewhat more extreme in the grassland than in the forest. The principal difference, however, is in precipitation. It is consistently less in the grassland than at the same latitudes to the east. Long droughts that grasses can tolerate but trees cannot are frequent.

The height of the grasses varies from more than 2 m in the east to only 0.5 m in the west. Though the depth of the vegetation is much less than in forest, in those parts of the grassland where moisture is relatively abundant, vegetation is very thick. And during summer the leaves of grasses grow continuously from their bases; therefore, as herbivores consume the tops, the grass crop is renewed. Many other herbaceous plants grow among the grasses, but except along watercourses woody plants are rare.

The most conspicuous first-order consumers are hoofed mam-

Use the results from Investigation 3.3 to explain this.

Harold Hungerford

Figure 8 • 23
Mid-latitude grassland
(Illinois).

Grant Heilman

Figure 8 • 24
Mid-latitude grassland
(eastern Nebraska). What
other herbivores might you
find here?

Fran Hall from Photo Researchers

Figure 8 • 25
Mid-latitude grassland
(South Dakota). How does
this grassland differ from
that shown in Figure 8 •23
and that in Figure 8 •24?

mals. Bison and pronghorns once thronged the North American grasslands; now most of them have been replaced by cattle and sheep. Less conspicuous herbivores are jackrabbits and such rodents as ground squirrels. And many kinds of insects feed upon the vegetation. At times grasshopper populations reach gigantic size; then swarms of them may devour the plants down to ground level.

Wolves and coyotes were once the chief larger predators; wolves have been nearly eliminated by man, but coyotes survive. Rattlesnakes and badgers are important predators on ground squirrels. Many insectivorous birds, such as meadowlarks, prey upon insects. Various kinds of hawks and owls prey upon small rodents and birds.

X 1/24

Figure 8 · 28
Pronghorn.

X 1/12

Figure 8 · 26
Black-tailed jackrabbit.

X 1/12

Figure 8 · 27
Badger.

Mid-latitude desert. In North America the western edge of the grassland is bordered by desert. The situation is complicated by the many mountains, but between the ranges various kinds of deserts occur from eastern Washington southward into Mexico.

The word *desert* is usually associated with low precipitation. Equally important in defining a desert climate, however, is the rate of evaporation. In deserts the evaporation rate is always high compared with the precipitation. This is partly a matter of latitude—the amount of precipitation that produces desert at the equator can support a fine grassland at higher latitudes. When precipitation does occur in desert, it is likely to be heavy but brief, and much of the water runs off instead of sinking into the soil.

Loss of heat from the earth's surface is greatly slowed down by water vapor in the air. Because desert air is very dry, the heat that builds up rapidly during the cloudless days is quickly lost again at night. Though temperatures of the air and soil surface vary greatly between day and night, temperatures underground are much more stable.

The roots of most desert plants spread far in all directions from the stems and are only a short distance below ground. When rains occur, these widespread roots soak up the moisture rapidly; the water is then stored in the tissues of the plants. Cacti, for example, store large quantities of water in their thick stems. Thorns and spines are

X 1/6

Figure 8 · 29
Meadowlark.

What does this abiotic-environment factor suggest about desert animals, especially cold-blooded ones?

You should now be able to make a generalization about the relationships between production of vegetation (in kg/hectare/year) and the abiotic environment.

David Muench

Figure 8 · 30

"Cool" desert (Nevada). What environmental factor most probably explains the distance between shrubs?

Josef Muench

Figure 8 · 31

"Hot" desert (Arizona) after spring rains.

Here are more statements of fact that require ecological explanations.

X 1/2

Figure 8 · 32

Pocket mouse.

numerous on desert plants. And most desert plants have small leaves or none at all.

Few large herbivores occur in mid-latitude deserts, but rodents are numerous. Most of these are burrowers. They obtain water in food they eat or from dew. A few—pocket mice, for example—survive with little intake of water because they use water that is produced from the chemical breakdown of foods in their bodies. As in all terrestrial biomes, insect herbivores are abundant.

Many birds and some reptiles, especially lizards, are insectivorous. Scorpions also prey upon insects. Among larger predators are coyotes, hawks, and rattlesnakes, all of which depend primarily upon rodents and rabbits for their food.

A.W. Kuchler

Figure 8 · 33
Tropical deciduous forest
(Thailand). In what season
do you think this picture was
taken?

SOME OTHER BIOMES

Tropical deciduous forest. The seasonless rain forests cover a relatively small part of the tropics. Most tropical regions have seasons;
but instead of being warm and cold seasons, they are wet and dry
seasons. Just as most of the broad-leaved trees and shrubs of high
latitudes are deciduous in winter—the season when frozen soil limits
available moisture—so many woody plants in the tropics lose their
leaves during the dry season. These plants are the basis for distinguishing a *tropical deciduous-forest biome.*

In this biome the canopy is neither as deep nor as dense as in
rain forest. Light filters all the way to the forest floor. Therefore, during
the rainy season there is a dense mass of undergrowth that man can
penetrate only by cutting his way with axes or large knives. It is this
biome that best matches the common notion of a "jungle."

Many animals go into a state of dormancy during the dry season.
This state is somewhat similar to hibernation; it is a response to unfavorable environmental conditions. But these are heat and dryness
rather than cold, so a different word—*estivation*—is used in referring
to it. Insects and reptiles, in particular, are likely to estivate.

Savanna. Where tropical dry seasons are especially long and severe, trees grow far apart, and between the trees the ground is cov-

Use Figure 8·10 to locate
regions of tropical deciduous
forest.

estivation [ĕs'tə vā'shən;
Latin: *aestas,* summer]

Figure 8 · 34

Tropical savanna in eastern Africa. Elephants, zebras, and giraffes (*background*); gnu and ostrich (*foreground*). What predators might you find here?

If you traveled from savanna to still drier regions, what changes would you expect to find in the vegetation?

hyenas. See page 106.

ered with tall grasses. This is *savanna,* a biome that covers large areas in South America and Africa.

In Africa savanna is the home of many large hoofed mammals, which graze and browse. These first-order consumers are followed by predators such as lions and leopards, and their kills are cleaned up by commensals such as hyenas and vultures.

Mid-latitude rain forest. In North America from southern Alaska to Oregon, the climate is milder—cooler in summer and warmer in winter—than we might expect at this latitude. In addition, there is much precipitation. These climatic conditions produce a *mid-latitude rain forest.*

The trees are mostly conifers, but they are much larger than those of taiga, some exceeding the height of trees in tropical rain forests. However, the canopy is much simpler than in the tropics, and there are relatively few species of trees. Lianas are uncommon. Epiphytes are abundant, but they are mostly mosses, ferns, and lichens. Shrubs are fairly numerous, but herbs are few. The ground is covered with deep cushions of moss.

Elk and deer browse on the shrubs. Many birds live largely on conifer seeds, as do many rodents. Compared with the tropical rain forest, this forest has few arboreal vertebrates, but insects are abundant. In the deep layers of humus on the forest floor there are small invertebrates that support populations of ground birds, such as thrushes.

What environmental factors explain "deep layers of humus"?

Ray Atkeson from DPI

Figure 8 • 35
Within mid-latitude rain forest (Washington).

Dennis Brokaw

Figure 8 • 36
Chaparral (California). At what season do you think this picture was taken?

chaparral |chăp'ə răl'|

To what environmental conditions do you think such leaves adapt a plant?

Chaparral. In California most of the precipitation comes in winter; summers are very dry. South Africa, western Australia, central Chile, and the region around the Mediterranean Sea have a similar climate. The biome characteristic of this climate has several names; in America the term *chaparral* is used.

Chaparral is composed of small trees and large shrubs with small, evergreen leaves that are thick and often coated with waxy material. The canopy is low and often discontinuous. Herbaceous plants have thick underground stems that survive the dry summers. Rodents and reptiles are numerous and show some of the adaptations of those in deserts. As in tropical deciduous forest, estivation occurs in the dry season.

Biomes in mountains. Because air is heated at the earth's surface, the higher the altitude, the cooler the air becomes. Temperature drops (on the average) about 2.7°C for each 500 m of elevation. So by climbing only a few hundred meters up the side of a mountain you get the effect—as far as temperature is concerned—of going many ki-

Haven Kolb

Figure 8 · 37

Zones on a mountain (Colorado). What environmental factors limit the upward range of trees?

lometers poleward. Ecosystems that resemble the circumpolar biomes of high latitudes develop as beltlike zones on mountains.

We might consider these zones as discontinuous biomes and attempt to relate them to similar biomes in less elevated regions, but
the similarities are somewhat superficial. For example, in the alpine
region of the Rockies the landscape looks much like tundra, and
many species of organisms are the same in both alpine and tundra.
But there is no permafrost in the ground, there is no long period of
darkness in the winter, and the amount of radiant energy received in
summer is much greater than that received at any time in the tundra.
It seems best, therefore, to think of mountainous regions as exceptions to the patterns of biomes, though mountainous regions from
one range to another throughout the world have many similarities.

> alpine: a mountain zone above
> the altitude to which trees grow

> Even at the equator mountains
> rise above the tree zone. Use
> geography books to find some
> such places.

BIOMES AND SUCCESSION

An ecologist standing in a coniferous forest watching a lynx leap-
ing through snow after a snowshoe hare would surely know he was in
the taiga biome. On the other hand, if he were watching a myrtle warbler in an aspen forest, a moose in a marshy pond, or some lichens
on an expanse of bare rock, he might not be so sure of the biome. Yet
he might well be standing in one of the taiga's successional ecosystems. And in any biome successional ecosystems can be found.

> Try to find successional
> ecosystems in your biome.

Events that clear an area of existing organisms provide the conditions from which succession starts. In the taiga region the great

Figure 8 • 38

Succession on rock. How might succession differ if it were to begin on a sandbar?

A
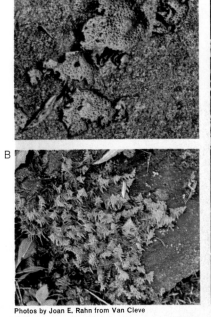
B

Photos by Joan E. Rahn from Van Cleve

C

D

Figure 8 • 39
Successional stages and animals of taiga.

crossbill
X 1/5

whitetail deer
X 1/60

porcupine
X 1/25

red squirrel
X 1/8

elk
X 1/80

meadow vole
X 1/6

bare rock ⟶ lichen ⟶ meadow ⟶ aspens ⟶ spruc

SUCCESSION FROM ROCK   CLIM

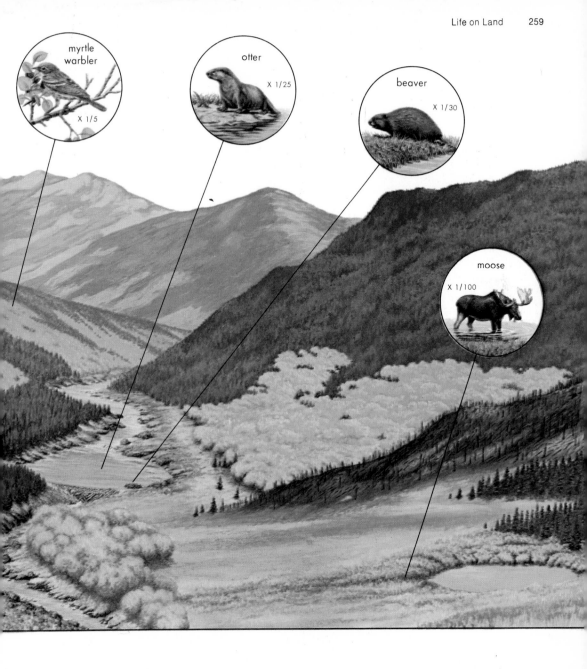

myrtle
warbler
X 1/5

otter
X 1/25

beaver
X 1/30

moose
X 1/100

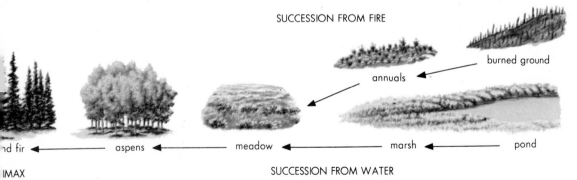

SUCCESSION FROM FIRE

burned ground

annuals

fir ← aspens ← meadow ← marsh ← pond

IMAX

SUCCESSION FROM WATER

glaciers have melted away so recently that there are still large areas of bare rock and of water surface (lakes and ponds). In all regions, erosion is constantly exposing bare rock. And fire is a normal occurrence in many biomes. Floods, blowing sand, and volcanic eruptions may also denude large areas.

If a fire burns a taiga spruce forest, not only is most life destroyed, but with it much of the organic matter of the soil. Soon, however, plants that have windblown seeds become established. At first, annual plants are most conspicuous; but within a few years they are replaced by perennials, particularly grasses and sedges, and a meadow is formed. The dead remains of these plants begin to rebuild the soil. Somewhat later, young aspen trees push up through the meadow vegetation. In the shade of this young forest, seeds of spruces and firs can germinate and the seedlings survive. After many years the conifers push up through the aspens. The shade-intolerant aspens die and the coniferous climax ecosystem is reestablished.

In the taiga biome, a succession can also start from bare rock or from the numerous taiga lakes and ponds (Figure 9 · 2). But if, within the established climax, a single spruce dies of old age, the space that it occupies is too shaded by neighboring spruces for aspen to replace it. So it is most likely that a young spruce will take its place. Thus, once established, the climax ecosystem is relatively permanent.

established [ĕs tăb'lĭshd; Latin: *stabilis*, firm]: here, become a part of an ecosystem, as discussed on page 232.

Investigation 8.2

TEMPERATURE, RAINFALL, AND BIOMES

GROUP 1
T = temperature (in degrees Celsius)   *P* = precipitation (in centimeters)

a. Tropical Deciduous Forest: Cuiabá, Brazil

	J	F	M	A	M	J	J	A	S	O	N	D
T	27.2	27.2	27.2	26.7	25.6	23.9	24.4	25.6	27.8	27.8	27.8	27.2
P	24.9	21.1	21.1	10.2	5.3	0.3	0.5	2.8	5.1	11.4	15.0	20.6

b. Chaparral: Santa Monica, California

	J	F	M	A	M	J	J	A	S	O	N	D
T	11.7	11.7	12.8	14.4	15.6	17.2	18.9	18.3	18.3	16.7	14.4	12.8
P	8.9	7.6	7.4	1.3	1.3	0.0	0.0	0.0	0.3	1.5	3.6	5.8

c. Savanna: Moshi, Tanzania

	J	F	M	A	M	J	J	A	S	O	N	D
T	23.2	23.2	22.2	21.2	19.8	18.4	17.9	18.4	19.8	21.4	22.0	22.4
P	3.6	6.1	9.2	40.1	30.2	5.1	5.1	2.5	2.0	3.0	8.1	6.4

d. Tropical Desert: Aden, Aden

	J	F	M	A	M	J	J	A	S	O	N	D
T	24.6	25.1	26.4	28.5	30.6	31.9	31.1	30.3	31.1	28.8	26.5	25.1
P	0.8	0.5	1.3	0.5	0.3	0.3	0.0	0.3	0.3	0.3	0.3	0.3

BACKGROUND INFORMATION

Climatograms show monthly variations in only 2 climatic factors. Other factors may greatly affect climate, but a climatogram does give a rough idea of climate in the location from which the data were obtained.

By daily observation you can easily associate the climate of your own locality with the biome found there. Only by extensive travel, however, can the relationship of particular climates with particular biomes be learned on a worldwide basis. This investigation is a poor substitute for such travel; but if it is carried out thoughtfully and with frequent reference to pictures and descriptions of biomes, it can help you to visualize relationships between the abiotic and biotic features in some of the earth's major ecosystems.

MATERIALS

graph paper, 3 to 17 sheets per student

PROCEDURE

First, draw climatograms from the data in Group 1. When these are completed, you will have 10 climatograms (6 being on pages 237 and 249) that represent the major land biomes of Earth.

Second, obtain monthly averages of precipitation and temperature from the weather station closest to your school. Because the National Weather Service of the United States is one of the very few still reporting in British units, these data will be expressed as inches of precipitation and as degrees Fahrenheit. Therefore, you will need to convert the data to centimeters of precipitation and degrees Celsius. To do this, use the information in Appendix 1. Then from the local data draw a climatogram.

Third, from the data in Group 2 draw climatograms as they are assigned by your teacher.

GROUP 2

		J	F	M	A	M	J	J	A	S	O	N	D
a.	T	1.1	1.7	6.1	12.2	17.8	22.2	25.0	23.3	20.0	13.9	7.8	2.2
	P	8.1	7.6	8.9	8.4	9.2	9.9	11.2	10.2	7.9	7.9	6.4	7.9
b.	T	10.6	11.1	12.2	14.4	15.6	19.4	21.1	21.7	20.0	16.7	13.9	11.1
	P	9.1	8.9	8.6	6.6	5.1	2.0	0.5	0.5	3.6	8.4	10.9	10.4
c.	T	25.6	25.6	24.4	25.0	24.4	23.3	23.3	24.4	24.4	25.0	25.6	25.6
	P	25.8	24.9	31.0	16.5	25.4	18.8	16.8	11.7	22.1	18.3	21.3	29.2
d.	T	12.8	15.0	18.3	21.1	25.0	29.4	32.8	32.2	28.9	22.2	16.1	13.3
	P	1.0	1.3	1.0	0.3	0.0	0.0	0.3	1.3	0.5	0.5	0.8	1.0
e.	T	−3.9	−2.2	1.7	8.9	15.0	20.0	22.8	21.7	16.7	11.1	5.0	−0.6
	P	2.3	1.8	2.8	2.8	3.2	5.8	5.3	3.0	3.6	2.8	4.1	3.3
f.	T	19.4	18.9	18.3	16.1	15.0	13.3	12.8	13.3	14.4	15.0	16.7	17.8
	P	0.0	0.0	1.5	0.5	8.9	14.7	12.2	8.1	2.0	1.0	0.3	0.8
g.	T	−22.2	−22.8	−21.1	−14.4	−3.9	1.7	5.0	5.0	1.1	−3.9	−10.0	−17.2
	P	1.0	1.3	1.8	1.5	1.5	1.3	2.3	2.8	2.8	2.8	2.8	1.3
h.	T	11.7	12.8	17.2	20.6	23.9	27.2	28.3	28.3	26.1	21.1	16.1	12.2
	P	3.6	4.1	4.6	6.9	8.1	6.9	6.4	6.6	8.9	5.1	5.6	4.6

(Group 2 is continued on page 262.)

i.	T	23.3	22.2	19.4	15.6	11.7	8.3	8.3	9.4	12.2	15.1	18.9	21.7
	P	5.1	5.6	6.6	5.6	2.8	0.9	2.5	4.1	5.8	5.8	5.1	5.3
j.	T	17.2	18.9	21.1	22.8	23.3	22.2	21.1	21.1	20.6	19.4	18.9	17.2
	P	0.3	0.5	1.5	3.6	8.6	9.2	9.4	11.4	10.9	5.3	0.8	0.3
k.	T	−20.0	−18.9	−12.2	−2.2	5.6	12.2	16.1	15.0	10.6	3.9	−5.6	−15.0
	P	3.3	2.3	2.8	2.5	4.6	5.6	6.1	8.4	7.4	4.6	2.8	2.8
l.	T	−0.6	2.2	5.0	10.0	13.3	18.3	23.3	22.2	16.1	10.6	4.4	0.0
	P	1.5	1.3	1.3	1.0	1.5	0.8	0.3	0.5	0.8	1.0	0.8	1.5

STUDYING THE DATA

Compare the climatogram based on local data with the 10 climatograms on pages 237 and 249 and in Group 1. • Which one of these does your local climatogram most nearly resemble?(1) • In what ways are they similar? In what ways are they different?(2) • Do they represent the same biome? If so, which is it?(3) • If they do not, what climatic differences account for the biome differences? If they do, what characteristics of climate seem to be related to characteristics of living things in your biome?(4)

Now attempt to associate biomes with the climatograms drawn from data in Group 2. In doing this, you will use generalizations made from studying climatograms of known biomes. Of course, you are working with only 2 variables; you have no data concerning winds or cloudiness, and you can only judge humidity indirectly. Nevertheless, by careful thinking you can make fairly accurate deductions.

Write the name of your hypothesized biome at the top of each graph. • For each biome relate the characteristics of its biota to the characteristics of its climate.(5) Afterward your teacher may give you the location of the places from which the data came. You can then check your reasoning.

GEOGRAPHIC RANGES AND HISTORY

polar bears. See Figure 4·5.

penguins. See page 112.

In polar regions of the Arctic and Antarctic, climate and other abiotic environmental factors are very similar. Yet only in the Arctic do polar bears roam the ice floes; in the Antarctic they are absent. Only in the Antarctic do penguins waddle about; in the Arctic there are none. Why are there no polar bears near the South Pole, no penguins near the North Pole?

From these and numerous other examples we must conclude that climates and other environmental factors do not entirely explain geographic ranges of organisms. Because an organism *can* live in a particular place does not necessarily mean that it *does* live there. To understand the geographic ranges of polar bears, penguins, and numerous other organisms, we must seek facts in addition to those from ecology.

We can start our search with two hypotheses: (1) all species once occurred everywhere and later disappeared from some places, or

(2) each species originated in a particular place and then spread into other places. For the first of these hypotheses biologists have no evidence; for the second the evidence is strong. Study of fossils from all parts of the world indicates that species populations originated in rather small areas and then spread.

DISPERSAL

If his fences are not kept in good repair, every farmer knows that his cattle will wander away. In all populations this tendency of living things to spread from places where they are to places where they are not may be observed.

In the case of motile organisms, such *dispersal* may be accomplished by flying, swimming, walking, running, crawling, or burrowing. In the case of nonmotile organisms, dispersal is passive. Seeds, spores, and eggs remain alive but in a dormant state for long periods. During this time they may be carried great distances in currents of air or water, or in mud on the foot of a bird. Even motile organisms may be passively transported much farther than they could actively travel.

dispersal [dĭs pûr'səl; Latin: *dis-*, apart, + *spargere*, to scatter]

passive: inactive but acted upon

How does this relate to the statement on page 202 about the geographical distribution of pond microorganisms?

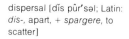
Carl Gans

Figure 8 • 40
The thick husk of a coconut is an excellent float. What do you predict if this scene is in Florida? In Massachusetts?

A polar bear may be carried hundreds of kilometers on floating ice. A spider attached to strands of its silk may be blown a long way by air currents.

Dispersal alone, of course, does not change a species' geographic range. Unless the organism survives and reproduces in the new location, its range has not changed.

BARRIERS

Since every kind of organism has some means of dispersal, either active or passive, it would be reasonable to expect that eventually every species might be found in every place on Earth where conditions occur that are ecologically favorable for it. Actually, such a broad geographic range is the exception rather than the rule. What, then, limits the dispersal of organisms? In the case of pastured cattle, it is a fence—a *barrier.* In nature, too, barriers of one kind or another are effective, to varying degrees, in preventing dispersal.

This is exactly what has happened in the case of at least one macroscopic species. Which?

A species' means of dispersal determines what will be a barrier for it. For most terrestrial animals, large areas of water are effective barriers. For most aquatic organisms, land areas are equally effective. Within a land area, mountains are barriers to many organisms.

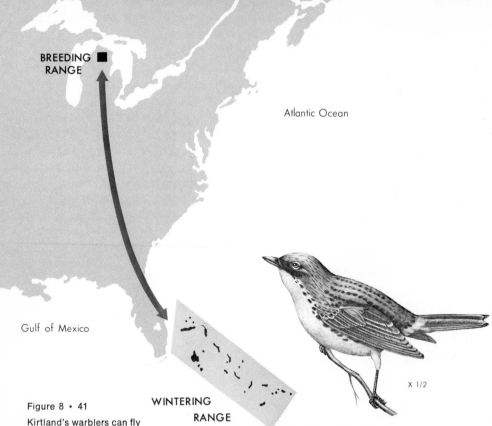

BREEDING RANGE ■

Atlantic Ocean

Gulf of Mexico

WINTERING RANGE

X 1/2

Figure 8 · 41
Kirtland's warblers can fly very well, yet they are found only in the small areas shown on the map. How might you explain this situation?

What barrier has probably kept tsetse flies out of South America?

See Figure 8·3.

What are some tree species that have seeds easily carried by wind?

Besides such physical barriers there are ecological barriers. For organisms adapted to life in a forest, a region of grassland or desert may be a barrier. And for grassland species, a forest region may limit dispersal.

Some barriers are best described as behavioral. It seems reasonable to suppose, for instance, that flying birds would be found almost everywhere. But many birds that can fly great distances remain inhabitants of very restricted regions. The Amazon River, in Brazil, serves as the northern or southern boundary of the ranges of many forest birds. Undoubtedly most of these birds *could* fly across the river, but they do not.

An increase in the population of a motile species encourages emigration into less densely populated areas. Then dispersal may take place rapidly. But the actual rate depends upon the barriers that are encountered. When barriers are great, dispersal may be slow even though the population is increasing rapidly. In passive dispersal the means of transportation may be the most important factor in determining rate of spread. Species of trees whose seeds are carried away and buried by squirrels have been estimated to spread about 1.6 km every thousand years. By contrast, organisms swept up in a tornado may be carried 30 km in a few hours.

RESULTS

If our reasoning is correct, we can now explain the absence of polar bears from the Antarctic as follows: Polar bears originated in the Arctic. Their ecological requirements are such that the tropical environment is a barrier to their dispersal. Throughout the existence of the polar-bear species, this wide barrier has existed, and thus far no part of the population has been able to move across it. So no polar bears are found in the Antarctic. Similar reasoning can be applied to the dispersal of penguins.

X 1/13

Figure 8 • 42
Cattle egret. This native of Africa is now found in much of America. Try to find out how it got here.

ICE
LIMIT
1916

Bettmann

Figure 8 • 43
A changing barrier. Dispersal of plants at the retreating edge of Mendenhall Glacier, Alaska.

MAN'S INFLUENCE ON TERRESTRIAL ECOSYSTEMS

Flying from Cleveland, Ohio, to Louisville, Kentucky, you cross the mid-latitude deciduous-forest biome, but you see only a few traces of forest. Flying from Chicago, Illinois, to Lincoln, Nebraska, you cross

Figure 8 · 44
Man's activities radically change natural biomes. (*A*) In this view (Ohio), little of the deciduous forest remains. (*B*) In this view (Iowa), little of the grassland remains. Which represents a greater change in the landscape?

the eastern part of the North American grassland, but here, too, you see only traces of the original climax ecosystem. In fact, in these two flights the landscapes below appear to be remarkably alike. Although in both cases climate remains an important factor, the chief molder of the present landscape has been man.

MAN AS AN AGENT OF DISPERSAL

Man has wandered more widely than any other organism, and in his travels he has carried other organisms with him. At first, perhaps, this meant merely the dispersal of his parasites, such as lice, and his commensals, such as mice and rats.

However, since man started the cultivation of plants, perhaps 10,000 years ago, he has become a deliberate agent of dispersal and one that has carried many organisms over barriers they might never have crossed otherwise. Oranges and lemons have been taken from

deliberate [dĭ lĭb′ər ĭt; Latin: *de*, from, + *librare*, to weigh]: done after weighing the facts and arguments

INTRODUCED INTO
NEW YORK CITY
IN 1890

x 1/5

Figure 8 · 45

Expansion of the range of the European starling in North America. It now extends to the Pacific.

Choose several domesticated animals or plants; find out where they originated and how they reached your region.

southeastern Asia and made an important part of landscapes in all the warmer regions of the earth. Wheat and barley have been taken from southwestern Asia and made to replace thousands of square kilometers once covered by forest. Cattle and horses from Asian grasslands now graze in almost every biome except tundra.

Man has also continued to disperse organisms unintentionally. Dandelions and hundreds of weeds have been carried along with crop plants. Modern airplane travel has made easy the rapid dispersal of many insects and microorganisms.

To transport banana plants to Pennsylvania in hopes of establishing a plantation is ecologically absurd. But it is not always so easy to determine whether an organism that man carries into a new area will thrive or fail. In some cases, organisms have easily become part of the ecosystems in the new areas. Wild orange thickets now thrive in many parts of the tropics. After man introduced a few European rabbits to Australia, they quickly spread without further help over much of the continent. In other cases, however, the organisms dispersed by man exist only through his continued protection. There has been wheat in England for two thousand years, but it soon disappears there when it is not cultivated. Dozens of species of European birds have been transported to North America, but less than half a dozen have become a real part of the North American biota.

What are they?

On the whole, success in transplantation of species by man is less frequent than failure. But there is always danger that in a new environment an organism may thrive *too* well to suit man's interests. The Australian rabbits became a disastrous pest in pastures. The fungus *Endothia parasitica,* unintentionally transported from Japan,

USDA

Figure 8 • 46

Plant quarantine. Foreign mail containing plants is examined by U.S. Department of Agriculture inspectors.

quarantine [kwôr′ən tēn′]

Many of the weeds of cultivated fields in eastern North America are immigrant species from Eurasia. Can you explain this?

erosion [ĭ rō′zhən; Latin: *e*, from, away, + *rodere*, to grow]

destroyed the valuable North American chestnut tree. Therefore, governments now require careful studies of the ecological relationships of any plant or animal that is proposed for introduction into a new area. And most governments have set up quarantine services to inspect automobiles, ships, and planes in hopes of preventing accidental introduction of organisms that might be undesirable.

CULTIVATION

By transporting organisms and then carefully cultivating them in new regions, man has changed ecosystems. In some cases the change has been small. Wheat, a grass from Asia, adapts well to the former grassland of Kansas because its tolerances are similar to those of the native grasses. And a Kansas wheat field is not unlike the native grassland it replaces except that it is composed of one species instead of a mixture of many. Wheat fields also do well in Virginia. But there man had to remove deciduous forest to plant the wheat. To the organisms that were a part of the Virginia forest ecosystem, the wheat-field ecosystem is an intolerable place to live, but organisms of the Kansas grassland can in many cases adapt to the wheat-field ecosystem.

In many parts of the world, man has changed ecosystems by cultivation even more than in the Virginia example. In some places he has actually made agricultural land: the Dutch have drained land once covered by the sea; the Filipinos have built terraces for rice on steep slopes in tropical forest. In many countries complex irrigation systems have been used to transform deserts into agricultural lands. For example, the thousands of hectares of irrigated land in the United States yield a considerable percentage of the country's total agricultural production.

Sometimes man has had setbacks in his attempts to spread his cultivated ecosystems. In the shortgrass plains of the North American grassland, there are periodic droughts and strong winds. The native grasses survived the droughts, and their matted roots protected the soil from erosion by the wind. But in the early part of the 20th cen-

Monsanto Company

Figure 8 • 47

The difference that irrigation makes (California). Where do you think the water comes from?

Figure 8 · 48
Dust-storm damage (Oklahoma), April, 1936.

tury, man rapidly plowed up the grasslands and established cultivated fields. Then, in the 1930's and again in the 1950's, great years-long droughts occurred. With the perennial grasses gone and the cultivated crops destroyed by drought, winds swept up the dry topsoil in great dust storms that left many areas barren. With the return of normal rains, neither the cultivated crops nor the native grasses could be easily reestablished on the remaining soil.

MAN AND SUCCESSION

What occurred in the shortgrass plains was only a case of setting a biome back to an early stage of succession. Many of man's activities do this. Plowing exposes bare earth. Dams and dikes cover land with water. The hundreds of hectares of concrete and asphalt paving that are laid down as roads each year in the United States create a kind of bare-rock condition that is similar to the result of an earthquake or landslide. And lumbering sets back succession several stages, much as does a lightning-set fire.

See Figure 3 · 19.

Figure 8 · 49
A lodgepole-pine forest (Wyoming). What is happening here?

It has sometimes been said that man's cultivated lands are a kind of artificial grassland biome. Is it more reasonable to say that a wheat field in Virginia is an artificial grassland ecosystem or that it is an early stage in a succession toward deciduous forest? Perhaps either viewpoint might be supported. Figure 8·44 might be used as evidence of the first. But suppose a Virginia wheat field is abandoned. In the first year, we can observe that the field becomes covered with annual weeds, such as ragweed. In the second year, perennial plants —goldenrods, asters, and grasses—become conspicuous. By the third or fourth year, young woody plants—shrubs and tree seedlings —are large enough to be seen among the herbs. Within a decade young trees shade out the earlier perennial herbs. As the trees grow larger, their fallen leaves begin to form a humus soil in which seeds of forest herbs and shrubs can germinate. And after a century of such succession, some abandoned Virginia fields have today actually developed an ecosystem that can be distinguished from climax deciduous forest only by an experienced ecologist.

X 1/8

Figure 8 · 50
Ragweed.

Investigation 8.3

EFFECTS OF FIRE ON BIOMES

BACKGROUND INFORMATION

Fire is an important ecological factor in terrestrial ecosystems. Some fires start from natural causes—lightning and volcanoes, for example—but many are caused by man, deliberately or accidentally. In whatever way they begin, fires have many effects upon the organisms in their paths. The most easily observed effects are on vegetation.

PROCEDURE

As you read each of the following sections, base your answers to the questions upon study of the pictures in Figure 8·51, 8·52, and 8·53.

A. Fire in mid-latitude grassland. Figures 8·51A to 8·51D picture a series of events that often occur in the southern part of the North American grassland. Two populations are involved: grasses of various species and mesquite shrubs. Study Figures 8·51A and 8·51B. • Which population is increasing in size?(1) Roots of mesquite have been found in mine shafts many meters below the surface of the soil. • What competitive advantage might this kind of root growth give mesquite over grasses?(2) • If the trend shown in these 2 pictures continued, what kind of community might result?(3)

Now refer to Figures 8·51C and 8·51D. In these figures plant parts shown in yellow at or below ground level represent unharmed tissue. • Do both kinds of plants survive fires?(4) • In which kind has more growing tissue been killed?(5) Grasses usually reach maturity and produce seeds in 1 or 2 years; mesquite usually requires 4 to 10 years. • Which kind of plant has lost more in terms of growing time?(6) • In Figure 8·51D which kind of plant occupies most of the land?(7) • What might you expect this area to look like 4 or 5 years after a fire?(8)

Now you can make a generalization on the effect of fire in this community. • Describe the probable landscape if fires did not occur

Figure 8 · 51

at all.(9) • What would be the appearance of the landscape if fires occurred every few years?(10)   • What environmental factor seems to be necessary for maintaining grassland in this region?(11)

B. Fire in a forest of the Great Lakes region. Around the Great Lakes of North America is a region of transition between taiga and mid-latitude deciduous forest. In many places much of the forest consists of pines (Figure

8 · 52A). But early in his settlement of the region, European man brought about a great change in the landscape (Figure 8 · 52B). • What was this change?(12) Fires had apparently been rare in this region, but following the change they became more frequent. • What might have brought about the increase in number of fires?(13)   • If fire does not occur, what might the area shown in Figure 8 · 52B look like in later years?(14)

Figure 8 · 52

Study Figures 8·52B, 8·52C, and 8·52D, which picture jack pine.   • What characteristic of jack pine gives that species a competitive advantage when there is a fire?(15)   • Describe the probable appearance of the area shown in Figure 8·52D 5 or 6 years later.(16)   Jack pines produce cones in 8 to 10 years but do not live to a very great age. Their seedlings do not thrive in shade. Suppose no further fires occur for 200 years.

Figure 8 · 53

• What changes in appearance might take place in this area during that period?(17) Suppose fires occur about once every 20 years. • What might the area look like at the end of 200 years?(18)

C. Fire in a forest of the southeastern United States. In the southeastern United States there are extensive forests in which longleaf pine is almost the only large tree, though seedlings and saplings of deciduous trees often occur. Until they are from 3 to 7 years old, young longleaf pines look somewhat like clumps of grass (Figure 8 • 53A). While in this "grass stage," the young trees develop deep roots in which a reserve supply of food is stored.

Fires in these forests generally are confined to the ground, where they burn grasses and the sparse growth of deciduous shrubs and saplings (Figure 8 • 53B). • What is the effect of fire on young longleaf pines in the "grass stage"?(19) • What is the effect on the deciduous shrubs and saplings?(20) • Which plants have a competitive advantage after a fire?(21) After the "grass stage," longleaf pines grow rapidly in height and develop a thick bark that resists scorching. • What is the effect of ground fires at this stage in the development of the pines (Figure 8 • 53C)? (22) • Which plants have a competitive advantage when fires do not occur (Figure 8 • 53D)?(23) • What factor seems to maintain a forest of longleaf pines within the deciduous-forest biome?(24)

DISCUSSION

Knowledge of ecological effects of fire on biomes can be useful to man. • If you were interested in raising cattle in the region described in Procedure A, would occasional fires be an advantage or a disadvantage? Why?(25) Jack pine is not as valuable a lumber tree as are other trees of the Great Lakes region. • If you were a landowner in that region, would fire be an advantage or a disadvantage? Why?(26) • If you were interested in maintaining a longleaf-pine forest to obtain turpentine, would ground fires be an advantage or a disadvantage? Why?(27) Suppose you wanted bobwhites (game birds that nest on the ground) in your turpentine forest • What effect might this have on your management of the forest?(28)

• What things must ecologists know before deciding whether to recommend fire as a method of management to a landowner?(29)

FOR FURTHER INVESTIGATION

Investigation 8.3 is based on "The Ecology of Fire," by C. F. Cooper (*Scientific American*, April, 1961). The article also discusses fire in Douglas-fir forests of the Northwest and in ponderosa-pine forests of the Southwest. Other information may be found in Gleason and Cronquist (see "Suggested Readings") and in books on forestry and range management. Prepare a comprehensive report on fire as a factor in terrestrial ecosystems.

GUIDE QUESTIONS

1. How are the ideas expressed by the ecological terms "biota" and "geographical range" related?

2. What must occur if a species is to survive as part of a particular ecosystem?

3. Why is it difficult to make precise measurements of an organism's tolerance for any single environmental factor?

4. A species may be able to survive a given set of abiotic conditions in an ecosystem but still not become a part of the ecosystem. Explain.

5. What are biomes?

6. What factors help to explain the abundant summer life in the tundra and the sparse winter life?

7. What structural and functional adaptations to long, severe winters are found among tundra organisms?

8. What is the most noticeable difference between tundra and taiga landscapes?

9. Why does taiga have many lakes and ponds?

10. What is hibernation?

11. What is the most noticeable difference between mid-latitude deciduous-forest and taiga landscapes?

12. Why must understory trees be more tolerant of shade than are trees of the canopy?

13. How do seasons affect the biological characteristics of landscapes in mid-latitude deciduous forest?

14. Contrast vegetation in mid-latitude deciduous forest with that of tropical rain forest and explain the difference.

15. What are epiphytes?

16. Explain the presence of large numbers of arboreal animals in tropical rain forest.

17. What climatic factor is chiefly reponsible for the presence of grasslands in the same latitudes with forests?

18. Many grassland animals are runners or burrowers. Explain.

19. What two abiotic environmental factors must be considered together in describing desert climate?

20. How are plants adapted to desert conditions?

21. What is the principal climatic factor related to the presence of deciduous trees in the tropics?

22. Compare and contrast hibernation and estivation.

23. If you went from savanna toward a region of greater precipitation, what changes would you expect in the vegetation?

24. Describe vegetation in mid-latitude rain forest by comparing it with that in mid-latitude deciduous forest and that in tropical rain forest.

25. What is chaparral?

26. How do conditions in an alpine ecosystem on mid-latitude mountains resemble conditions in the tundra? In what ways do the two sets of conditions differ?

27. What kinds of conditions start ecological succession?

28. What is meant by a climax ecosystem?

29. In addition to knowledge of biological tolerances, what information is needed to explain the geographic distribution of species?

30. What are some of the ways in which dispersal of organisms occurs?

31. How can a barrier to the dispersal of one species be a pathway for dispersal of another species?

32. In what ways has man acted as an agent of dispersal for other organisms?

33. How have the activities of man tended to produce "grassland landscapes" in mid-latitude deciduous forests and "deserts" in grasslands?

34. How can a study of succession reveal the biome pattern in a region that has been greatly modified by man?

35. Using fire as an example, explain how an abiotic environmental factor can have different effects in different ecosystems.

PROBLEMS

1. Make a list of terrestrial organisms that have been brought into your locality by man. Divide the list into two parts, as follows: (a) organisms that (in your opinion) survive because of man's activities, and (b) organisms that (in your opinion) would survive without man. Give reasons for your placement of each organism on the list.

2. Choose some small taxonomic groups (genera or families) that are present in your own state or locality. Investigate their distribution in the world as a whole, and construct maps to show this information. Try to explain the distribution shown on your maps.

3. A plant is growing in each of the following cities at the time of year indicated. In each list, arrange the cities in order of decreasing solar energy (from the one in which the plant receives the most solar energy at noon to the one in which it receives the least). (a) At the June solstice (vertical ray of the sun at the Tropic of Cancer): Winnipeg, Canada; New Orleans, Louisiana; Rio de Janeiro, Brazil; Anchorage, Alaska; Havana, Cuba; Caracas, Venezuela; Boston, Massachusetts. (b) At the December solstice (vertical ray of the sun at the Tropic of Capricorn): Singapore, Singapore; Hobart, Tasmania; Tokyo, Japan; Vladivostok, Soviet Union; Manila, Philippines; Brisbane, Australia; Canton, China; Little America, Antarctica. (c) At the equinox (vertical ray of the sun at the equator): Tananarive, Malagasy;

Cape Town, South Africa; Madrid, Spain; Nairobi, Kenya; Murmansk, Soviet Union; Copenhagen, Denmark; Cairo, Egypt. (d) To compare the possible amounts of photosynthesis in the plants per day, what additional information would you need?

4. In North America and Europe, a number of species of migratory birds now live at much higher latitudes during winter than they did 50 years ago. How might you explain this?

5. Before Europeans settled the grasslands of Australia, kangaroos were the ecological equivalents there of the bison of the North American grasslands. In other words, these animals had similar niches in the community structure of their regions—they were the largest grazing herbivores. (a) What are the ecological equivalents of these animals in most of the Australian and North American grasslands today? (b) What were the ecological equivalents of these animals in the steppes of Asia, the pampa of Argentina, and the veldt of South Africa before these regions were highly modified by man? (c) What are the ecological equivalents of these animals in the tundra? (d) In the desert of South Africa, what are the ecological equivalents of the cacti of North American deserts? (e) In the tropical forests of the Old World, what are the ecological equivalents of the hummingbirds of the New World tropical forests?

6. Explanations of the present geographic ranges of organisms may depend not only upon expansion from former ranges but also upon contractions of former ranges. What are some of the factors that might bring about contraction of ranges?

7. Make a series of photographs to illustrate succession in your biome.

8. The dispersal of starlings in North America is shown in Figure 8 · 45. Investigate these additional cases of dispersal: in North America—house sparrows, Japanese beetles, cotton-boll weevils, fungus of chestnut blight, gypsy moths; in Europe—muskrats, the Chinese mitten crab; in the islands of the Indian and Pacific oceans—giant African land snails.

9. Describe what you think would happen if man were removed from the following places: (a) a farm in Nebraska; (b) a sidewalk in New York; (c) a swimming pool in Seattle, Washington; (d) a landscaped park in Las Vegas, Nevada.

10. What factors of the lunar environment must astronauts overcome?

SUGGESTED READINGS

BARTHOLOMEW, G. A., and J. W. HUDSON, "Desert Ground Squirrels," *Scientific American,* November, 1961. Pp. 107–112+.

BATES, M. *The Forest and the Sea.* New York: Random House, Inc., 1960. Chapters 7 and 8: (A whole chapter on the tropical rain forest; then a contrasting chapter on biomes at middle latitudes. Fairly easy.)

BELL, R. H. V. "A Grazing Ecosystem in the Serengeti," *Scientific American,* May, 1971. Pp. 20–29.

ELTON, C. S. *The Ecology of Invasions by Animals and Plants.* New York: John Wiley & Sons, Inc., 1958. (Explains the ecological principles involved in dispersal and the establishment of organisms in new regions. Fairly easy.)

GLEASON, H. A., and A. CRONQUIST. *The Natural Geography of Plants.* New York: Columbia University Press, 1964. (The principles of plant distribution, with examples mostly from North America. Medium difficulty.)

GUTHRIE, R. D., and P. A. ZAHL. "A Look at Alaska's Tundra," *National Geographic,* March, 1972. Pp. 293–337.

HAAG, W. G. "The Bering Strait Land Bridge," *Scientific American,* January, 1962. Pp. 112–120+.

HARTESVELDT, R. J. "Fire Ecology of the Giant Sequoias," *Natural History,* December, 1964. Pp. 12–19.

KENDEIGH, S. C. *Animal Ecology.* Englewood Cliffs, N.J.: Prentice-Hall, Inc., 1961. Chapters 22–27. (A thorough description of biomes and their subdivisions. Fairly advanced.)

KILBURN, P. D. "Floras of the Tundra," *Natural History,* August, 1965. Pp. 52–59.

PRUITT, W. O. "Animals in the Snow," *Scientific American,* January, 1960. Pp. 60–68.

SIMPSON, G. G., and W. S. BECK. *Life: An Introduction to Biology.* Shorter ed. New York: Harcourt, Brace & World, Inc., 1969. Pp. 442–474. (Brief but well-expressed descriptions of biomes, with some consideration of the principles of biome distribution. Rather advanced.)

Life in the Water

THE HYDROSPHERE

"Planet Ocean" might be a better name than "Planet Earth." Whatever we call it, our planet, when viewed from outer space, is blue with water and water vapor.

All this water makes up the **hydrosphere,** just as all the air makes up the atmosphere. The hydrosphere is a vast heat reservoir; it absorbs, stores, and circulates the heat that results when solar radiant energy strikes the earth. It is also a reservoir of chemical elements and compounds. These are continuously being dissolved in waters that eventually drain into the oceans. And all the evidence from fossils indicates that ocean waters were the original home of life. In short, the hydrosphere is the center of biosphere events; terrestrial happenings are a sideshow.

hydrosphere [hī′drə sfĭr′; Greek: *hydor,* water, + *sphaira,* sphere]

reservoir [rĕz′ər vôr′]: a place where something is kept in quantity

NASA

Figure 9 • 1

Earth as seen from space.

Man, however, is a terrestrial organism. Historically, the majority of human beings have cared little about the great water area of the planet. And those who have cared have mainly just skimmed a little food from the edges of bodies of water or used the surface as a means of getting from one piece of land to another. Now, as terrestrial sources of foods and materials are becoming scarcer, man needs to use the hydrosphere as never before. Therefore, scientists in recent years have increased their attempts to understand aquatic environments and the organisms that inhabit them—aquatic ecosystems.

Environmental conditions a thousand meters beneath the surface of the ocean must certainly differ from those in a roadside puddle. Yet there is life in both of these extreme examples of aquatic ecosystems and in a multitude of intermediate ones. To make sense of the many observations that have been made in studies of aquatic ecosystems, we must again seek patterns—just as we did for terrestrial ecosystems.

The distinction between ocean waters and inland waters may serve as a beginning. In general, we can think of ocean waters as those forming the great interconnecting system that surrounds the continents and in which tides are clearly evident. Inland waters are the waters on the surface of the land. Being above the level of the oceans (with a few exceptions), they tend to flow downward to the oceans. Ocean waters usually contain a considerable amount of dissolved minerals; inland waters usually contain very little. But, again, there are exceptions.

INLAND WATERS

Inland waters are affected in many ways by the surrounding land, but they also have their own environmental characteristics. Puddles in South Dakota, Germany, and Australia contain very much the same kinds of protists. And, though the delta of the Nile is surrounded by desert and the delta of the Mississippi by forest, environmental conditions are similar within the slow-moving, warm, muddy waters of both places.

Inland-water ecosystems are grouped by *limnologists* as standing waters or as flowing waters. As is usual in ecological classification, the boundary between these is not sharp. A pond is an example of standing water. But most ponds are fed by springs or brooks and most have outlets, so some current of changing water passes through them. On the other hand, a river is an example of flowing water; yet in some places a river may have such a slow current that careful observation is necessary to detect it.

STANDING WATERS

Standing inland waters range in size from roadside puddles to the Caspian Sea. Puddles may last for only a few days or weeks; ponds,

---

In what places have people made the most use of aquatic food resources?

intermediate: between extremes

Where are some exceptions?

Where are some exceptions?

A good atlas will be useful while you study this chapter.

delta: so called because the deposit of soil at a river mouth is usually triangular, resembling the Greek letter "delta" (see page 39)

limnologists [lĭm nŏl' ə jĭsts; Greek: *limne*, marsh]: scientists who study the biology of fresh waters

Haven Kolb

Figure 9 · 2
This was once a taiga pond.
What happened to it?

for a few hundred to a few thousand years. In general, lakes are older. Standing waters vary from very shallow to very deep, from clear to muddy, and from fresh to salty.

A pond. In many parts of the United States, there are no natural ponds. But where natural ponds are fewest, man has been most active in constructing artificial ones. To gain a general understanding of inland waters, it does not matter much whether you study a pond that is natural or one that is artificial. As an example, we shall describe a natural pond in a region where such ponds are numerous—the northeastern United States. As you read, try to compare this pond with one you know.

See Figure 9 · 15.

We are standing on a hill overlooking the pond. As we walk down the tree-covered slope, mosquitoes start to annoy us; they began their life in the pond. We come out from the trees into a tangle of low shrubs. As we push our way through willows and alders, the ground becomes increasingly wet. As we leave the last shrubs behind us, our feet sink into mud. Before us lies a marsh of sedges and cattails with shallow water lapping about their stems. Dragonflies—lately emerged from the water—dart about; frogs sit on driftwood; a water snake slithers through the mixture of mud and water. A muskrat interrupts its meal of cattail stems and shuffles away. With wading boots, we can follow the muskrat through the cattails. At last we see the open water surface. Here and there it is dotted with leaves of water lilies. With our boots in deep mud and with water lapping at knee level, we are now in the midst of the pond ecosystem.

emerged [ĭ mûrjd′; Latin: *ex*, out of, + *mergere*, to dip]: risen out of (here) water

In studying any ecosystem, an ecologist first looks for its source of biotic energy. In a pond ecosystem the most important producers are not the most obvious ones. The large emergent plants such as cattails are conspicuous, but these produce little of the food in the ecosystem. Indeed, in some ponds—especially in artificial ones— emergent plants may be scarce or absent. Beyond the rim of emergent plants, we see many plants within the water itself—some floating on the surface, some submerged. Though such plants may become so

emergent [ĭ mûr′jənt]

submerged [səb mûrjd′; Latin: *sub*, under, + *mergere*]

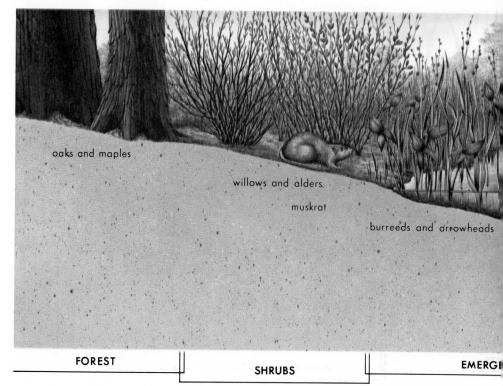

oaks and maples

willows and alders

muskrat

burreeds and arrowheads

FOREST   **SHRUBS**   **EMERGI**

Figure 9 • 3

Cross section through the edge of a natural pond in the northeastern United States.

erratically [ĭ răt′ĭk lĭ; Latin: *errare,* to wander]

Victor Hensen: 1835–1924. German zoologist

numerous at times that their thick mass may hamper a swimmer, these are not really important pond producers either.

Have you ever watched specks of dust moving in a bright beam of sunlight? In a beam of light shining into a pond, you can see erratically moving specks that resemble specks of dust—but they are living organisms. Some are plants, some are protists, and some are animals. All are microscopic or nearly so. Though few are really swimmers, all can stay afloat, carried hither and thither by the currents in the water. They are drifters. From the Greek word for ''drifter'' or ''wanderer,'' Victor Hensen in 1887 coined the term by which they are collectively known—*plankton.*

Figure 9 • 4

Some zooplankton organisms that are often found in ponds. Can you suggest the phylum and class in which each might be classified?

X 30

ostracod

X 15

amphipod

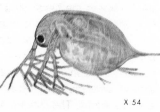

X 54

cladoceran

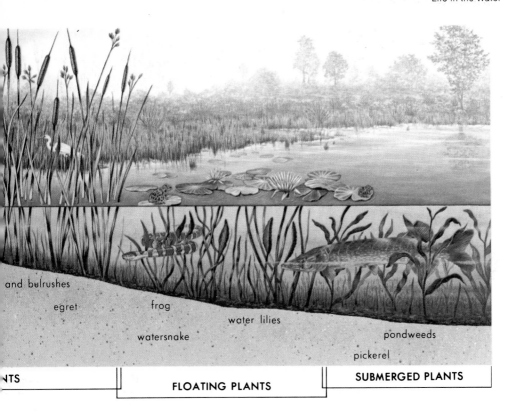

and bulrushes

egret   frog

water lilies

watersnake   pondweeds

pickerel

NTS | FLOATING PLANTS | SUBMERGED PLANTS

Slowly, early limnologists began to realize that plankton organisms made up for their smallness by their incredible numbers. Careful quantitative studies eventually showed that most food production in all parts of the hydrosphere—not just in ponds—is the result of photosynthesis by plankton organisms.

The plankton producers are referred to collectively as *phytoplankton*. Many are algae, but some are chlorophyll-bearing protists. The various kinds of phytoplankton vary in abundance from one body of water to another; but diatoms are usually the most numerous, though not the most conspicuous. Green algae, however, may become so abundant in late summer that a pond's whole surface becomes green.

Because the majority of pond producers are microscopic, you might expect the herbivores to be small also. Most of them are, and they form another part of plankton—*zooplankton.* There are protists —ciliates and flagellates; and there are animals—rotifers and a great diversity of tiny crustaceans. However, some pond herbivores are not part of plankton—for example, young fish, which are swimmers, not drifters, and mussels, which are bottom dwellers. Most pond fishes are carnivores. The smaller kinds are eaten by the larger; and fishes of all sizes eat aquatic insects, many of which are themselves car-

incredible [ĭn krĕd'ə bəl; Latin: *in-*, not, + *credare*, to believe]

phytoplankton [fī' tō plăngk'tən; Greek: *phyton*, a plant, + plankton]

X 1/3

Figure 9 · 5
A freshwater mussel.

See Figure 9 · 3.

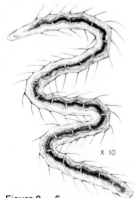

Figure 9 • 6
A tubifex worm.

tubifex [tū′bə fĕks; Latin:
tubus, tube, + *facere*, to make]

crayfish. See Figure 4 · 13.

nivores. Some pond food chains have many links. Most of the macroscopic carnivores are found near the pond margins, where the floating plants provide concealment, but some of the larger predatory fishes wander throughout the pond, ever on the alert for prey.

Dead organisms sink, so large quantities of organic matter accumulate on the bottom of a pond. Decomposers such as tubifex worms (phylum Annelida) burrow in this rich source of energy. As in all ecosystems, however, the most important decomposers are bacteria and fungi.

A pond ecosystem is not sharply bounded by the surface of the water. Above and around ponds, insects are usually conspicuous. Most of these begin their lives in the water, and many spend most of their lives there. For example, only the last few hours of a mayfly's life are spent in the air. Frogs live largely on those insects that spend their early lives in ponds. Water snakes consume fish and frogs. Many kinds of birds and some mammals are primarily consumers of such pond organisms as fish, crayfish, and mussels. Such consumers, though they spend much of their time on land, are truly part of pond ecosystems, since their energy supply can be traced back to phytoplankton.

stonefly nymph   X 1/2

mayfly nymph   X 2

stonefly adult   X 1/2

dragonfly nymph   X 1

Figure 9 • 7
Many insects occur in ponds only as wingless, immature forms called nymphs. For adult mayfly and dragonfly, see page 121.

penetrate [pĕn′ə trāt′; Latin: *penitus*, inward]: to pass into something

Lakes. To most people the word "lake" suggests a larger body of water than "pond." To a limnologist a pond is a body of water so shallow that light penetrates to the bottom; a lake, on the other hand, has depths that are always dark.

The largest of all freshwater lakes is Lake Superior. It covers an area about the size of South Carolina but has a maximum depth of only 410 m. The two deepest lakes are Baikal (1750 m), in Siberia, and Tanganyika (1449 m), in Africa. Lake Superior is perhaps 10,000 to 20,000 years old, but both Baikal and Tanganyika were formed millions of years ago. Such wide variation in the size, depth, and age of lakes means that conditions for life in lake waters also vary greatly.

Haven Kolb

Figure 9 • 8
A mountain pond in July
(Colorado). Compare and
contrast environmental
conditions here with those
in Figure 9 • 3.

Food produced by rooted aquatic plants is even less important in lakes than in ponds. Lake ecosystems depend upon phytoplankton. But the phytoplankton, unlike that of a pond, does not live throughout the lake. It can exist only to the depth to which light sufficient for photosynthesis penetrates. This depth depends upon variables such as the clearness of the water and the amount of cloudiness in the sky, but it probably does not average more than 80 m. In deep lakes, therefore, all the food production is in the upper part of the water.

Consumers are not limited by light. But for them an important abiotic factor is the amount of oxygen in the water. Surface waters receive dissolved oxygen continuously from photosynthesis and from air, particularly through wave action. Dissolved oxygen may move slowly downward from the surface, but before going very far it is largely used up by zooplankton. So the spread of oxygen into deep water depends upon other factors.

The sun heats the surface water of a lake, expanding it and making it less dense—lighter. Winds push this surface layer across the lake toward the shore. Here it must go somewhere, so it rolls downward. It cannot go down far, however, before it meets colder, denser (heavier) water. The warm water therefore doubles back across the lake, sliding just above the cold water and just below the warmer surface water. This process carries oxygen from the surface only a short distance downward; the colder, deeper water remains without oxygen. In the tropics this process goes on throughout the year; so tropical lakes, such as Tanganyika, have no deep-water aerobic organisms—no animals.

Outside the tropics, however, another process occurs. As the sun sinks lower in the sky in autumn, it heats the surface water less and less. Eventually this water cools to a point (4°C) at which it is more dense than the deeper water beneath. Then the denser surface water sinks and forces the deep water to the top—a large-scale turnover of the lake water. Oxygen is thus distributed yearly throughout the lake water. So lakes outside the tropics have many animals in their deeper water—at least to a depth of 600 m in Baikal.

Although animals are absent from the deeper water of some lakes, anaerobic organisms are probably present on all lake bottoms. There organic matter that decomposers can use as food is plentiful; it continually drifts down from above as organisms in the upper waters die and their bodies sink.

If a lake has no outlet, minerals washed in from the surrounding land accumulate. In arid regions this process is speeded up by the high rate of evaporation. The water becomes saturated with minerals, the most abundant usually being sodium chloride ($NaCl$), common table salt, as in Great Salt Lake, Utah. The result is an environment unfavorable to almost all organisms. In some parts of Great Salt Lake, only adult brine shrimp, a few species of blue-green algae, and two species of brine flies can survive.

See Investigation 2.4.

FLOWING WATERS

Some of the water that falls on land runs directly into lakes, ponds, and streams, and some immediately evaporates; but much of it soaks into the ground. This groundwater reappears in springs, from which its course downward toward the sea may be short or long.

What factors might affect the amount of water that sinks into the ground?

From brooks to rivers. Most springs give rise to small brooks. Such flowing water is usually cool—though some hot springs do exist. Tumbling through rapids and falls, the water traps many air bubbles, from which oxygen easily dissolves. Since cool water can hold relatively large quantities of gases in solution, brooks are usually well oxygenated.

Where might you find hot-water brooks?

In the swift-flowing water of brooks, plankton is absent. Producers —green algae, diatoms, and water mosses—grow attached to stones or other objects. Sometimes producer organisms completely cover a stream bottom, providing both food and shelter for aquatic insects,

Why does such water lack plankton?

Haven Kolb

Figure 9 • 9
A brook (Maryland). What
evidence can you see that
this aquatic ecosystem
probably has few producers?

which, in turn, are food for small fish. But most of the food supply of
a brook ecosystem comes from the land surrounding it. Small terrestrial organisms, such as insects, fall in and contribute to the diet of
stream inhabitants. And dead organic matter is washed in with every
rain. Anything not used immediately, however, is washed downward.
Thus, in the headwaters of a stream system there is very little food
for decomposers.

Brooks join, forming larger streams with wider beds and greater
volumes of water. Here the water moves more slowly, so solid substances that have been carried along are deposited as sediments.
Bits of organic matter, accumulating among the sediments, provide
food for decomposers.

sediments [sĕd′ə mənts;
Latin: sedere, to sit]

As the width of a stream increases, the amount of water surface
shaded by trees along its banks decreases; direct sunlight reaches
most of the water surface. Increased light increases the rate of photosynthesis. So some phytoplankton organisms may live in this slower
water, though many are swept downstream. Rooted plants similar to
those in ponds grow in sediments of a stream bottom; they, too, may

be washed away during floods.

Because of its greater number of producers, a stream supports a larger number of consumers than does a brook. On the bottom are mussels, snails, crayfish, and large numbers of different kinds of immature insects. Dependent upon these bottom dwellers are such larger consumers as turtles and fish.

Large bodies of flowing water are called rivers. As a river approaches the sea, it usually moves more and more slowly, dropping larger and larger quantities of sediments. Thus, near its mouth a river often builds up land instead of eroding it. The riverbanks may actually become higher than the land behind them. During floods a river often breaks through these natural levees and leaves behind water that is slow to drain away, thus forming swamps. In these swampy lands, many emergent and floating plants grow. Fruits, seeds, and other parts of these plants are swept into the river during floods, contributing to the food supply. But much of the food supply for consumers in large rivers comes from phytoplankton organisms, which grow well in the unshaded, slow-moving water.

Consumers in rivers are varied and numerous. Zooplankton organisms are food for larger predators. Mollusks, crustaceans, and fish often grow large. In tropical rivers crocodiles are common. Many terrestrial birds and mammals obtain their food from rivers, just as many do from ponds. And since ancient days mankind also has taken advantage of the abundant food in rivers.

eroding [ĭ rōd'ĭng; Latin: *ex*, out, + *rodere*, to gnaw]

levees [lĕv'ĭz; Latin: *levare*, to raise]

Many ancient riverside civilizations were agricultural. How did river ecosystems contribute to agriculture?

Figure 9 · 10

Part of the delta of the Mississippi River. What major kinds of ecosystems can you see here?

Litton Industries—Aero Service Division

Flowing waters as laboratories. Not all springs give rise to brooks. Some pour forth so much water that large streams flow from them. Many of the rivers of northwest Florida originated in this way.

About 20 years ago ecologists recognized that the short Florida rivers were fine outdoor laboratories because each had, along most of its length, almost stable conditions of volume, current, chemical composition, and temperature. They therefore used several of these rivers in a study of ecological *productivity*—the rate at which producers store chemical energy in the substances that make up their bodies.

See Figure 3·1.

Productivity can also be thought of as the rate of photosynthesis, and this can be measured indirectly. Photosynthesizing organisms give off oxygen in a known proportion to the amount of foods (energy-containing organic substances) that they produce. Therefore, if a biologist measures the oxygen given off during a measured period of time, he can calculate the amount of organic substance produced in that time—the productivity.

productivity [prō′ dŭk tĭv′ ə tĭ]

The ecologists measured the amount of oxygen in the water of Rainbow Springs and in the river water at several places downstream (Figure 9·11). Such measurements are expressed as "parts per million" (ppm), which is similar mathematically to percent. (For example 1 percent is 10,000 ppm, and 1 ppm is 0.0001 percent.)

Percents are "parts per hundred," which is much too crude for expressing amounts of oxygen dissolved in water.

Figure 9 · 11

Diagram of Rainbow Springs (Florida) and the river that flows from them.

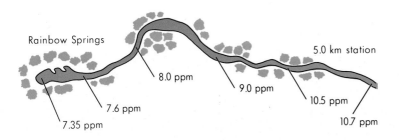

Rainbow Springs
5.0 km station
8.0 ppm
9.0 ppm
7.6 ppm
10.5 ppm
7.35 ppm
10.7 ppm

Any increase in the amount of oxygen in the springwater as it flowed downstream came largely from photosynthesis. In Figure 9 · 11 only the oxygen measurements are given. But knowing the oxygen content at a given place along the length of the river and the amount of water that flowed past that point per day, the investigators could calculate the total productivity of the water between its source in the springs and the place of measurement. This was expressed as grams of organic substance produced per square meter of stream surface per day. In nearby Silver Springs the investigators found an average productivity of 17.5 g/m²/day.

In further studies the investigators estimated the *biomass* of each

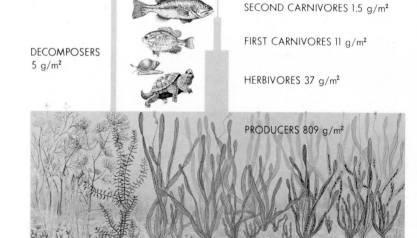

DECOMPOSERS
5 g/m²

SECOND CARNIVORES 1.5 g/m²

FIRST CARNIVORES 11 g/m²

HERBIVORES 37 g/m²

PRODUCERS 809 g/m²

other plants   tape grass   algae on tape grass

Figure 9 • 12

Average biomass measurements from Silver River, Florida. Largemouth bass are top carnivores.

Figure 9 • 13

Measuring populations. Working at night, one diver harvests tape grass as the other identifies individual largemouth bass from colored tags attached to their sides.

major species in the community. Biomass is the total mass of all individuals of a species in a given space. Figure 9 • 12 shows the result of these studies. This is one of the many studies on which the general diagram in Figure 1 • 18 is based.

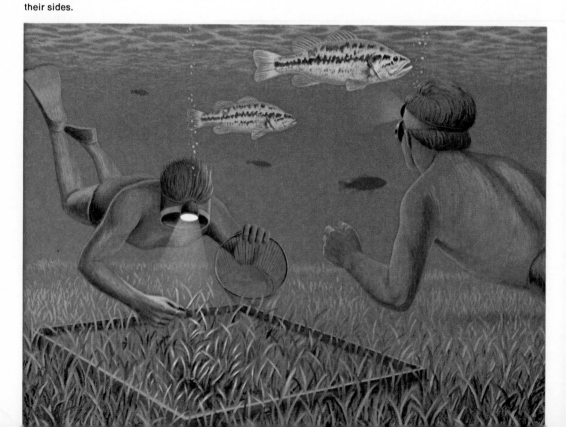

INLAND WATERS AND MANKIND

Man has greatly modified the ecosystems of inland waters. In water, as on land, his activities have benefited some organisms and caused others to disappear.

Drainage. Shallow ponds, lakes, and marshes are basins where organic mineral substances constantly accumulate. To channel such substances into crops, man need only remove the layer of water from the basins and plow the muck to mix air into it. Crops then thrive there.

With the invention of power machinery, man's ability to drain standing inland waters increased enormously. Throughout the 20th century, use of such machinery has resulted in a steady decrease in natural-water areas in many parts of the United States, especially in the grasslands of Minnesota and the Dakotas. An unfortunate effect of this drainage has been a decrease in duck populations; the grassland ponds and marshes were the main breeding areas for many species of ducks. But the drained areas have added considerably to the human food supply.

Artificial ponds and lakes. Although drainage of standing waters has continued, the surface area of inland waters has actually increased during the last 40 years. This has resulted from construction of dams, large and small, across running waters.

Some dams are erected solely for providing a fall of water to turn electric generators. Usually, especially in the western states, dams also form basins in which floodwaters are stored for irrigation or for supplying water to cities. Whatever the purpose, the result is a

modified: changed somewhat

Ducks and pond fish can be used as human food. How, then, does drainage increase the food supply?

Josef Muench

Figure 9 · 14

Lake Mead, formed by a large dam on the Colorado River. Even if shore slopes are gentle, such reservoirs seldom have emergent vegetation. Can you see why?

catfish. See Figure 9·17, far left.

How might a farmer increase the fish crop of his pond?

pond or lake—standing water where once there were streams and land. Such major changes in environment bring about major changes in biotic communities. A large dam may block the passage of species of fish that swim up rivers to lay their eggs in headwater streams; but it may greatly increase the amount of habitat favorable for other species, such as catfish.

Much of the new inland-water area is made up of small ponds that cover only a few thousand square meters. The number of ponds has particularly increased in regions where natural ponds are few. Some artificial ponds are dug merely to provide a supply of water in case of fire, but often they have several purposes. Many artificial ponds produce fish for food, sport, or both. In such cases the pond owners must know something about pond ecosystems so that they can make habitats in their ponds favorable for the kinds of fish they want.

In general, ecosystems in artificial ponds and lakes are simpler than those in natural ones. As they become older, however, artificial waters tend to become more and more like natural ones in the same region. And, as in natural ones, sediments accumulate, reducing their depth.

Pollution. Mankind's first major use of flowing waters—where they were large enough—was to float boats for transportation. To further this use, man has in modern times used machinery on a large scale to straighten rivers and dredge them deeper. These activities have clearly affected stream ecosystems, principally by simplifying community structure.

Almost as old as the use of flowing waters for transportation, perhaps, is their use to flush away unwanted substances. When people

Figure 9 • 15

What do you think are the uses of this farm pond?

Haven Kolb

Tennessee Game and Fish Commission

Figure 9 • 16
Why do you think this kind
of work is done on a stream
too small for ships?

come together into towns and cities, their accumulated biological
wastes—*sewage*—greatly affect nearby river ecosystems. Sewage
is mainly organic substances mixed with water. A small amount of it
in a large river increases the amount of life there by providing materials that promote the growth and multiplication of producers. However, if the amount of sewage relative to the volume of river water is
large, decomposers of the sewage substances use up the oxygen,
producing anaerobic conditions. This is disastrous for all organisms
that require dissolved oxygen. As the waters of the river flow onward,
however, the sewage may be diluted by addition of water from tribu-
tary streams. And in any case the decomposers eventually use up the
sewage materials. So river ecosystems tend to clean themselves of
sewage pollution.

How would this affect
consumers?

But what if another city is located close downstream from the first?
As human populations have increased, cities have been built closer
and closer together; so the cleansing action of a river ecosystem does
not have opportunity to occur before the river receives another load
of sewage.

As human technology has increased, new kinds of waste substances have been produced. After the Industrial Revolution, acids,
alkalis, ions of the heavy metal elements—such as chromium, lead,
and mercury—began to be dumped into the flowing waters of Earth.
All of these may be poisonous to living things. Further, some industrial processes, particularly the generation of electricity, result in
discharge of hot water into rivers. This makes an abrupt abiotic
environmental change that is difficult for many aquatic organisms to
tolerate. Finally, recent shifts to generating electricity with nuclear
reactors have added small amounts of radioactive substances that accumulate in the bodies of stream organisms, harming them and the
organisms that eat them.

SEWAGE

Sewage attacked by decomposers.

O_2 supply decreases.

Aerobic organisms die.

Figure 9 • 17

Diagram of sewage pollution in a stream. Organisms are not drawn to scale, and distances are greatly decreased.

Investigation 9.1

DISSOLVED OXYGEN

INTRODUCTION

The amount of free oxygen (O_2) dissolved in water is an abiotic environmental factor that is of basic importance in the study of any aquatic ecosystem. Oxygen measurements can be used in studying aquatic productivity and, indirectly, aquatic pollution.

Here you are given a procedure for measuring dissolved oxygen. But you must design your own investigation to make use of the procedure. Here are some suggestions from which you may develop hypotheses:

Aquariums: (1) oxygen in aquariums with and without artificial light; (2) oxygen in aquar-

iums with and without plants; (3) oxygen in aquariums with and without aerators; (4) oxygen in aquariums early in the morning and in the afternoon.

Standing waters: (1) oxygen in freshly collected rainwater compared with that in old rainwater puddles; (2) oxygen at various depths in a pond or lake; (3) oxygen in a natural pond compared with that in an artificial pond.

Running waters: (1) oxygen in a sewage-polluted stream at various distances from the source of pollution; (2) oxygen in a stream at various times of the year.

Sewage decreases.

O$_2$ supply increases.

Phytoplankton increases.

Aerobic consumers increase.

MATERIALS AND EQUIPMENT

(for each sample)

flask, 500-ml

stopper to fit flask, solid

pipette, graduated, 10-ml

manganese sulfate solution

alkali-iodide-azide solution

sulfuric acid, concentrated

starch solution

sodium thiosulfate solution

PROCEDURE

In a 500-ml flask collect a 250-ml sample of the water to be tested. Stopper the flask. Avoid disturbing the water in the flask and carry out the testing procedure as soon as possible after the sample is collected.

Using a pipette, add 2 ml of manganese sulfate solution to the sample. Wash the pipette thoroughly with running water and use it to add 2 ml of alkali-iodide-azide solution to the sample. *Handle this solution with care.* Stopper the flask and mix its contents by slowly inverting it. The contents should become cloudy.

Have your teacher add 2 ml of concentrated sulfuric acid to the flask. Mix as before. The flask contents should clear to a straw color.

Wash your pipette as before. Use it to add 2 ml of starch solution to the flask. The contents should become blue-black.

Wash your pipette as before. Fill it with 10 ml of sodium thiosulfate solution. Slowly add this solution drop by drop to the flask, swirling the contents as you do so. Continue until the blue-black color of the flask contents disappears. Record the volume of sodium thiosulfate solution that you used.

Each ml of sodium thiosulfate solution used in the final step indicates 1 part per million (ppm) of dissolved oxygen in the water sample.

DISCUSSION

• Assuming that the chemical materials were properly prepared, what sources of error may there be in the procedure?(1)   • What factors may cause an accurate measurement of oxygen in the sample to be different from the amount of oxygen in the water from which the sample was taken?(2)

OCEANS

The words "ocean" and "sea" are often not distinguishable in English. However, a sea sometimes means a smaller part of the hydrosphere than an ocean.

oceanographers
[ō′shĭ ə nŏg′rə fŭrz]

Knowledge of the oceans has grown rather slowly. Man has been moving about on the ocean surface for quite a while, but until rather recently observations were limited to the surface and the shore. Now, however, *oceanographers* can observe an ocean from within. They have developed instruments that send back to the surface information from the depths; they have also invented devices that permit deep diving. And the popularity of the very large aquariums called oceanariums has helped create public interest in the oceans and in the living things found there.

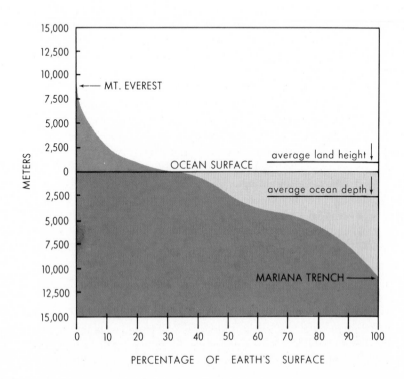

Figure 9 • 18

About what percentage of Earth's surface is covered by the ocean? How does the average depth compare with the average land height?

THE ABIOTIC ENVIRONMENT

Salinity. Ocean environments differ in many ways from inland-water environments. Perhaps the principal difference lies in the chemical composition of the water itself. Seawater—the water of the oceans—is about 3.5 percent minerals, or as oceanographers express it, about 35 parts per thousand. Most inland waters contain only small amounts of dissolved minerals. Most exceptions, such as Great Salt Lake, contain amounts of minerals much greater than in seawater.

The minerals dissolved in seawater are mostly substances called salts; therefore, the mineral content of seawater is referred to as *salinity.* Sodium chloride (table salt) is the most familiar salt. It is also the most common salt in the ocean, accounting for over 75 percent of the dissolved minerals.

Salinity varies somewhat at different depths and from place to place on the surface. It is greater where evaporation is high and precipitation is low, and lower where evaporation is low and much fresh water enters from rivers. For example, in the Red Sea it is over 45 parts per thousand and in the Baltic Sea it is sometimes less than 10 parts per thousand.

Evidence from rocks and fossils indicates that the ocean has had a rather high salinity for hundreds of millions of years. It seems, then, that the dissolved substances being constantly washed into the ocean from the land have only a slight effect on the composition of ocean water. Ocean water represents a steady state: substances are continually added but substances are also continually removed, and much of the removal is accomplished by marine organisms. Ocean water is the environment of marine organisms, but it is also, to a considerable extent, the product of the activities of these organisms. The hydrosphere, like the atmosphere, would undoubtedly have a much different composition if life were absent.

Other abiotic factors. The rapid changes that are characteristic of the atmosphere, and the resulting great differences in climates characteristic of terrestrial ecosystems do not occur in the hydrosphere. Even at the ocean surface, temperature changes between day and night are very small and seasonal changes are also small. However, the average 28°C temperature of surface water at the equator does differ considerably from the average of slightly below 0°C in antarctic and arctic surface waters. At a depth of 200 m, however, the pole-to-equator temperature range is only 0° to 22°C, and at greater depths temperature differences disappear almost entirely.

The amount of light energy available to photosynthetic organisms is greatest at the surface and decreases rapidly with depth of water. The turbidity of the water affects the rate at which light decreases; light penetrates much deeper into clear water than into turbid water.

Ocean currents bring about the distribution of chemical compounds useful to organisms. Currents also affect water temperatures and salinities at any given place in the ocean. Currents, in turn, are affected by the world pattern of winds and by the earth's rotation.

salinity [sə lǐn′ə tǐ; Latin: *sal*, salt]

What would this be in parts per million?

ELEMENT	SEA WATER (PARTS PER THOUSAND)
Chlorine	18.98
Sodium	10.56
Magnesium	1.27
Sulfur	.88
Calcium	.40
Potassium	.38
Bromine	.065
Carbon	.028
Strontium	.013
Silicon	.003
Fluorine	.001
Aluminum	.0005
Phosphorus	.0001
Iodine	.00005

Figure 9 · 19

Average mineral content of seawater. These elements occur as compounds; elemental nitrogen and oxygen dissolved from the air are not included.

From your own experience with weather, describe some of these rapid changes.

How can a temperature be below 0°C in *liquid* water?

turbidity [tûr bǐd′ə tǐ; Latin: *turbare*, to disturb]. In disturbed waters sediments do not settle out; hence "turbidity" has come to mean "cloudiness."

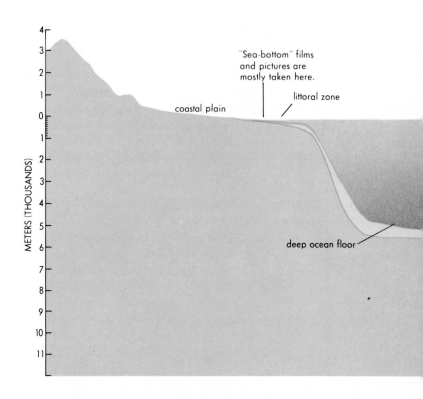

Figure 9 • 20
Diagram of an ocean in
cross section.

Salinity, temperature, light, current—on the basis of these and other factors, oceanographers are able to recognize many marine ecosystems. It is possible to group these ecosystems in several ways. One way distinguishes three major oceanic regions: open ocean, ocean depths, and coastal waters.

OPEN OCEAN

The chief producers of the open ocean are diatoms, other kinds of microscopic algae, and dinoflagellates. Upon this phytoplankton the entire life of the open-ocean ecosystem depends. Upon it the zooplankton depends directly, and from it extend food chains of varying lengths—to tuna, sharks, whales, and oceanic birds such as albatross.

Many efforts have been made to determine the density of plankton populations. Perhaps the most accurate results have come from the marine laboratory at Plymouth, England. The ocean water used in the investigations there contained, at the very least, 4,500,000 phytoplankton organisms in each liter of water! At present, oceanographers do not have enough data to give accurate averages for the ocean as a whole. But they do know that the oceans vary greatly in productivity.

The controlling factors in the oceans, as in many places on land, may be the availability of a few important chemical elements, espe-

dinoflagellates. See page 188.

For illustrations, see
Chapter 4.

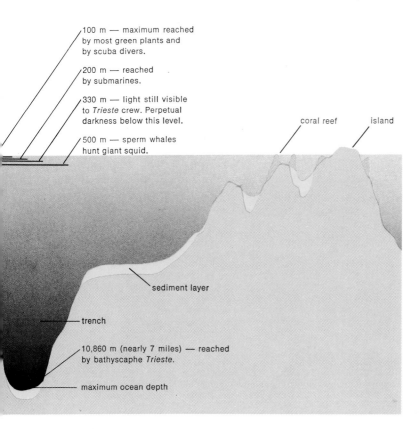

100 m — maximum reached by most green plants and by scuba divers.

200 m — reached by submarines.

330 m — light still visible to *Trieste* crew. Perpetual darkness below this level.

500 m — sperm whales hunt giant squid.

coral reef   island

sediment layer

trench

10,860 m (nearly 7 miles) — reached by bathyscaphe *Trieste*.

maximum ocean depth

M. Woodbridge Williams

Figure 9 · 21
A plankton net being cast from the *Horizon*, research vessel of the Scripps Institution of Oceanography, California.

cially phosphorus and nitrogen. Phytoplankton organisms are continuously using up these elements and so reducing their availability. Therefore, continued growth of phytoplankton depends upon the addition of these elements in sediments washed in from the land or in water welling up from below. Upwelling may occur as a result of seasonal changes, much as does the overturning of lake waters, or as a result of offshore winds' moving surface water away so that deep water rises to take its place. Thus, for chemical reasons ocean areas at higher latitudes and those close to the land, such as the North Sea and the Grand Banks of Newfoundland, are very productive. On the other hand, ocean regions far from land and especially those in the tropics —the Sargasso Sea in the Atlantic, for example—have very low productivity.

How does this relate to the location of great ocean fisheries?

Phytoplankton, of course, needs light, so its vertical distribution depends upon how deeply light penetrates. This, in turn, depends upon several factors, such as the angle at which the light strikes the water surface, the condition of the surface (whether smooth or broken by waves), and the transparency of the water itself. Within the water the longer wavelengths of light are absorbed most rapidly, which means that the reds and yellows disappear first, and the blues and violets penetrate farthest. Despite the deep penetration of blue light (550 m near Bermuda), phytoplankton is largely limited to the upper 100 m of water.

transparency [trăns pâr′ən sĭ; Latin: *trans*, through, + *parere*, to appear]. Transparency and turbidity are inversely related; as one increases the other decreases.

OCEAN DEPTHS

For a long time biologists thought that life could not exist in the dark and cold ocean depths because of the tremendous pressure of the water. The first clear evidence that this idea was wrong came in 1858, when one of the marine telegraph cables in the Mediterranean Sea broke and was hauled up for repair. It was encrusted with bottom-living animals, particularly sponges, some of which had grown at depths as great as 2000 m. Further investigation showed that water pressure in itself has no ill effect on organisms unless they contain spaces filled with air or other gases. Deep-sea organisms lack such spaces, so pressure is exerted equally inside and outside them.

Nina Leen

Figure 9 · 22
Eugenie Clark, marine biologist at the University of Maryland, gathers data during an investigation of sharks.

We terrestrial organisms, however, do have trouble with water pressure because we carry internal air-filled spaces into the water with us. Therefore, without using special apparatus, we can observe directly only the top few meters of the ocean. In the 19th century the development of diving helmets and air pumps enabled divers to go deeper and stay down longer. In the 20th century Jacques Cousteau's aqualung has allowed greater freedom of movement by eliminating the need for a hose connection to the surface. But neither of these devices enables a diver to descend beyond a depth of 100 m.

Jacques Cousteau [zhȧk kōōs tō′]: 1910—. French oceanographer. The aqualung is a device for breathing under water.

To reach greater depths some kind of vehicle is necessary. One of the first was constructed in 1935. It was a heavy steel sphere with thick quartz windows, built to withstand the great pressures of the deep and equipped with compressed oxygen and chemicals to absorb excess carbon dioxide and moisture. It was lowered into the sea on a cable. In it William Beebe was able to descend about 1000 m in the Atlantic Ocean near Bermuda and for the first time observed directly living things at such depths.

More recently Auguste Piccard designed the bathyscaphe, a vessel than can descend to great depths and come up under its own power. On January 23, 1960, Jacques Piccard, son of the designer, and Lieutenant Don Walsh of the United States Navy descended in the bathyscaphe *Trieste* to the bottom of Mariana Trench, in the Pacific Ocean—10,860 m below the surface. In doing so, they reached the deepest place in the oceans.

William Beebe [bē′bǐ]: 1877–1962. American zoologist and naturalist.

Auguste Piccard [ô gǔst′ pē′kär′]: 1884–1962. Belgian physicist

bathyscaphe [bǎth′ə skǎf; Greek: *bathos*, depth, + *skaphe*, boat]

U.S. Navy

Figure 9 • 23
The bathyscaphe *Trieste*.

The ocean depths are a very special ecosystem that requires unusual adaptations in the organisms that survive and flourish there. The depths are cold and dark and quiet. There are no producers. All the biological energy is in food that arrives as organic substances settling from the water above. Further, the adaptations of organisms to the pressures of the deep also make their ascent to upper levels fatal. So the consumers in the ocean depths form one of the most isolated communities of the biosphere.

In the eternal night of the ocean depths, most animals are either black or dark red and have very sensitive eyes. In the unending darkness of caves and underground streams, however, most are white and blind. The difference in eyes—and, perhaps, in color—is associated with the fact that in depths of the oceans many animals have the ability to produce light in their bodies, but this ability is not found in the

What other ecosystems contain no producers?

When brought to the surface, fishes caught at great depths often look as if they had exploded. Why?

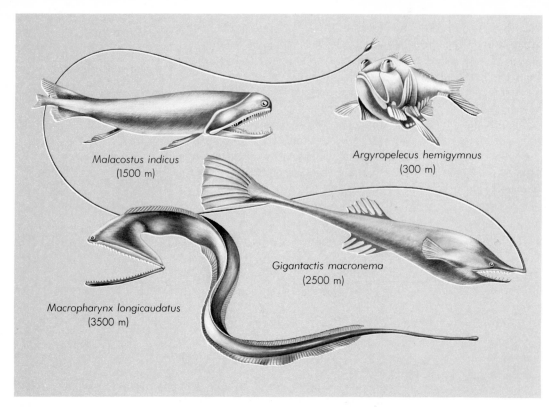

Figure 9 • 24

Some fishes of the ocean depths and the depths at which they have been caught. All are small; they are shown here X 1.

luminescent [lōō'mə něs'ənt]: light-giving

blackness of caves. Ability to produce light may serve several functions. One species of fish dangles a light in front of its mouth; apparently this lures unwary victims closer. Deep-sea shrimp are probably able to escape in the clouds of luminescent secretion that they

Lamont Geological Observatory of Columbia Univ.

Figure 9 • 25

An acorn worm on the ocean bottom (South Pacific, depth about 4800 m).

give off when disturbed. Patterns of light on the body may serve as marks of recognition in the depths, just as color patterns do among many organisms in the world of light.

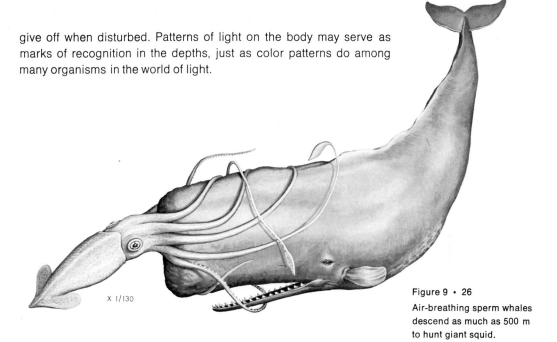

X 1/130

Figure 9 · 26
Air-breathing sperm whales descend as much as 500 m to hunt giant squid.

COASTAL WATERS

The littoral zone. With few exceptions, oceans are relatively shallow near the continents, as though the continents were partially flooded at their edges. These bands of shallow water—averaging less than 200 m in depth—tend to be widest at the mouths of large rivers and along areas of broad lowlands. They may be almost absent along mountainous coasts, as in California.

In this *littoral* zone a considerable amount of light reaches the bottom. Where there is plenty of light, a luxuriant growth of seaweeds may be found. In middle and higher latitudes, the most common and conspicuous ones are brown algae. Among these are kelps, which may reach a length of 35 m or more. Nevertheless, here, as elsewhere in aquatic ecosystems, phytoplankton organisms are the principal producers.

littoral [lǐt′ə rəl; Latin: *littus,* seashore, coast]

luxuriant [lŭg zhŏŏr′ĭ ənt]: rich, abundant

Brown Palmer from National Audubon Society

Figure 9 · 27
Large kelp washed up on a beach (California).   × 1/25

The physical characteristics of the bottom––presence of sand, rock, or mud—determine the kinds of organisms that live in the littoral zone. Sandy bottoms generally occur where wave or current action washes away the finer particles. Plants are not usually abundant on such unstable bottoms. However, many kinds of animals burrow into the sand, especially crustaceans, mollusks, and annelid worms. Muddy bottoms have even larger numbers of burrowers, and most of the species are unlike those adapted to sand. Sea cucumbers, clams, and some crabs plow through the mud. On rocky bottoms and on reefs made from the skeletons of corals, many animals (sponges, barnacles, and coelenterates, for example) attach themselves permanently to one place. Crabs, octopuses, and fishes hide in nooks and crannies among the rocks.

How might your knowledge of plants lead you to predict this fact?

octopus. See page 126.

Burton McNeely

Figure 9 · 28

Life on a coral reef (Florida Keys). Corals, sponges, and reef fishes are conspicuous.

Because it is shallow and close to land, the littoral zone offers more opportunity for human use than does the open ocean. From it has always come much of the marine food supply of man. Oil is now being obtained from wells drilled in its bottom. Underwater farming and mining are future possibilities. During the last decade much attention has been given to the development of devices in which scientists

U.S. Navy

Figure 9 • 29
Inside *Sealab II* a scientist wearing an electrically heated wet suit prepares to explore the surrounding water.

can directly explore littoral ecosystems. Within such devices they have already lived for several weeks at a time. By such continuous underseas observations, biologists have greatly increased knowledge of many marine organisms.

In the search for ways to adapt to such a life, a biologist looks for animals that are much like himself but that have made the adaptation successfully. Porpoises are such animals. Warm-blooded, air-breathing, and with large brains, porpoises have been the subject of much study. Experiments are being undertaken to learn the extent to which a porpoise can be trained to help a man. In one experiment a porpoise wearing a plastic harness carried tools and mail to under-

U.S. Navy

Figure 9 • 30
Tuffy, a trained porpoise, pushes a buzzer on the side of a boat.

304 PATTERNS IN THE BIOSPHERE

water scientists and carried a nylon lifeline to a diver who was pretending to be lost in turbid water. As man continues to explore the oceans, he may someday domesticate porpoises as he has domesticated dogs and horses on land.

The ocean edge. Everywhere along the margins of the oceans you can see the effects of waves and tides. In the Bay of Fundy, in Nova Scotia, the maximum vertical change between high and low tide is 15.4 m. At the other extreme, the average tidal difference in the Mediterranean is only 0.35 m. Wave action, too, varies greatly from place to place and from day to day. Some coasts, such as the coast of Maine, are pounded by heavy surf; others, especially in small, protected bays, may be no more exposed to wave action than are shores of small lakes. The zone between high and low tide, where twice a day organisms are submerged and exposed, is a difficult environment for life. Think of it: submerged in salt water; then, a few hours later, exposed to air—to bright, hot sun or freezing wind; and, between times, pounded by the advancing or retreating surf!

On rocky coasts life in this zone is surprisingly abundant. In cold waters brown algae of various kinds are able to cling to the rocks, protected from the drying sun by a gelatinous coating. These tangled algae then provide protection and support for other algae, for protists, and for numerous animals. In addition, barnacles, chitons, and snails cling firmly to rock or seaweeds, closing themselves up tightly to survive the periods when they are exposed to air.

On sandy coasts life in this zone is limited to organisms that can burrow in the sand or skitter over it. There are no attached producers. The burrowers, such as small crustaceans, eat food particles brought by the high tides. Shorebirds, a link with land ecosystems, prey on

X 1/5

Figure 9 • 31
Sanderling, a shorebird of sandy beaches.

gelatinous [jǐ lǎt′ə nəs]: jellylike

chitons. See page 127.

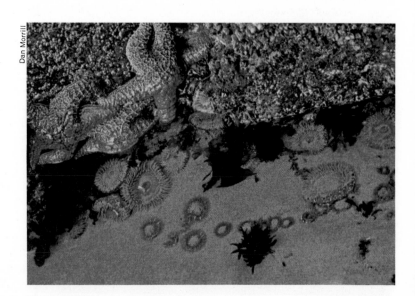

Dan Morrill

Figure 9 • 32
Tide pool. On rocky ocean shores many aquatic organisms live during low tides in pools left above the waterline.

Figure 9 · 33

"Drowned" river valleys (Delaware). Containing brackish waters, they form an ecosystem different from both marine and inland-water ecosystems.

the burrowers or forage in the debris left behind by the retreating tide. Land crabs go down to the water to release their young, and sea turtles crawl out on the beach to bury their eggs. Terrestrial and marine ecosystems merge.

debris [də brē']: rubbish, especially that resulting from destruction

Wherever ocean meets land there is constant change. With only a few years of observation, you can watch sediments deposited at the mouths of rivers building land into the ocean. Elsewhere you can observe the ocean pushing back the land. Through most of Earth's history, such changes have occurred.

Investigation 9.2

EFFECTS OF SALINITY ON AQUATIC ORGANISMS

MATERIALS AND EQUIPMENT

(per pair of students)
medicine dropper
microscope slides, 3
cover slips, 3
living specimens of small aquatic
    organisms
monocular microscope
paper towels
sodium chloride solutions (1%,
    3%, and 5%)

PROCEDURE

This is an experimental investigation.
• Study the procedure and then set up an appropriate hypothesis.(1)

Using a medicine dropper, place on a slide a drop of water containing the kind of organisms you are to study. Add a cover slip.

Using the low power of your microscope, observe the organisms for a few minutes to determine their normal appearance and actions. You can slow down the movement of some kinds of protists by adding a few wisps of cotton or a bit of shredded paper towel to the water. Record the name of the organism.

At one edge of the cover slip, place a drop of 1% salt solution. Draw the salt solution under the cover slip by holding a small piece of paper towel at the opposite edge. (See Figure A · 6.) As the salt solution moves under the cover slip, carefully observe the organisms. Notice particularly changes in movements and shape. Record the percentage of the solution and your observations.

Replace the salt solution with water from the original culture in the same way you added the salt solution.   • Are you making any assumption when doing this? If so, what?(2) Observe the organisms again and record any further changes in movement or shape that you can observe in them.

Using a new slide and specimen, repeat the procedure, using 3% salt solution. Repeat with 5%.

STUDYING THE DATA

Variability among individuals of a species in response to an environmental factor is usual. Therefore, all students who work with the same organism should discuss their results together.   • Did all the individuals of the species react in the same way? If not, what differences were noted?(3)   • Did the kind of reaction differ with different salt solutions? Try to explain any differences.(4)

Now exchange observations with teams that worked on different kinds of organisms. • Which kind was most tolerant to changes in salt concentration?(5)   • Which kind was least tolerant?(6)   • What kind of aquatic habitat do you think each kind of organism normally inhabits?(7)

CONCLUSIONS

• Which of your observations support the hypothesis you set up before beginning work? (8)   • Do you have any observations that tend to weaken your hypothesis? If so, which?(9) • Taking all your observations into account, restate your hypothesis in the form of a conclusion to the experiment.(10)

FOR FURTHER INVESTIGATION

All the organisms you studied in this investigation are small. Many larger ones (salmon, for example) regularly move from marine water into fresh water (or vice versa), apparently without harm; others cannot tolerate much change in salinity. You can devise means of testing the salinity tolerance of macroscopic aquatic animals such as crayfish, goldfish, guppies, or snails, using the principles employed in this exercise. If you use a marine species (for example, a clam worm) in your experiments, how should you modify your procedure? Caution: It is not necessary to kill the animals used in your experiments. Whenever they show signs of discomfort, return them to a more tolerable salinity.

GUIDE QUESTIONS

1. What is the hydrosphere?
2. How do ecologists divide Earth's waters for study?
3. What are the principal kinds of inland waters?
4. What are the characteristics of plankton organisms?
5. What is the function of phytoplankton in a pond ecosystem?
6. How is a pond ecosystem linked to surrounding terrestrial ecosystems?
7. How do limnologists distinguish between ponds and lakes?
8. Why are living animals found deep in Lake Baikal but not in the depths of Lake Tanganyika?
9. How do lakes become salty?
10. How does the source of biological energy in a brook differ from the source in a large river?

11. In which part of a stream system are consumers most numerous? Why?
12. What is meant by the biological productivity of any area?
13. Why is the rate of oxygen production a measure of an area's productivity?   •
14. What was the relationship of the biomass of producers to that of consumers in the study of a Florida river ecosystem?
15. In what ways has man changed the proportion of inland-water to land area?
16. What are the major kinds of stream pollutants?
17. What happens to sewage when it is dumped into a stream ecosystem?
18. Describe the chemical characteristics of seawater.
19. Compare variations of temperature in the oceans with those in the atmosphere.
20. Why do some parts of the oceans

have a higher productivity than others?

21. By what means have men explored the depths of the oceans?

22. Describe the environment of the ocean depths and adaptations of organisms that live there.

23. How does the littoral zone differ from the open ocean?

24. How do communities on sandy bottoms differ from communities on rocky ones?

25. Why is the ocean edge a particularly difficult place for the survival of living things?

PROBLEMS

1. Describe a pond in your area. In what ways does it resemble the pond discussed in the text? How does it differ?

2. To answer the following questions about inland waters you do not need further research but only further thought about what you have read in this chapter. (a) How would a cloudy, windy day affect the productivity of phytoplankton? (b) Is a layer of ice on the surface of a lake harmful to fish? Explain. (c) How do the sources of oxygen differ in a brook, a slow-moving river, a pond, and a lake? (d) Would you expect decomposers to be more active on the bottom of a pond or of a lake? Explain. (e) Why is a poisonous substance in a pond—such as a mercury compound—likely to be more concentrated in the flesh of a bass than of a cladoceran? (f) Why do household detergents, which kill bacteria, interfere with sewage purification?

3. A program designed to improve the fishing was introduced in a midwestern pond. First a fish poison was used to kill all the many small fish that were in the pond. Then the pond was restocked with game fish. Instead of large fish, the new population contained numerous but stunted individuals. Explain.

4. The concentration of hydrogen ions (H^+) and hydroxyl ions (OH^-) is as important in aquatic environments as in the soil. Where in North America can you find acid waters? Where can you find alkaline waters? What differences can you find among the living things in such waters?

5. Differences in the physical characteristics of water and air are important in understanding the contrast between aquatic and terrestrial environments. Consider such questions as these: (a) As the speed of a moving body increases, how does resistance change in air and in water? (b) What land organisms have the most-streamlined bodies? With what form of locomotion is this streamlining associated?

(c) What water organisms have the most-streamlined bodies? With what niches in aquatic ecosystems is this streamlining associated? (d) Why do most plankton organisms have little or no streamlining? (e) How does locomotion by walking on the bottom of the ocean differ from locomotion by walking on land?

6. If you collected 167 snails of a given species from five plots totaling 5 m² and found that their total weight was 534 g, what would be the biomass of the species?

7. Though 80 to 90 percent of the world's photosynthesis occurs in water, human food comes mostly from the land. Mankind might make much greater use of the hydrosphere as a source of food. Consider these questions: (a) What nations at present make the greatest use of marine food resources? (b) What kinds of marine organisms are eaten by man? (c) Man makes much use of terrestrial producers as food. Why is this difficult with aquatic producers? (d) How might man make greater use of aquatic producers as food? (e) Why does man's use of fish represent an inefficient harvesting of the ocean's energy resources?

8. The distribution of biologically useful mineral compounds is not the same as the distribution of oceanic salinity. Find out where in the seas of the world the largest amounts of such minerals are and explain why they occur there. What effects do concentrations of such minerals have on the marine biota?

9. Though the seas are very large, pollution of marine waters can occur. Investigate the kinds of oceanic pollution and their effects on the marine biota.

10. Estuaries, such as Chesapeake Bay and San Francisco Bay, represent a special kind of aquatic environment that has not been discussed in this chapter. Investigate the characteristics that distinguish estuarine environments from marine and inland-water environments and the resulting effects on aquatic life.

SUGGESTED READINGS

AMOS, W. H. "The Living Sand," *National Geographic,* June, 1965. Pp. 820–833.

———. "Teeming Life of a Pond," *National Geographic,* August, 1971. Pp. 274–298.

BATES, M. *The Forest and the Sea.* New York: Random House, Inc., 1960. Chapters 4–6. (Excellent discussion of water environments and water life—particularly the environment of coral reefs. Fairly easy.)

BOOLOOTIAN, R. A. *Biology of Coral Atolls.* (BSCS Pamphlet 10). Boulder, Colo.: EPIC, 1963. (This pamphlet describes the ecosystems in a special shallow-water marine environment of the tropics. Fairly easy.)

CARSON, R. *The Sea around Us.* New York: Simon and Schuster, Inc., 1958. (Beautiful account of the oceans and their life. Fairly easy.)

CHURCH, R. "Deepstar Explores the Ocean Floor," *National Geographic,* January, 1971. Pp. 110–129.

CLARK, J. R. "Thermal Pollution and Aquatic Life," *Scientific American,* March, 1969. Pp. 18–26.

COKER, R. E. *Streams, Lakes, Ponds.* Chapel Hill, N.C.: University of North Carolina Press, 1954. (The physical and chemical characteristics of water are discussed as background; then the living things in running and still waters are described. Somewhat advanced.)

DIETZ, R. S. "The Sea's Deep Scattering Layers," *Scientific American,* August, 1962. Pp. 44–50.

EARLE, S. A., and P. MION. "Tektite II: All Girl Team Tests the Habitat," *National Geographic,* August, 1971. Pp. 290–296.

ERICKSON, P. A. "The Ecology of a Reservoir," *Natural History,* March, 1969. Pp. 48–53.

HARRISON, R. J., and G. L. KOOYMAN. *Diving in Marine Mammals.* London: Oxford University Press, 1971. (A pamphlet that describes experiments and relates them to the structure of the animals. Rather advanced.)

HITCHCOCK, S. W., and W. R. CURTSINGER. "Can We Save Our Salt Marshes?" *National Geographic,* June, 1972. Pp. 728–765.

KENDEIGH, S. C. *Animal Ecology.* Englewood Cliffs, N.J.: Prentice-Hall, Inc., 1961. Chapters 5–7. (This reference is chiefly concerned with animals but has much background material on physical and chemical characteristics of both fresh and marine waters. Advanced.)

McELROY, W. D., and H. H. SELIGER. "Biological Luminescence," *Scientific American,* December, 1962. Pp. 76–87.

NIGRELLI, R. F. *Metabolites of the Sea.* (BSCS Pamphlet 7). Boulder, Colo.: EPIC, 1963. (This pamphlet considers the chemistry of organic substances that are found in seawater. Somewhat advanced.)

PINCHOT, G. B. "Marine Farming," *Scientific American,* December, 1970. Pp. 14–21.

REID, G. K. *Pond Life.* New York: Western Publishing Co., 1967. (Many pictures of pond organisms make this pocket-size book useful for field study of ponds.)

VAN DER WALKER, J. G., and B. LITTLEHALES. "Tektite II: Science's Window on the Sea," *National Geographic,* August, 1971. Pp. 256–289.

Life in the Past

EVIDENCE OF THE PAST

In 1808 there were no public tours through the White House in Washington, as there are today. If there had been, housewives on tour might have been shocked to discover piles of bones in one of the unfinished rooms. These were not leftovers from some official dinner. Nor did the hoard of over 300 bones belong to a favorite presidential dog. Indeed, some of the remains were gigantic—a leg bone large enough to use as a tent pole, for example. The truth of the matter was that Thomas Jefferson, the nation's science-minded President, had turned a part of the White House into a storage place for *fossils.*

hoard [hōrd]: a hidden supply of something

Jefferson was so interested in fossils that, at his own expense, he hired a crew of men to obtain specimens for him from famous Big Bone Lick in the hills of Kentucky. At about the same time, the first important natural-history museum in the United States grew up around the almost immovable mounted skeleton of a mastodon. But for centuries before the first museums were established, bones, shells, and other substances resembling living things or parts of living things had been dug from the ground by wandering men—and always they excited interest and thought.

fossil [Latin: *fossa,* ditch]: originally, anything found by digging

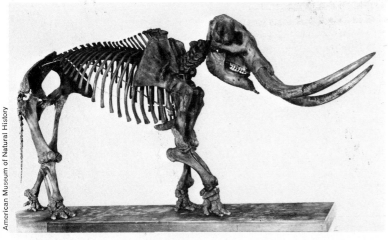

American Museum of Natural History

Figure 10 • 1
A mastodon skeleton.

309

WHAT IS A FOSSIL?

Great Flood: the flood recorded in Genesis of the Hebrew Bible

geologists [jǐ ŏl′ə jǐstz; Greek: *gea*, Earth, + *logos*, speech, reason]

An interest in fossils and an understanding of what they represent do not always go together. Some people once thought fossils were merely freakish accidents of nature. Others thought fossils were the result of the Great Flood (or perhaps many great floods). During the late 18th and early 19th centuries, *geologists* (scientists who study the earth) concluded that fossils are evidence of organisms that existed during past ages of the earth. Though they often resemble the parts of present-day organisms, fossils represent in most cases species that have long been extinct. This is the view held by most scientists today.

petrified [pĕt′rə fīd′; Latin: *petra*, stone, + *facere*, to make]

The majority of fossils represent the hard parts of organisms— wood, shell, bone. Sometimes these parts are unaltered. Usually, however, they have been *petrified.* In this process the original organic substances have been replaced, bit by bit, by minerals carried in soil water. The mineral substances may be quite different chemically from the substances they replace, but the form of the organism —even the microscopic detail, in many cases—remains.

component [kəm pō′nənt; Latin: *cum*, with, together, + *ponere*, to put]: a part of something

Fossils may also occur as thin films of carbon. The carbon, a component of all organic compounds, is all that remains after the living material has decomposed. Leaves of plants are often preserved in this form. Or fossils may be molds—hollows left in rock after the organic material has decayed. Or they may be casts—made of mud or some other sediment that filled the molds in the rocks and then hardened. Molds and casts preserve the shape but not the internal detail that petrified objects show.

In a very few cases soft parts of organisms have been directly preserved—for example, flesh of woolly mammoths frozen in tundra permafrost.

fossil footprints. See Figure 10 · 16.

Any indication of an organism's former presence is considered a fossil. Fossils may be footprints left by animals, burrows of worms,

Smithsonian Institution

Figure 10 • 2

Some kind of fossils.

Casts: brachiopods (New York).   × 1

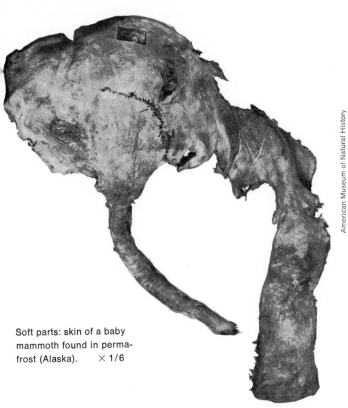

American Museum of Natural History

Soft parts: skin of a baby mammoth found in permafrost (Alaska).   × 1/6

Smithsonian Institution

Smithsonian Institution

Carbon film: primitive arthropod (British Columbia).   × 1

Mold: starfish (New York).   ×1

paleontologist
[pā lĭ ən tŏl′ə jĭst; Greek:
paleos, old, + *onta*, beings, +
logos, speech, reason]

nests of birds or insects, or even hardened dung. A *paleontologist*—a scientist who is trying to unravel the fossil records—frequently finds himself confronted with strange and unfamiliar objects that are often difficult to interpret.

THE GEOLOGICAL RECORD

sedimentary [sĕd′ə mĕn′tə rĭ]

Fossils are usually preserved in **sedimentary** rocks. Such rocks were once sediments—sand, mud, masses of shells. These were deposited by water, at the bottoms of oceans, lakes, and ponds and in beds of rivers and streams; by wind, often in the form of dunes; or by glaciers, in great masses left by the melting ice. Sediments have been forming as long as water, wind, and ice have been eroding the landscape in one place and depositing the products of the erosion elsewhere.

strata [strā′tə, străt′ə; Latin:
stratum, a covering]: singular,
stratum

The record in the rocks. The *strata* (layers) of sedimentary rocks are usually piled on each other like pages in a book. In general, the oldest strata are at the bottom and the newest on top. As a whole, the set of rock strata is now thought by geologists to represent about four billion years. But the portion particularly interesting to paleontologists is that which records the history of living things.

This "book of the earth" is not easy to read. For one thing many of the "pages" are blank—that is, many of the sedimentary strata contain no fossils. Perhaps no organisms existed at the time or place such strata were formed. Or conditions may not have been favorable

Figure 10 · 3

The sedimentary strata are orderly along the Colorado River (Utah).

Darwin Van Campen from DPI

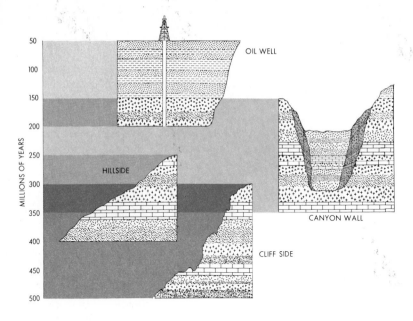

Figure 10 · 4

Geologists fit together strata from different places to construct the "book of the earth."

for the preservation of fossils. When you consider how few dead organisms you see around you today—because they have been rapidly consumed by decomposers—you may realize how seldom dead organisms become fossilized.

What conditions do you think would favor the preservation of organisms as fossils?

Further, during the history of Earth the strata have been subjected to breaking, folding, and sliding. Occasionally, folding has been so great that older strata have been turned so they are over younger. Sometimes fossils have been eroded from an older stratum and redeposited in a younger. And at any one place on Earth's surface, only some of the strata are found. To reconstruct the whole record, paleontologists must match strata from one place with strata from others.

Geological time scale. With evidence pieced together from many parts of the world, paleontologists have been able during the past two centuries to put most of the known rock strata in sequence. Thus they can say that Devonian strata are older than Cretaceous or that Miocene rocks are younger than Eocene (Figure 10 · 5). But how much older or younger?

Devonian [dǐ vō′nǐ ən]

Cretaceous [krǐ tā′shəs]

Miocene [mī′ə sēn′]

Eocene [ē′ə sēn′]

In early attempts to determine the ages of rock strata—and accompanying fossils—the total thickness of all sedimentary strata was estimated in meters. This was then divided by the estimated amount of time required for 1 meter of sediment to accumulate. But sediments do not accumulate at constant rates; therefore, this method was quite inaccurate.

radioactive [rā'dǐ ō ǎk'tǐv]:
substances that give off
radiations of energy such as
X-rays (Figure 1 · 15)

The most reliable method so far developed for dating rocks depends upon the presence of *radioactive* chemical elements. In such elements the atoms of the original element transform into atoms of a different element—and they do so at a predictable rate. Careful laboratory studies have determined for each radioactive element the half-life—the time in which half of any given amount of the original element is transformed. With this knowledge, it is possible to determine the age of a rock that contains a radioactive element by calculating the ratio between the amount of the radioactive element and the amount of the different element that has been formed.

ERAS	PERIODS	EPOCHS	YEARS SINCE BEGINNING OF PERIOD OR EPOCH
Cenozoic	Quaternary	Recent	10,000
		Pleistocene	2,000,000
	Tertiary	Pliocene	10,000,000
		Miocene	30,000,000
		Oligocene	40,000,000
		Eocene	60,000,000
		Paleocene	75,000,000
Mesozoic	Cretaceous		135,000,000
	Jurassic		165,000,000
	Triassic		205,000,000
Paleozoic	Permian		230,000,000
	Carboniferous		280,000,000
	Devonian		325,000,000
	Silurian		360,000,000
	Ordovician		425,000,000
	Cambrian		500,000,000
Pre-Cambrian			3,000,000,000+

Figure 10 • 5

The geologic time scale according to the best estimates now available.

For example, uranium breaks down through a series of steps to lead. In the same way, potassium breaks down to argon and rubidium breaks down to strontium. By selecting sample rocks from various geological periods and measuring the ratios between the elements in such pairs, the ages of the rocks have been approximated. The measurements are not perfect, but they have resulted in the establishment of a time scale that is probably more accurate than any previous one.

THE HISTORY OF LIFE

Despite all its shortcomings, the record of the rocks contributes to an important concept of modern science: Earth has had living inhabitants for a long time and has existed for even longer. And to biologists the fossils in the record are particularly important. They show that basic ecological processes and relationships have endured over long periods of time. They provide a basis for understanding the geographical distribution of life today. Finally, they are a major source of evidence for the great unifying theory in modern biology—the theory of evolution.

theory of evolution. For "theory," see page 59; for "evolution," see page 611.

ORIGIN OF LIFE

It seems natural for human beings to ask about the beginnings of things. Geologists inquire into the origin of our planet, and biologists inquire into the origin of life. The scientific evidence for these events is very meager; even the oldest fossils, for example, represent fully formed organisms. But in such a situation scientists sometimes start with a set of assumptions and develop from them a line of reasoning. This is called *speculation.* It may lead nowhere; but sometimes it leads to hypotheses that can be tested and thus becomes a part of science.

speculation [spĕk'yə lā'shən; Latin: *speculare*, to spy]

Some speculation. Geological evidence leads to the conclusion that Earth was very hot during its early history. Heat speeds up chemical activity, so at that time atoms must have been constantly combining and recombining to form many kinds of molecules. Geological evidence also indicates that the early atmosphere of Earth included methane, CH_4 (instead of present-day carbon dioxide, CO_2); ammonia, NH_4 (in addition to present-day nitrogen, N_2); some hydrogen, H_2; and much water vapor, H_2O.

methane [mĕth'ān]

Now the speculation begins. With the energy of heat and lightning, the gases of the early atmosphere *might* have combined to form such substances as amino acids—the simplest of which is $C_2H_5O_2N$. (Amino acids are substances that are found in all present-day organisms.) Then, during millions of years, an accumulation of such organic compounds within oceans, lakes, and pools *might* have produced a kind of "hot, thin soup," in which more complex organic molecules *might* have formed. Finally, these large, organic molecules *might* somehow have united to form a simple kind of reproducing "living thing." Such, at least, were the speculations of A. I. Oparin about 40 years ago.

amino [ăm'ə nō', ə mē'nō]

Alexander Ivanovich Oparin [ăl'ĭg zăn'dər ĭ vä'nŏ vĭch ō pä'rĭn]: 1894 — . Soviet biochemist

But did not Louis Pasteur show a century ago that living things cannot come from nonliving materials? Do not these speculations contradict his solid evidence? Not necessarily. Pasteur was concerned with conditions on Earth today, while Oparin's speculations assume very different environmental conditions.

Some experiments. A curious investigator might wonder what would happen if he exposed a simulated primitive atmosphere to an energy source. One did. In 1953 Stanley Miller at the University of Chicago passed electric sparks—simulating lightning—through ammonia, methane, water, and hydrogen. When he later analyzed the substances in his apparatus, he found that some simple amino acids had indeed been produced!

simulated [sĭm'yə lāt'ĭd; Latin: *similis*, like]: made like something; modeled (see Investigation 2.2)

Stanley Lloyd Miller: 1930 — . American chemist

synthesis |sĭn'thə sĭs; Greek: *syn-*, together, + *tithenai*, to place|: constructing by putting two or more things together

Miller's experiment has received ample verification. Other investigators have employed ultraviolet light instead of electric sparks and have obtained the same kind of results. Continuing research has been directed toward the synthesis of organic molecules more complex than amino acids. And some success has been achieved.

Do these experiments suggest a way in which life might have originated in the distant past? Perhaps. But it is a long way from amino acids to even the simplest of known organisms.

THE OLDEST FOSSILS

Somewhere, somehow, at some time, life on Earth *did* originate. So let us return to the factual evidence of fossils. How far back into time does the fossil record extend?

Cambrian [kăm'brĭ ən]

Fossils are fairly abundant in sedimentary deposits of the last 500,000,000 (0.5 billion) years. In deposits older than the Cambrian period few traces of life are found. Within the past decade, however, exploration of remote areas and the study of rock specimens by electron microscopy have revealed new evidence of the antiquity of life on our planet.

antiquity [ăn tĭk'wə tĭ]: great age

In 1965 a report was published announcing the discovery of fossils in South African rocks that had been dated at 3.1 billion years old. Naming the ancient organisms *Eobacterion isolatum*, the discoverers noted that "these organic remnants comprise the oldest known evidence of biological organization in the geologic record."

Eobacterion isolatum [ē'ō băk tĭr'ĭ ən   ī'sō lā'tŭm]

Elso S. Barghoorn

Figure 10 • 6

Electron micrograph of *Eobacterion isolatum* (*left*) and its imprint (*right*).

How can you explain the presence of consumers before the presence of producers?

Not all paleontologists agree that the South African finds are undoubtable evidence of living things. But microscopic rod-shaped and spherical fossils that clearly resemble modern bacteria have been found in 1.9 billion year-old rocks in Ontario. Further, chemical compounds definitely related to chlorophyll have been found in rocks dated at 1.1 billion years of age. And well-preserved fossils classified

M. F. Glaessner, University of Adelaide

Figure 10 • 7
One of the oldest-known animal fossils—probably a worm. The rocks are more than 0.6 billion years old (South Australia).

as green and blue-green algae have been collected in central Australia from pre-Cambrian limestones that have been dated at 0.7 to 0.9 billion years old.

In still more recent pre-Cambrian rocks are burrows of worms, skeletons of sponges, and shells of radiolarians. But everywhere the pre-Cambrian fossil record is scanty.

STUDYING ECOSYSTEMS OF THE PAST

From the beginning of the Cambrian to the present, the paleontological view of the past improves. Some speculation must remain, of course, and careful interpretation of the evidence is always essential. But the evidence itself is more abundant in rocks from each succeeding age.

For a century after scientists began to realize that fossils represent ancient forms of living things, no clear meaning could be obtained from the accumulating collections. Then, in the middle of the 19th century, the theory of biological evolution linked in a great kinship group all the beings of the past and present. From that time on, biologists have been busy with the task of discovering the lines of ancestry that link the organisms of the present to those of the past. This task is far from complete, but the broad outline of the history of organisms has been worked out.

Why do you think fossils become more abundant as we study more recently formed rocks?

CAMBRIAN 500

ORDOVICIAN 425

SILURIAN 360

DEVONIAN 325

CARBONIFEROUS 280

PERMIAN 230

TRIASSIC 205

JURASSIC 165

vascular plants

Figure 10 · 8
Half a billion years of Earth
history. On what kinds of
evidence is this illustration
based?

Appalachian Mountains

Rocky Mountains   Cascade Mountains

al-age forest

cone-bearing plants

flowering plants

ACEOUS 135

PALEOCENE 75

EOCENE 60

OLIGOCENE 40

MIOCENE 30

PLIOCENE 10

PLEISTOCENE 2

In recent years many paleontologists have turned their attention to a study of the ecological relationships that existed among the organisms of past ages. Beginning with the fossils themselves, but also using geological evidence from the chemical and physical characteristics of the rocks in which the fossils occur, they have reconstructed both the biotic relationships of ancient communities and their abiotic environmental conditions. Let us take a look at some of these *paleoecosystems.*

paleoecosystems
[pā′lĭ ō ĕk′ō sĭs təmz; Greek: *paleos,* old, + ecosystem]

The biosphere in Cambrian time. If this textbook could have been written during the Cambrian period, the contents would have been very different. The chapter "Life on Land" would have been entirely missing—there is no evidence of terrestrial life during the Cambrian. However, both "Life in the Water" and "Life in the Microscopic World" would have been present, though the mentioned organisms would have been different. Section Two, "Diversity Among Living Things," might have made dull reading, because the majority of our familiar organisms, from grass and palm trees to mosquitoes, whales, and man himself, could not have been included. They had not yet arrived on the scene. On the other hand, the major ecological ideas in Section One would still have had a place in our Cambrian book; ecological relationships were apparently much the same then as now.

Although there were no terrestrial ecosystems, marine ecosystems were well developed. There were shallow-water and deep-water organisms, floating and swimming and bottom-dwelling kinds. The chief marine producers then, as now, were probably microscopic plankton species—though their remains are not abundant.

The major animal phyla known today were present—except the chordates. The most abundant fossil animals of the Cambrian were brachiopods and arthropods. Many of the brachiopods were not greatly different from species living today. But the arthropods were so different that none of them could be placed in any of the modern arthropod classes.

Figure 10 • 9

Fossil trilobites (New York). Which of the kinds of fossils (pages 310–311) are these?

American Museum of Natural History

Figure 10 • 10

An artist's reconstruction of life in a Cambrian sea. How many kinds of organisms can you identify?

Among Cambrian arthropods, the ones that left the most abundant fossils were the trilobites. Most trilobites were small—2 to 6 cm in length—though a few were more than 50 cm long. From Cambrian rocks alone more than a thousand species have been described. Most species had two large eyes, but some had no eyes at all; these probably burrowed in the mud of the ocean bottom. Some trilobites were smooth; others had long, hollow spines over most of the body These spines may have served as protection against predators, though some paleontologists think they were helpful in floating. In any case, the many trilobite adaptations suggest that there were many ecological niches in the Cambrian seas.

trilobites [trī′lə bīts; Latin: *tri-*, three, + *lobus*, lobe]

What reason can you give for this conclusion?

Paleozoic [pā′lĭ ə zō′ĭk; Greek: *palaios*, ancient, + *zoion*, animal]

era [ĭr′ə]

Carboniferous [kär′bə nĭf′ər əs; Latin: *carbo*, coal, + *ferre*, to bear]

The trilobites disappeared from the fossil record at the end of the Paleozoic era. Apparently they left no descendants. Many other groups of organisms have a similar history: they are abundant for millions of years and then become extinct. On the other hand, the brachiopods still exist, as do sponges and coelenterates—though the species are different from the ones that flourished in Cambrian seas.

A Carboniferous ecosystem. In rocks that are dated between the Cambrian and the Carboniferous periods, fossils that indicate freshwater and terrestrial organisms are found. By Carboniferous time the first forest ecosystems fringed shallow seas that then covered much of the present North American continent. The trees in these forests were mostly relatives of the present-day horsetails, club mosses, and ferns. Some were gymnosperms—at least, strata of the late Carboniferous age contain some gymnosperm fossils. But the most familiar plants of today, the angiosperms, were absent.

Though some of the trees had branches, others bore their leaves at the top of a single stem in large clumps, as palms do today. When older leaves fell, they left scars in a characteristic pattern on the trunks. But the leaves did not fall all at once; the forests were evergreen.

Beneath the trees was thick undergrowth, mostly of ferns. Stream banks were lined with a dense growth of giant, reedlike plants related

☐ Water and swamp
☐ Land

Figure 10 • 11

North America in the Carboniferous period. What kind of evidence did geologists use to draw this map?

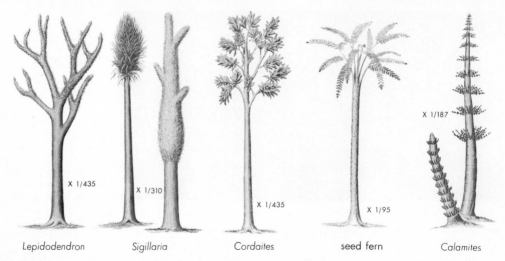

Lepidodendron   Sigillaria   Cordaites   seed fern   Calamites

X 1/435   X 1/310   X 1/435   X 1/95   X 1/187

Figure 10 · 12

Some trees of the coal-age forests: *Lepidodendron* and *Sigillaria* were lycopsids; *Cordaites* were primitive gymnosperms; the seed ferns have no living species; *Calamites* were sphenopsids.

Compare these sizes with those of the trees shown in Figure 8 · 18.

Why? What would have been the result if decay had been rapid?

to the horsetails of today. Thick tangles of moss probably covered the ground, but few of these soft and delicate plants have left traces in the fossil record.

The kinds of plants suggest to paleontologists that the climate in which these forests grew was warm and humid, with little or no seasonal change. Compared with tropical forests of today, however, the Carboniferous forests were shallow. The larger trees reached a height of about 30 m and had trunks 2 m in diameter.

Though fossils of Carboniferous decomposers are rare, decay certainly occurred. But the accumulation of great beds of organic remains in which there is a large proportion of carbon indicates that decay was rather slow. These beds, hardened and compressed, we now call coal. In coal itself remains are usually so altered we cannot see much detail; but in the beds of shale (mud turned to stone) that lie above and below the coal are many well-preserved fossils. From them we can form an excellent picture of the coal-age forests.

Figure 10 · 13

A fossil fern from the Carboniferous period.

Harold Hungerford

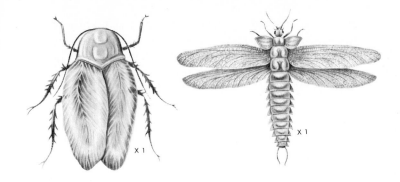

Figure 10 • 14

Insects from the Carbon-
iferous period: a cockroach
(*left*) and a possible ancestor
of the dragonflies (*right*).

X 1/24

Figure 10 • 15

An artist's drawing (based on
fossil bones) of an amphibian
of the Carboniferous period.

Insects were numerous. Predatory dragonflies that darted about in these forests were similar to modern kinds; but one was the largest insect ever known, with a wingspread of almost 75 cm. Cockroaches were abundant. Except for differences in size—a few were nearly 10 cm long—some were almost identical to modern species. But most of the insects belonged to orders now extinct. And some orders familiar today—mayflies, beetles, and mosquitoes—were not present.

Land snails glided over the vegetation; they probably were important herbivores. Scorpions, centipedes, and spiders were frequently encountered predators. The spiders (or perhaps we should call them spider-like animals) had no organs for producing silk, so they probably did not make webs.

Why do the paleontologists think that the land snails were herbivores and the scorpions and centipedes were predators?

The only large land animals were amphibians. Of these there were many kinds. Most had four legs, but they could not really stand; they waddled their way through the muck. Some were snakelike, without legs. None were like present-day frogs. All were probably predators, preying mostly on fishes in the streams and ponds.

A Triassic ecosystem. In the Connecticut Valley of New England are rocks that contain large, three-toed footprints. When these were

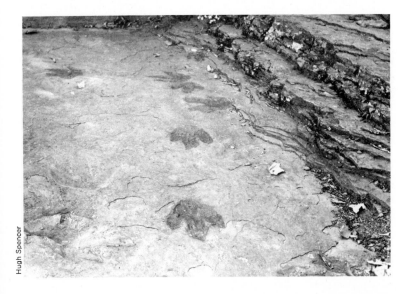

Hugh Spencer

Figure 10 • 16

Fossil footprints in the
Connecticut Valley.

discovered, many people—including paleontologists—believed that they had been made by giant birds. But because they are associated in many places with skeletons of reptiles, and because fossils of birds are unknown in the valley, it is now clear that the footprints were made by some of the early dinosaurs. Numerous other fossils help us build up a picture of the ecosystem that occupied the Connecticut Valley late in the Triassic period.

Triassic [trī ăs'ĭk]

The characteristics of the rocks there indicate to geologists that a slow, winding stream flowed through a valley. The stream carried materials from highlands, which lay on both sides, to a broad, flat plain, where it deposited them. The rocks show cracks similar to those found today in drying mud; these cracks are filled with material that once was sand or dust. Moreover, the deposits show the luster seen on dried clay and rocks that have been exposed to the polishing of desert winds. There are occasional impressions of large raindrops, suggesting that the region had sudden hard showers such as are common in arid regions today.

luster: shining with reflected light

Narrow bands of coal-like rocks indicate that small ponds were present in this arid region. Almost all the fossil plants are from such rocks. There are remains of ferns and horsetails that probably grew around the ponds. There may have been a scanty vegetation of small horsetails between the ponds. Fossils of the large lycopsid and sphenopsid trees that had been abundant in the coal age are lacking, but there are fossil logs of gymnosperms such as cycads, conifers, and ginkgoes. Though some of these are 50 cm in diameter, it is unlikely that trees grew in the region. Probably the fossils were formed from trees that were uprooted and swept down from the uplands when the river was in flood.

Why is it unlikely?

lungfish. See Figure 18 · 8.

The ponds were inhabited by aquatic insects and several kinds of fishes. Fossils of lungfishes, which could obtain oxygen from the air, suggest that the ponds sometimes dried up, just as do ponds where modern lungfishes live. But there were also swift predatory fishes that were not able to breathe air; so there must have been at

Figure 10 · 17

Fossil of a Triassic fish from the Connecticut Valley. How does it compare with fish of today?

X 1/23

Figure 10 · 18
A Triassic dinosaur.

Paul Eric Olsen

Margaret Matthew Colbert

Figure 10 • 19
An artist's reconstruction of a streamside scene from the Triassic period. How many of the organisms can you identify?

least some permanent ponds. Numerous tracks of worms are found in rocks that were once mud along edges of pools.

Reptiles were abundant. In the ponds lived large crocodile-like reptiles, but they were only distantly related to modern crocodiles. Paleontologists believe they were fish-eaters, because many fish bones have been found within their skeletons. Scurrying among the horsetails were lizard-like reptiles. The structure of their leg bones suggests they were fast-moving; and their small, sharp teeth indicate an insect diet. Several species of slender dinosaurs about 2.5 m high roamed the mud flats and left the tracks that first called attention to this paleoecosystem. All the dinosaurs were active and agile carnivores, preying upon smaller reptiles.

An Eocene ecosystem. During the Eocene epoch in the region now called the Geisel Valley of central Germany there was an ecosystem that can be visualized almost as clearly as if it existed today. An unusual combination of conditions brought about the fossilization of large numbers of organisms that seldom are formed into fossils. Organic materials that usually decay quickly and leave no trace were preserved in great detail.

epoch [ĕp′ək]
Geisel [gī′səl]

Trees of this ancient ecosystem are clearly represented by fossils of stems, leaves, seeds, and even pollen. Among the most common are fossils of sequoia, rubber, palm, fig, and cinnamon. And there are various lianas. Fossils of mosses are common, and fossils of algae are numerous. Among the remains of fungi are some that resemble the living genus *Penicillium*.

Snails are represented by fossils of both land and freshwater species. There are remnants of a number of species of crayfish. The most common insect remains are those of beetles, but mayflies and stone flies are also present. Fossil scales from the wings of butterflies provide some of the earliest known evidence of these insects. And the fossilized larva of a fly was discovered in the nostrils of a fossilized

stone fly. See Figure 9 · 7.

Figure 10 · 20

An artist's reconstruction of a scene in North America during the Eocene. Most of the vegetation and the turtle are little different from those of today. But the mammals are classified in orders that are now extinct.

X 1/32

Figure 10 · 21
A creodont.

heron. See Figure 3 · 2.

tapir. See page 105.

creodonts [krē′ə dŏnts′; Greek: *kreas*, flesh, + *odous*, tooth]

mammal—evidence of a kind of parasitism that still exists today.

Thousands of fish skeletons have been found. They represent many modern families, such as those to which bass and salmon belong. Scattered among the fish are remains of frogs and toads in all stages of development, from tadpoles to adults. A study of chemical substances in the preserved frog skin has made it possible to conclude that the frogs were green in color. Evidence of color is extremely rare in organisms of the past.

The Geisel Valley beds include fossils of many reptiles. Snakes have been found—some of them so small that they appear to have just hatched. There were long-tailed, tree-climbing lizards; there were terrestrial lizards; and there were burrowing lizards, some almost legless. Turtle skeletons are found lined up side by side in shallow depressions; perhaps death overtook the turtles while they were dormant. The Geisel crocodiles had stubby snouts and limbs well adapted to swimming. Many of their eggs have been discovered, some with the embryos still visible inside. But bird remains are rare, as they usually are. There are bones—some quite fragmentary—of herons and cranes, and of an owl-like bird.

Among the fossil mammals in the Geisel Valley is an opossum-like marsupial. Not only the skeletons of bats but even fragments of wing membranes, muscles, cartilage, and hair are preserved. Among rodents are species related to the present-day kangaroo rats of American deserts. All the primate fossils come from relatively small species, including several kinds of lemurs and tarsiers.

Representing the hoofed mammals are fossils of animals that resembled tapirs and of species of the horse family. The carnivores known from this deposit are all very primitive kinds, the most important being the creodonts. Some of these were large predators that were strong enough to kill even the biggest of hoofed mammals of that time; others were small, weasel-like forest dwellers that probably preyed on rodents.

Finally, in the Geisel Valley deposits we even have evidence of protists. So perfect is the preservation here that traces of bacteria can be clearly identified in the eye cavities of fish skulls, in fossil frog skin, and in fossil insect muscle. Usually we have to assume the presence of these pathogens in ancient ecosystems; in this one we have evidence.

What additional evidence would you need to show that these protists were indeed pathogens?

From the evidence represented by these fossils and from geological study of the layers of rocks, paleontologists can describe the ecosystem of the Geisel Valley during the middle Eocene.

A river floodplain was dotted with numerous ponds and water holes. Along the river and around the ponds grew a thick forest, and on the surrounding hills was a grassland. The animal remains crowded around the ancient ponds and water holes indicate a lack of water elsewhere, so evidently there was a dry season. The turtles that apparently died while dormant were probably estivating rather than hibernating. This opinion is supported by the fact that some trees in the ecosystem (cinnamon and palm) are species known to be intolerant of cold weather. Indeed, the whole assemblage of organisms was much like that of present tropical regions where wet and dry seasons alternate.

Altogether, this scene is much more familiar to us than the ecosystems of the Paleozoic and Mesozoic. But it still is not modern. Most of the families or genera of animals and plants are familiar, but the species are not. And the assemblage of living things seems odd, too; some of the kinds of organisms living together in the Eocene are widely separated in the 20th century A.D. Sequoias, now found in California, then grew side by side with rubber trees, now native to the Amazon Valley. Opossums, now of America and Australia, inhabited the Eocene forest with lemurs, now found only in Madagascar. Most of the Geisel turtles are classified in a genus now inhabiting Southeast Asia and tropical America. And what was a tropical forest doing in Germany? As is so frequently the case in science, the more we know, the more questions we raise.

Mesozoic [měs′ə zō′ĭk]

THE WORK OF PALEONTOLOGISTS

Collecting facts is the first job in any science. Fossils are the facts of paleontology, so fossil collecting is a basic task for a paleontologist. Chipping fossil ferns from a cliff in Greenland, uncovering an ancient human skull in Africa, stumbling upon a nest of fossil dinosaur eggs in Mongolia—such activities give paleontology a certain air of adventure. But an exciting and important discovery may come only after months or even years of searching. And fossil digging often

Figure 10 · 22

Excavating a dinosaur (Montana). What information do you think the paleontologist should record in the field?

Figure 10 · 23

Fossil dinosaur eggs. In some cases the bones of the unhatched young have been found within the shells.
× ½

turns out to be a hot, dusty, and monotonous occupation, with the paleontologist lying on the ground and slowly brushing dirt away from a delicate bone.

STUDYING THE EVIDENCE

Collecting fossils may be nothing more than a hobby. But to a paleontologist it is only the beginning of his work. From careful study of all the varied remains of organisms—often mere fragments—he attempts to reconstruct the appearance of living things of past ages, to understand the ways in which they changed during the long centuries of geological time, and to describe the ecosystems of which they were a part.

One of a paleontologist's first tasks when he returns from the field is to make measurements of his specimens. This enables him to report his findings to other scientists in an exact manner. And from comparisons of such measurements some conclusions may be drawn.

Investigation 10.1

PALEONTOLOGICAL COMPARISON

BACKGROUND INFORMATION

Members of the early Eocene genus *Hyracotherium* are the oldest known animals of the horse family, Equidae. In rocks of the late Eocene and of succeeding epochs of the Cenozoic, fossil remains of the family are abundant. Paleontologists have classified the animals represented by these fossils into about 20 genera. By combining many kinds of structural evidence, they have arrived at some agreement about the relationships among 17 of these genera, as shown in Figure 10 · 25. In this investigation you will study only one of the many structural characteristics that paleontologists have used.

In horses the grinding teeth are in the back of the mouth, separated from the front teeth by a toothless space. On each side of each jaw the grinding teeth (cheek teeth) consist of 3 premolars and 3 molars (Figure 10 · 26). The structural characteristic you are to study is the distance spanned by the cheek teeth.

X 1/16

Figure 10 · 24

Artist's drawing of *Hyracotherium*.

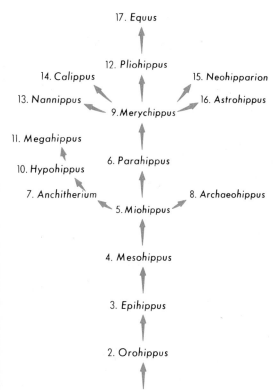

17. *Equus*

12. *Pliohippus*

14. *Calippus*   15. *Neohipparion*

13. *Nannippus*   16. *Astrohippus*

9. *Merychippus*

11. *Megahippus*

6. *Parahippus*

10. *Hypohippus*

7. *Anchitherium*   8. *Archaeohippus*

5. *Miohippus*

4. *Mesohippus*

3. *Epihippus*

2. *Orohippus*

Figure 10 · 25   1. *Hyracotherium*

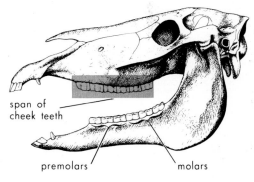

span of
cheek teeth

premolars   molars

Figure 10 · 26

MATERIALS

(per student)
graph paper, 1 sheet

PROCEDURE

The span of the cheek teeth has been measured in many horse fossils. Averages of the data are presented in Figure 10 · 27. When plotted on a graph, these data suggest certain relationships. Figure 10 · 28 shows the most

GENERA OF EQUIDAE	TIME OF EXISTENCE	SPAN OF CHEEK TEETH (IN CM)
1. Hyracotherium	Early Eocene	4.3
2. Orohippus	Middle Eocene	4.3
3. Epihippus	Late Eocene	4.7
4. Mesohippus	Early Oligocene	7.2
	Middle Oligocene	7.3
5. Miohippus	Late Oligocene	8.4
	Early Miocene	8.3
6. Parahippus	Early Miocene	10.0
7. Anchitherium	Early Miocene	11.3
8. Archaeohippus	Middle Miocene	6.5
9. Merychippus	Middle Miocene	10.2
	Late Miocene	12.5
10. Hypohippus	Late Miocene	14.2
11. Megahippus	Early Pliocene	21.5
12. Pliohippus	Early Pliocene	15.5
	Middle Pliocene	15.6
13. Nannippus	Early Pliocene	11.0
	Late Pliocene	10.7
14. Calippus	Early Pliocene	9.3
15. Neohipparion	Middle Pliocene	13.1
16. Astrohippus	Middle Pliocene	11.8
	Late Pliocene	11.8
17. Equus	Late Pliocene	18.8
	Pleistocene	17.6

Figure 10 · 27

convenient kind of grid. Construct such a grid, making it as large as possible so that the plotted points will not be crowded. As each point is plotted on the graph, place beside it the number of the genus it represents.

Connect the points representing the genera *Hyracotherium, Orohippus, Epihippus, Mesohippus,* and *Miohippus.* • What seems to have been the trend of evolution in the span of equid cheek teeth during Eocene and Oligocene times?(1) • Is it possible to continue to connect the points with a single line farther to the right on the grid?(2) • Without drawing such a line, describe the trend of evolution in cheek-teeth span during the Miocene, Pliocene, and Pleistocene.(3)

Now you can find out whether the data on the span of the cheek teeth fit other relationships among the equid genera—relationships worked out by paleontologists from evidence provided by other structural characteristics. To do this, draw lines between the plotted points so that they correspond to the arrows on Figure 10 · 25. For example: Draw a line from the dot for *Miohippus* to that for *Anchi-*

Figure 10 · 28

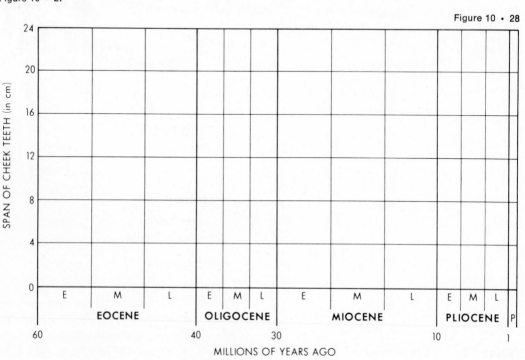

therium, continuing through that for *Hypohippus* to that for *Megahippus.* Draw another line from the dot for *Miohippus* to that for *Archaeohippus.* Draw a 3rd line from *Miohippus* to *Parahippus,* and so on.

CONCLUSIONS

If data on a single characteristic conflict with relationships worked out from other characteristics, the data will produce a set of crossing lines when graphed. • Do the data on the span of the cheek teeth support the relationships shown in Figure 10 • 25, or do they conflict with those relationships?(4)

• What was the average change in the span of the cheek teeth per million years from *Hyracotherium* to *Miohippus*?(5)   • What was the average change per million years from *Miohippus* to *Megahippus*?(6)   • From *Miohippus* to *Equus*?(7)   • From these results, what generalization can you make about the rate of evolutionary change within the Equidae?(8)

• What evidence do you have that the direction of an evolutionary change can be reversed?(9)

INTERPRETING THE EVIDENCE

Visualizing fossil organisms. Even when all the hard parts of an organism are preserved, they are seldom found in perfect order. The parts must not only be carefully excavated from the rock in which they are found; they must also be reassembled and placed in proper relation to each other. To do this well, a paleontologist must know the ways in which the parts of modern organisms are arranged—he must know the **anatomy** of modern organisms. Then, to picture the fossil organism as it was in life, he must imagine the placement of muscles and other "soft parts" that have left no trace. Again he is guided by his knowledge of the anatomy of modern organisms. Finally, he may paint the restoration. In his choice of colors he must be guided almost entirely by what he knows of color in modern organisms, because evidence of pigments is among the rarest of all paleontological data.

excavate [ĕks′kə vāt′; Latin: *ex,* out of, + *cavus,* a hollow]: to dig out

anatomy [ə năt′ə mĭ; Greek: *ana,* on, up, + *temnein,* to cut]: structure of an organism

In all this work it is possible for different paleontologists to interpret the evidence differently. The farther we go from the basic evidence—the fossils themselves—the greater is the possibility of differing interpretations.

Decisions about classification. Structural—anatomical—characteristics are more often used by taxonomists than any other kind. This emphasis on anatomy is, at least in part, because usually no other characteristics are found in fossils. And a kinship classification depends heavily upon knowledge of the ancestors—represented by fossils—or organisms now living. But if you look back at Section Two, you will see that many anatomical characteristics used in defining taxonomic groups are not likely to be preserved in fossils.

Consider the problem posed by a fossil from the early Mesozoic era—when the first mammals must have been evolving. How can we distinguish a mammal fossil from a fossil of one of the many reptiles of that time? Characteristics that distinguish present-day mammals from reptiles include simple jaw bones, definite kinds of teeth (incisors, molars, etc.), hair, milk glands, and the warm-blooded con-

A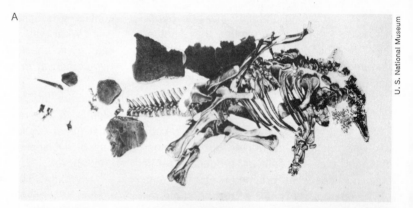

U. S. National Museum

B

Smithsonian Institution

Figure 10 • 29
Stegosaurus, a late Mesozoic
reptile.   ×1/50
A. Fossil bones laid out as
they were found.
B. Bones of another specimen, mounted in a
museum.
C. An artist's reconstruction.
D. Another artist's
reconstruction.

C

Peabody Museum of Natural History

D

Smithsonian Institution

dition. Suppose a fossil shows a jaw and teeth strongly resembling those of present-day mammals. A fossil is not likely to indicate hair or milk glands—certainly not warm-bloodedness. Does the fossil represent a mammal? Might there not at one time have been animals with mammal-like jaws and teeth without the other characteristics by which we define mammals today? Or suppose we discover a similar fossil together with an impression of hair. We may speculate that the hair helped the animal to maintain a warm-blooded condition. But did it have milk glands? Is it *fully* a mammal, or is it a mammal-like reptile?

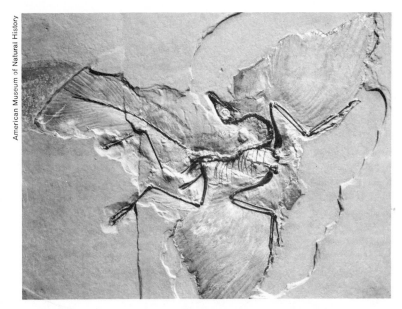

American Museum of Natural History

Figure 10 • 30

Archaeopteryx, earliest-known fossil of a bird. Most of the bones are much like those of dinosaurs. What is the evidence that shows it to have been a bird?

Such problems make the work of taxonomists difficult. But the problems' existence is evidence for the theory of evolution. If mammals evolved from reptiles, animals must once have existed that showed combinations of reptilian and mammalian characteristics.

A principle. From the foregoing examples of paleontological work, we can see a principle emerging: "The present is the key to the past." This means that unless we have evidence to the contrary, we interpret the past on the basis of our knowledge of the present. This applies to the structure of organisms, their function, their environment—indeed, it applies to the whole history of ecosystems.

How was this principle used in describing the paleoecosystems on pages 320–327?

SOME PALEONTOLOGICAL CONCEPTS

From years of studying fossils, paleontologists have been able to picture for us the living things and the ecosystems of the distant past. Paleontologists have also developed important scientific concepts that greatly influence the ways in which we think about our world.

Change and stability. No one can examine a large collection of fossils, especially if arranged in chronological order, without being impressed by change. Changes have occurred in single species of organisms, in large groups of species, in environmental conditions. Whole ecosystems have changed: where once there was coal-age swamp in Pennsylvania there is now dry, hilly oak forest. Such eco-system changes are further examples of ecological succession. But instead of successions involving a few centuries or millennia, these successions involve millions of years.

What geoecological successions have occurred in the region where you live?

It has been estimated that at least 130,000 species of animals are known only from their fossil remains. Perhaps no group of large vertebrates has left so many fossils as have the dinosaurs. But no fossils of dinosaurs have been found in rocks younger than the Mes-ozoic. Many other large groups of organisms have likewise become extinct—disappeared from the earth.

Can you name any?

What caused such extinctions? This problem has been a sub-ject for speculation among paleontologists for a long time. There are many hypotheses, but, unfortunately, paleontological hypotheses are not often testable by experimentation. Perhaps we shall never learn what brought about the extinction of the dinosaurs, for example. But as long as there are rocks that have not been opened by the paleon-tologist's pick, new evidence on the problem may be found.

Brontosaurus [brŏn′tə sôr′əs]

Evolution moves in only one direction—forward in time. This idea is termed "Time's Arrow." It took many distinct biological steps over millions of years to produce, let's say, *Brontosaurus*. The same evolutionary steps will never occur in the same sequence again on

X 1/200

Figure 10 · 31

Brontosaurus, a reconstruc-tion (*right*) and a fossil skeleton (*below*).

American Museum of Natural History

Earth. Thus no *Brontosaurus*—indeed, none of the thousands of known species of extinct organisms—will ever live on Earth again.

Though many species have died out and left no descendants, others seem to have merely changed through generation after generation until they are no longer recognizable as the same species. You might suspect that the most advanced forms in one geological period would give rise to the advanced forms in the next. But the fossil record does not support this view. For example, reptiles did not become more and more advanced during the Mesozoic and finally, at the end of the geological period, give rise to mammals—which are considered more advanced than reptiles. On the contrary, the ancestors that had given rise to the varied reptilian groups were apparently also the ancestors of the mammals (Figure 10 · 32). Thus, the ancestors of mammals were early and primitive reptiles rather than recent and

"Advanced forms": If you have forgotten this term, review Investigation 5.2.

Figure 10 · 32

Relationships among reptiles, birds, and mammals, according to the existing fossil evidence.

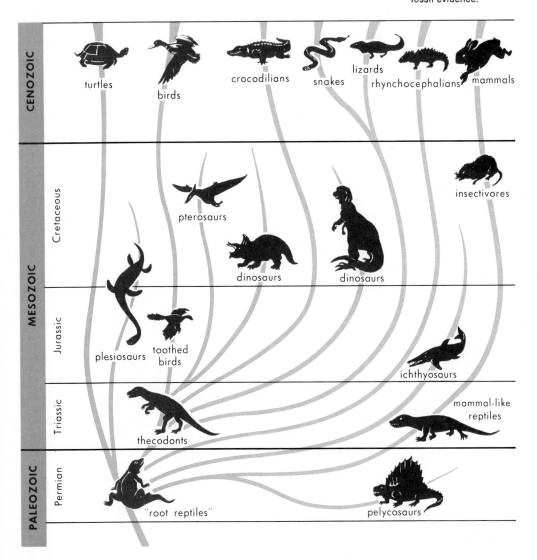

advanced reptiles.

Though the fossil record shows abundant evidence of change, it also provides evidence of great stability. Brachiopods much like those of the Paleozoic seas are found in 20th-century oceans. Except for their larger size, many of the fossil ferns and horsetails that lie in the coal beds are much like the ones that still grow a few meters above them in the Illinois woods. The Triassic lungfishes have disappeared from Connecticut, but lungfishes still inhabit the lakes of Africa and Australia. And turtles and frogs—slightly different kinds—survive from the Eocene in Germany.

Adaptation. What happens to organisms and ecosystems through time depends largely upon the kinds of changes a particular environment undergoes and upon the adaptability of the associated organisms. In Section Two the concept called "structural adaptation" was repeatedly mentioned: many structures of organisms seem to be fitted to the ecological niches that the organisms occupy. But a structure that adapts an organism to one environment might be a hindrance in a different environment. The fossil evidence indicates that structural adaptations slowly change as environmental conditions change or as organisms disperse into new environments.

Again and again during the history of life on Earth, the descendants of a small group of organisms that were originally adapted to a narrow range of ecological conditions dispersed into a great variety of ecosystems. As they did so, many features of their structure changed—as indicated by their fossil remains—in ways that adapted them to their new ecosystems.

This process, known as *adaptive radiation,* is well demonstrated

Marine organisms have probably changed less than land and freshwater ones. If this is indeed true, can you explain it?

Figure 10 · 33

Adaptive radiation in the class of mammals. Only the still-living mammals (*outer arc*) are listed in Chapter 4.

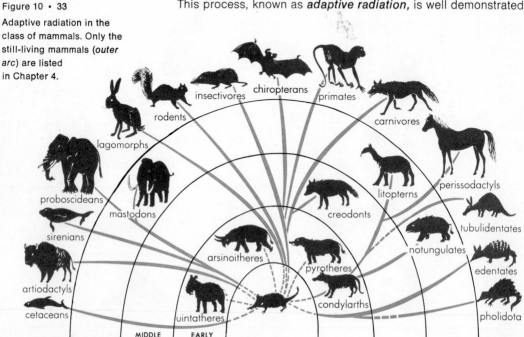

by mammals. The few fossils of mammals from the Mesozoic era indicate that they were small animals much like present-day shrews. From such ancestors the great variety of Cenozoic mammals apparently developed by adapting to a great variety of ecosystems. The fossil record of the bony fishes, which probably originated in small, freshwater streams, shows a history of adaptive radiation into the world's aquatic ecosystems. And among plants, the angiosperms have adaptively radiated into almost all terrestrial ecosystems.

On the other hand, the fossil record also shows examples of *adaptive convergence.* In such cases, descendants of quite different ancestors have developed similar structures as they adapted to similar ways of life. Animals that have adopted a burrowing life are similar in having appendages shorter than those of their ancestors (or no appendages at all), but the animals may be from very different taxonomic groups—earthworms and caecilians, for example. Another example is the development in distantly related species of a body form that enables animals to swim swiftly through the water as aquatic

Figure 10 · 34

Adaptive convergence in vertebrates: (A) toothed bird; (B) shark; (C) ichthyosaur—an extinct reptile; (D) whale.   × 1/24

Gottscho-Schleisner

Haven Kolb

Figure 10 • 35
A euphorbia (*left*) and a
cactus (*right*).

discontinuous
[dĭs′kən tĭn′yō̄ əs]: separated,
not connected

predators. Adaptive convergence is also known among plants. Compare (Figure 10 • 35) the spiny, leafless euphorbia of the African desert with a cactus of the Mexican desert; yet flower structure and other characteristics show that euphorbias and cacti are members of two different families.

Light on the present from the past. In discussing the distribution of organisms in Chapter 8 (pages 262–263), two hypotheses were presented. On the whole, fossil evidence favors the second: each species originated in one place and then spread into other places. But regardless of which hypothesis is correct, some taxonomic groups of organisms were undoubtedly once more widespread than they are today. As a result, there are now *discontinuous distributions*—geographic distributions in which taxonomically related organisms are found today in widely separated regions and are absent from intervening regions.

Consider tapirs, for example. During the Eocene, they were present in the Geisel Valley of Germany. Germany is about midway between tropical America and Malaysia, the present-day homes of tapirs. Fossils from other places show that tapirs once existed in many parts of regions that separate their modern geographic ranges.

And fossil marsupials of the Geisel Valley show that these mammals were once not restricted to America and Australia as they are today.

Recall now the principle presented earlier in the chapter: "The

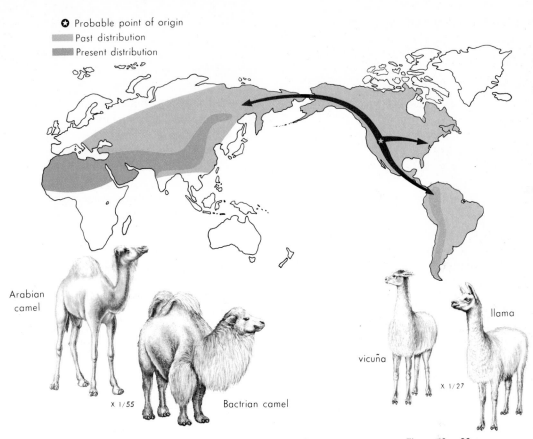

● Probable point of origin
▨ Past distribution
▧ Present distribution

Arabian camel

× 1/55

Bactrian camel

vicuña

llama

× 1/27

present is the key to the past." In the study of discontinuous distribution, we can see that sometimes the reverse is true: the past sheds light upon the present. A paleontologist travels far and wide over the earth to seek evidence; to interpret that evidence, he must allow his mind to move freely back and forth between present and past.

Figure 10 • 36

Past and present distribution of the camel family. How can paleontologists determine the part of the world where the family originated?

Investigation 10.2

COAL BALLS

BACKGROUND INFORMATION

Usually the plant and animal remains that make up coal have been so compressed that individual fossils are difficult to distinguish. In structures known as "coal balls," however, the organic matter of dead organisms was invaded at an early stage of decomposition by waters containing calcium carbonate or calcium magnesium carbonate. These waters left a mass of limy substance in which the organic remains were embedded and protected.

For study, a coal ball is sawed into pieces of convenient size and the sawed surface is ground smooth with Carborundum [kär′bə rŭn′-dəm] powder. The smooth surface is then etched—that is, enough limy material is removed, by flushing with an acid, to leave cell walls and other structures minutely elevated.

Plant and sometimes animal remains can then be made to adhere to a cellulose acetate sheet.

MATERIALS AND EQUIPMENT

Carborundum powder, #600
glass plate
medicine dropper
coal ball, slice
beaker, with water
culture dish
hydrochloric acid, 2% solution
acetone
cellulose acetate sheet, a little larger
    than the coal-ball specimen
tape, adhesive, cellulose
microscope

PROCEDURE

Sprinkle a pinch or two of Carborundum powder on the glass plate. With a medicine dropper add a few drops of water. Place the flat surface of the coal-ball slice on the Carborundum and grind for about 2 minutes. This exposes a new, clean layer of organic material. Rinse the ground surface in water.

Lay the specimen in a culture dish, ground side up. Flood the surface with a 2% hydrochloric acid solution and allow it to stand for 2 minutes. The surface will turn cloudy with bubbles as the acid reacts with the lime. Rinse the acid from the surface of the specimen with water. Remove the specimen; empty the culture dish and rinse it with water. Allow the specimen to air dry.

Now prop the specimen at a slight angle in the culture dish. Flood the surface with acetone. Smoothly lower a sheet of cellulose acetate onto the acetone-covered surface, starting at the lower edge of the specimen and using a rolling motion so that the acetone is evenly spread and air bubbles are forced out. Allow about 20 minutes for drying. Now take one edge of the sheet between your fingers and slowly peel it from the surface.

Tape the peel to a glass slide. Using either a dissecting or a compound microscope, scan all parts of the peel. Low power is best for recognizing the forms of the fossils that are present in the sliced surface of the coal ball. Look for leaf and stem outlines, and for fossils of spores, seeds, or insect parts. Record your observations by means of sketches.

Using high power, examine details of structure. You should be able to see different kinds of plant cells. Sketch any that you can see. You may be able to identify some of the kinds of cells that you observe by referring to Figure 13 · 3, 13 · 10 or 13 · 15, which show the structure of modern plants.

SUMMARY

Your coal ball was formed during the Carboniferous period. · Referring to Figure 10 · 5, what is the least possible number of years since your fossils were formed?(1) · Based on your observations, state your opinion concerning the amount of structural change that has occurred during this time.(2)

GUIDE QUESTIONS

1. From what evidence do paleontologists obtain their ideas of life in past ages?
2. How was the paleontological evidence formed?
3. Why are sedimentary rocks the most important kind of rocks for paleontologists?
4. What difficulties do paleontologists encounter in reading the "book of the earth"?
5. By what methods do geologists determine the age of a sedimentary rock?
6. According to geologists, how were environmental conditions on Earth during its early history different from conditions today?
7. Pasteur showed that spontaneous generation does not occur. How, then, is it possible to speculate about the origin of life from nonliving materials?
8. What experimental evidence supports the *possibility* of such an occurrence?
9. How far back in time do the oldest fossils now known date?
10. Which organisms of today do the ear-

liest undoubted fossils most resemble?

11. In what kind of environment did all the organisms known from Cambrian fossils live?

12. What were trilobites?

13. Compare a forest of Carboniferous time with a forest of today.

14. Name some groups of land animals that are *not* known from Carboniferous time.

15. What class of land vertebrates apparently originated between Carboniferous and Triassic times?

16. What evidence indicates to geologists that the Connecticut Valley was an arid region in Triassic time?

17. What class of land vertebrates apparently originated between Triassic and Eocene times?

18. How is each statement about ecological relationships in the Geisel Valley ecosystem supported by evidence?

19. In what ways would the assemblage of organisms in the Eocene Geisel Valley seem strange to a person living there today?

20. Why is collecting fossils only the beginning of a paleontologist's work?

21. If you were shown paintings by two different artists of an organism known only from fossils, how might the paintings differ?

22. By what reasoning would a paleontologist decide whether a particular fossil represented a reptile or a mammal?

23. By what principle is the interpretation of paleontological evidence guided?

24. How does the fossil record support both the idea of change and the idea of stability in living things?

25. Contrast the processes of adaptive radiation and adaptive convergence.

26. How can fossils help to explain discontinuous distribution in today's organisms?

PROBLEMS

1. The broad view of the history of life has been developed through study of fossils from all parts of the world. In any one region, such as a state, rocks representing only a few of the geological time divisions are likely to be found. Obtain a geological map of your state. From it construct a geological time scale, indicating the time divisions that are represented in your state and those that are not. Use the map as a guide to places where you may be able to collect fossils yourself.

2. In Greenland and in Antarctica, beds of coal occur. These were formed from abundant plant remains; today the regions are covered with ice caps. How can you account for this evidence of great photosynthetic activity at high latitudes?

3. Investigate the origin of the names given to the geological time intervals listed in Figure 10 • 5.

4. In eastern Colorado and western Nebraska there are extensive deposits of fossils in rocks of Oligocene age. Known as the White River deposits, these rocks were formed from silts in which there were streaks of gravel. The fossils represent, among others, the following organisms: grasses, reeds, hickories, and hackberries; freshwater clams, several kinds of freshwater fish, frogs, snakes related to the boas, and several species of large land tor-

toises; among mammals, saber-toothed cats and species closely related to the modern dogs, members of the camel family, four species of horses, and several species of rhinoceroses. Some of the rhinos were much like those of the present day; others had long, slender legs much like those of horses; still others, much like the hippos of today, had heavy bodies with short legs and large feet. Using the evidence given here, describe the ecosystem represented by the White River deposits. Does your interpretation agree with those of other students? How do you support your interpretation in places where it differs from theirs? What additional evidence would give further support to your interpretation?

5. By means of research and the kind of reasoning used in this chapter, try to reconstruct ecosystems represented in the fossil remains found in the La Brea tar pits of Los Angeles and in the Florissant region of Colorado. You will need to find out what geological times these deposits represent, the conditions under which the fossils were formed, and the kinds of fossils present.

6. Fossil skeletons of ichthyosaurs have been discovered with fossil skeletons of small ichthyosaurs inside them. What possible interpretation of this situation can you devise? What additional evidence would you look for to sup-

port your interpretation?

7. Investigate the hypotheses that have been advanced to explain the extinction of the dinosaurs. You may think that one seems more reasonable than the others. If so, explain why you think so.

8. Two groups of hoofed mammals, the litopterns and the notungulates, inhabited South America for a long time. During this time there was no land connection between South and North America. Soon after the Panama land bridge was reestablished in the Pliocene, these animals became extinct. How can you account for this?

9. The fossil record of the rhinoceroses is nearly as good as that of the horses, but it has not been described in easily obtained pub-

lications. If you have the necessary library resources and the ability to tackle technical literature, you can work out the rhinoceros story on your own. Begin with Henry F. Osborn, "The Extinct Rhinoceroses," *Memoirs of the American Museum of Natural History,* Vol. 1, pp. 75–164, 1903; and Horace E. Wood, "Trends of Rhinoceros Evolution," *Transactions of the New York Academy of Sciences,* 2nd Series, Vol. 3, pp. 83–96, 1941.

10. In recent years many geologists have begun to support the theory of continental drift. This theory holds that the present arrangement of continents is different from what it was in the geological past. Investigate the theory and especially its use in explaining the geographical distribution of plants.

SUGGESTED READINGS

AUFFENBERG, W. *Present Problems about the Past.* (BSCS Pamphlet 6). Boulder, Colo.: EPIC, 1963. (Contains a good description of a Miocene ecosystem. Fairly easy.)

BARGHORN, E. S. "The Oldest Fossils," *Scientific American,* May, 1971. Pp. 30–41.

BONE, Q. *The Origin of Chordates.* London: Oxford University Press, 1972. (A pamphlet that discusses one of the major problems of the history of life. Fairly easy.)

COLBERT, E. H. *Dinosaurs: Their Discovery and Their World.* New York: E. P. Dutton & Co., Inc., 1971. (A nontechnical account of the best-known group of extinct animals. Fairly easy.)

ERICSON, D. B., and G. WOLLIN. "Micropaleontology," *Scientific American,* July, 1962. Pp. 96–104+.

GLAESSNER, M. F. "Pre-Cambrian Animals," *Scientific American,* March, 1961. Pp. 72–78.

GORDON, W. D. *A Pleistocene Ecosystem.* Chicago: Rand McNally & Co., 1969. (A detailed account of paleontological study, part of which was carried out by high school students. Easy.)

MATTHEWS, W. H. *Fossils: An Introduction to Prehistoric Life.* New York: Barnes and Noble, Inc., 1962. (A full but simple outline of paleontology. Includes information on fossil collecting. Easy.)

MILES, A. E. W. *Teeth and Their Origins.* London: Oxford University Press, 1972. (Because they are so hard, teeth are among the most abundant fossils. Fairly easy.)

NEWELL, N. D. "Crises in the History of Life," *Scientific American,* February, 1963. Pp. 76–92.

RHODES, F., H. W. ZIM, and P. R. SHAFFER. *Fossils—A Guide to Prehistoric Life.* New York: Golden Press, 1962. (An inexpensive, easy, and well-illustrated pocket guide to fossils.)

SCHAEFFER, B., and M. MANGUS. "Fossil Lakes from the Eocene," *Natural History,* April, 1965. Pp. 10–21.

SIMPSON, G. G. *Life of the Past.* New Haven, Conn.: Yale University Press, 1953. (For students who want more than just a description of strange organisms.)

WEST, R. G. *Studying the Past by Pollen Analysis.* London: Oxford University Press, 1971. (A pamphlet that describes a method that is much used for research on Pleistocene ecosystems. Fairly easy.)

YOUNG, R. S., and C. PONNAMPERUMA. *Early Evolution of Life.* (BSCS Pamphlet 11). Boulder, Colo.: EPIC, 1964. (The title is somewhat misleading. Deals with the origin of life. Requires some background in biochemistry.)

WITHIN THE
INDIVIDUAL ORGANISM

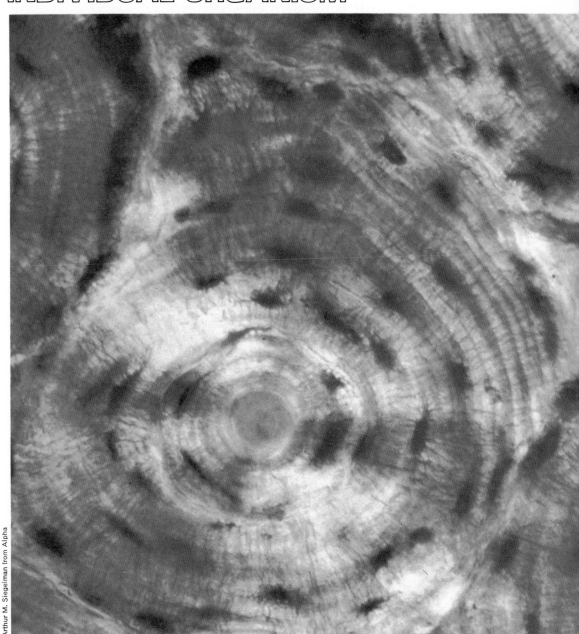

WITHIN THE INDIVIDUAL ORGANISM

Individual organisms vary greatly in size. A redwood tree may extend 100 m from root to tip, and a blue whale may weigh 150 metric tons. Near the other extreme, a single bacterium may be only 0.4 μ wide and weigh a small fraction of a milligram. But regardless of their size, we have been treating all of these as equal units—as individuals interacting with other individuals and with the abiotic environment.

We have viewed living things somewhat as a traffic engineer looks at automobiles. He is concerned with the way they move about, with what happens when they collide, and with how they may be managed. He is not concerned with the way their motors are constructed, with the principles involved in their braking systems, or even with their source of energy. The mechanic, on the other hand, is concerned with the structure of automobiles—with gears, pistons, and valves—and with the way the energy of gasoline is transformed into motion of turning wheels. One looks at automobiles from the outside; the other, from the inside.

The two views are not independent, of course. The way a machine is constructed determines what it can do. The same is true of organisms. So the time has now come to shift from the outside view of organisms to the inside view. What activities within an organism produce the activities we have seen from the outside? To understand these internal activities of an organism, we must examine its parts. Is there any basic internal unit from which the parts are constructed? Internal activities imply internal energy. We have seen how energy goes from organism to organism in the biosphere, but what happens to this energy within an organism?

These are some of the questions we shall consider in the following chapters.

Cells

SOME HISTORY

If you examine a fairly large organism—yourself, perhaps—you can easily identify a number of parts. Externally there are eyes, arms, and hair; inwardly are teeth and tongue; and after a bit of dissection (imaginary, of course!) you find heart, liver, stomach, and other organs. Proceeding with the dissection, you will find smaller and smaller parts.

In the case of the human body, investigation of structure through dissection had almost reached the limits of unaided vision by the 16th century. When, in 1543, Andreas Vesalius published his great work, *De Humani Corporis Fabrica* ("Concerning the Structure of the Human Body"), many persons no doubt considered that the subject had been completed.

DISCOVERY OF CELLS

Today it seems that Vesalius began, rather than ended, the scientific study of human anatomy, because in the next century the microscope was developed.

In the turbulent 17th century Leeuwenhoek was not the only curious observer, though no other had lenses as fine as his. However, 11 years before the Royal Society published Leeuwenhoek's letters, Robert Hooke, a secretary of the society, found interesting microscopic structures in cork, the bark of a Mediterranean oak, and in stems of various plants. In cork he observed neat rows of thick-walled compartments that reminded him of honeycomb. Because beekeepers called the compartments in honeycomb "cells," Hooke called the cork compartments *cells.*

The story of Hooke's cells closely parallels the story of Leeuwenhoek's "little animals." During the following century and a half many men saw both cells and "little animals," but no one at that time fully understood them.

Hooke himself found that in many living materials (the cork, of course, was dead) the cells were filled with a liquid substance. Gradually attention shifted from the walls to this liquid within. In 1809 Jean Baptiste de Lamarck wrote: "Every living body is essentially a mass

dissection [dĭ sĕk′shən; Latin: *dis-*, apart, + *secare*, to cut]

American Museum of Natural History

Figure 11 • 1

Andreas Vesalius [än′drē əs və sā′li əs]: 1514–1564. Flemish anatomist.

Robert Hooke: 1635–1703. English physicist, mathematician

The word "cell" originally meant a small room.

Jean de Lamarck [zhän də lə märk′]: 1744–1829. French naturalist

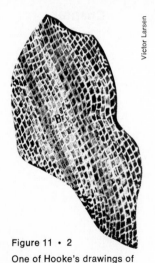

Victor Larsen

Figure 11 • 2

One of Hooke's drawings of cork (*Micrographia*, 1665).

Henri Dutrochet [äN rē′ dōō′trə shĕ′]: 1776–1847. French physiologist

Matthias Schleiden [mə thī′əs shlī′dən]: 1804–1881

Theodor Schwann [thē′ə dōr shvän]: 1810–1882

aggregations [ăg′rə gā′shənz; Latin: *ad*, to, + *gregare*, to herd]

Cell dyes came to be called stains by microscopists. What stains have you used?

of cellular tissue in which more or less complex fluids move more or less rapidly."

Lamarck was a bold originator of generalizations, but he was not good at seeking out facts to support them. His statement was not supported until 1824, when Henri Dutrochet wrote that "the cell is truly the fundamental part of the living organism." Because the boundaries of plant cells are easier to see than those of animal cells, this idea was at first more acceptable to botanists than to zoologists. But by 1839 the generalization was fully developed with respect to both animals and plants. Two Germans, Matthias Schleiden, a botanist, and Theodor Schwann, a zoologist, did much to convince their co-workers of its usefulness. As Schwann wrote, "We have thrown down a great barrier of separation between the animal and vegetable kingdoms."

THE CELL THEORY

Thus "cell," which once referred to an empty space, came to mean a unit of living matter. Leeuwenhoek's "little animals" were interpreted as the least possible degree of cellular organization—that is, single cells. All other organisms could then be regarded as aggregations (groupings) of cells—very highly organized aggregations, to be sure, but nevertheless reducible to cell units.

This idea did not lead immediately to a great new era of research. Despite the microscope's usefulness, detailed studies of cells had to await another technological development—the discovery of dyes that make cellular structures more clearly visible. This came with a

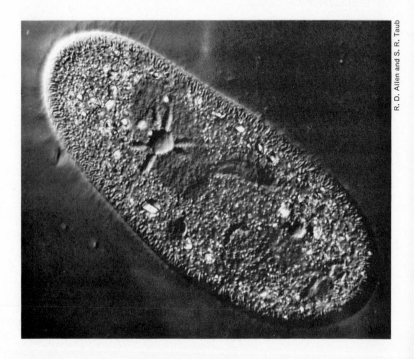

R. D. Allen and S. R. Taub

Figure 11 • 3

Paramecium. The complex structure of this protist has led some biologists to regard it not as a single cell but as an organism that has lost cellular structure.   × 450

great spurt in chemical knowledge in the 1850's and 1860's. Soon thereafter every life process was being associated with one type of cell or another. Cells quickly came to be regarded as not only the units of structure but the units of function as well.

Already, in the decade after Schleiden and Schwann, investigators had begun to find that cells normally and regularly come into being through the division of parent cells. Soon the idea was established that since the beginning of life there had been no break in the descent of living cells from other cells of the past.

Today the cell theory may be summarized as three main ideas: (1) Cells are the units of structure in living organisms. (2) Cells are the units of function in living organisms. (3) All cells come from pre-existing cells.

Why is this called a theory rather than a generalization?

Investigation 11.1

OBSERVING CELLS

MATERIALS AND EQUIPMENT

(for each student or pair of students)
onion, cut into pieces about 1 cm²
forceps, fine-pointed
microscope slide
scalpel
medicine droppers, 3
cover slips
monocular microscope
iodine - potassium-iodide solution (I₂KI)
paper towels
elodea leaves
toothpicks (sterile)
physiological saline solution
methylene blue solution
dissecting needles, 2
frog blood
frog skin

PROCEDURE

You will be provided with small pieces of onion. On the inner, concave side of each piece, the **epidermis** (ĕp'ə dûr'mĭs)—skin— may be readily peeled off with forceps. Place a small piece of epidermis (*much* smaller than a cover slip) on a slide, avoiding overlapping or wrinkling. Add 1 or 2 drops of water and a cover slip.

Examine the onion epidermis under the low power of the microscope. Look for cell boundaries. Draw a *small part* of the field of view to show cell shapes and arrangement.

Place a drop of I₂KI stain along one edge of the cover slip. Pull it under the cover slip, using the technique shown in Figure A•6. Record any changes that occur as the stain spreads across the onion epidermis. Then switch to high power and draw a single cell, including as much detail as you can see. Label any parts you can identify.

With forceps remove a young leaf from near the tip of an elodea plant. Place it on a clean slide and add a drop of water and a cover slip. Observe the leaf under low power. • By slowly turning the fine adjustment back and forth, determine the number of cell layers in the leaf.(1) Switch to high power. Select an average cell and focus on it carefully. • Is there any evidence that the cell is living? If so, what is the evidence?(2) Make a drawing of the cell, including as much detail as you can see. Label any parts you can identify.

Using the blunt end of a sterile toothpick, gently scrape the inside surface of your cheek. You should obtain a barely visible mass of material. Rub this material on a *clean* slide. Add a drop of physiological saline solution and stir thoroughly with the toothpick. Examine under low power. By carefully using the fine adjustment, try to observe the three-dimensional shape of the cells. • Would you describe them as spherical, disk-shaped, or neither?(3) Add a drop or two of methylene blue and a cover slip. Find several cells well separated from the others. Draw one or two of them, including as much detail as you can see. Label any parts you can identify.

Place a drop of diluted frog blood on a clean slide. Add a drop of methylene blue and a cover slip. Most of the cells you see are red blood cells. Find an area where the cells are neither too crowded nor too scarce and center it in the field of view. Switch to high power. Draw one or two cells and label any parts you can identify.

Place scrapings from a frog's skin on a clean slide. Add a drop of physiological sa-line, a drop of methylene blue, and a cover slip. Using low power, locate cells and then switch to high power. Draw one or two cells and label any parts you can identify.

SUMMARY

In your data book construct a chart. In the first column list all the kinds of cells you have observed. Head other columns with the names of cell parts that you have identified. Then review your sketches and notes. For each kind of cell examined, place an X beneath the name of each cell structure observed. • Does the lack of an X indicate that the structure was not present in the cells observed? Why or why not?(4)

• On the basis of your observations, which kind of cell (plant or animal) seems to have more angular, less rounded shapes?(5) • Which has more clearly defined boundaries?(6) • What cell structure may be involved in these characteristics?(7)

CELL STRUCTURE

Study Figure 11 • 4. Not all structures shown in the diagram are to be found in all cells, nor are all structures known to occur in cells shown

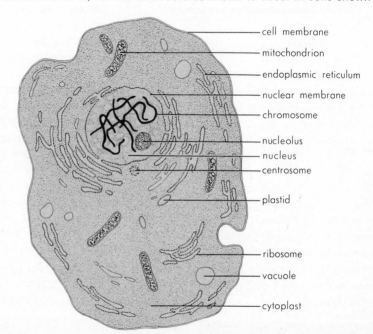

Figure 11 • 4

Cell structures. This is a diagram; it does not picture any particular kind of cell.

- cell membrane
- mitochondrion
- endoplasmic reticulum
- nuclear membrane
- chromosome
- nucleolus
- nucleus
- centrosome
- plastid
- ribosome
- vacuole
- cytoplast

in the diagram. It is intended only to assist you in remembering some principal cell structures.

Nearly every cell contains at least one **nucleus** (plural, "nuclei"). Under an ordinary microscope the nuclei of living cells are usually difficult to see, but they are readily visible when stained with various kinds of dyes. Nuclear substances take up larger amounts of stains than do substances in the rest of a cell. This causes a contrast between the nucleus and the surrounding parts. Unfortunately, most stains kill cells; but the phase-contrast microscope, a kind not usually found in school laboratories, allows biologists to see nuclei in unstained living cells.

Within nuclei are one or more small bodies that usually stain

nucleus [nōō'klĭ ŭs; Latin: *nux*, nut]

Figure 11 • 5
Diversity among cells.

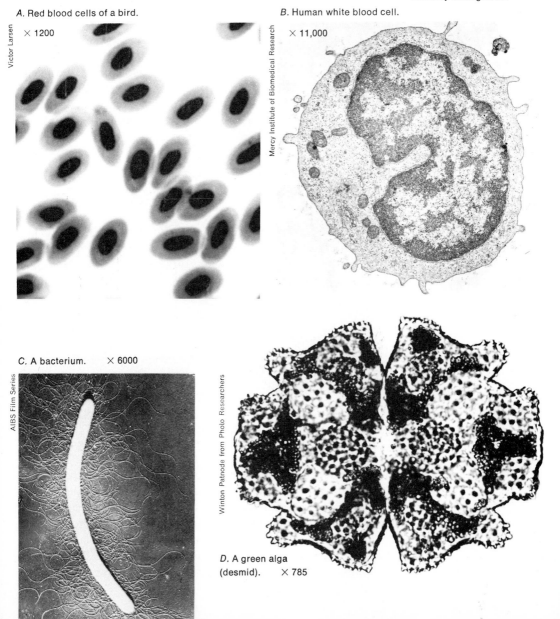

A. Red blood cells of a bird.
Victor Larsen
× 1200

B. Human white blood cell.
Mercy Institute of Biomedical Research
× 11,000

C. A bacterium.   × 6000
AIBS Film Series

D. A green alga
(desmid).   × 785
Winton Patnode from Photo Researchers

nucleoli [nōō klē'ə lī']

centrosome [sĕn'trə sōm'; Greek: *kentron*, center, + *soma*, body]

cytoplast [sī'tə plăst; Greek: *kytos*, a vessel, + *plassein*, to form, mold]

organelles [ȯr'gə nĕlz']: "little organs"

chloroplasts [klōr'ə plăsts; Greek: *chloros*, green, + *plassein*]

mitochondrion [mī'tə kŏn'drē ən; Greek: *mitos*, thread, + *chondros*, cartilage]

more deeply than the nucleus itself. These are the *nucleoli* (singular, "nucleolus"). In almost all animal cells, in most protist cells, but in rather few plant cells, a small structure, the *centrosome,* is found just outside (or in a few cases, just inside) the nuclear membrane.

The body of a cell outside the nucleus is known as the *cytoplast.* The cytoplast surrounds the nucleus, although the position of the nucleus varies in different kinds of cells—sometimes it is near the center, sometimes far to one side.

Within cytoplasts are various kinds of small structures that are called *organelles.* Even without stains it is easy to see *plastids,* for most of them are colored by pigments. Plastids are found in cells of plants and some protists. Among the variety of plastids, *chloroplasts,* containing green pigments (chlorophylls), are of major concern to us, because they are involved in photosynthesis.

Under a light microscope *mitochondria* (singular, "mitochondrion") appear only in specially stained material as very tiny, rod-shaped bodies that may be either scattered throughout the cytoplast or concentrated in certain places. Under an electron microscope, however, each mitochondrion shows up as a somewhat sausage-shaped body containing parallel infolded layers of membranes.

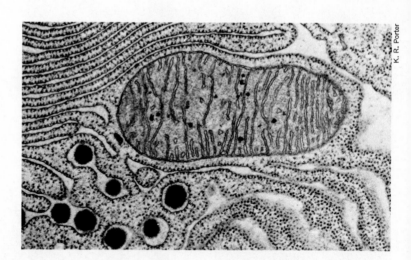

K. R. Porter

Figure 11 · 6
Mitochondrion in a cell from a bat.   × 14,700

The *cell membrane* is the boundary between a cell and its environment. Under a light microscope the membrane appears merely as the outer surface of the cytoplast, but under an electron microscope it clearly has a two-layered structure. Chemical investigations show that a cell membrane is composed of protein and fatlike substances. A membrane having a similar structure surrounds the nucleus.

endoplasmic reticulum [ĕn'də plăz'mĭk rĭ tĭk'yə ləm; Greek: *endon*, within, + *plassein*, and Latin: *retum*, a net]

Electron microscopy also reveals within a cytoplast a membranous network called the *endoplasmic reticulum.* This network branches throughout a cytoplast and appears to connect its cell

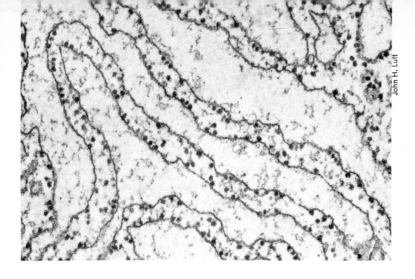

John H. Luft

Figure 11 · 7
Detail of an endoplasmic
reticulum.   × 160,000

membrane with its nuclear membrane. Adhering to the endoplasmic
reticulum are organelles called **ribosomes.**

The substance of a cytoplast is a complex and constantly changing mixture of a great variety of organic, and some inorganic, substances in water. Some of these substances clump together to form
granular bodies that are sometimes visible under high magnification
of a light microscope. Both animal and plant cells contain **vacuoles**—
droplets of liquid that sometimes contain solid particles. Vacuoles are
usually small and few in the cells of animals and protists, but are
frequently large and numerous in plant cells.

In addition to their cell membranes, the cells of plants and some
protists are surrounded by nonliving cell walls. In a living cell the two
structures are pressed so closely together that under a light microscope they are frequently difficult to distinguish from one another.

ribosomes [rī'bə sōmz']

vacuoles [văk'yŏŏ ōlz'; Latin:
vacuus, empty]

SOME CELL PHYSIOLOGY

You might study the parts of a clock and still not understand how the
clock runs. But it is certain that you could never understand how a
clock runs without studying its parts. Investigation of a mechanism's
structure is chiefly aimed at learning how it operates. You have been
studying some of the visible parts of cells—the structure of cells. Now
you can try to understand how a cell runs—how it functions. The study
of biological function is called **physiology.**

physiology [fĭz'ĭ ŏl'ə jĭ; Greek:
physis, nature, + *logos,*
speech, reason]

METABOLISM

The activities of organisms require energy changes. Since cells
are the basic functional units of organisms, it follows that these energy changes must take place within cells. For example, you can
move your arm because muscle cells can change chemical energy
into the mechanical energy of a shortening muscle. In one way or

another all activities or functions of organisms involve energy changes. The resulting very large number of continuing chemical reactions in cells are collectively known as **metabolism.**

In obtaining energy for its activities, a cell constantly uses up energy-rich molecules, converting them into energy-poor molecules that are useless for metabolism. However, one of a cell's most striking characteristics is its always shifting but, on the average, constant composition—its steady state. Maintaining this steady state, while the stock of useful energy-rich substances is always being reduced and the burden of energy-poor substances is always being added to, demands that substances continually enter and leave a cell.

TRANSPORT

A cell, then, is an open system. Yet there is a definite boundary —the cell membrane—between a cell and its environment. While the cell membrane acts as a barrier between the living substance and the environment, it must also allow various substances to pass through. Furthermore, there are internal membranes—the nuclear membrane, for example—through which substances must pass. And of course substances must move from one part of a cell to another. All this adds up to a complex physiological problem: How do substances move into cells, out of cells, and within cells?

Diffusion. Biologists constantly use concepts developed by physicists and chemists. At this point we need to use the physicists' molecular theory of matter. According to this theory all matter is made up of tiny particles that are in continuous motion. Originally all the particles were called molecules—hence the name of the theory; now some may go by other names, such as ion. The higher the temperature, the faster the molecules move. In solids each molecule's motion is restricted to vibration. In liquids, gases, and dissolved solids the molecules vibrate, but, in addition, they move easily from one place to another. These movements are helter-skelter in direction—one molecule bumps into another, and both go off in new directions. This is described as **random** movement.

molecules [mŏl′ə kūlz′; Latin: moles, a mass]

vibration [vī brā′shən; Latin: vibrare, to shake]

Do you know any of the evidence on which the molecular theory is based?

If you place a colored, soluble solid in a test tube of water, you observe that the color gradually spreads throughout the water. According to the molecular theory, as the colored substance dissolves, its molecules begin to move in a random manner. This random movement gradually carries them from a place where they are more abundant per unit volume (that is, where their concentration is greater) to places where they are less abundant per unit volume (that is, where their concentration is less). This process is called **diffusion.** At the same time that the molecules of colored substance are diffusing, the water molecules are also diffusing. Originally there was a *low concentration of water molecules* where the concentration of the colored substance was high and a *high concentration of water molecules* where the concentration of the colored substance was low.

diffusion [dĭf yū′zhən; Latin: dis-, apart, + fundere, to pour]

After the solution is completely uniform, collisions and rebounds

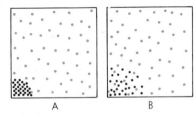

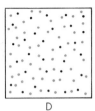

Figure 11 • 8

Diagram of stages in diffusion. In *D* the particles continue to move; but because each moves randomly, they remain evenly distributed in the available space.

continue. But for every molecule that moves from right to left there is another that moves from left to right. Thus the movement is continuous among the molecules without a net change in their distribution—and therefore there is no more diffusion.

Movement always involves energy. Where do you think the energy for diffusion comes from?

Investigation 11.2

DIFFUSION THROUGH A MEMBRANE

MATERIALS AND EQUIPMENT

(for each team)
cellulose tubing, 20-cm lengths, 2
soluble-starch solution, 15 ml
rubber bands, 2
glucose solution, 15 ml
iodine solution
beakers, 600- or 1000-ml, 2
glass-marking crayon
Tes-tape or piece of Clinitest tablet
in test tube

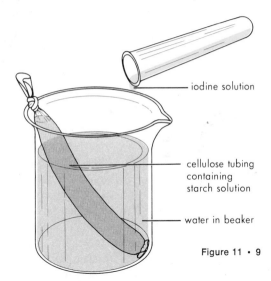

iodine solution

cellulose tubing containing starch solution

water in beaker

Figure 11 • 9

PROCEDURE

Open the cellulose tubing by moistening and then rubbing it between the thumb and forefinger. Tie a tight knot about 1 cm from one end of each piece of tubing.

Into one tube pour soluble-starch solution to within about 5 cm of the top. Pinch the top of the tube together tightly and rinse the tube under running water to remove any starch from the outside. Fasten the top of the tube tightly with a rubber band at a point not more than 2 cm above the top of the liquid. Place the tube in a beaker of water. Mark the beaker *A*. Add enough iodine solution to give the water a distinct yellowish color.

Into the second tube pour glucose solution to within about 5 cm of the top and repeat the procedure given in the previous paragraph

—but do not add iodine solution to the water in the beaker. Mark this beaker *B*.

Allow the tubes to stand about 20 minutes. Then dip a piece of Tes-tape into the water in Beaker B (or pour a small quantity of the water into a test tube containing a fragment of a Clinitest tablet). Record the color. Observe the tube in Beaker A. Record any color change you see in either the tube or the water in the beaker.

Let Setup B stand overnight. The next day record any change observed.

STUDYING THE DATA

• On the basis of the chemical test for starch, what must have happened to the iodine molecules in Setup A?(1)   • On the basis of the chemical test for glucose, what must have happened to the glucose molecules in Setup B?(2)   • From the evidence obtained by allowing Setup B to stand overnight, what other substance must pass through the membrane?(3)   • Which substance did not pass through a membrane? How do you know that it did not? (4)

CONCLUSIONS

Physicists can show that the molecules of any one substance are all about the same size but that the molecules of different substances are different in size. Measurements show that iodine molecules and water molecules are very small, glucose molecules are considerably larger, and starch molecules are very large.   • On this basis suggest a hypothesis to account for the observations made in this investigation.(5)   • What assumption did you make about the structure of the membrane?(6)

Cell membranes. The contents of cells are largely solutions or suspensions of substances in water. And all active (that is, not dormant) cells exist in a water environment. Cells of the human body are no exception. Every one of our living cells (cells of the outer skin are dead) is coated with moisture. Therefore, an active living cell is a mixture of things in water, separated by its cell membrane from another mixture of things in water. The cell membrane is the boundary that separates this unit of living substances from the rest of the universe. Within cell membranes occur all the activities that, taken together, make up what we mean by "life." (Actually, the membrane is living too, so the word "within" must be thought of as including the membrane itself.) Through the cell membrane must pass everything that a cell obtains from its environment and also everything that a cell returns to its environment.

Diffusion through membranes. A paper bag holds potatoes, but it does not hold water very long. A plastic bag holds water, but oxygen passes through the plastic fast enough to keep a goldfish alive in the water. The paper bag is permeable to water but not to potatoes; the plastic bag is permeable to oxygen but not to water. Any membrane that is permeable to some substances and not to others is said to be *differentially permeable.*

But not fast enough to keep *you* alive! You use oxygen more rapidly than a goldfish.

permeable [pûr′mǐ ə bəl; Latin: *per,* through, + *meare,* to glide]

differentially [dǐf ə rěn′shǐ ə lǐ]

Among molecules that diffuse easily through cell membranes are those of water, carbon dioxide, and oxygen. Many ions of inorganic substances also diffuse easily. But the molecules of many compounds that are dissolved or suspended inside cells are too large to pass through cell membranes by diffusion.

The *direction* in which any given kind of substance diffuses is determined, as we have discussed above, by concentrations. If concentration is greater *outside* than inside a cell, the direction of diffusion is into the cell. If concentration is greater *inside,* the direction of diffusion is outward.

What evidence do you have that different substances can diffuse in different directions at the same time?

Differential permeability is of special importance when we consider the water-diffusion relationships of a cell. Let us assume that Substance X, whose molecules are too large to diffuse through the cell membrane, is found in a relatively high concentration within a cell but does not occur in the fluid outside that cell.

First, imagine that the cell has no membrane. The tendency for the solution to become uniform results in the diffusion of the molecules of X from the area of their higher concentration to the area of their lower concentration (Figure 11 • 8). Also *water* molecules diffuse from the area of their higher concentration (which is where the concentration of X is lower) to the area of their lower concentration (which is where the concentration of X is higher).

Now consider the real situation. The high and low concentrations of X are separated by the differentially permeable cell membrane. Only *one* of the two movements of molecules can occur—the movement of water molecules through the cell membrane into the cell. Therefore water accumulates inside the cell. This creates pressure on the membrane from the inside. The pressure may even be sufficient to burst the membrane.

Why *must* the concentration of water molecules be lower where the concentration of other molecules is higher, and vice versa?

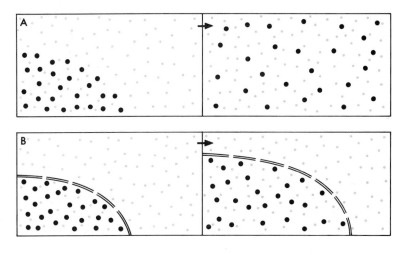

Figure 11 • 10
Diagram of diffusion (*A*) without a differentially permeable membrane, (*B*) with such a membrane.

A paramecium lives in a freshwater environment. Within a paramecium there is a much higher concentration of molecules that cannot diffuse through its cell membrane than there is outside. Just as in Figure 11 • 10, water diffuses from the environment into the paramecium because the concentration of the *water* is higher outside the paramecium than it is inside. In the paramecium, however, the excess water is continuously accumulated in a vacuole and periodically expelled to the exterior. The paramecium must constantly "pump" water out or it will be flooded. This, of course, is work—it costs energy.

Review your data from Investigation 9.2. Can you now give a fuller explanation of your results?

Active transport. Many movements of substances through cell membranes cannot be explained by diffusion. For example, in most cells the concentration of potassium ions is many times greater inside than it is outside. It can be demonstrated that potassium ions readily pass through cell membranes by diffusion. Why is it that these ions do not leave the cell by diffusion?

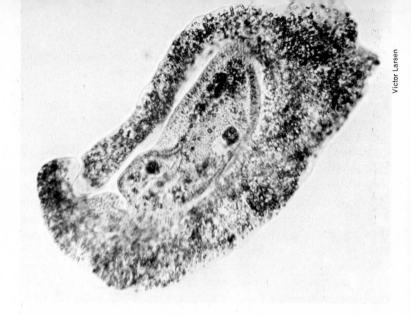

Victor Larsen

Figure 11 • 11

This ameba has a para-
mecium in a large food
vacuole, from which digested
substances diffuse into the
ameba's cytoplast. Why is
there a hazy area over part
of the vacuole? Compare
this photograph with
Figure 6 • 8.   × 350

In fact, there *is* a constant diffusion of potassium ions from cells. Careful investigation has shown, however, that cells can take in potassium ions from the environment at a rate at least as great as the rate at which the ions are lost by diffusion. Cell physiologists use the term "ion pumps" for mechanisms that move ions from a region of low concentration to one of high concentration. Of course these are not mechanical devices, but their action requires the expenditure of energy—work—just as it is necessary to use energy to operate a water pump or an air pump.

Movement of substances from lower to higher concentrations—opposite to the direction of diffusion—occurs not only through external cell membranes but also through the membranes of mitochondria and nuclei. Any such movement is called *active transport.*

Cyclosis. Diffusion probably accounts for much of the distribution of substances within cells. In many kinds of cells, however, substances are also distributed by the motion of the matter making up the cytoplast. Especially in plants and protists it is possible to observe this "streaming," called *cyclosis,* with the high power of an ordinary laboratory microscope. Although the exact way in which cyclosis occurs is not known, it is clear that it requires the expenditure of energy, just as active transport does.

cyclosis [sī klō′səs]

CELL DUPLICATION

The third major idea in the cell theory is that all cells are produced from preexisting cells. Why and when does one cell become two? Indirectly such cell duplication is probably related to the maximum size that a *given kind* of cell can maintain. Among cells of different kinds there is an enormous variation in size. For example, the yolk of an ostrich egg (a single cell) is about 300,000 times larger than a rickettsial cell. But there may be a maximum limit to the size a given kind of cell can maintain. If so, then continued growth of a cell must result in division, even though reaching a certain size is not the direct cause of division.

Whatever the cause, cells *do* divide. Usually nucleus and cytoplast divide almost simultaneously. However, sometimes the nucleus may divide, but not the cytoplast. Such division, if repeated, will give rise to a structure like the hypha of *Rhizopus* (Figure 11 · 12). Or the nucleus may divide, with division of the cytoplast occurring at some later time, as in spore formation by ascomycetes.

simultaneously [sī'məl tā'nē əs lĭ; Latin: *simul,* together with]: refers to two things happening at the same time

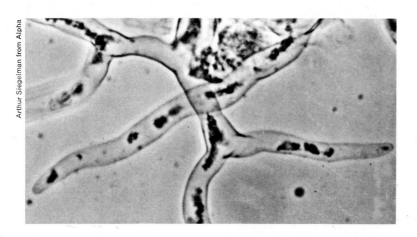

Arthur Siegelman from Alpha

Figure 11 · 12

A fungus, *Rhizopus,* containing several nuclei not separated from each other by cell membranes. Is the structure of *Rhizopus* an exception to the cell theory?   × 200

MITOSIS

Division of the nuclear substances seems to be an important part of cellular duplication. Mature human red blood cells, which have no nuclei, never divide; instead, they survive a short time (about 110 days) and then disintegrate. On the other hand, cells of blue-green algae divide even though they have no definitely organized nuclei.

In the great majority of cells there *is* a definite nucleus, and nuclear division is observable as a clear sequence of events. So much attention has been concentrated on this sequence that the name for it, *mitosis,* is sometimes incorrectly applied to the whole process of cell division.

disintegrate [dĭs ĭnt'ə grāt'; Latin: *dis-,* apart, + *integer,* whole]

mitosis [mī tō'sĭs; Greek: *mitos,* a thread]

CELL DIVISION IN ANIMALS

In mitosis of an animal cell, the first observable event is the division of the centrosome. The two parts of the centrosome separate and begin to move around the nucleus. (Refer to Figure 11 · 13 as you read on.) Fiber-like structures develop around them, radiating from each half centrosome like the spokes of a wheel. As the two centrosome parts continue to move away from each other, the fibers between them lengthen, forming a structure called a *spindle.* While these events are taking place, the nucleolus diminishes in size and disappears. The nuclear membrane disintegrates and likewise disappears.

While the centrosome halves are moving, the nuclear material increases in stainability. In the stained nucleus an observer can see a set of threadlike parts, called **chromosomes**. Close examination

chromosomes [krō′mə sōmz; Greek: *chroma*, color, + *soma*, body]

Figure 11 · 13

Six photographs of mitosis in the cells of an embryonic whitefish. In *A* the process is just beginning, and in *F* it is nearly completed; but the times between photographs are not equal. How many cell parts can you identify?   × 1000

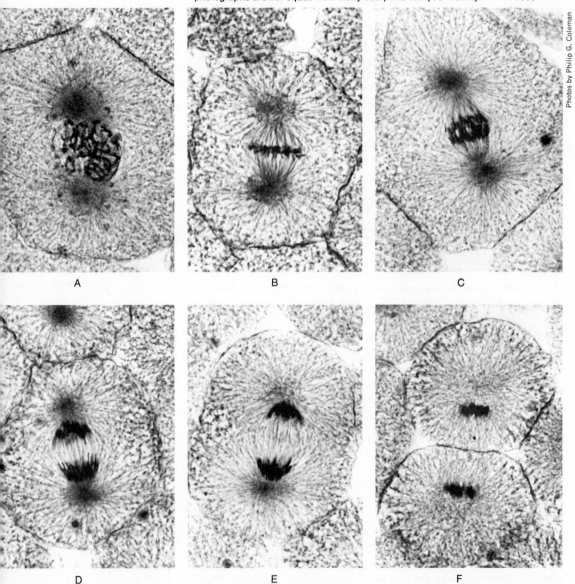

Photos by Philip G. Coleman

A   B   C

D   E   F

shows that each chromosome is double from the time it can first be seen. Each strand of a chromosome is called a *chromatid.* The chromatids are attached to each other at a single point, the **centromere.** Gradually the chromosomes become shorter, thicker, and more distinct. Under high magnification it becomes clear that this is due to coiling, just as a long, thin wire can be coiled into a shorter and thicker spring.

centromere [sĕn'trə mĭr; Greek: *kentron*, center, + *meros*, a part]

By the time the spindle is complete—that is, when the centrosome halves are 180° apart on the circumference of the nucleus—the chromosomes are fully coiled. If we call the positions of the centrosome halves the **poles** of the spindle, then we can imagine a plane across the center of the spindle and equidistant from the poles. This is the **equatorial plate.** (Because of high magnification the cells in the photographs appear two-dimensional, so the equatorial plate seems to be a line rather than a plane.) The chromosomes move toward the equatorial plate, and their centromeres become attached to spindle fibers. The centromere of each chromosome now divides, so the paired chromatids separate from one another; however, each centromere remains attached to a fiber of the spindle.

equidistant [ē'kwə dĭs'tənt; Latin: *aequus*, equal, + *distare*, to stand apart]

The chromatids from each chromosome move apart. Once separated from its former partner, each chromatid of a pair is referred to as a chromosome. One member of each pair moves away from the equatorial plate and toward one pole of the spindle; the second moves toward the other pole. Each centromere leads the way as though pulled by a shortening of the spindle fibers; the rest of the new chromosome trails along.

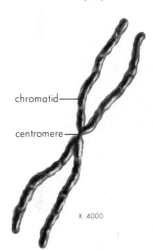

chromatid

centromere

X 4000

Figure 11 · 14
A chromosome before separation of chromatids.

Now the fibers of the spindle begin to fade and the chromosomes start to uncoil. At each pole a new nuclear membrane forms around the group of chromosomes, leaving the centrosome outside. A nucleolus appears within each new nuclear membrane. At some time before the next nuclear division occurs, the chromosomes become double (with two chromatids) again; but this cannot be seen. The formation of new nuclei ends mitosis.

Usually division of the cytoplast begins as new chromosomes approach the poles. A furrow forms around the cytoplast in the equatorial plate and deepens until the original cell is cut in two. Because they cluster near the equatorial plate, the mitochondria in the cytoplast are distributed more or less equally between the two new cells. The division of the cytoplast, unlike that of the nucleus, is not always equal, but its completion ends cell division.

SIGNIFICANCE OF MITOSIS

Nuclei were discovered and named by Robert Brown, who in 1831 reported seeing small bodies within plant cells he had studied. How little he understood the importance of his discovery is shown by the fact that he merely mentioned it in a footnote. Because the unstained nucleus is difficult to see with ordinary microscopes, practically nothing was learned about it until stains came into use. Thus,

Robert Brown: 1773–1858. Scottish botanist

the behavior of the nucleus during mitosis was first described only about a century ago.

The sequence of events in mitosis appears to be a device to ensure exact, equal division of the nuclear substance—which suggests that this substance is very important. Research during the past eight decades has amply supported this idea. Abundant evidence shows that complex nuclear substances regulate the activities of a cell and that the characteristics of a cell, both structural and functional, are expressions of these activities. Thus, maintaining characteristics from one cell generation to the next depends upon the duplication of the chromosomes in the parent cell, with full, identical sets being transmitted to the daughter cells. Apparently each bit of chromosome material is duplicated to form the paired chromatids before they become visible. Then the events of mitosis result in one chromatid of each pair ending up in each new cell.

Investigation 11.3

MITOSIS AND CELL DIVISION IN PLANT CELLS

BACKGROUND INFORMATION

If an onion is placed with its base in water and kept in the dark for several days, slender white roots sprout from it and grow into the water. This growth occurs partly by repeated duplication of cells. Therefore, in the end of a root you might expect to see cells in the process of mitosis. With proper procedures cells in mitosis can indeed be seen under a microscope. One such procedure can be accomplished within an hour.

In an alternative, more lengthy procedure a root is stained and then gradually saturated with a supporting substance such as paraffin. It is then cut into a series of very thin slices with a microtome, and the slices are mounted on slides. The mounting medium is one that hardens, making a permanent preparation.

Arthur Siegelman from Alpha

Figure 11 · 15

A microtome. The material is embedded in a block of paraffin that forms a continuous ribbon of slices. These slices are then used for making permanent mounts on slides.

MATERIALS AND EQUIPMENT

hydrochloric acid - alcohol solution
watch glasses, Syracuse, 2
forceps, fine-pointed
onion roots, in 70% alcohol
Carnoy's fluid (with chloroform)
microscope slide
scalpel or razor blade
aceto-orcein solution
cover slip
cleansing tissue
monocular microscope
prepared slide, long sections of
onion-root tip

PROCEDURE

Pour hydrochloric acid - alcohol solution into a Syracuse watch glass to a depth of about 3 mm. Using forceps, pick up a root that has been fixed in 70% alcohol, *grasping it by the cut end* and not by the pointed end. (Caution: In all later operations handle the root by the cut end only.) Transfer the root to the watch glass. Allow it to remain in the solution for 5 minutes. This treatment breaks down the cementing material that holds the cells together. Shortly before the 5 minutes are up, pour Carnoy's fluid into a second watch glass, again to a depth of 3 mm. Using forceps, transfer the root to this second watch glass and allow it to remain there for 3 minutes. This treatment hardens the material, which has been softened by the acid treatment, and reduces damage to the cells in subsequent procedures. Again using forceps, transfer the root to the center of a clean slide. Using a scalpel or razor blade, cut off the tip (the last 2 mm or less of the root) and discard the rest. Immediately add one or two drops of aceto-orcein solution. Cut the tip into small pieces and allow these to remain in the solution for 5 minutes. This solution stains certain cell structures, including nuclei and chromosomes. Do not let the preparation dry up; if it appears to be doing so, add another drop of solution. Next, place a clean cover slip over the pieces of root tip and tap lightly on the cover slip with the point of a pencil held vertically. This will

separate the cells and spread them out under the cover slip. Now fold a cleansing tissue several times so it is the same shape as but slightly larger than the slide. Then make a final fold in the tissue, bringing its ends together. Place the tissue on the table and insert the part of the slide where the cover slip is located into the final fold, making a "sandwich," with several layers of tissue under the slide and several on top of the cover slip. With the "sandwich" resting flat on the table, press down vertically with your thumb on the upper layer of cleansing tissue. This will further spread the cells and flatten them. Be careful to apply pressure without twisting so that the cover slip is not moved laterally in relation to the slide. Finally, carefully remove the slide from the cleansing tissue. You have now made a "squash" preparation.

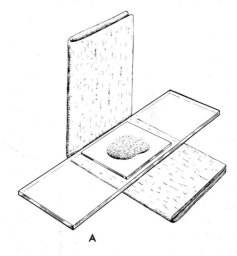

A

Figure 11 · 16
Making a "squash"
preparation.

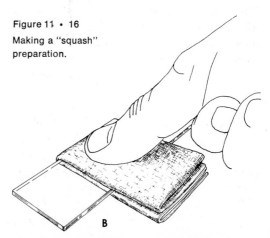

B

OBSERVATIONS

Examine the slide under low power of the microscope. Move the slide so that you scan the entire area under the cover slip. Look for cells containing nuclei that appear to be made up of distinct threadlike parts. Such cells were undergoing mitosis at the time they were killed. Locate an area where cells in various stages of mitosis are numerous. Switch to high power and examine this area carefully. If necessary, adjust the diaphragm of your microscope to increase the clarity of the image. Draw at least 5 entire cells, each in a different stage of mitosis. Then number your drawings in the order in which you think the stages occur during mitosis.

Now examine a prepared slide containing longitudinal sections of onion-root tip. Study each section first under low power and then under high power. • In what region of the root tip are most of the cells that are undergoing mitosis?(1) • How does the shape of cells undergoing mitosis compare with that of cells located in other parts of the sections?(2) Study a number of cells in different stages of mitosis, plus several which do not appear to be dividing. • Are any structures visible in these cells on the prepared slide that you could not see in the "squash" preparation? If so, draw one or more cells showing these structures.(3) Refer to the illustrations of dividing animal cells on page 358. • What differences, if any, can you find in the ways mitosis and cell division occur in animal cells and in plant cells?(4)

FOR FURTHER INVESTIGATION

1. If you were attempting to determine the number of chromosomes present in cells of a root, would it be better to use "squash" preparations or sections of the root?

2. Suppose you suspected that frequency of mitosis in onion roots varied with the time of day. How would you go about getting data to confirm or refute your suspicion?

3. Do all the events in mitosis take about the same time, or do some of them occur faster than others? How would you proceed experimentally to obtain information to answer this question?

DIFFERENTIATION

After cell division one of two things may follow: either the daughter cells separate or the daughter cells remain together. In the first case there are two unicellular individuals; in other words, cell duplication is identical with the reproduction of an individual. In the second case repeated cell divisions result in groups of connected cells. If the cells in the group remain approximately alike, the group is a colony. But if the cells come to differ from each other in various ways, the group becomes a multicellular individual. Because cells usually increase in size between divisions, repeated cell divisions usually result in the growth of a colony or multicellular individual.

unicellular [ū′nə sĕl′yə lər; Latin: *unus*, one, + *cella*, cell]

multicellular [mŭl′tĭ sĕl′yə lər; Latin: *multus*, many, + *cella*]

A PUZZLE

paradox [păr′ə dŏks; Greek: *para*, beyond, + *doxa*, opinion]: an apparently contradictory statement

Buried in the last paragraph is a paradox. If, as we reasoned on page 360, the process of mitosis ensures that both daughter cells will have the *same characteristics*, then how can any of the cells in a group derived from the same parent cell come to differ from the others? But differ they do, as you know from observing blood and skin cells of the frog; both of these descended from a single cell! Indeed,

John H. Luft

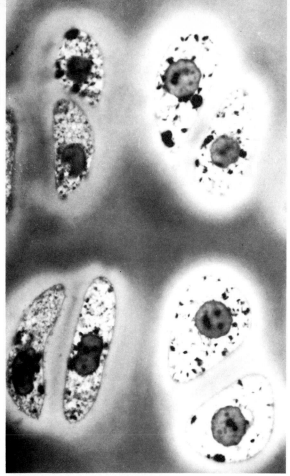

A. Cartilage of a frog.   × 1350

Figure 11 • 17
Diversity among tissues.

Martin H. Zimmerman

C. Pith of a grape stem.   × 60

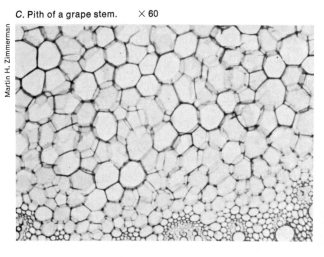

Runk/Schoenberger from Grant Heilman

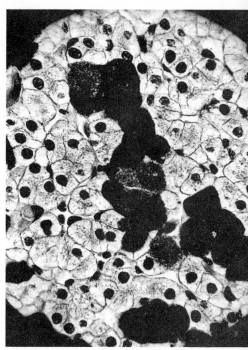

B. Outer skin of a salamander.   × 170

D. Wood.   × 35

Harold v. Green

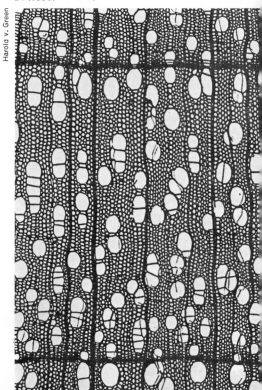

every multicellular organism—an oak tree, a cow, a man—develops from a single cell; yet the adult contains cells of a great many kinds.

ingenious: clever, inventive

differentiation
[dĭf'ə rĕn'shĭ ā'shŭn]

In the past 70 years many ingenious experiments have provided biologists with information about the puzzle of **differentiation.** It is now clear that differentiation involves (1) selective use of information stored in the chromosomes, (2) ways in which adjacent cells affect each other in the developing organism, and (3) factors in the environment. Yet the fundamental question—How does differentiation occur?—remains unanswered.

RESULTS OF DIFFERENTIATION

Differentiation is an orderly process. Cells do not become endlessly different; they become different in limited and predictable ways. Further, they become different in groups rather than individually. Microscopic examination of a multicellular organism therefore reveals the same basic structural characteristics in each member of a particular group of cells. In another group, all cells may be similar to each other but different from those in the first group. Groups in which all cells have similar structural and functional characteristics are called **tissues.**

Some of the money that is available for cancer research goes into studies of cell differentiation. Why?

A tissue might be considered a population of similar cells, just as a species is a population of similar individuals. In both cases one population is surrounded by other populations—in the first case, by other kinds of cells; in the second, by other kinds of individuals. In both cases a population has many close and necessary relations with adjacent populations. And just as we can artificially remove a portion of a population of individual organisms—a mouse colony, for example—from its ecosystem and keep it in a laboratory, we can also remove a population of similar cells—muscle tissue, perhaps—and cultivate it in a test tube. In such laboratory situations many valuable things can be learned about tissues and about the structure and functioning of the whole organism. But under natural conditions neither a mouse colony nor a muscle tissue lives alone.

See Figure 11 · 18. What things would you have to do in order to maintain a tissue culture?

Some multicellular organisms, such as sponges and some algae, seem to have no organization other than that of tissues. But most have different tissues grouped into body parts that perform one or more functions for the whole organism. Such a body part—a leaf or a heart, for example—is called an **organ.** Organs, like tissues, can be removed from the organism and cultured artificially, but this is not done as often as with tissues.

AGING

No individual cell lives forever. But a unicellular organism never grows old. Unless it is killed by unfavorable environmental effects (lack of food, accumulation of poisonous wastes, being eaten by other organisms), it simply disappears as an individual when it becomes two new individuals by dividing.

In multicellular organisms, however, the situation is not as simple. Some cells do not continue to divide, and they are not killed directly. Instead, they seem to gradually lose their vigor and die: they become old, we would say. Why do cells of multicellular organisms age and die? Do aging and death of such cells result from harmful environmental effects? Or do they result from internal changes that are caused by differentiation?

Perhaps in vertebrates the cells of the outer layer of skin and of the lining of the intestine die as a result of unfavorable environmental conditions. On the other hand, an internal cause—lack of nuclei— has been suggested as the cause of the early death of red blood cells of mammals. But the red blood cells of birds, which *do* contain nuclei, also have a short life-span.

Some evidence exists that changes occur early in the differentiation of some kinds of cells. Some of these changes may be harmful to the metabolic processes. In recent years some biologists have come to believe that the accumulation of such harmful changes may "slow down" a cell and result in what we call aging. But why do not such changes also occur and accumulate in reproductive cells and in unicellular organisms?

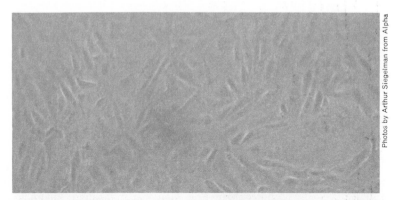

Photos by Arthur Siegelman from Alpha

Figure 11 • 18

Culture of human embryonic kidney tissue (*above*).   × 175 Tissue-culture chambers in an incubator (*below*).

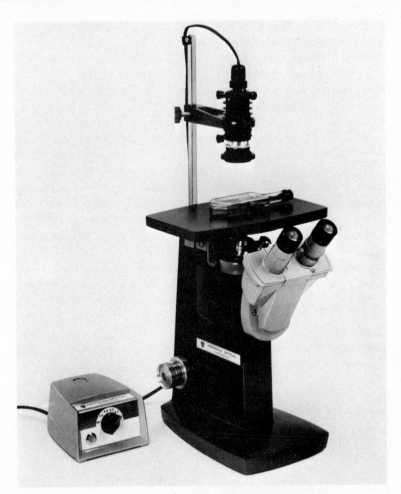

Figure 11 • 19
In what ways is this microscope that is used for examining tissue cultures different from other micro-scopes you have seen?

Many kinds of cells that are grown in tissue cultures, where they are maintained in an excellent environment, survive and go through cell division almost indefinitely. This suggests that aging, failure to divide, and death may be caused by the cellular environment within the body. But differentiation of cells is itself, at least in part, depen-dent upon that internal environment. In many respects, therefore, tissue-culture cells may not be "normally" differentiated, so we can-not have complete confidence in such evidence.

Like the problem of differentiation, the problem of aging and death of cells is complex. But it is a very important problem. Today in the human population more and more individuals are living to a point where the aging of their cells shows up in problems of health. Therefore, many cell biologists devote themselves to the study of aging both because aging is an interesting biological process and because such study may result in increased understanding of practical problems of human aging.

What effects does an increasing number of old people have on the lives of the rest of the human population?

GUIDE QUESTIONS

1. How has the meaning of the word "cell" changed since Hooke's time?

2. Why are staining techniques useful in the study of cells?

3. What is the cell theory?

4. Compare and contrast cells of plants, animals, and protists, using the principal cell structures as the basis for distinguishing them.

5. Distinguish between anatomy and physiology.

6. What is meant by the metabolism of a cell?

7. Why must a cell be constantly taking in and getting rid of substances?

8. What are the *facts* of diffusion? How does the molecular theory explain the facts?

9. Cell membranes are differentially permeable. What does this mean?

10. If water molecules are less concentrated outside a cell membrane than they are within the membrane, what will be the direction of water diffusion?

11. Molecules of different sizes can pass back and forth through a cell's membrane, yet the substance of the cell remains easily distinguishable from the substance of its environment. Explain.

12. What observations by cell physiologists have led to the theory of active transport?

13. Which of the processes by which substances move into and out of cells require the use of a cell's energy?

14. The terms "mitosis" and "cell division" are not synonymous. Explain.

15. In your own words describe the principal events that occur during mitosis.

16. What seems to be the biological meaning of mitosis?

17. How does cell differentiation seem to contradict this meaning?

18. How are cells related to tissues?

19. How are tissues related to organs?

20. How do unicellular and multicellular organisms differ with respect to aging?

21. What ideas do biologists have about the aging of cells?

PROBLEMS

1. During the late 19th century, most knowledge of detailed cell structure was gained by studying stained dead cells. Some biologists objected to many conclusions drawn from such observation, arguing that the processes of killing, staining, and mounting cells on slides might cause cell structure to appear very different from cell structure in living cells. What kinds of evidence are available today to meet at least some of these objections?

2. Examine various kinds of cells from multicellular organisms, either under the microscope or by means of photomicrographs in books. Discuss the relationships between the structural forms of the different cells and their functions.

3. Working in a police laboratory, you are given a tiny sample of material and asked to identify it as either plant or animal matter. How could you decide which it is?

4. On the basis of your understanding of the diffusion of water, describe what would happen to (a) a marine jellyfish placed in a freshwater stream, and (b) a frog placed in ocean water. Some fish (for example, shad and striped bass) annually swim from the ocean into freshwater rivers and back. How are they able to do this?

5. In this chapter mitosis in cells that have single, well-defined nuclei was described. Investigate what is known about the behavior of nuclear material (chromatin) during division in (a) a cell that lacks a nucleus (a blue-green alga, for example), and (b) a "cell" that has more than one nucleus (*Paramecium,* for example).

6. Much of the money available for cancer research goes into studies of cell differentiation. Why?

7. In unicellular organisms, cells usually separate shortly after division. In some, however, they remain attached, forming colonies. In multicellular organisms they remain attached, but more strongly in some cases than in others. Investigate the ways in which the cells are held together.

8. The living substance of cells is often called "protoplasm." Many biologists object to the use of the term. Find out why.

9. Much of the modern understanding of cell structure has resulted from invention of new optical instruments. What kinds of information have been provided by means of electron microscopes? By means of phase-contrast microscopes?

SUGGESTED READINGS

(See also books by Mercer and by Baker and Allen, listed at the end of Chapter 12.)

FOX, F. "The Structure of Cell Membranes," *Scientific American,* February, 1972. Pp. 30–38.

GREEN, D. E. "The Mitochondrion," *Scientific American,* January, 1964. Pp. 63–66+.

GURDON, J. B. "Transplanted Nuclei and Cell Differentiation," *Scientific American,* December, 1968. Pp. 24–35.

HOLTER, H. "How Things Get into Cells," *Scientific American,* September, 1961. Pp. 167–174+.

JOHN, B., and K. R. LEWIS. *Somatic Cell Division.* London: Oxford University Press, 1972. (Emphasis on the details of mitosis and on the problems that cell biologists are exploring. Advanced.)

MAZIA, D. *Cell Division.* (BSCS Pamphlet 14.) Box 3406, Boulder, Colo.: EPIC, 1964. (Emphasis on the details of mitosis and the problems that cell biologists are exploring.)

ROBERTSON, J. D. "The Membrane of the Living Cell," *Scientific American,* April, 1962. Pp. 64–72.

SIMPSON, G. G., and W. S. BECK. *Life: An Introduction to Biology.* Shorter ed. New York: Harcourt, Brace & World, Inc., 1969. Chapter 3. (Fine illustrations and clear writing make this one of the best accounts of cells written for college freshmen.)

SOLOMON, A. K. "Pumps in the Living Cell," *Scientific American,* August, 1962. Pp. 100–108.

SPRATT, N. T. *Introduction to Cell Differentiation.* New York: Reinhold Publishing Corp., 1964. (A clear discussion of present-day understanding of cell differentiation based on experimental investigation. Requires some knowledge of genetics.)

SWANSON, C. P. *The Cell.* 3rd ed. Englewood Cliffs, N.J.: Prentice-Hall, Inc., 1969. (An excellent summary of modern cell studies. Fairly advanced.)

WESSELLS, N. K. "How Do Living Cells Change Shape?" *Scientific American,* October, 1971. Pp. 76–82.

Bioenergetics

LIFE, ENERGY, AND CELLS

A sequoia seed is but a few millimeters in diameter. Yet if it is planted in a favorable environment, it may develop—after many centuries—into a towering tree, almost 90 m high and more than 30 m in circumference. Where does the energy to build these tons of organic compounds come from? In a park on a summer afternoon, you run, squirrels leap, birds fly, bees buzz. What is the source of the energy for all this activity?

sequoia. See Figure 5·12.

Life always involves energy. In Sections One and Three we examined the flow of energy through the biosphere. Now, as we look *into* organisms, we should ask, What are the chemical means by which the cells of living things perform the various kinds of energy changes that result in growth and movement? This is the question that is basic to *bioenergetics.*

bioenergetics [bī'ō ĕn'ər jĕt'ĭks; Greek: *bios*, life, + *en*, in, + *ergon*, work]

If a cell has a pigment that can trap radiant energy, it stores energy in a chemical form (food) by the process of photosynthesis. If a cell does not have such a pigment—or if it has the pigment but lacks a supply of radiant energy—it must obtain energy from food. In any case, energy to carry on moment-to-moment cell processes comes from food, whether the food be made within the cell or taken in from its environment. Because the release of energy from food occurs in all living cells at all times, it is appropriate to begin the consideration of bioenergetics with the energy-releasing processes of cells.

photosynthesis. Review pages 16–20.

Within multicellular producers many *individual cells* function as consumers. Can you give some examples?

Investigation 12.1

BIOENERGETICS: AN INTRODUCTORY VIEW

MATERIALS AND EQUIPMENT

(for each team)
pea seeds, 80
beakers, 2
volumeter
graduated cylinder, 100-ml

glass beads, a volume of about 100 cc
paper towels
glass rod
nonabsorbent cotton
spatula, porcelain

Ascarite, about 3 cc
medicine dropper
water, colored with eosin

(for special team)
pea seeds, a volume of about 400 cc
beakers, 400-ml, 2
vacuum bottles, 2
nonabsorbent cotton
rubber stoppers, 1-hole, to fit vacuum
    bottles, 2
thermometers ($-10°$ to $+110°C$), 2
glycerin

PROCEDURE

Day 1. Place 40 pea seeds in a beaker and add water until the seeds are well covered. Place another 40 pea seeds in a second beaker without water. Set the beakers aside for 24 hours.

Assemble a volumeter as illustrated in Figure 12 • 1. Before continuing this investigation, you must understand how this apparatus works. Your teacher will demonstrate its use.

A special team in each class will place 2 additional lots of peas (each having a volume of about 200 cc) in beakers, adding water to

Figure 12 • 1
Volumeter.

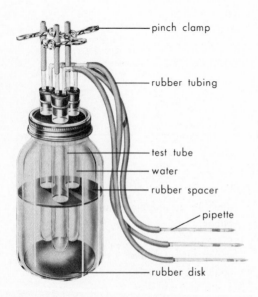

pinch clamp

rubber tubing

test tube
water
rubber spacer

pipette

rubber disk

cover the seeds in one beaker and leaving the second without water. Set the beakers aside for 24 hours.

Day 2. Remove the stoppers from the volumeter tubes. Pour 50 ml of water into a 100-ml graduated cylinder. Add the 40 soaked seeds to the cylinder and record the level of the water in the cylinder. Remove the soaked seeds and put them in one of the volumeter tubes. Again pour 50 ml of water into the cylinder. Add the 40 dry seeds. Then add glass beads until the water reaches the level recorded for the soaked seeds. Remove the seeds and glass beads. Dry them on a paper towel and place them in a 2nd tube of the volumeter. Again pour 50 ml of water into the cylinder. Add glass beads until the water reaches the level recorded for the soaked seeds. Remove the beads and dry them. Then put them in the 3rd volumeter tube.

• What is the role of this 3rd tube in the experimental design?(1) • What is the purpose of the glass beads?(2) • How do you think the soaked seeds differ from the dry seeds?(3)

Using a glass rod, loosely pack cotton to a depth of 1 cm over the material in each tube. With a porcelain spatula, add about 1 cc of Ascarite to the top of the cotton in each tube. *Caution: Ascarite burns. Be very careful not to get it on your skin or clothes.* Replace the stoppers. Place the tubes in the volumeter. Arrange the volumeter pipettes so they are level on the table.

Place a drop of colored water in the end of each pipette. In each of the 2 pipettes attached to the tubes containing peas, adjust the drop to a position near the outer end. In the 3rd pipette, adjust the drop to a position near the middle. To make each adjustment, open the clamp at the top of the tube to which the pipette is attached and, using a medicine dropper, draw or push air through the system.

Leave the apparatus set up for 5 minutes. During this pause, assign 3 team members to read the 3 pipettes; assign a 4th student to time the readings. Record the position of each marker drop at time zero. Then record the position of each drop at 2-minute intervals for a total of 20 minutes.

Meanwhile the special team should proceed as follows: Mark 2 vacuum bottles *A* and *B*. Place a layer of moist cotton in the bottom of Bottle A. Then add the 200 cc of seeds that have been soaked for 24 hours. Lubricate a thermometer with glycerin and insert it through a 1-hole stopper that fits the vacuum bottle. Position the stopper in the vacuum bottle so that the bulb of the thermometer is among the peas but the mercury is visible above the stopper. Now place in the bottom of Bottle B a layer of dry cotton and add the dry seeds. Fit Bottle B with a thermometer as you did Bottle A. Wait 5 minutes; then record the temperature in each bottle. Set both bottles in a place designated by your teacher.

Day 3. Record the temperature in each vacuum bottle.

STUDYING THE DATA

For each tube of the volumeter, subtract the reading at time zero from each of the subsequent readings. • What does a positive number indicate about the volume of air in the tube-pipette system?(4) • What does a negative number indicate?(5)   Graph all the data on one grid, using lines of different colors to represent the 3 tubes. • Which line represents changes in a tube not associated with living things?(6)   Compare the other two lines with this. • Which one of these two most resembles it?(7)

• State a hypothesis to account for any difference you found between the data from the tube containing the dry peas and the data from the tube containing the soaked peas.(8)

At the beginning of the investigation, each tube-pipette system contained air, a mixture of gases. • If you found changes in the position of the marked drops, which of these gases do you think changed in amount?(9) Ascarite is a substance that absorbs carbon dioxide. • Why do you think it was included in each tube-pipette system?(10)

CONCLUSIONS

• What evidence does this investigation provide that physiological activity involves chemical change?(11) • What evidence does it provide that physiological activity involves energy change?(12)

FOR FURTHER INVESTIGATION

You can use the volumeter to investigate these problems: (1) How do advancing stages of seed germination affect the rate of the biochemical process measured by the apparatus? (2) Do small animals such as grasshoppers produce results in the volumeter like those obtained with seeds?

ENERGY-RELEASING PROCESSES

SOME BASIC POINTS

Foods as fuels. Foods are carbon compounds that contain hydrogen, oxygen, and often other elements as well. Chemically, foods are somewhat like the fuels burned in furnaces. Indeed, furnace fuels such as wood, coal, and oil are carbon compounds derived from dead cells. They serve as fuels because they contain chemical energy. During the chemical reactions of burning, this energy is released.

coal. See page 20.

Chemical energy in foods is likewise released during chemical reactions that occur in cells. But in cells the chemical reactions are quite different from those in furnaces; they occur at temperatures much below those of burning. And only a small amount of the energy

calories [Latin: *calor*, heat]

is released in the form of heat and light.

Energy is customarily measured in units called **calories**. A calorie is defined by physicists as the amount of heat energy required to raise the temperature of 1 g of water 1°C. Thus, by definition, a calorie is a unit of heat. But since all forms of energy are interchangeable, the calorie can be used as a unit of measurement for energy of all kinds. Biologists generally use the big Calorie—capitalized—which is equal to 1000 of the physicists' small calories.

In some books the Calorie is abbreviated Kcal. Can you explain this abbreviation?

Catalysts and enzymes. How can energy-releasing chemical reactions occur at the low temperatures in cells? Chemists have discovered that small quantities of certain substances can greatly speed some chemical reactions without themselves being used up in the reactions. For instance, a small quantity of finely powdered platinum will cause some gases that normally do not react together to react with explosive rapidity; yet the quantity of platinum does not change. Platinum is a **catalyst** for these reactions.

catalysis [kə tăl'ə sĭs; Greek: *kata*, down, + *lyein*, to loosen]

In cell chemistry, also, catalysts accelerate reactions. Cell catalysts, however, are not simple metals, such as powdered platinum, but are complex organic compounds made by living cells. Because they differ so greatly from inorganic catalysts, they have a special name —*enzymes.*

enzymes [ĕn'zīmz; Greek: *en*, in, + *zyme*, a material to raise bread dough]

According to present evidence, each enzyme in a living cell catalyzes just one chemical reaction. Though many chemical reactions *could* take place among the hundreds of compounds in a living cell, **biochemists** have found that only those reactions *do* occur for which there are appropriate enzymes. Moreover, these reactions are orderly. Their timing depends in part on the location of the enzymes in the cell. One reaction, catalyzed by a certain enzyme, occurs at one place; then the products of this reaction pass on to another place, where another enzyme catalyzes a second reaction. Thus the chemical changes in a cell are controlled as to location and sequence as well as to kind.

Investigation 12.2

A STUDY OF BIOCHEMICAL REACTIONS

BACKGROUND INFORMATION

Hydrogen peroxide (H_2O_2) is a highly active chemical, often used for bleaching; it is sold as a 3% solution in water. Within cells, hydrogen peroxide is thought to be formed continually as a by-product of biochemical processes. Because it is *toxic,* or poisonous, it would soon kill cells if not removed or broken down immediately.

MATERIALS AND EQUIPMENT

(for each team)

test tubes, 13- x 100-mm, 9
glass-marking crayon
test-tube rack
graduated cylinder, 10-ml
hydrogen peroxide solution, 3%,
     about 100 ml

scalpel
manganese dioxide powder
forceps
liver, fresh, 3 pieces, each about
    6 mm in diameter
sand, fine
mortar and pestle
bunsen burner
ring stand
beaker
potato, fresh

PROCEDURE

Arrange the test tubes in the rack and number them from *1* to *9*. Measure 2 ml of water in a graduated cylinder and pour into Tube 1. Mark each of the other tubes at the 2-ml level, and pour hydrogen peroxide solution into each to the level of the marks. After each of the following steps, record your observations. Compare observations on different tubes whenever you think it appropriate.

Into Tube 1 sprinkle a small amount (about half as much as a scalpel blade will hold) of manganese dioxide powder. Repeat for Tube 2.

Using forceps, select a small piece of fresh liver and drop it into Tube 3.

Into Tube 4 sprinkle sand in an amount equal to that of the manganese dioxide used in Tubes 1 and 2.

Place in a mortar a piece of fresh liver (about the size of that used in Tube 3). Add a little fine sand and grind the liver. Transfer the resulting mixture to Tube 5.

Place a 3rd piece of liver in boiling water for a few minutes. Drop the boiled liver into Tube 6.

Place an amount of manganese dioxide equal to that used in Tube 1 in a test tube with about 2 ml of water. Place the test tube in boiling water for a few minutes. Then pour the tube's contents into Tube 7.

Using the scalpel, cut 2 cubes of fresh potato, each the size of the liver used in Tube 3. Place 1 potato cube in Tube 8.

Wash the mortar thoroughly. Grind the other potato cube with sand. Place the potato-sand mixture in Tube 9.

DISCUSSION AND CONCLUSIONS

• What was the purpose of Tube 1?(1)
• Do you have any evidence that manganese dioxide catalyzes the breakdown of hydrogen peroxide instead of reacting with it?(2)
• What additional steps in the procedure would be needed to confirm this?(3)   Biochemists have obtained experimental evidence that manganese dioxide is indeed a catalyst in this reaction. Consider the formula of hydrogen peroxide and the kind of reaction you observed in Tube 2.   • What are the most likely products of the breakdown of hydrogen peroxide? (4)   • How might you confirm your answer?(5)
• How do you explain the difference in activity resulting from the whole piece of liver and from the ground liver?(6)   • Why is Tube 4 necessary for this explanation?(7)   • How do you explain the difference in activity resulting from fresh and boiled liver?(8)   Suppose that someone comparing Tubes 2 and 3 concluded that liver contained manganese dioxide.
• What evidence do you have either for or against this conclusion?(9)   • If you cannot support the conclusion, explain the reaction in Tube 3.(10)
• What additional information do the results from Tubes 8 and 9 provide?(11)

CELLULAR RESPIRATION

Biologists refer to the main kind of energy-releasing process as *cellular respiration.* This may be a little confusing to you at first because the term "respiration" is often used to mean breathing. Breathing is related to cellular respiration but is not directly a part of it.

During burning, the chemical energy of fuels is released as light and heat. During cellular respiration, the chemical energy in foods is either transformed into motion (on a large scale, as in muscle, or on a small scale, as in the movement of molecules or ions by active transport). Or it energizes reactions that form new chemical compounds. Or, to a very small extent, it may be transformed into light (as in fireflies). And some heat is released—but this is lost energy as far as cell processes are concerned.

Glucose. The principal carbon compound that is broken down when energy is released in cells is *glucose*. Many complex carbon compounds in cells can be converted to glucose, so it is by way of glucose that energy release can best be explained.

A glucose molecule contains a series of six linked carbon atoms with oxygen and hydrogen atoms attached. Its formula is $C_6H_{12}O_6$; however, the numbers and kinds of atoms shown in this formula can be arranged in many patterns, each pattern having its own characteristics and thus representing a distinctly different chemical compound. So biochemists often write the formula for glucose as shown in Figure 12 • 2A. This is known as a *structural formula.* Of course, atoms in a molecule do not occur in the flat shape of a formula on paper. To show the three-dimensional shape of a molecule, biochemists use a model such as that in Figure 12 • 2B.

Although lost for cell processes, how may this heat be of advantage to a warm-blooded animal?

glucose [gloo′kōs; Greek: *glykys*, sweet]

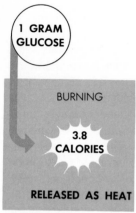

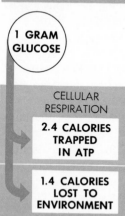

Figure 12 • 3

Does the amount of energy obtained from a food depend upon the way it is released?

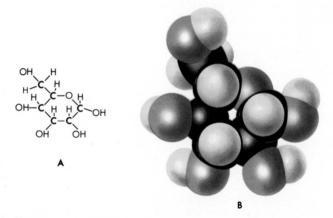

Figure 12 • 2

Structural formula (*A*) and model (*B*) of a molecule of glucose. Atoms are shown as spheres, each kind in a separate diagrammatic color. Try to find in the model the atoms shown by symbols in the formula.

Energy in small packets. If you had only a hundred-dollar bill, you might find it difficult to make everyday purchases—a hamburger, notebook paper, a comb. You would find purchasing much easier if you exchanged the large bill for a hundred one-dollar bills. So, too, with energy in cells. The bigger bursts of energy from glucose are put into "small change." This "small change" is the chemical energy in what are called energy-transfer compounds. The most important of these is a complex substance known as *adenosine triphosphate,* usually abbreviated ATP.

adenosine triphosphate [ă dē′nə sĭn trī fŏs′fāt]

Each molecule of this substance includes a main section, symbolized as A. Attached to this section are three identical groups of atoms called phosphates. Each phosphate may be symbolized as ℗. ATP may thus be written A–℗~℗~℗. Each wavy line indicates the attachment of a phosphate group whose removal is accompanied by the release—or transfer—of a small amount of energy.

identical: exactly the same

Wherever energy is required in a cell, ATP is the usual source. Each ATP molecule releases a bit of energy whenever the terminal phosphate group breaks off, leaving A–℗~℗ . This molecule, with only two phosphate groups, is called *adenosine diphosphate*— ADP. We can show its formation from ATP as follows:

$$A-℗{\sim}℗{\sim}℗ \longrightarrow A-℗{\sim}℗ + ℗$$
$$\downarrow$$
$$\text{energy}$$

You cannot keep spending money from your pocket without eventually facing the necessity of putting money in again. Likewise, a cell cannot continually use its ATP as in the above reaction without also rebuilding some ADP back into ATP:

$$\text{energy}$$
$$\downarrow$$
$$℗ + A-℗{\sim}℗ \longrightarrow A-℗{\sim}℗{\sim}℗$$

This energy comes from the breakdown of food substances such as glucose.

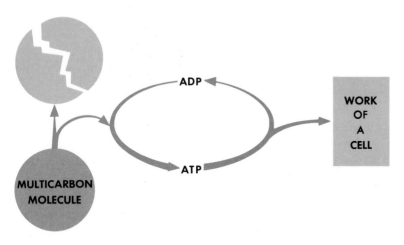

Figure 12 · 4
The ATP-ADP cycle.

From glucose to carbon dioxide and water. Now let us consider a little further the process of cellular respiration. It is biochemically complex, but basically it consists of a series of reactions in which glucose molecules are broken into fragments. In the course of this breakdown, hydrogen is removed from the fragments. Each hydrogen atom becomes a hydrogen ion and a high-energy electron—an electron that carries some of the energy that was in the glucose. The whole process

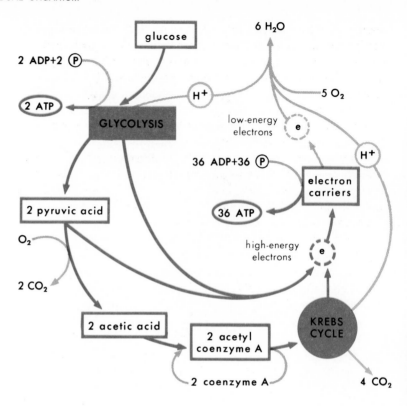

Figure 12 • 5

The principal events in
cellular respiration.

glycolysis |glī kăl'ə səs|

Named for Hans Krebs,
1900—. British (German-born)
biochemist

pyruvic [pī rū'vĭk|

acetic [ə sĕt'ĭk]

can be considered in three major sets of reactions: *glycolysis,* the
Krebs cycle, and an electron-carrier system. (Refer to Figure 12 • 5
as you study the rest of this section.)

Glycolysis consists of a series of reactions, each catalyzed by its
own enzyme. As a result of these reactions, energy is released, and
each 6-carbon molecule of glucose is changed to 2 molecules of
a 3-carbon compound, pyruvic acid. No outside source of oxygen
is required for these reactions.

Each of the 2 pyruvic acid molecules is then changed to a molecule of a 2-carbon compound, acetic acid, releasing still more

Figure 12 • 6

Structural formulas (*A*) and models (*B*) of two kinds of molecules. Can you see how
the change of pyruvic acid to acetic acid leaves a molecule of CO_2?

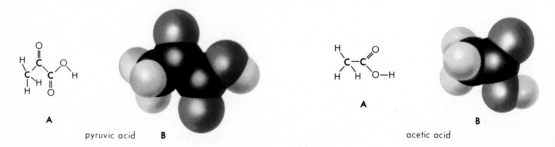

A   A

                                                                            B

pyruvic acid   B   acetic acid

energy. Oxygen is required for this reaction, and CO_2 is released. The acetic acid molecules are immediately attached to a molecule of co-enzyme A, forming acetyl coenzyme A. A *coenzyme* is a molecule that works in cooperation with an enzyme. Coenzyme A is formed from one of the B vitamins.

acetyl coenzyme A
[ə sēt'əl kō ĕn'zīm' ā']

What effect might a lack of B vitamins in your diet have?

After the formation of acetyl coenzyme A, the second part of cellular respiration—the Krebs cycle—begins. Acetic acid from acetyl coenzyme A is transferred to a molecule of a 4-carbon compound, oxaloacetic acid. This forms a 6-carbon compound, citric acid. Then, through a series of reactions, hydrogen, high-energy electrons, and 2 carbon atoms (each forming a molecule of CO_2) are removed from the citric acid molecule. Left over is a molecule of the 4-carbon oxaloacetic acid. This molecule is now available to start the Krebs cycle again by receiving acetic acid from another molecule of acetyl coenzyme A.

oxaloacetic [äk'sə lō'ə sĕt'ĭk]
citric [sĭ'trĭk]

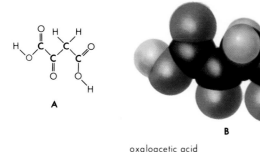

A

oxaloacetic acid

B

Figure 12 • 7

Structural formulas (*A*) and models (*B*) of two kinds of molecules. In the citric acid molecule try to find the atoms of the two molecules from which it is formed.

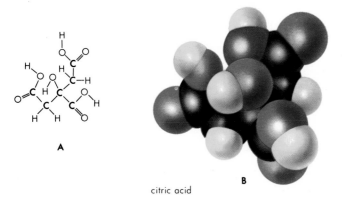

A

citric acid

B

Each glucose molecule yields 2 molecules of acetyl coenzyme A, and 2 molecules of carbon dioxide are formed from each 1 of acetyl coenzyme A. Therefore, the Krebs cycle produces 4 CO_2 molecules from the breakdown of 1 glucose molecule.

The high-energy electrons resulting from glycolysis and the Krebs cycle are passed to a series of substances we may call electron car-riers. In going from one carrier to another, the electrons give up en-ergy, which is used to form ATP from ADP molecules. The electrons are finally united with hydrogen ions and oxygen to form water.

We can now summarize cellular respiration in the following chemical expression:

$$C_6H_{12}O_6 + 6\ O_2 \xrightarrow{\text{enzymes}} 6\ CO_2 + 6\ H_2O$$
$$\downarrow$$
$$\text{energy to ATP}$$

Why do you think some
biochemists refer to
mitochondria as the
"powerhouses" of a cell?

The many enzymes that catalyze cellular respiration are not distributed evenly throughout a cell. Those concerned with the reactions of glycolysis are in the cytoplast. Those concerned with the Krebs cycle and the electron-carrier systems are in the mitochondria.

OTHER PATHWAYS OF ENERGY RELEASE

What happens if a cell does not have sufficient oxygen to complete the process of cellular respiration? In our own bodies, for example, rapid muscular exercise may require that energy be released faster than oxygen can be supplied. Under such circumstances glucose is partially broken down by *fermentation.*

fermentation
[fûr′měn tā′shən; Latin:
fervere, to be frothing]

Fermentation is a general term for anaerobic energy release. The various anaerobic pathways differ in their end products, but they are alike in releasing only a small fraction of the energy in a glucose molecule. Figure 12 · 3 shows that cellular respiration traps in ATP about 2.4 Calories of the 3.8 Calories in a gram of glucose—that is, 2.4 ÷ 3.8 = .6 = 60% of glucose energy is trapped in ATP. If you contrast Figure 12 · 8 with Figure 12 · 5, you see that fermentation produces only 2

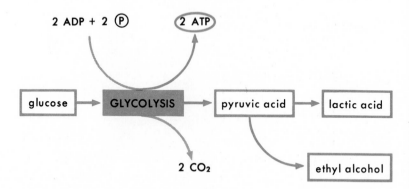

Figure 12 · 8

Two fermentation pathways.
Which occurs in mammalian
muscle and which in yeasts?

ATP molecules per glucose molecule, as compared with 38 produced by cellular respiration. So in fermentation only about 2/38 × 60%, or 3.2%, of glucose energy is trapped in ATP. Thus fermentation is somewhat like a faulty furnace that allows unburned coal to pass through with the ashes.

Like all analogies, this one is
imperfect (see page 58).
In what way?

The cells of man and other animals can survive for a time on the limited amount of energy released by fermentation. But eventually they must have oxygen for the more efficient cellular respiration. However, some organisms—for example, *Clostridium tetani,* the bacterium of

Would you expect *Clostridium*
cells to have mitochondria?
Why or why not?

lockjaw—exist entirely by the inefficient fermentation process. Others, such as yeasts, can exist very well anaerobically; but if oxygen is available, they change to the more efficient aerobic method.

Some of the waste products from fermentations are useful to man. Can you give examples?

Investigation 12.3

FERMENTATION

MATERIALS AND EQUIPMENT

(for each team)

vacuum bottles, 2
stoppers, 2-hole, to fit bottles, 2
glass tubing, lengths of about 8 cm, 2
thermometers, 2
glycerin
rubber tubing, lengths of about
    35 cm, 2
beakers, 250-ml, 2
limewater, 300 ml
molasses, 25% solution in water,
    400 ml
glass-marking crayon
dry yeast, about 1/4 package
drinking straw

PROCEDURE

Assemble 2 sets of apparatus, each as shown in Figure 12 • 9. Lubricate glass tubing and thermometers with glycerin before attempting to insert them in the stoppers. Label one vacuum bottle A and the other B. When both setups are complete, remove the stopper from Bottle A and add 1/4 package of dry yeast. Mix the yeast with the molasses solution by gently swirling the bottle. Then replace the stopper.

Wait 5 minutes. While you are waiting, blow your breath through a drinking straw into a sample of limewater. Record the result. At the end of 5 minutes, record the temperature in each bottle and the time. As frequently as possible during the next 48 hours, record the temperatures in the 2 bottles, the time at which each reading is made, and the appearance of the limewater.

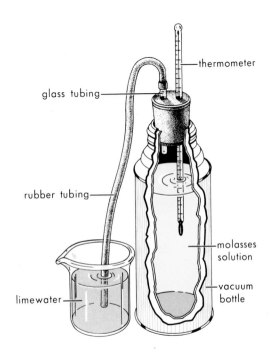

Labels: thermometer, glass tubing, rubber tubing, molasses solution, vacuum bottle, limewater

Figure 12 • 9

STUDYING THE DATA

Graph your data. Use blue for plotting the data from Bottle A and red for Bottle B.
• What evidence do you have that chemical reactions have occurred during the period of your observation?(1) • Did reactions occur in Bottle A, Bottle B, or both? If both, was any difference evident in amount of reaction?(2)
• Are conditions within the bottles aerobic or anaerobic? Explain your answer.(3) • What evidence do you have that a gas is produced in the bottles?(4) • Was it produced in both bottles? If not, in which one was it produced?

(5)   • In what way does the gas resemble the gas in exhaled breath?(6)   • Did the contents of the bottles smell alike at the end of the experiment? If not, how did they differ?(7)

CONCLUSIONS

• What variable in the setup accounts for any differences you may have observed between results in Bottle A and Bottle B?(8)   • In what ways did the fermentation in this investigation resemble respiration as observed in Investigation 12.1?(9)   • In what way did fermentation differ from respiration?(10)

FOR FURTHER INVESTIGATION

1. If you can obtain some unpasteurized milk, you can use this same apparatus to investigate another kind of fermentation. Compare it with the kind you observed in this investigation.

2. The amount of gas produced by yeasts can be used as a measure of the amount of fermentation. Use the apparatus of Investigation 1.2 to investigate the effects of environmental variables on fermentation (for example, kind of food, temperature, light).

SYNTHESES

synthesis [sĭn′thə sĭs]; plural, syntheses

The release of chemical energy in cells involves the breaking down of large molecules into smaller ones. You might suppose, therefore, that the building up of large molecules from smaller ones—*synthesis*—would require energy, and this is actually the case. The growth of a cell results from adding new molecules to its substance, and most of these must be synthesized. So growth is one of the processes for which a cell requires energy.

You probably know something about the groups of chemical compounds called carbohydrates, fats, and proteins. These are ordinarily thought of as foods. A hungry lion can make use of the carbohydrate, fat, and protein of your cells as food. And you can do the same with the cells of a bean. These substances are present in all cells and, to varying extents, cells have abilities to synthesize them. There are also many other groups of substances in cells. Biochemistry is an enormously complex subject.

CARBOHYDRATES

Carbohydrates contain only the elements carbon, hydrogen, and oxygen; the hydrogen and oxygen atoms are usually in a 2 to 1 ratio. Sugars, starches, and cellulose are examples of carbohydrates.

Glucose is one of the *simple sugars*—sugars that contain between 3 and 7 carbon atoms. Glucose molecules can be chemically changed in many ways, and the synthesis of many cell substances may be thought of as beginning with glucose.

sucrose [sōō′krōs; Latin: *saccharum*, sugar]

The most familiar sugar is sucrose, table sugar. Its formula is $C_{12}H_{22}O_{11}$. This looks much like the result of putting together two glucose molecules ($C_6H_{12}O_6$), except that 2 hydrogen atoms and 1 oxygen atom are lacking. Actually, the chemistry of the matter is rather more complicated than this. In the first place, the atoms in a molecule of another 6-carbon sugar called fructose are rearranged, forming a molecule of glucose. Then the newly made glucose molecule is combined with a molecule of fructose to form a molecule of sucrose. In the process, 2 hydrogen atoms and an oxygen atom are split off and they combine to form water. The process can be summarized as follows:

$$\underset{\text{(glucose)} \quad \text{(fructose)} \quad \text{enzymes}}{C_6H_{12}O_6 + C_6H_{12}O_6} \xrightarrow[\text{enzymes}]{\text{energy from ATP}} \underset{\text{(sucrose)}}{C_{12}H_{22}O_{11} + H_2O}$$

This reaction is termed **dehydration synthesis** because it produces water.

Sucrose is called a **disaccharide,** because it is built with *two* simple-sugar units. Larger carbohydrate molecules may be formed by dehydration synthesis from larger numbers of simple-sugar units. When there are many of these units, the carbohydrates are called **polysaccharides.** Starch and cellulose are polysaccharides.

FATS

Like carbohydrates, **fats** are composed of carbon, hydrogen, and oxygen atoms only, but in fats the ratio of hydrogen to oxygen atoms is always greater than 2 to 1. Weight for weight, fats contain more chemical energy than do carbohydrates: 1 gram of fat contains about 9 Calories of chemical energy; 1 gram of carbohydrate contains only about 4 Calories.

Fats are synthesized from **glycerol** and **fatty acids.** Glycerol (glycerin) is perhaps best known as an ingredient of candies and cough medicine. It can be formed in cells from glucose. The simplest fatty acid is acetic acid (Figure 12 • 6), the acid in vinegar. Other fatty acids are built up from acetic acid, so they usually have even numbers of carbon atoms. The ones most commonly used in building fats have from 14 to 18 carbon atoms. Because the $-COOH$ group of atoms is characteristic of the molecular structure of the organic acids, we can symbolize any fatty acid as $R-COOH$; here R stands for the rest of the molecule.

fructose [frŭk'tōs; Latin: *fructus,* fruit]

dehydration [Latin: *de,* from, + Greek: *hydor,* water]

disaccharide [dī săk'ə rīd'; Greek: *dis,* twice, + *sakcharon,* sugar]

poly- [Greek: *polys,* much, many]

Fats that are in the liquid state at room temperature (about 20°C) are termed "oils."

In motile organisms food is usually stored as fat rather than as carbohydrate. Can you suggest an explanation?

glycerol [glĭs'ə rŏl']

What use have you recently made of glycerin in your laboratory work?

Figure 12 • 10
Formation of a fat.

The —COOH group of a fatty acid can react with the —OH groups of glycerol in the manner shown in Figure 12 • 10. Note that 3 molecules of fatty acid react with 1 molecule of glycerol. The 3 fatty-acid molecules may all be the same kind, or they may be different kinds. As in the synthesis of carbohydrates, water molecules are split off in the process, so this reaction is also a dehydration synthesis.

Fats are only one group within a broader chemical grouping, *lipids.* All lipids are formed from organic acids, but not necessarily in combination with glycerol. Many organisms produce nonfat lipids; an example is the plant wax that is used in floor and automobile polishes.

lipids [lī′pĭdz, lĭ′pĭdz; Greek: *lipos*, fat]

PROTEINS

Molecules of fat are large, and those of polysaccharides larger; but still larger and more complex than these are *protein* molecules. Ordinarily, protein molecules contain thousands of atoms—sometimes tens of thousands. Proteins occur in bewildering variety. Undoubtedly every species of organism has characteristic proteins shared by no others.

The basic building units of protein molecules are *amino acids.* Amino acids always contain at least four kinds of atoms: carbon, hydrogen, and oxygen (as in carbohydrates and lipids), plus nitrogen. Some amino acids also contain sulfur. As in the case of the fatty acids, *R* may be used to represent all the variable parts of an amino acid; thus *any* amino acid may be symbolized as in Figure 12 • 11.

amino [ăm′ə nō′, ə mē′nō]; related to ammonia, which is NH_3

Approximately 20 different amino acids occur in proteins. Apparently most green plants and some bacteria can synthesize all of these from inorganic materials. Animals, on the other hand, must obtain amino acids ready-made in their food, though many animals can

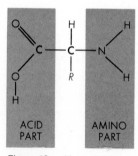

ACID
PART   AMINO
            PART

Figure 12 • 11

Basic structure of an amino acid. In a glycine molecule what is the *R*?

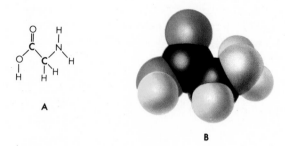

A

B

Figure 12 • 12

Structural formula (*A*) and model (*B*) of a molecule of the simplest amino acid, glycine.

In human nutrition we speak of essential amino acids. What does this mean?

change one kind to another within their bodies. Human cells can transform about ten amino acids in this manner.

The synthesis of proteins is a matter of linking the amino acids together. When a bond between amino acids is made, a water molecule is split off—another case of dehydration synthesis. This can be illustrated in the combining of three amino-acid units (Figure 12 • 13).

The resulting molecule is called a tripeptide. A longer chain is a **poly-peptide.** The name "protein" is used when the chain becomes about a hundred amino acid units long. Such a chain is coiled up like a

polypeptide [pŏl'ĭ pĕp'tĭd; Greek: *polys*, many, + *peptein*, to digest]

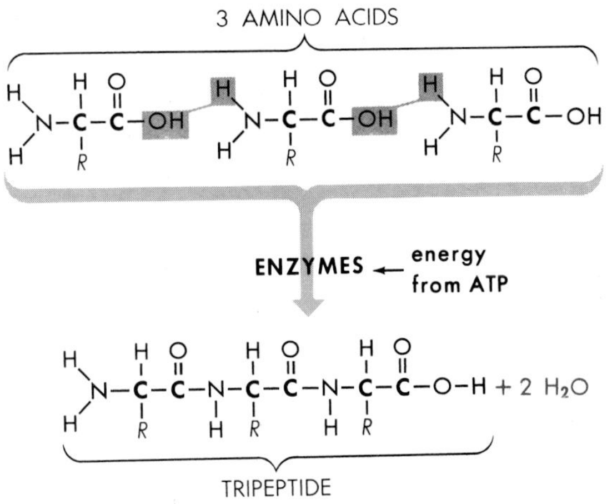

3 AMINO ACIDS

ENZYMES ← energy from ATP

TRIPEPTIDE

Figure 12 • 13
Formation of a tripeptide.

spring and has weak cross bonds between sulfur-bearing amino acids (Figure 17 • 27).

The number of ways in which 20 different amino acid units can be combined into hundred- or thousand-unit structures is almost beyond imagination. Thus, the number of possible kinds of protein is almost without limit.

NUCLEIC ACIDS

Much of the dark-staining material in the nucleus of a cell is composed of substances called **nucleic acids.** In some cases nucleic acids may make up more than 50 percent of a cell's dry weight.

nucleic [noo klē'ĭk]

There are two different series of nucleic acids: **ribonucleic** acids (RNA) and **deoxyribonucleic** acids (DNA). RNA molecules are built from units that contain ribose, a 5-carbon sugar; DNA molecules are built from units containing deoxyribose, another 5-carbon sugar that differs from ribose in having 1 less atom of oxygen. Ribose—or deoxyribose—is attached, at one point, to a phosphate ($-PO_4$) and, at another, to one of five different kinds of carbon-nitrogen structures called **bases.**

ribonucleic [rī'bō noo klē'ĭk]

deoxyribonucleic
[dē ŏk'sə rī'bō noo klē'ĭk]

ribose [rī'bōs]

base ——— 5-carbon sugar ——— phosphate

Such a unit is called a **nucleotide.**

nucleotide [noo'klē ə tĭd]

In addition to being the units from which nucleic acids are built, nucleotides have other functions in biochemistry. Figure 12 • 14, for example, shows how a nucleotide, adenosine monophosphate (AMP), is chemically related to ATP and ADP.

The ribonucleic acids (RNA) are found throughout cells. They are involved in the synthesis of proteins. In most cells deoxyribonucleic acids (DNA) occur mainly in nuclei; but in cells of blue-green algae, which have no organized nucleus, they are distributed throughout.

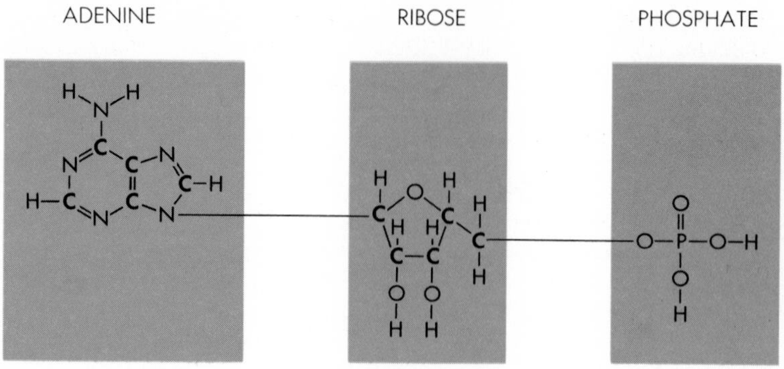

ADENINE   RIBOSE   PHOSPHATE

Figure 12 • 14

Structural formula of a nucleotide. Adenine is one of the bases. Addition of a phosphate group would make this ADP; addition of two phosphate groups would make it ATP.

PHOTOSYNTHESIS

All living cells release energy, and all put energy into synthesizing new cell molecules. But in the long run all living cells (except a few bacteria) are dependent upon the sun for their energy. Thus photosynthesis can be considered the *first* bioenergetic process when we view the biosphere as a whole. But because only certain specialized cells of plants and of a few protists can trap solar energy, we have delayed the discussion of the bioenergetics of photosynthesis.

DISCOVERY OF PHOTOSYNTHESIS

Joseph Priestley: 1733–1804. English clergyman, chemist

In 1772 Joseph Priestley placed a shoot of a mint plant in a container of water and inverted a glass jar over it so that air could not enter. Much to his surprise, the shoot remained alive for several months. On the other hand, he noted in another experiment that a burning candle was quickly extinguished when covered with a jar. Then after the candle had burned out, Priestley placed a shoot of mint under the same jar, and in a few days the candle, when lighted, burned again for a short time. And as he phrased it, "The restored air was not at all inconvenient to a mouse which I put into it." However, other investigators were unable to verify Priestley's experiments. He himself failed when he tried again, six years later.

Jan Ingen-Housz [yän ĭng'ən hous]: 1730–1799. Dutch physician and naturalist

The reason for his failure became clear in 1779, when Jan Ingen-Housz showed that plants act in the manner described by Priestley only when they are exposed to light. He found, moreover, that only the green tissues of plants act in this manner. Soon the effects of Priestley's "restored air" were traced to the release of oxygen by plants. Next it was discovered that plants growing in light absorb carbon dioxide. And in 1804 Nicolas de Saussure showed that the increase in plant weight is greater than the weight of the carbon dioxide taken in. He concluded that plant growth results from the intake of both carbon dioxide and water.

Nicolas de Saussure [nĭk ə ləs dē sō'sŏor']: 1767–1845. Swiss chemist and naturalist

By 1845 Julius Robert Mayer was able to recognize the main events in photosynthesis: the absorption of energy in the form of light and the transformation of this light energy into chemical energy, which is then stored in compounds that cells form from water and carbon dioxide. Thus, more than a century ago scientists in western Europe had already worked out the basic scheme of photosynthesis.

Julius Robert Mayer [jül'yəs mī'ər]: 1814–1878. German physicist

MACHINERY OF PHOTOSYNTHESIS

Mayer's description of photosynthesis was clear, but it left many questions unanswered. If you are developing some scientific understanding, you should be able to list several. One certainly is: Does photosynthesis occur everywhere in a cell or only at certain places?

Chloroplasts. Botanists had observed long ago that oxygen is produced in photosynthesizing cells only in the vicinity of chloroplasts. To demonstrate clearly that photosynthesis occurs only in chloroplasts, it is necessary to remove them from the rest of the cell. Removal of

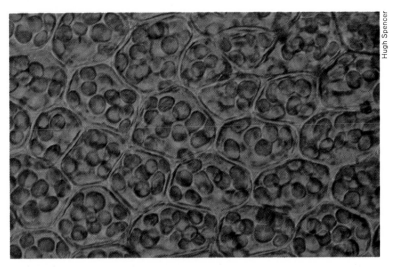

Hugh Spencer

Figure 12 • 15
Chloroplasts in cells of a moss.

chloroplasts was accomplished in the 1930's, but it wasn't until 1954 that Daniel Arnon and his co-workers at the University of California were able to demonstrate that isolated chloroplasts can indeed carry on the entire process of photosynthesis.

Daniel Arnon: 1910—. American (Polish-born) plant physiologist

Chloroplasts are easily observed with almost any microscope. But knowledge of the internal structure of a chloroplast has come from electron-microscope observations. These show that many chloroplasts contain small, disk-shaped bodies each of which is made up of a number of flat plates. Biochemists have found that each plate is composed of layers of chlorophyll, protein, and lipid molecules. The layered structure allows maximum exposure of chlorophyll molecules to light. It also brings chlorophyll in contact with the protein layers, where the enzymes required for photosynthesis are located.

Why would you predict that enzymes might be located in the protein layer?

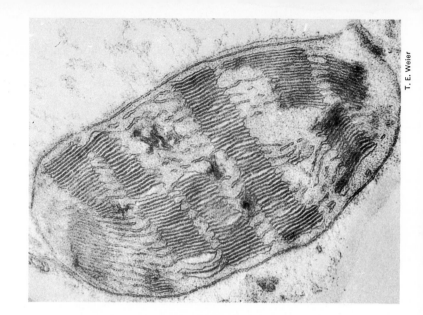

T. E. Weier

Figure 12 · 16

Electron micrograph of a single tobacco chloroplast. × 20,000

Chlorophylls. Five different kinds of chlorophylls are now known, identified as *a, b, c, d,* and *e.* Chlorophyll *a* is believed to be present in all photosynthetic plants. In green algae, bryophytes, and tracheophytes, there is also some chlorophyll *b.* In diatoms and brown algae, chlorophyll *c* occurs instead of *b;* in red algae, chlorophyll *d* is present instead of *b;* and in a small group of yellow-green algae chlorophyll *e* replaces *b.*

Chlorophyll molecules are quite complex; the formula for chlorophyll *a,* for example, is $C_{55}H_{72}O_5N_4Mg$. Although the structural formulas of the chlorophyll molecules have been worked out by biochemists, little is yet understood about how organisms produce them. It is known, however, that they are produced inside chloroplasts—except, of course, in the case of blue-green algae—and that very few are formed in the absence of light.

Can you demonstrate that a plant requires light for the formation of chlorophylls?

Investigation 12.4

SEPARATION OF LEAF PIGMENTS

INTRODUCTION

How does a biochemist know that color of leaves is the result of a mixture of several kinds of pigments? Obviously he cannot know unless he has some method of separating them from the leaves and from each other. Separating the multitude of cell substances from each other is an important step in any biochemical study. Many methods are used to accomplish this. Substances that are soluble in water (sugars, for example) are easily separated from substances that are insoluble in water (fats, for example). But many substances found in organisms are so much alike that the usual methods of separation employed by chemists fail.

In the late 19th century the principle of **chromatography** (krō′mə tŏg′rə fĭ) was discovered by a Russian chemist. At first this method was used, as its name (Greek: *chroma,* color, + *graphein,* to write) implies, only to separate pigments. By the 1930's, however, chromatography was being used for the separation of colorless substances. And to the original technique—separation on paper—had been added techniques for separation on other materials.

Much of the enormous progress that has occurred in biochemistry during the past 40 years has resulted from the use of chromatography and related techniques.

MATERIALS AND EQUIPMENT

(for each team)
paper clip
test tube, 25 x 200 mm
cork (to fit the test tube)
filter or chromatography paper,
    several strips
scissors
glass-marking crayon
developing solution (8% acetone,
    92% petroleum ether)
test-tube rack
spinach leaves
fine sand
acetone
mortar and pestle
cheesecloth, a square about
    10 x 10 cm
cleansing tissue
funnel
funnel support
test tube, 18 x 150 mm
pencils, 2
pipette, with a very fine tip

PROCEDURE

Using the larger test tube, assemble the apparatus shown in Figure 12 • 17, but do *not* add the developing solution and pigments. Handle the paper with care, because even a slight bit of oil from your fingers will affect the results. When you have the length of the paper properly adjusted, mark on the test tube the level of the lower end of the notch. Remove the paper strip from the hook. Then pour developing solution into the test tube to a depth about 5 mm below the mark that you made. Place the cork, with the hook attached (but

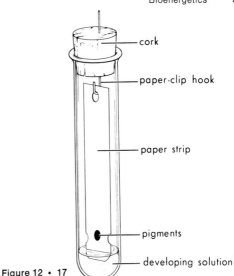

Figure 12 • 17

cork
paper-clip hook
paper strip
pigments
developing solution

without the strip of paper), in the test tube. Place the tube in an upright position in a rack.

Put 2 or 3 spinach leaves, a little fine sand, and about 5 ml of acetone into a mortar; grind thoroughly. Place a layer of cheesecloth in a funnel, and add a layer of cleansing tissue. Pour the acetone (which now contains extracted pigments) into the funnel, and collect the filtrate in the smaller test tube • What is the color of the filtrate?(1) • Is there any evidence that more than one pigment is dissolved in the acetone?(2)

Support the strip of paper across 2 pencils so that the portion between the notches does not touch the table. Using a fine-pointed pipette, place a drop of the pigment extract on the paper between the notches. Allow it to dry. Add another drop in the same place, and allow it to dry. Repeat until you have placed at least 4 drops on the paper—one on top of another. When the final drop has dried, remove the cork from the large test tube and hang the strip on the hook. Insert the cork, with the paper strip attached, into the test tube. Be sure that the pigment spot does not touch the surface of the developing solution. If necessary, adjust the length of the hook to avoid this. Be sure the cork is tight. Watch the developing solution rise. When its upper edge almost reaches the hook, remove the cork from the tube and hold it until the paper has dried.

STUDYING THE DATA

Examine the chromatogram.   • How many bands of color can you see?(3)   • How many bands might be made up of chlorophylls?(4) • What other colors can you see in the chromatogram?(5)   • Why were you unable to see these colors in the leaf?(6)   • Do you think that all the leaf pigments were soluble in the acetone? Why or why not?(7)   • Suggest a hypothesis to explain the change of color that often occurs when a leaf dies.(8)

Now consider the process by which the pigments were separated.   • From what point did all the pigments start as the developing solution began to rise?(9)   • When did all the pigments start to move, and when did they all stop?(10)   • In what characteristic, then, must the pigments have differed?(11)

FOR FURTHER INVESTIGATION

1. Why were the pigments studied in this investigation extracted with acetone? Why was water not used? What liquids besides acetone can be used to extract these pigments from the leaf?

2. Are there any leaf pigments that are not extracted by acetone? If so, what are the pigments, and how can they be extracted?

3. What effect does the kind of developer have on the success of chromatography? Try 100% acetone, 100% petroleum ether, 100% alcohol, and different mixtures of any 2 of these or of all 3. Does the nature of the pigments you are trying to separate affect the success of the chromatography? Using some of the developers listed above, try separating other pigments, such as those in ball-point pen inks.

BIOCHEMISTRY OF PHOTOSYNTHESIS

Following Mayer's summary of photosynthesis, biochemists made many measurements of the amounts of CO_2 and H_2O taken in by illuminated, chlorophyll-bearing cells. They also measured the amounts of oxygen and energy-rich carbon compounds that were formed. Although there are many such carbon compounds, we can use glucose as an example and summarize these investigations as follows:

$$6\ CO_2 + 6\ H_2O \xrightarrow[\text{enzymes}]{\text{light energy}} C_6H_{12}O_6 + 6\ O_2$$

See page 378.

You no doubt recognize that this chemical equation is the opposite of that for cellular respiration—except for the form of the energy. Of course, such summary equations merely indicate the reacting materials and the products. They show nothing of the chemical steps and the intermediate substances that lead to the products. So biochemists realized that cellular respiration and photosynthesis were not necessarily the reverse of each other.

Chemical reactions occur so rapidly in photosynthesis that identification of the intermediate substances seemed impossible. By 1905, however, biochemists had obtained evidence that two distinct sets of reactions occur during photosynthesis. One set—the "light reactions" —occurs only while a chlorophyll-bearing cell is exposed to light. This one is followed by a set for which light is *not* required—the "dark reactions."

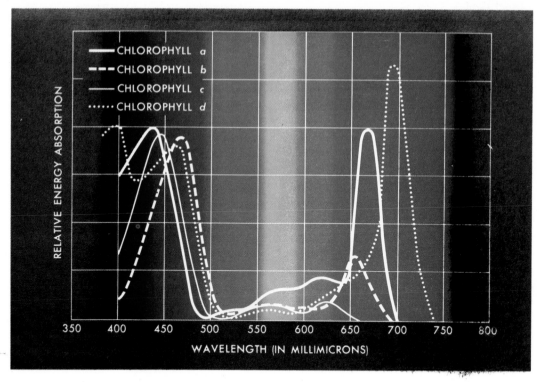

Figure 12 • 18

Energy absorption of visible light by four chlorophylls. The background shows the appearance of the wavelengths to our eyes. What wavelengths (colors) do these chlorophylls absorb least?

The source of oxygen. Basic to any further understanding of the details of photosynthesis was the question, Where does the oxygen come from? For many years CO_2 was considered the most likely source. But the problem could not be solved until a way was found to distinguish between oxygen derived from H_2O and oxygen derived from CO_2.

An atom of ordinary oxygen is 16 times heavier than a hydrogen atom. But there is an *isotope* of oxygen—another form of the oxygen atom—with an atomic weight 18 times that of hydrogen. This isotope, O^{18}, can be distinguished from O^{16} with an instrument called the mass spectrometer. In 1941 Samuel Ruben and Martin Kamen exposed photosynthesizing plants to CO_2 that contained only O^{18}. The mass spectrometer showed that all the O_2 given off by these plants was O^{16}. Ruben and Kamen then exposed other plants to ordinary CO_2 but supplied them with water containing O^{18}. With the mass spectrometer, the oxygen given off by these plants was identified as O^{18}. Clearly, the oxygen came only from the water, not from the carbon dioxide.

Methods of investigation. The work of Ruben and Kamen succeeded through the use of a new technique. At the same time, other inves-

isotope [ī′sə tōp′; Greek: *isos*, equal, + *topos*, place]

spectrometer [spĕk trŏm′ə tər]

Samuel Ruben: 1913–1943. American chemist. Martin Kamen: 1913——. American (Canadian-born) biochemist

technique [tĕk nēk′; Greek: *techne*, an art]: a method or procedure

tigators were applying other new techniques. The result has been a rapid increase in knowledge of photosynthesis during the past half century.

Ian E. Bush, "Automation of Steroid Analysis," SCIENCE, Vol. 154, pp. 77–83, Oct. 7, 1966

Figure 12 • 19

As biochemists attack more complex problems, they develop more complex tools. The apparatus shown increases the speed with which chromatographic records can be obtained.

All the substances that are involved in respiration are present in a cell together with all the substances involved in photosynthesis. Even when all these substances are separated and identified, how can biochemists decide which are involved in respiration, which are involved in photosynthesis, and which are, perhaps, involved in both processes? In chloroplasts only the substances of photosynthesis occur. Thus, the use of isolated chloroplasts makes it easier to trace the steps in photosynthesis because the steps by which multicarbon compounds are broken down are removed.

You have seen how chromatography can be used to separate a mixture of substances. A combination of techniques involving both isotopes and chromatography has been especially useful. For example, in one procedure, carbon dioxide that contains carbon-14 (C^{14}), a radioactive isotope of carbon, is supplied to single-celled algae. Shortly afterward, the algae are killed and the substances in them removed. These substances are then separated by chromatography, and the ones that have taken up C^{14} can be detected by a device sensitive to radioactivity. By killing some of the algae every few fractions of a second, the investigator can determine the order in which the substances containing C^{14} are formed. From information gathered by these techniques, diagrams such as Figures 12 • 20, 12 • 21, and 12 • 22 are constructed.

The "light reactions." The experimental evidence now available indicates that within chloroplasts light energy is transformed to the

radioactive. See page 314.

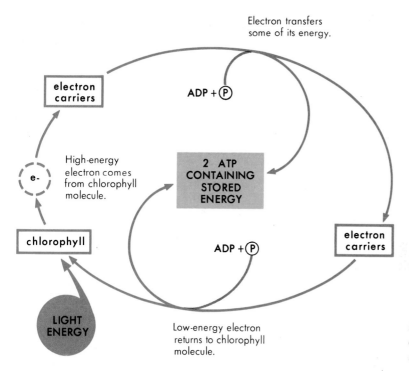

Figure 12 • 20
Cyclic part of the "light
reactions" in photosynthesis.

chemical energy of ATP in two different ways. The first is a cyclic set
of reactions (Figure 12 • 20). Light energy is absorbed by a molecule
of chlorophyll. Somehow this causes an electron that carries much energy to be expelled from the molecule. This high-energy electron is
passed along a series of electron carriers. These are not necessarily
the same electron carriers that operate in respiration, though some
may be the same. As the electron moves along this series, its energy
is transferred to enzyme systems that catalyze the change of ADP to
ATP. Before this electron—now with low energy—returns to a chlorophyll molecule, 2 or more molecules of ATP have been formed.

The second way is a noncyclic set of reactions (Figure 12 • 21).
A pigment as yet unidentified—probably either one of the chlorophylls
other than *a* or one of the yellow pigments present in chloroplasts—
absorbs light and expels a high-energy electron. Picked up by electron
carriers, its energy goes into the formation of an ATP molecule from
ADP. At the same time, light is absorbed by a chlorophyll *a* molecule; it
expels another high-energy electron, which, however, is replaced in
the chlorophyll by the first electron—minus its high energy. High-
energy electrons from 2 chlorophyll *a* molecules operate in pairs. A
pair of them joins 2 hydrogen ions (H^+)—which are formed by the
ionization of 2 water molecules—and a molecule of NADP (oxidized
nicotinamide adenine dinucleotide phosphate). The result of this activity is another kind of energy-rich molecule: $NADPH_2$ (reduced
nicotinamide adenine dinucleotide phosphate).

nicotinamide [nĭk′ə tēn′ə mīd]

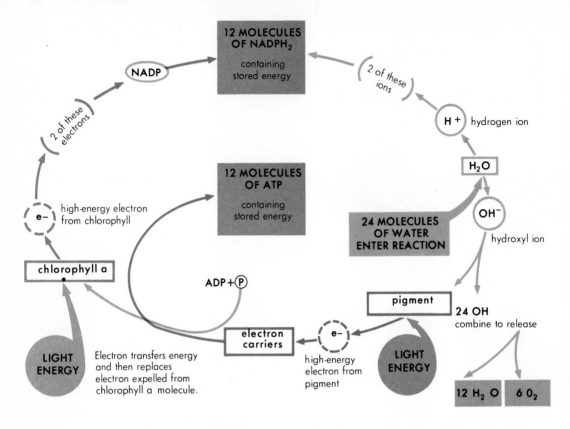

Figure 12 • 21

Noncyclic part of the "light reactions" in photosynthesis. How many molecules of ATP and NADPH$_2$ are formed for each 24 molecules of water?

$H_2O \longrightarrow H^+ + OH^-$

Formation of hydrogen ions from water provides OH$^-$ ions also. Each OH$^-$ ion furnishes an electron to replace the ion that light energy removed from the molecule of the unidentified pigment. Each OH$^-$ ion then becomes an OH *radical*—a chemical term for a group of atoms that is neither an independent molecule nor an ion. Twenty-four of these OH radicals combine to form 12 molecules of water and 6 molecules of oxygen—the oxygen that is given off by photosynthesizing organisms.

Many details of these "light reactions" are still uncertain. Future biochemical discoveries may change our understanding of them in many ways.

The "dark reactions." Through years of ingenious investigation, Melvin Calvin and his colleagues have worked out many of the more than 20 reactions involved in the "dark reactions." The basic result of this phase of photosynthesis is the formation of multicarbon molecules containing chemical energy.

The carbon source in the "dark reactions" is carbon dioxide. Carbon dioxide is combined with complex molecules that already exist in

Melvin Calvin: 1911—. American biochemist. In 1961 he received the Nobel Prize. What does this mean?

cells, and in a series of steps phosphoglyceraldehyde (PGAL), a 3-carbon molecule, is formed. For every 6 molecules of CO_2 taken in by a photosynthesizing cell, 12 molecules of PGAL result. But 10 of these are cycled back into the reactions. Only 2 molecules of PGAL are left to form carbohydrates such as glucose—and eventually all the other multicarbon compounds in cells.

phosphoglyceraldehyde
[fŏs′fə glĭ′sər ăl′də hīd′]

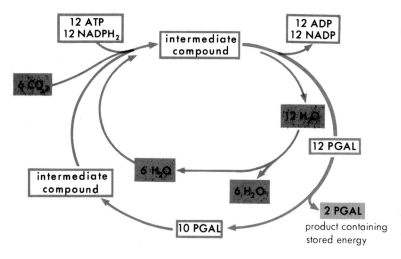

Figure 12 • 22
The "dark reactions" in photosynthesis.

To accomplish all this, a supply of energy is required. It comes from the compounds formed during the "light reactions"—ATP and $NADPH_2$. As the energy is released from ATP, ADP is formed. This ADP is then available for conversion into ATP during the "light reactions." Likewise, as energy is released from $NADPH_2$, NADP is formed. And this is also available for conversion into $NADPH_2$ during the "light reactions." Thus, ATP and $NADPH_2$ act as carriers of energy from sunlight to multicarbon compounds. And from the chemical energy of these multicarbon compounds, all the activities of living things result.

Some biochemists have argued that the formation of carbon compounds from carbon dioxide should not be considered a part of photosynthesis. How might this viewpoint be defended?

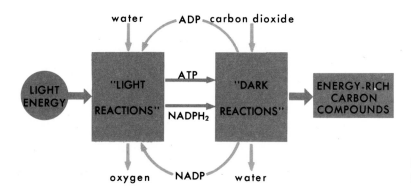

Figure 12 • 23
Summary of photosynthesis.

Investigation 12.5

PHOTOSYNTHETIC RATE

BACKGROUND INFORMATION

Because oxygen is only slowly soluble in water, visible bubbles of oxygen may be formed by a photosynthesizing aquatic plant. If the bubbles are of uniform size, the number of bubbles formed per time unit indicates photosynthetic rate—provided all other factors affecting rate are held constant.

MATERIALS AND EQUIPMENT

(for each team)
sprig of elodea
glass rod
string
graduated cylinder, 250-ml
sodium bicarbonate solution (0.25%
    in pond or aquarium water), 250 ml
battery jar
thermometer
ring stand with clamp
lamp with reflector and 150-watt bulb
razor blade
forceps
watch with second hand

PROCEDURE

First read through this procedure.   • Now state a hypothesis for the experiment.(1)

Prepare the setup shown in Figure 12 • 24, as follows: With string fasten a healthy sprig of elodea to one end of a glass rod. Place this in a 250-ml graduated cylinder so the tip of the sprig is located at the bottom. Add sufficient 0.25% bicarbonate solution to the cylinder to cover the cut end of the sprig to a depth of 5 cm. Place this whole setup in a battery jar filled with water at room temperature. Using a ring stand and clamp, suspend a thermometer with the bulb located near the cylinder. Place a lamp with a 150-watt bulb 10 cm from the elodea sprig.

Turn on the lamp and observe the base of the sprig. If all goes well, after several minutes

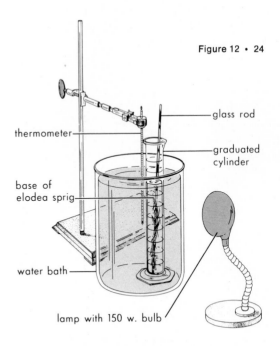

Figure 12 • 24

glass rod

graduated cylinder

thermometer

base of elodea sprig

water bath

lamp with 150 w. bulb

small bubbles will appear and rise through the bicarbonate solution at regular intervals. If no bubbles appear, lift the rod out of the cylinder and, with a sharp razor blade, cut off a short section of the sprig base. Immediately return the rod to the cylinder. If large bubbles are formed that become detached only after an extended time, gently crush the base of the sprig with a pair of forceps.

When the rate of bubble formation has become fairly uniform, count the number of bubbles formed during each of 5 one-minute intervals, allowing a couple of minutes between counts. Record the average number of bubbles produced per minute. Increase the distance of the lamp from the sprig to 20 cm. Observe, count, and average the data as before. Increase the lamp distance to 40 cm and make a final determination of average rate of bubble formation per minute. At frequent intervals throughout the experiment, check the temperature of the water in the battery jar. If the temperature rises more than 2°C, add sufficient cold water or ice cubes to reduce it to the original temperature.

DISCUSSION

Graph the data, placing the distance between lamp and sprig on the horizontal axis and the average number of bubbles per minute on the vertical axis. • What is the general direction of the slope of the line?(2) • How is the change in distance of lamp from plant related to the change in light intensity received by the plant?(3) • What, then, is the relationship between light intensity and photosynthetic rate as indicated by your data?(4)

• Why do you think the plant was placed in sodium bicarbonate solution?(5) • What other environmental factors may affect photo-synthetic rate?(6) • In the design of this experiment, which of these factors are controlled? How?(7)

FOR FURTHER INVESTIGATION

1. Plan and carry out an experiment in which light intensity is held constant and some other factor affecting photosynthetic rate is varied.

2. In terms of exchange of gases, what process in living organisms is the opposite of photosynthesis? How does this process affect attempts to measure photosynthetic rate? Using measurements of gaseous exchange as a basis, plan and carry out an experiment designed to eliminate the errors introduced by this process.

GUIDE QUESTIONS

1. Why is the study of energy in living things—bioenergetics—of basic importance to an understanding of biology?

2. What experimental evidence do we have for the idea that living things lose energy to their environments?

3. What characteristic is shared by all substances that can act as fuels?

4. How are many chemical reactions brought about in living things at relatively low temperatures?

5. How can chemical energy in a substance be measured?

6. What is an enzyme?

7. Only certain chemical reactions occur in cells. Why?

8. How is cellular respiration different from burning?

9. Into what does the energy released by cellular respiration go?

10. What part does ATP play in the use of energy by cells?

11. What are the main steps in the breakdown of a glucose molecule to carbon dioxide and water?

12. In cellular respiration which reactions require oxygen? Which occur without the presence of oxygen?

13. What part of cellular respiration occurs in mitochondria?

14. In what ways does fermentation differ from cellular respiration? In what ways are cellular respiration and fermentation alike?

15. Where does a cell obtain energy for syntheses?

16. What are some common kinds of carbohydrates?

17. From what chemical units are polysaccharides synthesized?

18. Contrast the energy contents of fats and carbohydrates.

19. In what ways are all lipids alike? How do fats differ from other lipids?

20. How do proteins differ from carbohydrates and lipids with respect to the chemical elements they contain?

21. From what chemical units are polypeptides synthesized?

22. How does a protein differ from a polypeptide?

23. In what ways are the syntheses of polysaccharides, lipids, and proteins alike?

24. How is ATP related chemically to the nucleic acids?

25. How were the main events in photosynthesis discovered?

26. How is the structure of a chloroplast related to its function?

27. How can acetone-soluble pigments in leaves be separated? How many kinds of

chlorophyll usually occur in leaves?

28. In what general ways are photosynthesis and cellular respiration similar? How do they differ?

29. What seems to be the effect of light energy on chlorophyll molecules?

30. How do water molecules enter into the light phase of photosynthesis?

31. How does the light phase of photosynthesis prepare for the dark phase of photosynthesis?

32. How have isotopes of chemical elements played a part in the investigation of photosynthesis?

33. How has the technique of isolating chloroplasts been important to the investigation of photosynthesis?

34. Contrast the energy sources used to change ADP to ATP in cellular respiration and in photosynthesis.

35. List the conditions necessary for photosynthesis.

PROBLEMS

1. In Simpson and Beck (Chapter 2) or another reference find out how biochemists picture the way enzymes act in metabolic reactions. Then use this model to explain enzyme specificity.

2. A certain chemical substance is known to increase the activity of an enzyme called nitrate reductase. This enzyme reduces nitrate ions to nitrite ions, which are then used in the synthesis of amino acids. What practical use might be made of this information?

3. Calculate the surface area and volume of ten spheres having diameters of 1 mm, 2 mm, 3 mm, and so on to 10 mm. Plot the two sets of results on the same grid, allowing the vertical axis to represent both mm^2 and mm^3. Keeping in mind the requirements of all living cells for energy and materials from which energy is released, comment on the meaning of your graph. How might cells grow large while avoiding the biological consequences of large size?

4. As you are running in a track meet, your rate of breathing increases. When the race is over, your breathing rate continues to be high for a considerable period. Explain this phenomenon, using your knowledge of cellular physiology.

5. You may have seen some fats and cooking oils referred to as "polyunsaturated." Find out what "polyunsaturated" means in chemical terms.

6. Proteins in the cells of a wheat plant differ from the proteins in your cells. How can the differences be explained? What must happen when you use wheat as a nutrient for the formation of your protein?

7. Experiments with photosynthesizing tracheophytes have shown that when they are grown in an atmosphere without oxygen they take up carbon dioxide at 1.5 times the rate in natural atmosphere, which is about 20 percent oxygen. (a) What does this information indicate about the relationship between photosynthesis and cellular respiration? (b) How might this relationship affect the composition of the earth's atmosphere? (c) How does this information affect Oparin's speculations (Chapter 10)?

8. Many botanists believe that the concentration of carbon dioxide in the air was much greater during the Carboniferous period, when most of the large coal deposits were being formed, than it is at present. What might be the basis for their belief? Is there any reason to suppose that the concentration of carbon dioxide in the air has increased during the last 150 years?

9. According to the theory of the origin of life discussed in Chapter 10, energy for the first living things must have come from chemical compounds formed by the heat and electrical energy in the earth's atmosphere at that time. Later some organisms apparently began to use energy from sunlight to build up foods. What might account for this change in energy source?

10. Gather whatever information you can find about conditions on the surfaces of Mars and Venus. Then, using your knowledge of cell metabolism, comment on the possibility of life existing on these planets. What life-supporting equipment would probably be desirable for astronauts planning trips to these planets?

11. What pigments are lacking along the edges of the geranium leaves pictured below? What pigments do the leaf edges contain? Do you think these pigments are also present in other parts of the leaves? Refer to Investigation 12.4.

12. The coleus plant pictured above carries on photosynthesis. How could you show that it does so? Explain how it can photosynthesize despite its color.

SUGGESTED READINGS

BAKER, J. J. W., and G. E. ALLEN. *Matter, Energy, and Life*. Palo Alto, Calif.: Addison-Wesley Publishing Co., Inc., 1965. (A very useful introduction to the chemical and physical aspects of living systems. No previous knowledge of physics or chemistry is assumed.)

BASSHAM, J. A. "The Path of Carbon in Photosynthesis," *Scientific American,* June, 1962. Pp. 88–100.

CHANGEUX, J. "The Control of Biochemical Reactions," *Scientific American,* April, 1965. Pp. 36–45.

CHAPPELL, J. B., and S. C. REES. *Mitochondria.* London: Oxford University Press, 1972. (Considers the functions of mitochondria in the biochemistry of cellular respiration. Advanced.)

DAWKINS, M. J. R., and D. HULL. "The Production of Heat by Fat," *Scientific American,* August, 1965. Pp. 62–67.

DICKERSON, R. E. "The Structure and History of an Ancient Protein," *Scientific American,* April, 1972. Pp. 58–72.

LEHNINGER, A. L. *Bioenergetics.* New York: W. A. Benjamin, Inc., 1965. (Extremely well-written account of most aspects of bioenergetics at a somewhat advanced level.)

LEVINE, R. D. "The Mechanism of Photosynthesis," *Scientific American,* December, 1969. Pp. 58–70.

McELROY, W. D. *Cell Physiology and Biochemistry.* 3rd ed. Englewood Cliffs, N.J.: Prentice-Hall, Inc., 1971. (Contains excellent diagrams of biochemical processes and many structural formulas. Advanced.)

MARGARIA, R. "The Sources of Muscular Energy," *Scientific American,* March, 1972. Pp. 84–91.

MERCER, E. H. *Cells: Their Structure and Function.* New York: Doubleday & Co., Inc., 1962. (An inexpensive book that emphasizes present theories in biochemistry. Fairly easy.)

PHELPS, C. F. *Polysaccharides.* London: Oxford University Press, 1972. (A good short account of a set of fairly complex biochemical substances. Advanced.)

RABINOWITCH, E. I. and GOVINDJEE. "The Role of Chlorophyll in Photosynthesis," *Scientific American,* July, 1965. Pp. 74–83.

SIMPSON, G. G., and W. S. BECK. *Life: An Introduction to Biology.* Shorter ed. New York: Harcourt, Brace & World, Inc., 1969. Chapters 2

Photos by Victor Larsen

and 4. (Fine illustration and clear writing make this one of the best accounts of cell physiology written for the level of college freshmen.)

STEGNER, R. *Plant Pigments*. Chicago: Rand McNally & Co., 1967. (Considers leaf pigments as well as other plant pigments. Contains suggestions for laboratory investigations. Fairly easy.)

STEIN, W. H., and S. MOORE. "Chemical Structure of Proteins," *Scientific American*, February, 1961. Pp. 81–86.

WHITTINGHAM, C. P. *Photosynthesis*. London: Oxford University Press, 1971. (A short account of the biochemistry of photosynthesis. Rather advanced.)

YOUNG, V. R., and N. S. SERIMSHAW. "The Physiology of Starvation," *Scientific American*, October, 1971. Pp. 14–21.

Functioning Plants

PLANTS AS ORGANISMS

As producers, green plants are of primary importance to other organisms in the web of life. But plants carry on many activities other than photosynthesis. Like other living things they use nutrients, grow, reproduce. Photosynthesis was discussed in Chapter 12; here you will consider some of the other processes that go on in plants.

VASCULAR PLANTS

An estimated 80 percent of the photosynthetic activity on Earth occurs in the seas—mostly in single-celled plants and protists. But we are land animals, and thus far in many parts of the world we have made only limited use of the seas' productivity. By and large we obtain our food, directly or indirectly, from land plants.

Moreover, land plants are plants with which we are most familiar, the plants with which we most like to surround ourselves—even in hot, dry houses and dim hotel lobbies. It seems reasonable, therefore, to use tracheophytes—the group to which almost all familiar land plants belong—as the chief examples in continuing this discussion of how plants function.

We may begin our study by taking a look at a potted house plant —perhaps a geranium placed near a window at home. Unlike many animals, such a plant actually lives in two very different environments —one the air, the other the soil. The part above ground—the shoot— made up of stems, leaves, and, perhaps, flowers and fruits, is surrounded by air, which provides almost no support to offset the effects of gravity. In nature, wind, rain, sleet, or snow may exert powerful forces, which the shoot must withstand if it is to remain whole and maintain its position. Because the air is usually not saturated with water and because the shoot has a relatively large surface in contact with the air, loss of water to the atmosphere continually occurs. But, being in air, the shoot has an abundant oxygen supply, a limited supply of carbon dioxide, and—depending upon where it grows— varying intensities of light.

See Figure 8 · 5.

saturated: with a relative humidity of 100 percent. (See Investigation 3.3.)

opaque: not allowing light to
go through

Quite different is the root's environment—the soil. Soil is comparatively dense, moist, and opaque. Support is firm; water is usually absorbed rather than lost; and light is lacking.

Like all attempts to identify differences, this simplified view of a plant as consisting of shoot and root runs into difficulties. There are roots that live above ground and stems that live underground. As a generalization, however, this view can be helpful in understanding the wide variety of structure and function shown by plants.

LEAVES

What are some tracheophytes
that lack leaves?

The shoots of the first tracheophytes probably had chlorophyll in most of the cells that were exposed to light. But very early in the history of land plants, flat, green structures developed that were exposed more or less perpendicularly to the sun's rays. These structures—leaves— were well developed on plants long before the end of the Paleozoic era, and they are characteristic of almost all tracheophytes today.

In general, botanists consider leaves as organs. To call a leaf an "organ" may seem somewhat strange. In the human body, organs are usually one of a kind or, as in the case of eyes and lungs, two; on the other hand, a large land plant may have thousands of leaves. However, according to the discussion in Chapter 11, a leaf is an organ—a structure composed of a number of tissues and performing some general function in the life of an organism.

Figure 13 • 1

Variation in leaves taken
from a single white poplar
tree.

X 1/2

See Investigation 5.1.

External view. Variability is a characteristic feature of leaves. Examine the leaves on any one plant. No two are exactly alike. Shapes and sizes vary according to the age of the plant, the amount of light received, and other factors. Yet for any particular species of plant, the leaf shape is usually distinctive and constant enough to be useful in identification.

A leaf may or may not have a petiole connecting the blade to the plant stem. In the needle leaves of many conifers there is neither blade nor petiole. In *simple* leaves the blade is in one piece, but it is divided into separate leaflets in *compound* leaves. Or leaves may be so highly modified that they no longer function in photosynthesis—spines of cactus, for example. Whatever the form, however, there is no doubt that the primary function of most leaves is photosynthesis.

cactus. See Figure 10 · 35.

X 1/4   X 1/4   X 1/4

horse chestnut   locust   meadow rue

Figure 13 · 2

In these compound leaves each blade is divided into separate parts. What other plants with compound leaves can you name?

Inside a leaf. Figure 13 · 3 shows the cellular structure of a leaf blade. Several different tissues can be distinguished in the figure. With your knowledge of photosynthesis, you can set up a number of hypotheses about the functions of these tissues. As cells in a multicellular organism differentiate in structure, they usually acquire special functions—they become *specialized.*

Photosynthesis requires chlorophyll, and chlorophyll is usually

Upon what generalization are your hypotheses based?

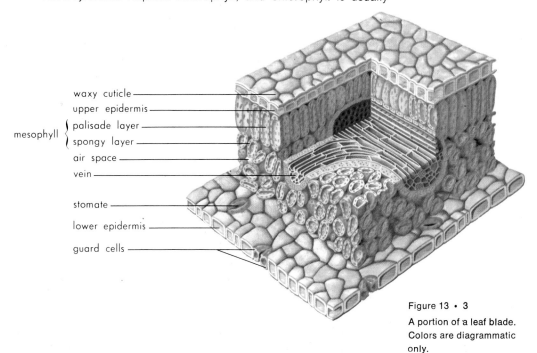

waxy cuticle
upper epidermis
mesophyll { palisade layer
spongy layer
air space
vein
stomate
lower epidermis
guard cells

Figure 13 · 3

A portion of a leaf blade. Colors are diagrammatic only.

mesophyll [měs'ə fĭl; Greek: *mesos*, middle, + *phyllon*, a leaf]

stomates [Greek: *stoma*, mouth]

located in chloroplasts. Since the *mesophyll* cells (palisade and spongy tissues) contain chloroplasts, you can confidently hypothesize that the mesophyll is the specialized tissue in which photosynthesis occurs. The upper leaf surface usually gets the most light, and you therefore might suspect that more photosynthetic activity takes place in the closely packed upper layers of mesophyll. (The epidermis covers the leaf but allows light to pass through.)

Both of the raw materials of photosynthesis—H_2O and CO_2—are present in air. Although the amount of water vapor varies a great deal, water molecules are never as abundant in air as in living leaf cells. Thus, according to the principles of diffusion, leaves should lose H_2O to the air. The amount of CO_2 in the air does not normally vary much, but, depending upon relative rates of respiration and photosynthesis, it does vary within chlorophyll-bearing cells. CO_2, therefore, might either be given off or taken in by them. Further, an exchange of gases between inner-leaf cells and the air is suggested by the numerous slitlike pores, *stomates,* leading from the outside of a leaf through the leaf's epidermis and into the air spaces of the mesophyll. Therefore, you might hypothesize that gas exchange occurs through stomates.

If water is lost through these stomates, how does it enter the leaf? Look at the tubular structure labeled *vein* in the figure. As it evidently is a structure through which liquids could flow, you might hypothesize that water comes to the leaf from other parts of the plant by way of veins.

Through years of experimentation, mostly during the 19th century,

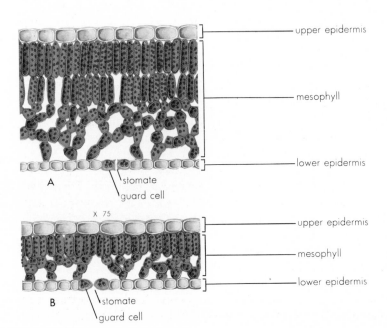

Figure 13 • 4

Leaves vary internally as well as externally. Sections through two leaves from one plant: (*A*) A leaf that was exposed to full sun. (*B*) A leaf that was shaded most of the day. How many structural differences can you see?

upper epidermis

mesophyll

lower epidermis

A

stomate

guard cell

X 75

upper epidermis

mesophyll

lower epidermis

B

stomate

guard cell

plant physiologists have confirmed these hypotheses. Now we shall go a little beyond the hypotheses and discuss matters that are not quite so obvious.

Loss of water from leaves. Air contains less water than cells do. As air moves among mesophyll cells, water must diffuse into the air—the plant loses water. And the drier the air, the more rapidly the water is lost. Each stomate that lets air in and out of the mesophyll is surrounded by a pair of specialized cells, *guard cells.* The inner walls of the guard cells are thickened. When their water content and thus their volume increases, the cells bend outward and the stomate opens. When the water content decreases, the stomate closes (in a relative sense—never tightly). We might hypothesize that this is a mechanism for opening stomates when the air is moist and closing them when the air is dry.

Figure 13 • 5
Stomate action. Diagrammatic sections through open and closed stomates.

STOMATE CLOSED

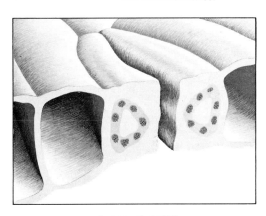

STOMATE OPEN

But this hypothesis is not confirmed by observation. In most land plants the stomates are open during daylight hours, when the water content of the air is usually relatively low, and closed at night, when the water content is usually higher. Moreover, experiments have shown that changes in the shape of guard cells are related not to the water content of the air, but to the concentration of CO_2 dissolved in the cell substance. Therefore, the action of guard cells seems to be associated more with supply of CO_2 than with control of water loss. However, this still does not explain another observation of plant physiologists: that stomates of potato plants are closed for only about three hours after sundown. Botanists still have much to learn about how stomates work.

What metabolic process in guard cells affects their supply of CO_2?

Regardless of the action of guard cells, land plants lose much water through the stomates of their leaves. But they also lose some water directly through their epidermal cells—not only through the leaf

cuticle [kū′tə kəl; Latin: *cutis*, skin]

epidermis but through the surface of the whole shoot. This loss is reduced, but never completely stopped, by the **cuticle,** composed mostly of a waxy material that covers the outer surface of the shoot's epidermal cells. The cuticle is very thin in some cases, as on lettuce leaves, and rather thick in others, as on pine leaves.

All loss of water vapor from plants, both through the stomates and through the external surfaces of the epidermal cells, is called

transpiration [Latin: *trans*, across, + *spirare*, to breathe]

transpiration. Plant physiologists have made many measurements of transpiration rates. Black raspberries lose water through their leaves at the rate of 3.8 ml per cm² of leaf surface per day. Mature apple trees lose water at the rate of 15 liters per tree per hour. A single corn plant has been found to transpire 200 liters of water during a growing

What variables in the environment might have effects on such measurements?

season. Such data clearly indicate that many land plants require large amounts of water.

Investigation 13.1

TRANSPIRATION

MATERIALS AND EQUIPMENT
(for each team)

container, deep, 30-liter

(for entire class)

cork, 1-hole, split
tubing, rubber, about 20 cm long
battery jar and bowl, large
plant, leafy, potted (all teams but 1)
glass rod, solid (1 team only)
scalpel
water at room temperature
pipette, 1-ml
burette clamp
ring stand
petri dish, bottom half
beaker, 400-ml
towel, paper
watch
plastic bag
string, 15 cm long

PROCEDURE

• Read the procedure and then state a hypothesis appropriate to the design of the experiment.(1)

All teams except a control team proceed as follows: Immerse a potted plant in a deep 30-liter container of water (at room temperature) so that the base of the shoot is covered to a height of 5 to 10 cm. Have a team member support the shoot and another team member make a diagonal cut through the base of the shoot, under the water and close to the soil surface. *Quickly* transfer the cut shoot to a large bowl of water and hold it so that the cut end is kept under water and the rest of the shoot remains dry.

Immerse the rubber tubing in the bowl. Squeeze it to force out air so that it is completely filled with water. Then, keeping it under the surface of the water, force an end of the tubing over the cut end of the shoot so that it is covered by the tubing for a distance of about 1 cm.

Fill the bottom half of a petri dish with water, almost to its brim. Immerse the tip of a graduated 1-ml pipette in the dish and suck on it to fill it completely with water. Place a finger over the tip of the pipette and then remove it from the petri dish. Insert the other end of the pipette to a distance of 2 cm in the free end of the rubber tubing, keeping both pipette end and rubber tubing under water. As this is being done, remove your fingertip. Water will spurt out of the tip of the pipette. (Caution: Remove books and papers from the immediate vicinity.) Immediately replace the tip of the pipette in the petri dish of water. Then position the shoot as in Figure 13 • 6, supporting it by means of ring stand, clamp, and split cork. The base of the shoot should be about 15 cm above the table surface.

Figure 13 • 6

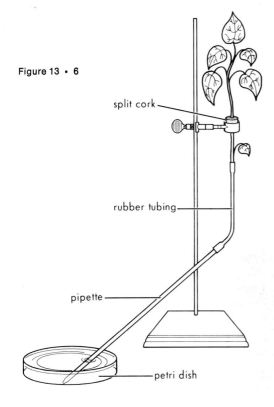

split cork

rubber tubing

pipette

petri dish

Now raise the tip of the pipette out of the petri dish and rest it, in a horizontal position, on the top of a small beaker. Place a small piece of paper towel against the pipette lip. Gently apply pressure to the rubber tubing so that a small volume of water is forced out of the pipette and absorbed by the towel. This water will be replaced by air when the pressure is removed. If the setup is operating satisfactorily, the air column should move slowly along

the length of the pipette. Wait until the air column reaches a .1-ml graduation and then determine the time it takes to move through the next three .1-ml sections of the pipette.

As soon as you have recorded the time, place the pipette tip in the petri dish and gently squeeze the rubber tubing until a few bubbles of air are forced out; then release pressure. Now cover the shoot loosely with a plastic bag. Gather the mouth of the bag together and, using a piece of string, tie it shut around the base of the stem. After 5 minutes repeat the above procedure for measuring the rate of movement of the air column.

One team will prepare a control setup substituting a glass rod for the leafy shoot. Except for this difference, procedures identical to those described above should be carried out.

STUDYING THE DATA

Calculate the volume of water per minute removed from the pipette attached to the shoot when uncovered. Calculate the same for the shoot when covered. Make the same calculations for the control setup.

Compare the results from the experimental setup with the results from the control setup. • Where do you think water may have been lost from the apparatus in either of the setups? (2) • In the case of the experimental setup, does the use of the plastic bag provide any confirmation of this? If so, how?(3)

Use the data from the control to correct the data from the experimental setup.

CONCLUSIONS

• Do your data support your original hypothesis? Explain.(4)

FOR FURTHER INVESTIGATION

How could you determine the rate of water loss from the shoot of a growing potted plant of the same species and size as that from which you obtained the shoot used in this investigation? Would you expect the rate of water loss of this plant to be lower, the same as, or greater than the rate of uptake of the cut shoot? Explain.

Investigation 13.2

STOMATES AND PHOTOSYNTHESIS

MATERIALS AND EQUIPMENT

(for each team)

For Part A

    leaves, fresh (several kinds)
    razor blade
    microscope
    slide
    cover slip
    forceps
    droppers

For Part B

    plants, potted, 2
    scissors
    beakers, 400-ml, 3
    forceps
    hot plate
    beaker, 1000-ml
    alcohol, 95%
    petri dishes, 4
    iodine solution
    test tubes, 4
    petroleum jelly
    paper towel
    cotton, absorbent
    benzine
    water at room temperature

PART A

PROCEDURE

Tear a leaf at an angle while holding the lower surface upward. The tearing action should peel off portions of the lower epidermis, which will appear as a narrow, colorless zone extending beyond the green part of the leaf. Using a razor blade, cut off a small piece of the epidermis and immediately place it in a drop of water on a slide. Do not allow the fragment to dry out. Add a cover slip.

Using the low-power objective of your microscope, locate some stomates. Then switch to the high-power objective. Make a sketch to show the shape of a stomate, its guard cells, and a few adjacent cells in the epidermis.

Count the number of stomates in 10 high-power fields of the microscope and average. Referring to Appendix 2, calculate the diameter of the high-power field. Use this figure to calculate the area. Then calculate the average number of stomates per mm^2 of leaf surface.

In the same manner, count the stomates on the upper epidermis of the same leaf. Examine as many other kinds of leaves as possible and compare the number of stomates per mm^2 for the upper and lower surfaces of each kind of leaf.

STUDYING THE DATA

• Did you find exactly the same number of stomates per mm^2 in different areas of a piece of leaf epidermis?(1)   • What variations in the extent to which the stomates are open can you observe? Can you explain this variation?(2)   • If you wished to compare the number of stomates per mm^2 for 2 species of plants, what steps should you take to assure a reliable comparison?(3)

CONCLUSIONS

• What do your data suggest concerning the distribution of stomates in leaves of your species of plant?(4)   • What assumption must you make in drawing this conclusion?(5)

PART B

PROCEDURE

If carbon dioxide enters a leaf through the stomates, then plugging up the stomates should prevent photosynthesis. The following experiment will test this hypothesis.

Select 2 healthy plants of the same species. Place one where it will receive no light and the other where it will be exposed to sunlight. After 3 days remove a leaf from each plant, identifying the illuminated one by placing a small notch in its margin. Immediately drop the leaves into a beaker of boiling water. When they are limp, transfer them to a beaker half full of alcohol. Place this beaker in an electrically heated water bath. *Never heat alcohol over an open flame or permit its vapor to come into contact with an open flame.*

Heated alcohol extracts chlorophyll from leaves; it also makes them brittle, because most of their water is removed. As soon as the leaves are no longer green, use forceps to take the leaves out of the alcohol. Then drop the leaves into a beaker of water at room temperature. After a minute or so, the leaves will become quite soft. Spread each leaf out in a petri dish and cover it with iodine solution.

Allow the iodine solution to act on the leaves for several minutes. Then remove both leaves from the iodine solution, rinse them in water, and spread them out in petri dishes of water placed on a white piece of paper. Record the color of each leaf.

Select 4 similar leaves on the plant that has been kept in the dark. Do not remove them from the plant. Thoroughly coat the upper surface of one of these leaves with petroleum jelly. Cut 1 notch in its margin. Coat a 2nd leaf on its lower surface and cut 2 notches in its margin. Coat a 3rd leaf on both upper and lower surfaces and cut 3 notches in its margin. Do not coat the 4th leaf, but cut 4 notches in its margin. A layer of petroleum jelly, though transparent, is a highly effective barrier across which many gases cannot pass. • In what ways would you suspect that coating a leaf with petroleum jelly would alter the exchange of gases between it and the air?(6)   Place the plant where it will be exposed to sunlight.

After 3 days remove all 4 leaves, place them on paper towels, and remove the petroleum jelly by gently rubbing the leaves with absorbent cotton saturated with a solvent such as benzine. Following the procedure used before, perform the iodine test on each leaf. Devise a scheme for comparing the color reactions of the 4 leaves, and record your observations.

STUDYING THE DATA

• In the design of this experiment, what was the purpose of the 1st set of iodine tests? (7)   • If you use this test as an indication of photosynthetic activity, what assumption are you making?(8)

• In the design of this experiment, what is the purpose of the leaf that is marked with 4 notches?(9)

• In which of the leaves did photosynthetic activity appear to have been greatest?(10) • In which of the leaves did photosynthetic activity appear to have been least?(11)

CONCLUSION

• Do your data support the hypothesis? Explain.(12)

ROOTS

Water is lost by terrestrial tracheophytes principally through their leaves. Except for epiphytes, terrestrial plants obtain water from the soil through their roots. With water they absorb soluble mineral nutrients. Roots have three additional functions: anchorage, storage of food, and the transportation of absorbed water and dissolved minerals. This last function will be discussed later in connection with stems.

Anchorage. Anyone who has pulled weeds in a garden or removed dandelions from a lawn is well aware that the roots of a plant anchor it firmly in the soil. In some species the lower end of the uprooted plant is a tough mass of roots. This is a *fibrous-root* system, and it is characteristic of corn, beans, and clover, for example. In other species the plant is anchored by a long, tapering root with slender, small lateral branches. This is a *taproot* system, found in dandelions

To what ecological conditions do you think each of these kinds of root systems is adapted?

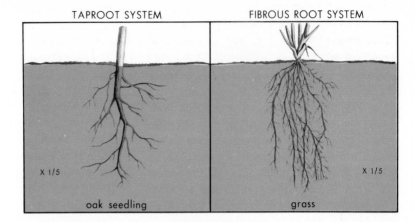

TAPROOT SYSTEM

FIBROUS ROOT SYSTEM

X 1/5

X 1/5

oak seedling

grass

Figure 13 • 7

Two kinds of root systems.

Figure 13 • 8

A radish seedling. What part of the plant was first to emerge from the seed coat? × 9

Hugh Spencer

Review pages 354–355.

and young oak trees.

When a plant is pulled up, most of a root system remains in the soil. But if a stream of water is used to gently wash away the soil, the smaller branch roots remain undamaged and the root system can be seen more completely. When carefully exposed in this way, the root system of a rye plant less than 60 cm in height was estimated to have a total length of about 480 km and a total surface area of more than 600 m²—twice that of a tennis court.

Absorption. If radish seeds are germinated in a moist petri dish, the structure of the young root can readily be seen. The tip of such a young root is pointed and bare. Just back of the tip is a region that appears to be covered with a fuzzy white growth. Observed over a period of several days, this fuzzy zone seems to move in the direction of growth as the root lengthens.

The fuzzy zone owes its appearance to the presence of numerous *root hairs.* Each root hair is a thin-walled extension of an epidermal cell. The central part of a root-hair cell is occupied by a large vacuole; this is filled with water in whicn sugars, salts, and a variety of other compounds are dissolved. Root hairs penetrate the spaces between soil particles and are in contact with soil water. It is principally through these specialized cells that the water and many other substances required by a plant are obtained.

Substances dissolved in soil water are seldom as concentrated as the same substances dissolved in the vacuole of a root hair. Because cell membranes are differentially permeable, many substances inside root-hair cells cannot pass out through the membranes. Under such conditions there is a net inward diffusion of water.

Thus, we can explain the entry into land plants of the two materials required for photosynthesis: carbon dioxide enters chiefly through leaf cells by way of stomates; water enters chiefly through the root hairs.

But in addition to CO_2 and H_2O, a plant requires mineral nutrients. The many elements that are needed by plants are obtained from soil water in the form of dissolved ions or compounds. Roots take in nitrogen, for example, in the form of ammonium ions or nitrate ions. Because the mineral nutrients are continually being used in the synthetic metabolic activities of a plant, they are usually less concentrated inside root-hair cells than in the surrounding water. They, therefore, pass into root hairs by diffusion.

Frequently, however, certain substances needed by a plant are *less* concentrated in soil water than in the root-hair cells. Under these circumstances, diffusion would carry the substances *from* the cells *into* the soil water: ions would be most concentrated in the soil water, less concentrated in the root hairs, and progressively less concentrated the farther a cell is from the root hairs. But experiments have shown that plants can absorb substances that exist only in low concentrations in soil water. In certain tissues in roots, minerals accumulate at even higher concentrations than in root hairs themselves. Further, when cells are moving dissolved substances in a direction opposite to that of diffusion, cell respiration speeds up. Clearly, absorption of mineral nutrients involves active transport as well as diffusion.

Root-hair cells are the usual places of entry for water and mineral nutrients. On their inner sides these special epidermal cells are in contact with other root cells (Figure 13 · 9). Absorbed substances move deeper into the root by diffusion or active transport from one layer of cells to another. Eventually they reach the conducting tissues, through which they move upward to the stem and leaves.

Recall the roles of plants in the nitrogen cycle, Figure 7 · 26.

Why is a speeding up of cell respiration an indication of active transport?

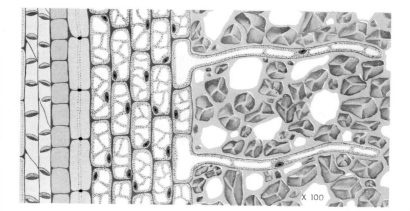

X 100

Figure 13 · 9

Root hairs penetrating into soil. On the left are conducting tissues of the root; soil is shown as in Figure 7 · 18.

Storage. The *cortex* of a young root may be sloughed off as the root grows older, or it may form part of the bark around the root. Sometimes a plant stores food in the cortex, and sometimes in modified cells of the conducting tissues. The food is usually stored as insoluble starch, but sometimes as sugars.

slough [slŭf]: to shed by rubbing off (usually implying something no longer needed)

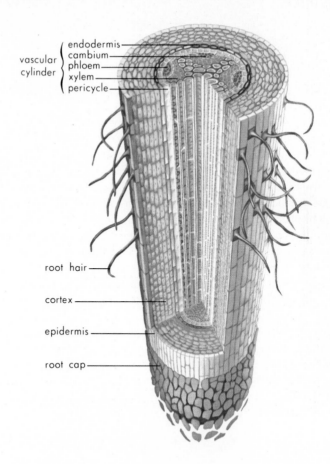

Figure 13 • 10

The terminal portion of a root. Colors are diagrammatic only.

Taproots and some fibrous-root systems may have parts where food storage is concentrated. In polar regions, middle latitudes, and those tropical biomes with dry seasons, perennial plants usually store a considerable amount of food in roots.

What plant stores so much sugar in its root that we use it as a sugar source?

STORAGE ROOTS

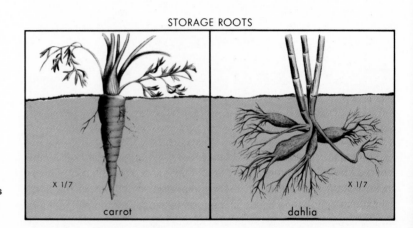

Figure 13 • 11

When large quantities of food are stored, both taproots (*left*) and fibrous roots (*right*) may be thickened.

Figure 13 · 12

In some plants, roots sprout from stems, grow downward, and penetrate into the soil. This banyan tree grows near the state capitol of Hawaii.

STEMS

For botanists the distinction between a root and a stem—usually the principal part of a shoot—is based on the arrangement of tissues in these structures and on the way the structures originate in embryos within seeds. But the easiest way to make the distinction is to look for *buds*—each a miniature shoot, consisting of a short length of stem, tiny leaves, and (sometimes) flowers. The eyes of a white potato are buds, and it is therefore an underground stem. A sweet potato has no buds; it is a root. Most stems, however, grow above ground, supporting leaves and reproductive organs in light and air.

Macroscopic structure. Stems differ greatly in structure, but it is convenient to use a portion of a woody twig from a deciduous plant as a starting point in discussing stem structure. Such a twig, when the leaves have fallen, usually bears conspicuous buds. Growth from a *terminal* bud lengthens the twig; growth from a *lateral* bud starts a new branch. A bud may or may not be covered with protective *scales* (modified leaves). If present, scales fall off, leaving scars on the twig, when growth is resumed in the spring. For a few years, old scale scars may remain visible, and from their positions growth in different years can be compared. The places where the petioles of fallen leaves were attached to the twig are also marked by scars. Openings in the

terminal [Latin: *terminare*, to end, limit]

lateral [Latin: *latus*, a side]

Figure 13 • 13
An opening hickory bud.

lenticels [lĕn′tə sĕlz′]

Figure 13 • 14
A dormant woody twig.

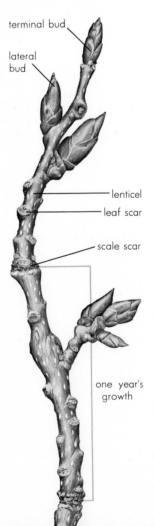

terminal bud

lateral
bud

lenticel

leaf scar

scale scar

one year's
growth

bark—*lenticels*—through which atmospheric gases diffuse into and out of the living cells may be very conspicuous in some species, but hard to see in others.

Older woody stems—tree trunks, for example—are best viewed in cross section. A rather thick bark is characteristic of both older stems and older roots. The bark surrounds the wood. Wood usually shows annual growth rings. Wood *rays* extend radially from the center

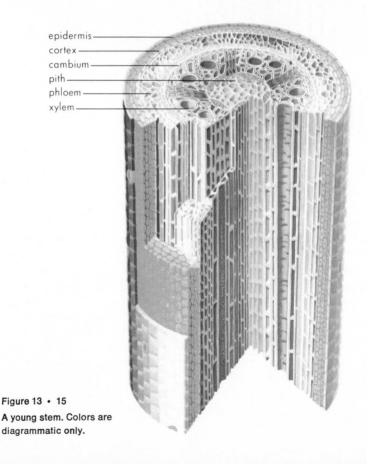

epidermis
cortex
cambium
pith
phloem
xylem

Figure 13 • 15
A young stem. Colors are diagrammatic only.

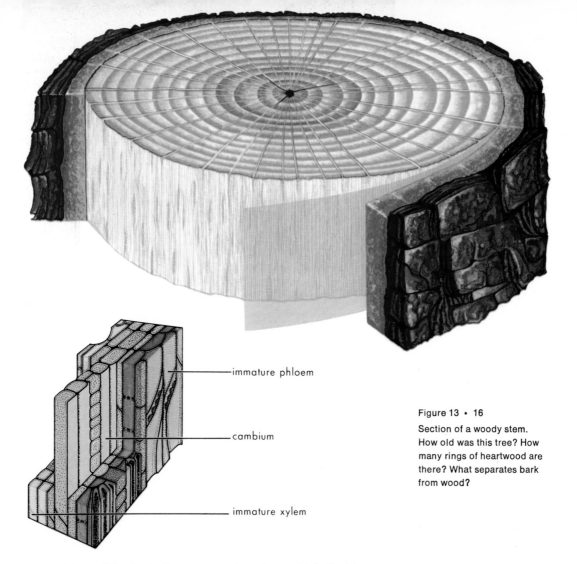

immature phloem

cambium

immature xylem

Figure 13 • 16

Section of a woody stem. How old was this tree? How many rings of heartwood are there? What separates bark from wood?

outward toward the bark; these are routes along which liquids move laterally.

Only the tissues of the inner bark and the outer part of the wood are alive; the rest of the wood and bark is composed of dead cell walls such as Hooke saw in cork. Most of the plant liquids (*sap*) move up and down stems through dead cells—upward through wood, downward through bark. Wood through which sap moves upward is called *sapwood.* Eventually the center wood loses its conducting function; it is then called *heartwood.* It may serve to support the upper parts of a tree, but this is not always important—many trees stand erect and live for years after much of the heartwood has rotted away.

Microscopic structure. Figure 13 • 15 shows in three dimensions the microscopic structure of a young stem. This is a stém from a dicotyledonous plant. By examining thin slices of several different kinds of stems with a microscope, you can find—as with roots and leaves—that there are many variations.

In ebony wood there are no growth rings. In what biome do you think ebony grows?

See Figure 11 · 2.

cambium [kăm′bĭ əm; Latin: cambiare, to exchange]

xylem [zī′lĕm; Greek: xylon, wood]

phloem [flō′ĕm; Greek: phloos, bark of a tree]

The fibers of some plant stems are commercially valuable. What are some examples?

See Figure 5·9

tracheids [trā′kĭ ĭdz; Greek: trachea, windpipe, + eidos, shape]

Pith is usually conspicuously present in young stems, but in older plants of many species it does not persist as an organized tissue. The *cambium* tissue consists of cells that divide and form new tissues of other kinds. It separates the bark from the rest of the stem. *Xylem* cells are continually being formed at the inner surface of the cambium. Most of the stem eventually consists of xylem; this forms the wood of an old stem. *Phloem* is continually being formed at the outer surface of the cambium. It makes up much of the bark of an old stem, and the outer layers are eventually sloughed off.

Xylem and phloem are primarily vascular tissues, but they also contain *fiber* cells, which form a tissue that strengthens the stem. Sometimes fibers and vascular cells occur in bundles. In monocot-yledonous plants these *fibrovascular bundles* are scattered in pith tissue. They can be seen macroscopically in corn stems.

Within xylem there are *tracheids* and *vessels*. Tracheids develop from elongated single cells that form thick walls and then die. Pits occur at many points in the walls of these dead cells. In most cases these pits are so closely paired on adjacent cells that only a thin layer of cell wall separates two adjoining tracheids. At these points, water and dissolved materials can easily pass from one tracheid into another.

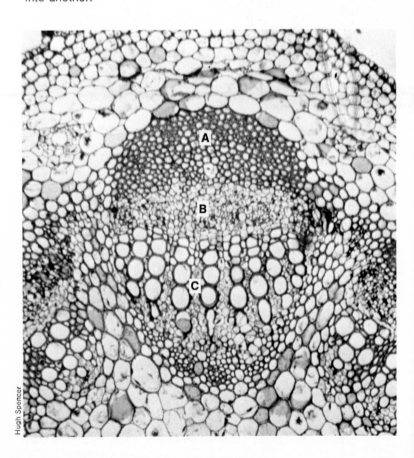

Figure 13 • 17

Fibrovascular bundle in a cross section of a sunflower stem. In the bundle the dark outer region is composed of fiber tissue (*A*); next within is conductive phloem (*B*); and inside that, xylem (*C*).
× 110

Hugh Spencer

Vessels are made up of elongated, thick-walled cells joined end to end. When a vessel cell is fully formed, a hole develops in the wall at each end of the cell; then, as in the tracheids, the living substance dies and disappears. Thus tiny, elongated pipes are formed, extending through the stem. Because water and salts can pass from one end of a vessel to the other without having to pass through pits, vessels would seem to be more efficient for transporting sap than tracheids. However, some of the tallest trees are gymnosperms, which possess no vessels.

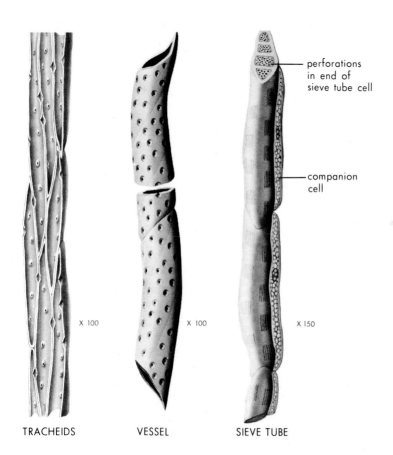

perforations
in end of
sieve tube cell

companion
cell

X 100   X 100   X 150

TRACHEIDS   VESSEL   SIEVE TUBE

Figure 13 • 18
Cells from conducting tissues
of tracheophytes.

Within phloem are long lines of cells making up structures called *sieve tubes*. As the cells of a sieve tube develop, small holes form in their end walls. Through these holes the cells are interconnected. As a sieve tube matures, the nuclei in the cells disintegrate. Located beside each sieve-tube cell are smaller *companion cells*. These do have nuclei and are believed to regulate the activity of the adjacent sieve-tube cells.

Conduction. Through the two series of tissues—xylem and phloem —moves sap, a complex mixture of minerals, foods, and other materials in solution. Unlike the blood in your vascular system, the sap in a plant is not moved by the pumping action of a heart. How, then, do liquids move in a plant?

To date, all the observations of botanists do not add up to an entirely satisfactory answer. Many experiments show that water from roots rises through xylem—from root xylem to stem xylem to xylem in the veins of leaves. Even in the tallest trees, water moves *against the force of gravity* from the roots to the topmost leaves. Let us consider this upward movement.

Suppose you have a bottle of ginger ale. You place a straw in the liquid, put your lips on its upper end, and suck. Immediately you are rewarded: the liquid rises to your mouth through the straw. Now consider a similar but less familiar situation. You place a beaker of water on the ground next to a school building. You climb up to the third floor, 13 m above the ground, and, using a long piece of glass tubing, you attempt to draw the water up from the beaker. Try as you may, you never succeed. You then borrow a vacuum pump from the physics lab, connect it to the tubing, and turn it on. This is also unsuccessful. If the school is near sea level, the water will rise about 10.3 m above the beaker, but no farther. In Denver, Colorado, at an

How does a physicist explain these results?

altitude of 1609 m, the water in the tube can be raised only to a height of about 8.4 m. Yet in many trees, water rises to a much greater height. Clearly, something more than a suction force is required.

Now a new experiment—one involving a living plant. Suppose you hold a leafy shoot under water and cut off the top 20 cm with a sharp knife. You insert this cut tip into a short piece of water-filled rubber tubing. You then connect the other end of the tubing to a 14-m length of slender (less than 0.5-mm internal diameter) glass tubing that is filled with water. You make certain that there are no leaks in the system. Now you place the lower end of the glass tube in a beaker of boiled water containing a dye so that the tube can be easily seen. (Boiling removes dissolved air that could form bubbles in the tube.) The entire setup makes a continuous, water-filled system extending from the mesophyll cells in the leaves down through the xylem tissue of the stem into the rubber tubing and the long glass tube, ending in the container on the ground. Gradually the dyed water from the container begins to rise—first 3 m, then 6, 9, and finally to the tip of the shoot—more than 14 m (that is, 3.7 m above the limit reached with a vacuum pump). How is this possible?

Before we can attempt an explanation, you need to understand an important characteristic of water. Under certain conditions a column of water has remarkable resistance to breaking when pulled lengthwise. Here are the conditions: (1) the water must be contained in tubes of very small diameter; (2) the walls of the tubes must be made of a

adhere [ăd hǐr'; Latin: *ad*, to, + *haerere*, to stick]

material to which water molecules will adhere; (3) the water must not contain gas bubbles that break the column of water. If, under these conditions, water molecules are lost by evaporation from the upper

cohesion [kō hē'zhən; Latin: *cum*, with, together, + *haerere*]

end of the column, their cohesion—attraction for adjoining water

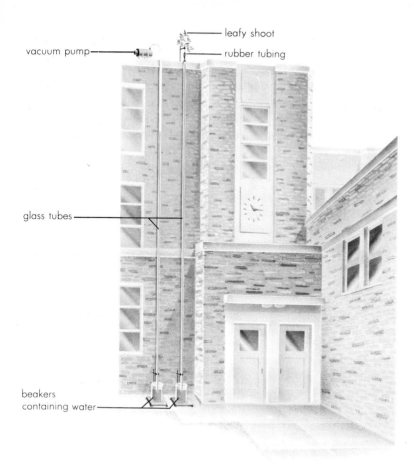

vacuum pump

leafy shoot

rubber tubing

glass tubes

beakers
containing water

Figure 13 · 19
An experiment on rise of
liquids in stems.

molecules—results in a pull, which is transmitted throughout the length of the system. This causes more water to move up into the tube from below. In this way, water can be moved upward in columns many times higher than 10.3 m. The water column is pulled up just as a wire would be pulled, rather than being pushed up by atmospheric pressure, as it is in a vacuum-pump system.

In 1915 these physical facts were used by H. H. Dixon to develop the "transpiration-tension" theory for explaining the rise of liquids in plant stems. According to this theory, the system of vessels in the xylem of a living tree corresponds to the slender glass tubing. Soil water in contact with root surfaces corresponds to the dyed water in the container. Sugars produced by photosynthesis are contained within the mesophyll cells. As water evaporates from the mesophyll tissue and passes out through the stomates (transpiration), the concentration of dissolved materials increases. Water molecules then diffuse into these mesophyll cells from the xylem vessels and tracheids. As they move into the mesophyll, cohesion between these water molecules and water molecules in the xylem tissues develops

Henry H. Dixon: 1869–1953.
British botanist

tension [těn'shən; Latin:
tendere, to stretch]

Robert J. Rodin

Figure 13 • 20

Storage stem of a South African plant. In this environment what do you think might be the chief substance stored?

Under what circumstances would the xylem liquids contain a large amount of dissolved food?

Figure 13 • 21

Structural adaptations of underground stems. What do you think is the principal function of each kind?

a force (tension) that pulls more liquid up the stem.

However, some experimental results do not fit this theory. If the shoot of a well-watered grapevine is cut off and a vertical glass tube is sealed to the rooted stump, sap rises in the tube. In this situation one condition assumed in the transpiration-tension theory is not present—there is no transpiration. Here it seems that the rise of the sap must come about through a push from below rather than a pull from above. This push has been called *root pressure.* Measurements of the force of root pressure have indicated that water might be pushed to a height of 90 m under some conditions.

In spite of these measurements, plant physiologists doubt that root pressure is an important factor in the rise of liquids in plants. For one thing, not all plants develop root pressure when their shoots are cut—and some that do not are tall trees. Secondly, in plants that do develop root pressure, the pressure is lowest in the summer, when the largest volume of liquids is being transported. Moreover, root pressure is simply a name for an observed fact; it is not an explanation. As yet no botanist has fully explained where the force of root pressure comes from. So Dixon's theory still remains the most reasonable *single* explanation for the rise of liquids in tall plant stems.

Now consider the phloem. Liquids moving through phloem contain much dissolved food, in contrast to the inorganic nutrients that are usually the principal contents of xylem liquids. In general, movement in the phloem is from the leaves, where foods are produced by photosynthesis, downward through stems to roots, where much of the food may be stored. But this is not always so; occasionally, movement in the phloem is reversed.

You might think the downward movement in the phloem is easily explained—gravity alone might be the cause. But the sieve cells of the phloem are not merely empty tubes; they contain living cytoplasts, through which liquids must pass. Of course, substances can diffuse through cytoplasts, but the rate at which the food-rich liquids move through the phloem is known to be thousands of times faster than

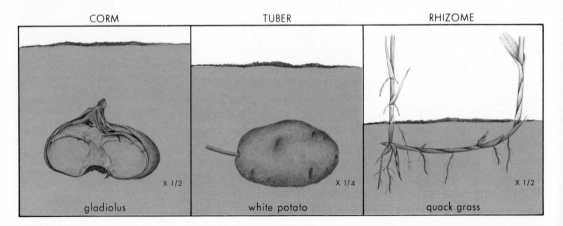

CORM

gladiolus   X 1/2

TUBER

white potato   X 1/4

RHIZOME

quack grass   X 1/2

diffusion could account for. And in many cases the direction of movement is from lesser concentration to greater concentration—opposite to that of diffusion. Some kind of active transport may be involved.

Other stem functions. Conduction of liquids is a principal function of stems. But in most plants, stems perform other functions also. Some stems carry on photosynthesis. In most herbaceous plants photosynthesis occurs in chlorophyll-bearing cells just beneath the stem epidermis. Even in woody plants young twigs contain photosynthetic tissues. In most terrestrial plants mature stems are not directly involved in photosynthesis. However, they make food production possible by conducting water to photosynthetic tissue and by supporting leaves where they may be exposed to sunlight. In forests, sturdy trunks hold leaves of trees far above the surface of the ground; plants with weaker stems grow in the shade below, where they are adapted to the reduced light.

What are some kinds of plants that carry on most of their photosynthesis in mature stems?

Some plants are almost stemless. The leaves of dandelions, for example, spread out on the surface of the ground, appearing to grow directly from the top of the root. Some such "stemless" plants are shade tolerant; others grow mostly in places where few taller neighboring plants cut off solar radiation.

In many plants stems serve as storage organs. Sugarcane plants store sucrose in their stems. Quantities of water as well as food are stored in most cactus stems. When the storage function of stems is highly developed, other functions may be less evident.

Can you give an example of a stem that seems to have a storage function but no conduction or support functions?

Investigation 13.3

WATER AND TURGOR PRESSURE

INTRODUCTION

The ability of a shoot to maintain its position above ground, resisting the forces of gravity, wind, and precipitation, is directly related to 2 different factors. One is the rigidity of the plant body, resulting from the mechanical strength of cell walls. This is of primary importance in woody plants in which much of the plant body consists of nonliving thickened cell walls. In herbaceous plants many cell walls are thin and structurally weak; therefore support depends primarily upon a 2nd factor —the pressure that the contents of individual cells exert against their walls. This *turgor pressure* varies as the volume of the cell contents changes. Such changes result from the intake or loss of water. Maintaining position in

such plants is directly related to maintaining shape. Maintaining shape depends upon turgor pressure. Turgor pressure, in turn, is dependent upon the water relationships of individual cells.

MATERIALS AND EQUIPMENT
(for each team)

knife, 12-cm blade
white potato, large
cork borer, 1-cm diameter, with rod
cardboard, heavy, 15-cm square
petri dishes, 100- x 20-mm, 4
beaker, 250-ml
sucrose solutions, 0.2 M, 0.4 M, 0.6 M,
    75 ml of each

metric scale, graduated in
    millimeters
balance
paper towels
glass-marking crayon
refrigerator
graph paper

PROCEDURE

• Read the procedure and then state a hypothesis appropriate to the design of the experiment.(1)

Using the knife, cut off one end of a potato, perpendicular to its long axis. Then make another cut parallel to the first one and approximately 7 cm from it. Discard the end pieces. Place one cut surface on top of the cardboard square, resting on the laboratory table. Force the cork borer down through the potato, with a twisting motion, to cut a core of tissue. Then, using the rod, force it out of the borer into the bottom half of a petri dish. Repeat this coring procedure until you have prepared 4 dishes. Line up the dishes and label them in order, *0.0 M, 0.2 M, 0.4 M, 0.6 M.* (M = *molar.* A molar solution [1.0 M] of sucrose contains 342 g of this sugar per liter. This is a convenient unit of concentration.)

Weigh each core and record. Then, using the metric scale, measure and record the length of each core. Determine the rigidity of each core by holding it at each end between your fingertips and gently bending it. Are there any marked differences in rigidity among the cores? If so, record them. Replace each core in its dish.

Now add to the dish labeled *0.0 M* enough tap water to cover the core. Add to each of the other 3 dishes enough of the appropriate sucrose solutions to cover the cores.

After 30 minutes, remove the core from the 0.0-M dish. Dry it gently by rolling it between 2 pieces of paper towel and lightly pressing each end on the paper. Repeat for each of the other cores. Determine if there has been any change in rigidity among the cores. If so, devise a system to describe the differences and record. Return each core to its

dish. Then place the dishes in a refrigerator. After 24 hours remove the dishes from the refrigerator. Repeat the drying procedure for each core and immediately determine and record rigidity, weight, and length. Calculate the differences, if any, between initial and final weight and initial and final length of each core and record, using a + sign to indicate increase and a − sign to indicate decrease.

Graph these differences, using a grid as shown below. Then graph increase and decrease of weight on a similar grid, with weight units substituted for length units.

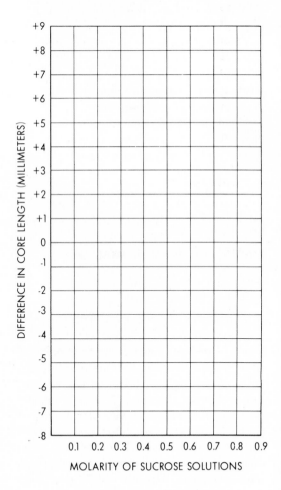

STUDYING THE DATA

Review the discussion on diffusion in Chapter 11, pages 352–356, and in Investigation 11.2. Potato tissue is almost entirely made up of cells with membranes highly permeable to water and highly impermeable to sucrose molecules. The thin cell walls are highly permeable to both. The walls of these cells can be either stretched or contracted only to a limited extent. Their shape when contracted can, however, be readily changed. • Upon what basis can you explain differences in rigidity, if any, among the cores placed in various concentrations of sucrose solution?(2) For each of the cores compare the rigidity change, if any, after 30 minutes. • In which core was there the greatest change in rigidity? (3) • In which core was there the least change in rigidity?(4)

• Is there any relationship between your observations on rigidity and differences between initial and final lengths of the cores? If so, explain the relationship.(5) • Between initial and final weights? If so, explain the relationship.(6)

CONCLUSIONS

• Do your data support the hypothesis you stated at the beginning of this investigation? (7) • On the basis of this experiment, write a general statement explaining the relationship between water content and the rigidity of plant structures that are made up of thin-walled cells.(8)

FOR FURTHER INVESTIGATION

1. Using the same experimental approach, investigate the effects of sucrose solutions having concentrations of 0.8 M and 1.0 M. Compare data obtained with those derived from your original experiment.

2. Investigate the effects on elodea leaves of sucrose solutions of the same range of concentrations as used in Investigation 13.3. Mount detached leaves on a microscope slide in the sugar solution, add a cover slip, and observe first under low and then high power over a period of 5 minutes.

GROWTH

You may still be growing, but you know that a time will come when you will cease to grow—at least in height. Mammals, birds, and insects have definite limits to growth, but many other animals and all multicellular plants continue to grow throughout their lives—usually at a gradually lessening rate. Nevertheless, there is a fundamental difference between growth in animals and growth in multicellular plants.

Meristems. Growth in multicellular organisms occurs primarily by means of the addition of new cells, followed by enlargement of these cells. In most animals, new cells are added so that growth occurs throughout the body. This is so because most kinds of animal cells retain the ability to reproduce even though they differentiate in other respects.

In vascular plants, most cells that have differentiated—into xylem, phloem, and mesophyll, for example—lose their ability to divide. Each cell of such tissues is formed from another kind of tissue, an undifferentiated tissue that continues mitosis and cell division as long as the plant lives. This tissue, no matter where it occurs in a plant, is called a *meristem.*

In root tips meristematic tissue is located just behind a *root cap* (Figure 13 • 10). This meristem forms root-cap cells on the side toward the tip. These cells do not accumulate, because they are constantly worn away as the root pushes through the soil. On the other side, this

meristem [měr′ə stěm′; Greek: *meristos*, divided]. Note that there is no relation to the word "stem."

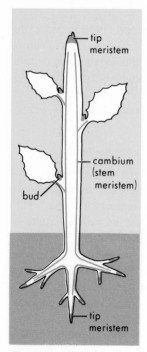

Figure 13 • 22
Diagram showing location of principal meristems.

meristem forms cells that differentiate into specialized root tissues, which become a permanent part of the root.

As a stem lengthens, the tissue at its tip remains meristematic. Small masses of meristem are also left behind, and from them branches and leaves develop. Each branch has a meristem at its tip. In most leaves, however, all the cells differentiate into xylem, phloem, mesophyll, etc. This differentiation takes place at an early stage in leaf formation. For example, in deciduous woody plants, cells in leaves for the following year are fully formed within a bud before the end of the growing season. They are, however, quite small. In spring, leaves expand mostly by the enlargement of these small cells. Leaves of grasses and some other plants are an exception: in them a meristem remains at the base of the leaf, and the leaf can increase in length even after most of the blade has been cut off by a grazing animal or a lawn mower.

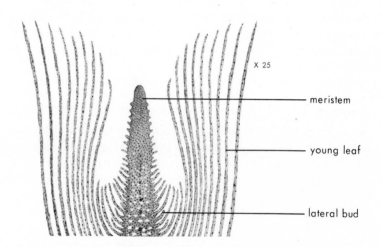

Figure 13 • 23
Tip of an elodea shoot.

Not all the cells left behind along a lengthening root or stem branch off or differentiate. Except in monocots, the layer of meristem called the cambium remains along the length of each stem and root. From cambium new xylem and phloem are formed, increasing the diameter of the stems and roots. Cambium remains as a boundary between the central core of wood (xylem) and the outer layer of bark (phloem). Bark can usually be peeled from a tree trunk rather easily, because the walls of cambium cells are thin and easily broken (Figure 13 • 16).

Chemical control of growth. For a long time it has been known that most green plants grow toward light—a response often called *phototropism.* This is easily observed in plants growing on windowsills, where almost all the light comes from one side. A century ago, Charles Darwin and his son, Francis, investigated the mechanism of

phototropism [fō tŏt′rə pĭz′əm; Greek: *photos*, light, + *tropos*, turning]

Charles Darwin: 1809–1882. English naturalist

this response. From previous studies the Darwins knew that several zones can be distinguished in a developing plant stem. At the tip is the meristem; just behind it is a zone of elongation, in which the newly formed cells enlarge lengthwise; behind this is a zone in which the cells become differentiated into tracheids, vessels, fibers, and other tissues.

The Darwins observed that bending toward light occurs not at the very tip, but in the zone of elongation, a few millimeters behind it. They experimented with very young seedlings of grasses and oats, which have a closed tubular structure called the *coleoptile,* within which the first leaves develop. When they placed a tiny opaque cap over the tips of the coleoptiles, the zones of elongation no longer bent. Somehow, light shining on the tip affected the cells in the zone of elongation below it. The Darwins concluded that "when seedlings are freely exposed to a lateral light some influence is transmitted from the upper to the lower part, causing the latter to bend."

What was this "influence"? In later years this investigation was pursued by others. In 1910 Boysen-Jensen performed an experiment based on the hypothesis that the "influence" carried from the tip to the cells in the region of elongation was a chemical substance. He placed oat seedlings in a container that provided light from only one side. He cut off the coleoptile tips of some and left others intact. The intact seedlings bent toward the light source; the tipless seedlings grew straight upward. Then he used gelatin to fasten the tips to the stumps of the tipless coleoptiles. These seedlings now began to bend toward the light in the same way as the controls (intact plants). Something had evidently passed from the tip through the nonliving gelatin to the stumps—most probably a chemical substance.

X 1/10

Figure 13 • 24

Bark and cambium were removed from a strip around the trunk of this tree a year before the top was cut off. Can you explain this result?

coleoptile [kō′lĭ ŏp′tĭl; Greek: *koleos,* sheath, + *ptilon,* feather]

Peter Boysen-Jensen: 1883–1959. Danish botanist

intact [ĭn tăkt′; Latin: *in-,* not, + *tangere,* to touch]: here, whole, uncut

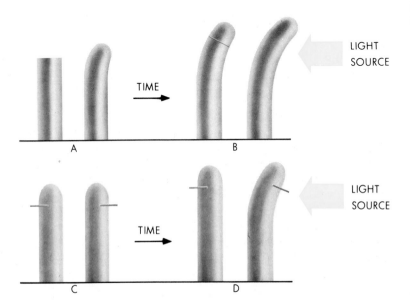

TIME

A   B

LIGHT SOURCE

TIME

C   D

LIGHT SOURCE

Figure 13 • 25

Boysen-Jensen's two experiments. *A* and *B* show the first experiment; *C* and *D* show the second.

How did the supposed chemical substance cause the bending toward the light? A year later, in an attempt to obtain information on this question, Boysen-Jensen inserted thin pieces of mica partway through oat coleoptiles and just behind the tips. In designing this experiment, he assumed that the chemical substance from the tip of the plant could not pass through the mica as it evidently had done through the gelatin. When the seedlings were placed so that the mica was on the side toward the light source, they bent toward it. When they were placed so that the mica was away from the light source, they did not bend. From these results Boysen-Jensen concluded that some substance produced by cells in the coleoptile tip moved down the coleoptile on the side opposite to the light and increased elongation of cells on that side. Greater lengthening of cells on the "dark" side made the plant bend toward the light.

Figure 13 • 26

**How differential elongation
of cells on opposite sides of
a shoot produces bending.**

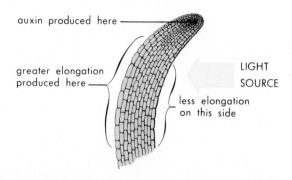

In 1928 Frits Went worked out techniques for collecting the substance Boysen-Jensen had concluded must exist. He cut off the tips of oat coleoptiles and placed them on thin layers of agar. Later he cut the agar into blocks. He then removed the tips from the agar and discarded them. He placed each small agar block on the edge of a seedling from which the tip had been removed. Without exposure to light the seedling bent—and always away from the side on which the piece of agar was placed. Evidently the substance in the tip had diffused into the agar and from there into the coleoptile. Further, Went found he could measure the amount of the substance in the agar block by measuring the angle of bending that it produced in a seedling.

Because the substance produced in the seedling tip stimulated increased elongation, it has been referred to as a growth substance and named **auxin,** but its exact chemical nature has not yet been determined. However, many known chemical substances have the same effect on the growth of plants. One of these, indoleacetic acid, is effective in extremely small amounts. For example, 0.0000005 mg applied to one side of an oat seedling will bring about a clearly visible bending. Indoleacetic acid has been found to be present in

Leaves pulled out
to support agar block

Figure 13 • 27

Went's method of measuring
auxin production.

LAYER OF AGAR
WITH SEEDLING TIPS

TIPS REMOVED AND AGAR
CUT INTO SMALL BLOCKS

AGAR BLOCK ATTACHED
TO TIP OF SEEDLING

plants; it is very possible that it is a natural auxin.

Many man-made chemical substances have effects similar to those of indoleacetic acid. One, called "2,4-D," stimulates growth when used in small quantities; but larger quantities of it kill many kinds of plants. Since, at the concentrations usually used, it does not affect members of the grass family, it is used to control weeds in lawns and in grainfields.

How might a growth substance kill a plant when present in large quantities?

There are other naturally occurring growth substances. Many years ago, Japanese rice farmers noticed that rice plants sometimes grow gigantically tall and then fall over and die. Japanese botanists found that these *bakanae* ("silly seedlings") are infected with a fungus. They studied the disease and discovered that certain substances formed by the fungus—***gibberellins***—bring about the strange growth. It is now known that some tracheophytes and algae as well as fungi produce gibberellins.

bakanae [bä kä nä ĕ]

gibberellins [jĭb′ər ĕl′ĭnz; named after the fungi in which they were first found, the genus *Gibberella*]

When treated with gibberellins, many kinds of plants grow to double or triple their normal height; but many species are only slightly affected by such treatment. The study of gibberellins and their many effects is an active field of botanical research.

USDA Photo

Figure 13 • 28

The top row of holly cuttings was treated with a chemical similar to indoleacetic acid; the bottom row was not treated. How might this growth substance be used commercially?

Investigation 13.4

RATE OF GROWTH

INTRODUCTION

On page 422 it was pointed out that the multiplication of cells by which a leaf is formed takes place chiefly while the leaf is still in a bud. And the expansion of the leaf from the bud is largely a result of the enlargement of cells. A simple and convenient study of growth can be made by beginning with the embryonic leaves in a seed.

MATERIALS AND EQUIPMENT
(for each team)

bean seeds, 18
beaker, 250-ml
fungicide solution
scalpel
hand lens
metric scale, graduated in
   millimeters
seed flat or box
sand or vermiculite
graph paper, 1 sheet per student

PROCEDURE

Select 18 bean seeds of approximately the same size. Place in a beaker. Add fungicide solution to the seeds until the volume of the solution is approximately twice that of the seeds. Allow the seeds to remain in the fungicide 20 minutes. Then pour off the solution and rinse the seeds thoroughly with water. Fill the beaker with just enough water to cover the seeds and leave overnight.

After 24 hours take 3 seeds from the beaker and, using a scalpel, cut carefully through the seed coat of each. Remove the seed coats and open the beans. Using a hand lens, find the embryo plant that lies between the 2 large cotyledons in each seed. Measure the length of the embryo leaves in each seed. In your data book, record the measurements and calculate the average length.

Plant the remaining 15 seeds about 1.5 cm deep and 5 cm apart in sand or vermicu-lite. After planting, water thoroughly; provide abundant light and a relatively constant temperature; keep damp.

On Days 3, 6, 10, 13, 17, and 20, after planting, measure the length of the first 2 leaves of 3 plants to the nearest millimeter. Make the measurement along the center vein (midrib) of each leaf, from the apex to the base; do not include the length of the petiole. Average the measurements each day. On Day 3 (and possibly on Day 6 also) you may find it necessary to dig up 3 germinated seeds, since the plants may not have grown above the surface. After the plants appear, measure the leaves on the same 3 plants each measurement day.

STUDYING THE DATA

Plot the data (time on the horizontal axis, average length of leaves on the vertical axis) on a graph. The rate of growth is indicated by the slope of the graph line.   • Does the slope change? If so, describe the change.(1) • When did the most rapid growth occur?(2) • Are there fluctuations? If so, try to explain them.(3)

Compare this graph with the ones you drew in Investigations 2.1, 2.2, and 2.3. • Which of these does this most resemble?(4) • In which part of the graphs—beginning, middle, or end—is there most resemblance?(5)

SUMMARY

• From your study of the graphs, what general statements can you make that apply to all of them?(6)

FOR FURTHER INVESTIGATION

1. Obtaining data on growth of individual plants through maturity usually requires a considerable amount of time. Figure 13 • 29 shows data on the growth of a bamboo—a plant that grows quite rapidly. Draw a graph from these

AGE (IN WEEKS)	AVERAGE HEIGHT (IN METERS)
1	0.7
2	1.5
3	2.5
4	4.0
5	6.2
6	8.3
7	10.2
8	12.0
9	13.2
10	13.8
11	14.1
12	14.2

Figure 13 • 29

data. Compare it with the graph of leaf growth.

2. Is the shape of the growth-rate graph influenced by the kind of measurement recorded? Weight rather than a linear measure-ment has frequently been used in growth studies. The data in Figure 13 • 30 were obtained from a field of corn. Every 2 weeks after the seedlings appeared above ground, several plants were pulled and weighed. The weights were averaged and recorded. Graph these data, and compare the graph with other growth-rate graphs.

AGE (IN WEEKS)	AVERAGE WEIGHT (IN GRAMS)
2	21
4	28
6	58
8	76
10	170
12	422
14	706
16	853
18	924
20	966

Figure 13 • 30

NONVASCULAR PLANTS

The great majority of multicellular plants are tracheophytes. However, bryophytes, most fungi, and many algae are also multicellular. Their structures differ from those of tracheophytes, but the plants carry on the same basic functions—absorption of nutrients, transportation of dissolved substances, storage of food, growth.

Many bryophytes appear to have roots, stems, and leaves. Microscopically, however, none of these parts resemble the roots, stems, and leaves of tracheophytes. In particular, they lack vascular tissues. Because botanists use the terms "root," "stem," and "leaf" to indicate vascular organs, these words should not be used in describing liverworts or mosses.

More important than the naming of the structures, however, is the effect that the lack of vascular tissues has on the physiology of these plants. A few bryophytes live in water, but most are land plants, getting their water from soil. Because they lack vascular tissues, the upward transportation of soil water in them is, apparently, not efficient enough to permit growth to heights above 40 cm. At least, this is the maximum height achieved among bryophytes—and they reach such heights only in environments with a high humidity, where transpiration rates are very low. On the other hand, many mosses are able to go into a dormant state when the water supply is low. Such species survive in some very dry places, as in deserts and small crevices in rocks, where they grow actively only during a few days after each rain.

Photos by Nathan W. Cohen

A

B

Figure 13 · 31

(A) A clump of dry moss.
(B) The same clump two minutes after water was added at its base. What has happened to the moss plants?
× 2

What can you predict about the height of fungal stalks above ground level?

Multicellular algae also lack vascular systems; but because they live in water, this is no hindrance to their growth. Indeed, some of the brown algae reach a length of 45 m, far longer than the height of most middle-latitude deciduous trees. Such seaweeds, however, are seldom more than a few centimeters thick, so none of their cells are far from the surrounding water and the mineral nutrients it contains.

All algae carry on photosynthesis. Many contain chlorophylls *c*, *d*, or *e* instead of chlorophyll *b*, which is characteristic of tracheophytes and bryophytes. Apparently this does not cause any great difference in the biochemistry of photosynthesis. However, most groups of algae have a physiological characteristic that is useful in classification—the kind of food they store. Although most plants store food principally as starch, some of the algae store it in the form of other polysaccharides or even oils.

Fungi, too, lack conducting tissues. But the lack of chlorophyll is a much more distinctive characteristic in the physiology of fungi. Fungi, like animals and many protists, are consumers. They must obtain their energy from food—multicarbon compounds that they get from their environments. Unlike animals, however, they seldom need to take in such molecules as amino acids. Except for photosynthesis, they are like other plants in their ability to synthesize the organic substances they require. During their metabolic activities, many fungi produce substances that are rare or unknown among other organisms —the complex acids of lichen fungi, for example. Biochemists have become very interested in the special physiology of fungi.

For example, see pages 590–592.

GUIDE QUESTIONS

1. In what ways do the usual environments of a plant root and of a plant shoot differ?

2. On what basis can we call a leaf a plant organ?

3. What characteristics of the internal structure of a leaf seem to be related to photosynthesis?

4. How do stomates function?

5. What is transpiration?

6. What are the principal functions of a root?

7. How does a fibrous-root system differ from a taproot system?

8. Through what root structures does a plant take in most of its water and nutrients?

9. What evidence indicates that absorption of substances from the soil involves more than simple diffusion?

10. What is the surest way to distinguish a stem from a root?

11. How can the yearly growth of young woody stems be measured?

12. What is the function of lenticels? Of wood rays?

13. How do heartwood and sapwood differ?

14. What are the principal differences between xylem and phloem?

15. Why might a botanist *expect* to find vessels rather than tracheids in the xylem of tall trees?

16. Using your own words, explain the transpiration-tension theory of conduction.

17. In what ways is the idea of root pressure unsatisfactory as a general explanation for the rise of liquids in stems?

18. How does conduction occur through phloem tissue?

19. Summarize the functions that plant stems perform.

20. What is the function of meristems?

21. Where are meristems located in vascular plants?

22. Why is bark usually peeled easily from a woody stem?

23. What is phototropism?

24. How did the Darwins study phototropism?

25. How did Boysen-Jensen demonstrate that tissue at the tip of a shoot produces a substance causing elongation of stem cells?

26. How did Boysen-Jensen's experiments provide an explanation for phototropism?

27. How did Went measure the amount of growth substance that diffused into an agar block?

28. In what ways do gibberellins resemble auxin?

29. Mosses never grow very tall. What seems to be the principal reason for this?

30. Some algae may grow to 45 m in length even though they have no conducting tissues. How may this growth in length be explained?

31. Metabolically fungi resemble both animals and plants. How?

PROBLEMS

1. Water-lily plants are rooted in mud at the bottom of ponds, but their leaves float on the water surface. How might the cellular structure of the roots, stems, and leaves of water lilies differ from cellular structure in terrestrial tracheophytes?

2. A few species of tracheophytes do not carry on photosynthesis. In what ways might you expect their roots, stems, and leaves to differ from those of the photosynthetic tracheophytes?

3. How is the gas exchange between an underground root and its environment different from the gas exchange between a leaf (in sunlight) and its environment?

4. During the growing season farmers spend considerable time cultivating their crops —loosening the soil between plants. What advantage does this have for the crop plants? Investigate the practice called "dry farming." How is it related to the physiology of plants?

5. Ten years ago a farmer built a fence 1.5 m high and attached one end of it to a tree that was 7 m high. Now the tree has grown to a height of 14 m. How far above the ground is the attached end of the fence? Explain.

6. The following questions concern lateral growth in woody stems: (a) How is an annual ring formed in the wood of a tree? (b) Within a given biome, how would the annual ring formed in a wet year differ from one formed in a dry year? (c) Sometimes two rings are formed in one year. How might this happen? (d) What is the science of *dendrochronology* and how is it used? (e) What happens to phloem as the trunk of a tree increases in diameter? (f) Would you expect to find annual rings in the bark of a tree?

7. A plant is placed in an atmosphere containing abundant carbon dioxide, but no growth occurs. What are some possible explanations for this?

8. In a middle-latitude biome a pine and an apple tree are growing side by side. Compare the requirements of these two trees for water throughout the year.

SUGGESTED READINGS

CLOWES, F. A. L. *Morphogenesis of the Shoot Apex.* London: Oxford University Press, 1972. (A short but detailed discussion of meristems at the tips of shoots. Rather advanced.)

DOYLE, W. T. *Nonvascular Plants: Form and Function.* Belmont, Calif.: Wadsworth Publishing Co., Inc., 1964. (Emphasizes use of nonvascular plants in biological research.)

FOGG, G. E. *The Growth of Plants.* Baltimore: Penguin Books, Inc., 1963. (Though growth is the focus of attention, all phases of plant physiology are discussed. Somewhat advanced.)

FRITTS, H. C. "Tree Rings and Climate," *Scientific American,* May, 1972. Pp. 92–100.

RUTTER, A. J. *Transpiration.* London: Oxford University Press, 1972. (Contains descriptions of some methods of measuring transpiration. Advanced.)

VAN OVERBEEK, J. "The Control of Plant Growth," *Scientific American,* July, 1968. Pp. 75–81.

———. *The Lore of Living Plants.* New York: Mc-Graw-Hill Book Co., Inc., 1964. (An excellent discussion of plant physiology. Contains suggestions for student investigations. Fairly easy.)

WENT, F. W., and Editors of LIFE. *The Plants* New York: Time, Inc., Book Division, 1963.

WILSON, C. L., W. E. LOOMIS, and T. A. STEEVES. *Botany.* 5th ed. New York: Holt, Rinehart & Winston, Inc., 1971. (Contains excellent college-level discussions of structure and functions of tracheophytes.)

WOODING, F. B. P. *Phloem.* London: Oxford University Press, 1971. (Illustrated with good micrographs, this booklet discusses both structure and function. Rather advanced.)

WOOLHOUSE, H. W. *Aging Processes in Higher Plants.* London: Oxford University Press, 1972. (Discusses aging in plant parts and aging and life-spans of whole plants. Advanced.)

ZIMMERMANN, M. H. "How Sap Moves in Trees," *Scientific American,* March, 1963. Pp. 132–138+.

Functioning Animals

Investigation 14.1

ANIMAL STRUCTURE AND FUNCTION

INTRODUCTION

No one species can fully illustrate animal structure and function. But for a long time frogs have been favorite laboratory animals. And frogs have some advantages: they are of a convenient size, they are easily obtained, and they are comparatively inexpensive. Still more important, they are vertebrates—enough like ourselves to throw some light on our own structure and function, yet sufficiently unlike us to provide some important contrasts.

MATERIALS AND EQUIPMENT

(for each team)

For Procedure A
   frog, live
   gauze bandage, 60 cm
   aquariums, each at least 60 cm long
      and containing water to a depth
      of at least 10 cm, 2 per class

For Procedure B
   frog, pithed
   dissecting pan
   pins, 10
   forceps, 2
   scissors
   scalpel
   watch with a second hand

pipette
sodium chloride crystals
petri dish
distilled water
microscope slide
sugar solution, warm
medicine dropper
monocular microscope
paper towels
saline solution (0.7% sodium
      chloride)
plastic bag
glass-marking crayon
rubber band
refrigerator

For Procedure C
   frog (from Procedure B)
   dissecting pan
   pins, 10
   forceps
   hand lens
   scissors

PROCEDURE A

Moisten the top of the table where you will place the frog. To aid you in handling the animal, a piece of gauze bandage has been tied to one of its legs. Tie the other end to a table leg or to any other fixed object. Sit quietly and allow time for the frog to become accustomed to its surroundings. By avoiding sudden motions, you will increase your opportunities for making accurate observations.

Compare the general structure of the frog's body with that of your own. Think of your body as consisting of a head, neck, trunk, and 4 appendages.   • Are any of these lacking in the frog? If so, which?(1)   Consider a cat, cow, or lizard. • What major division of the body is present in these and many other vertebrates but is lacking in the structure of both the frog and you?(2) • What kind of symmetry does the frog's body have? What kind does your body have?(3)

Locate the frog's eyes. • In what ways do its eyes differ from yours?(4)   Its ears are located behind and below the eyes. Its eardrums are stretched across the ear openings. • How do your ears differ from those of the frog?(5) • In what ways does the skin of the frog differ from yours?(6)

In a human each of the upper appendages consists of a series of parts: upper arm, forearm, wrist, hand, and fingers. Each of the lower appendages consists of: thigh, shank, ankle, foot, and toes. • Are any of these parts lacking in the appendages of the frog? If so, which?(7) • In what ways do the *terminal* parts (those that are farthest from the trunk) of the frog's appendages differ from yours?(8)

Using the eraser end of a pencil, gently prod the frog until it jumps. • What is the function of each pair of appendages in jumping?(9)   You can leap somewhat as the frog does, but the frog cannot stand erect as you do. • By examining the structure of the frog's legs and trunk, give evidence to support the preceding statement.(10)

You must watch very carefully to see how the frog breathes. First locate its nostrils. (Ducts lead from its nostrils to its mouth cavity.) Then, without touching the frog, watch the floor of its mouth (upper throat). When the floor is lowered, the mouth cavity enlarges. • From where can air come to fill the enlarged mouth cavity?(11)   Observe the motion of the nostrils. • How does this motion relate to the motion of the floor of the mouth?(12)   • As the mouth is raised, where can the air in the mouth cavity go?(13) • When you breathe, where does the principal motion occur?(14) • Can you breathe with your mouth open? Can the frog?(15)

Remove the gauze bandage from the frog's leg. Place the frog in the water at one end of a large aquarium. Observe the motion it uses to swim. • How does it use its toes in swimming?(16) • What structures are associated with the toes in swimming?(17) • Are these structures present on the fingers?(18) Try to get the frog to float. • What is the position of its eyes, ears, and nostrils with respect to the surface of the water?(19) • Hold the frog under water for 2 minutes. Do you observe any breathing movements? Try to explain.(20) • While the frog is under water, do you see any eye structure that you lack? If so, describe it. (21)   Return the live frog to the container designated by your teacher.

PROCEDURE B

Each team will be provided with a frog in which the brain and spinal cord have been destroyed—a *pithed* frog. Such an animal can have no sense of feeling. However, its tissues remain active for a number of hours, making it possible for you to observe directly several kinds of functions.

Place the frog on the dissecting pan, ventral side up. Fasten the frog to the wax in the pan by inserting pins through the ends of the appendages and into the wax. The skin of the frog is attached quite loosely to its muscles. With forceps, hold the skin free from the muscles of the ventral body wall; use scissors to make a small crosswise cut through the skin at the midline of the abdomen (Figure 14 • 1A). Insert one tip of the scissors into this opening, and cut anteriorly along the midline of the body to the region of the throat. Then cut posteriorly along the midline as far as possible (Figure 14 • 1B). Next cut laterally from the ends of the longitudinal incision (Figure 14 • 1C). There are now 2 flaps of skin that you can open to the side. To open them fully and pin them down (Figure 14 • 1D), you must separate the skin from the body wall in a few places; a sharp scalpel is the best instrument to use for this job.

Open the muscular body wall, following the procedure you used to open the skin. The organs of the body cavity lie just inside the body wall; therefore, be sure to lift the body wall from the organs beneath and to insert only the tip of your scissors when cutting. As you cut anteriorly, you will run into the breastbone. In opening the body wall laterally, you may remove about 8 mm of the breastbone. Some effort may be required to open the body wall at the anterior end.

Observe the beating of the heart. • How many times does it contract per minute?(22) Carefully slit the thin, transparent membrane that surrounds the heart. • Do the contractions travel from the anterior toward the pos-

Figure 14 • 1

Steps in opening the body cavity of a frog.

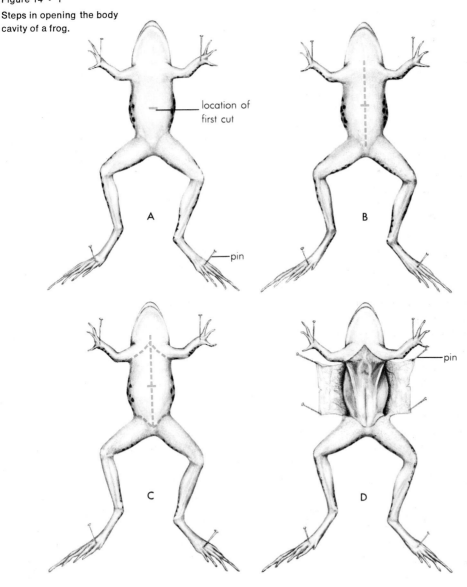

location of first cut

pin

A

B

C

D

pin

terior part of the heart? Vice versa? In neither direction?(23)

Open the mouth and locate a slitlike opening in the floor of the mouth. Insert the end of a pipette into the opening, and blow gently on the other end of the pipette. If you have located the right opening, the lungs will become inflated. • Describe their appearance.(24)

Female frogs may contain so many eggs that it might be difficult for you to see the organs in the posterior part of the body. If this is true of your specimen, use forceps to carefully pick the eggs out a few at a time. Attached to the egg masses are white, coiled tubes, through which the eggs pass when they are laid. Remove these also.

Sprinkle a few crystals of sodium chloride along the surface of the intestine. Observe for at least 2 minutes.   • Describe any movements of the intestine.(25) Using scissors, snip across the small intestine about 1.5 cm from the stomach and the same distance from the large intestine. Free the small intestine from the *mesentery* (the membrane that holds it in place) and drop it into a petri dish containing distilled water. • Describe any reaction.(26) Now cut off a piece about 5 mm long. Slit the piece open and spread it out, inner side up, on a slide. Add a drop or 2 of warm sugar solution and observe (without a cover slip) under low power of a monocular microscope. Note the small projections on the inner wall of the intestine. • Describe their activity.(27)

Remove the pins from the frog. Close the body wall and the skin over the body cavity. Wrap the frog in a paper towel that has been dipped in saline solution. Mark a plastic bag with your team symbol. Place the frog in the bag, fasten the bag with a rubber band, and store in a refrigerator.

PROCEDURE C

Remove the frog from the plastic bag and paper towel. Pin it to the dissecting pan, as in Procedure B.

Just posterior to the heart is the reddish-brown liver. • How many sections does it have?(28) On the frog's right side the liver covers the *gall bladder.* Using forceps, raise the liver and find the gall bladder. • What color is it?(29)

On the left side, the liver partially covers the stomach. The diameter of the stomach depends upon the amount of food it contains. • Toward which side does the stomach curve from anterior to posterior end?(30) At its posterior end the stomach leads into the small intestine. Where these 2 portions of the alimentary canal join, a narrow constriction, the *pyloric* (pī lôr′ ĭk) *valve,* is visible. Between the inner edge of the curved stomach and the 1st loop of the intestine is the long, light-colored *pancreas.* Nearby, within the mesentery, is a dark body, the *spleen.*   • What is its shape? (31)   After you have located these organs, remove the stomach. Using scissors, slit the stomach along its outer curvature and spread it open. Observe the inner surface with a hand lens. • Describe it.(32)

You have already removed most of the small intestine. Now push the mesentery and remaining organs aside and look for the kidneys, which are attached to the back. They are reddish-brown in color. • Describe their shape.(33)   Using a hand lens, locate the thin tube that leads from the posterior end of each kidney. • To what does it lead?(34)

Dispose of your frog as directed by your teacher.

SUMMARY

• On the basis of this investigation and your understanding of your own body, write a brief comparison of the structures and functions of frog and man.(35)

FOR FURTHER INVESTIGATION

1. Divide a group of live frogs into 2 sets, each containing the same number of individuals. Weigh and mark each frog. Leave one set overnight in a container with a small amount of water; leave the other overnight in a container without water. The next day weigh all frogs again. Compare the data from the 2 sets of frogs. Suggest an explanation.

2. Prepare one of the frogs as a skeleton.

First, using scalpel and forceps, remove as much flesh as possible. This is a rather difficult task, because many of the bones are small and delicate; be careful not to cut through the small ones in the appendages and the thin ones in the head. Second, gently simmer the roughed-out skeleton for about 30 minutes in a little water to which some soap powder has been added. Third, using a scalpel and a stiff-bristled toothbrush, gently scrape the remaining flesh from the bones. Finally, using thin wire, assemble the bones in their natural relationship to each other and attach them to a piece of stiff cardboard.

ACQUIRING ENERGY AND MATERIALS

There is one striking similarity among animals—they spend a great deal of time either eating or hunting for things to eat; they are all consumers. As they eat, animals obtain, in addition to foods in the narrow sense, minerals (such as iron and calcium ions or compounds), vitamins (used in regulating various body functions), and water. And for the release of energy, all animals must also obtain oxygen, which is usually not classified as a nutrient. Acquiring energy and materials, then, is a matter of taking in things from the environment.

foods. See pages 24–25.

nutrient. See page 53.

NUTRITION

The processes by which animals obtain, distribute, and use nutrients are known collectively as *nutrition.* Nutrition can be considered under three heads: ingestion, digestion, and absorption.

nutrition [nōō trĭsh′ən; Latin: *nutrire,* to suckle, nourish]

Ingestion. A microscopic particle of food might be overlooked by many animals, but to a sponge it is a meal. Sponges have no special organs for food-getting. Indeed, they have no organs at all; their bodies are merely collections of cells. One kind of sponge cell has a flagellum. The beating of many flagella keeps a current of water moving through the sponge. When a food particle comes by, one of the cells may engulf it and draw it into a vacuole, just as an ameba does. This process of taking particles of food into some cavity of the body (*ingestion*) is a characteristic of animals. It distinguishes them from consumer plants but not from all protists.

See Figures 6 · 8 and 11 · 11.

ingestion [ĭn jĕs′chən; Latin: *in,* in, + *gerere,* to carry]

Some other aquatic animals also ingest nutrients that are brought to them by water currents. Many, however, actively pursue nutrient objects. And for land animals, mere waiting seldom provides a sufficient supply. In any case, most animals have some means of capturing food objects.

Can you think of a land animal that waits for its prey to come by?

One way in which predators do this is by poisoning the prey. For example, the tentacles of coelenterates are equipped with stinging capsules. Each capsule contains a long, spirally coiled, hollow thread with barbs near its base. When some food organism brushes one of the tentacles in passing, the thread is shot out with such force that it pierces the body of the victim, injecting it with a paralyzing poison. The prey is then drawn into the body cavity by the tentacles.

paralyzing [păr′ə līz′ĭng]: causing to lose the power of movement

When a leech finds a victim, it attaches itself by means of a

What other animals that you know poison their prey?

What liquid-sucking arthropods do you know?

disengaged [dĭs′ĕn gājd′]: taken apart

posterior sucker. Then it makes a wound with its three-toothed jaw, and sucks the blood of the victim. Many arthropods also obtain liquid nutrients.

Among vertebrates, jaws, beaks, and teeth are structures that aid ingestion. There are numerous adaptions of these structures. For example, the lower jaw of a snake can be completely disengaged from the upper jaw, and the two can be moved independently so that the prey, held by backward-curving teeth, is forced into the throat. This adaptation permits a snake to swallow prey with a diameter greater than its own head.

New York Zoological Society

Figure 14 · 2

The long, sticky tongue of an anteater is an organ of ingestion. How do you think it is used?

Digestion. Ingested food enters some sort of cavity within an animal's body—a digestive cavity. Digestive cavities are of three main kinds: temporary, completely enclosed food vacuoles; sacs; and tubular alimentary canals.

By and large, only relatively small molecules can pass readily through cell membranes. But most nutrient particles that animals ingest are not of molecular size. Even the microscopic particles taken in by sponges are much too large to pass through cell membranes. But until a substance is actually within a cell, until it has passed through the cell's membrane, it cannot be of use to that cell. In almost all cases, then, substances taken in by animals must be broken down into small molecules. The processes by which this breakdown is accomplished are known collectively as *digestion.*

Although most nutrient substances must be changed chemically during the course of digestion, chemical reactions proceed very slowly unless the substances are in relatively small pieces. This breakdown of large pieces into smaller particles is the physical part of digestion.

Most mammals have teeth that cut or grind. But in many animals most of the physical part of digestion is accomplished by muscular movements of the digestive cavity. The gizzard of a bird, for example, is a specialized part of the stomach that grinds food into small particles; in some species its effectiveness is increased by bits of sand and small pebbles that the bird swallows. But in some animals the physical part of digestion is unimportant. For example, a snake may swallow a whole rat and then lie quietly for as long as a week while chemical digestion proceeds.

digestion [dĭ jĕs'chən; Latin: *dis-*, apart, + *gerere*]

gizzard [gĭz'ərd]

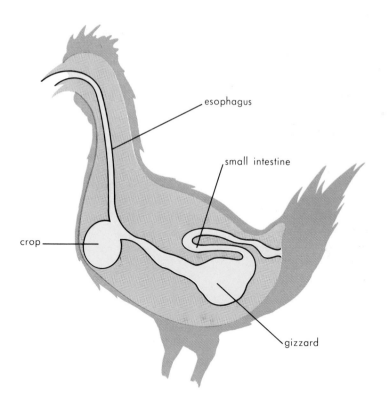

esophagus

small intestine

crop

gizzard

Figure 14 • 3
Alimentary canal of a bird. Food is swallowed without being chewed and is stored temporarily in the crop.

In sponges and to some extent in coelenterates and flatworms, chemical digestion takes place within a vacuole, which is *intracellular* —inside a cell. But because a cell forms a vacuole by surrounding a particle with a section of cell membrane, a vacuole really is an enclosed bit of an organism's environment. Enzymes that catalyze the reactions of the chemical phase of digestion are secreted into

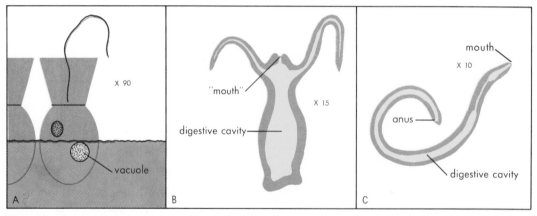

Figure 14 • 4

Kinds of digestive cavities:
(*A*) Intracellular (vacuole)—
in a cell of a sponge.
(*B*) Extracellular with one
opening (sac)—in a hydra.
(*C*) Extracellular with two
openings (alimentary canal)
—in a roundworm.

In addition to enzymes, what
substance is required to
reverse a dehydration
synthesis?

the vacuole. As chemical digestion proceeds, the resulting small molecules pass from the vacuole into the cytoplast. Only then are the nutrients truly inside the cell. In most animals, however, digestion takes place largely or exclusively in an *extracellular* space—enzymes are secreted *from* cells into a digestive cavity. Thus a digestive cavity is really only an extension of the environment of the animal—part of the environment more or less surrounded by the body of the organism.

The chemical part of digestion is simply the reverse of the synthetic processes described in Chapter 12 and is basically similar in all animals. However, there is great variation in the form and complexity of the digestive system in which it occurs. In the digestive sac of a coelenterate, some of the cells lining the cavity are specialized as enzyme-secreting cells, and some have flagella that move the foods through the cavity; but there is no grouping of cells with a common structure and function into tissues. In the simple alimentary canal of a roundworm, digestive enzymes are produced entirely by

Figure 14 • 5

The complex stomach of a
cow. Food is swallowed
without being chewed and is
stored in the rumen. Later it
is brought back into the
mouth for chewing. Bacteria
in the other parts of the
stomach carry on cellulose
digestion, for which a cow
has no enzymes. What
ecological relationship exists
between cow and bacteria?

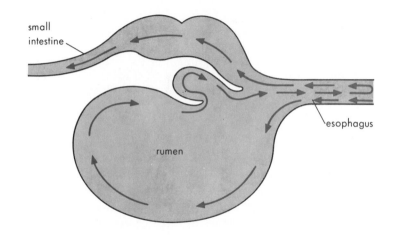

cells in the lining, but in most animals with alimentary canals there are specialized digestive glands. Some herbivorous vertebrates have special digestive chambers that contain great numbers of cellulose-digesting microorganisms. Vertebrates have no cellulose-digesting enzymes but can use compounds produced by these microorganisms.

Absorption. The rate at which small molecules resulting from digestion can leave an alimentary canal to pass into the cells of an animal's body is dependent upon the surface area of the lining. The larger the surface area, the greater the rate of transfer of digested substances out of the digestive cavity. Folding is a common method by which surface area is increased. In addition to folds, the lining of a part of the alimentary canal of a mammal has many minute, finger-like processes known as *villi*. These increase internal surface as much as a hundred-fold.

Where did you observe such folding?

villi [vĭl'ī; Latin: tufts of hair]; singular, villus

A. John Geraci

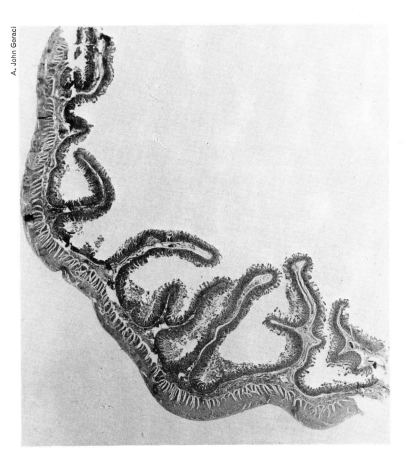

Figure 14 · 6
Portion of a small intestine. You can see small villi on the surfaces of the folds of the inner side.   ×8

Digestion in man. Now let us examine in some detail the digestive system of a complex animal—man.

Digestion begins in the mouth, where teeth break large pieces of food into smaller pieces. *Saliva,* secreted by three pairs of salivary

saliva [sə lī'və]; salivary [săl'ə vĕr'ē]

glands, flows into the mouth cavity, where it moistens the food and begins to change it chemically. However, it is usually not in the mouth long enough for much chemical digestion to occur there. The tongue keeps the food in position between the teeth during chewing and then pushes the chewed substances to the back of the mouth cavity. There muscular contractions carry it into the **esophagus** and thence into the stomach.

esophagus [ē sŏf'ə gəs; Greek: *oisein*, to carry, + *phagein*, to eat]

gastric [găs'trĭk; Greek: *gaster*, stomach]

In the stomach muscular contractions continue physical digestion. They also mix in **gastric juice,** secreted by gastric glands in the

Figure 14 • 7
Digestive system of man (*right*). The appendix, attached to the large intestine, is a sac that has no known function.

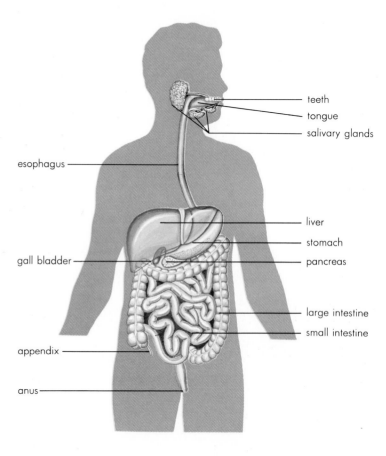

teeth
tongue
salivary glands
esophagus
liver
stomach
gall bladder
pancreas
large intestine
small intestine
appendix
anus

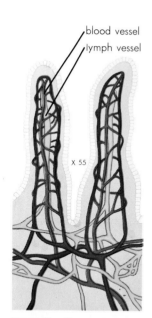

blood vessel
lymph vessel

X 55

Figure 14 • 8
Diagram of two villi.

pH: Where have you already met this term?

wall of the stomach. Gastric juice is mostly water; the contents of the stomach, therefore, soon acquire the consistency of a cream soup. Gastric juice also contains hydrochloric acid, which provides the low pH required for the action of an enzyme that catalyzes the breaking of peptide bonds in some protein molecules, producing large fragments called polypeptides. Contraction of the pyloric valve (a circular layer of muscle in the wall of the alimentary canal between the stomach and the small intestine) holds the partially digested food—now called *chyme*—in the stomach for about five hours.

From time to time the pyloric valve relaxes, permitting some of the chyme to pass into the small intestine. There three more digestive juices are added. These juices have a high pH and therefore neutralize the hydrochloric acid of the chyme. This is important because the enzymes that are active in the small intestine require an approximately neutral medium.

The first of the juices is *bile,* which is secreted by the liver and stored in the gall bladder. Human bile contains no digestive enzymes. But bile, in addition to being very alkaline, contains substances that cause large globules of fat to be broken up into fine droplets. This speeds up the chemical digestion of fats into fatty acids and glycerol. Pancreatic juice secreted by the pancreas contains several enzymes that catalyze the digestion of carbohydrates, proteins, and fats. Additional enzymes are in the intestinal juice secreted by glands in the wall of the small intestine. Most chemical digestion occurs in the upper part of the small intestine.

In the lower part, almost all absorption of nutrients occurs. Through the surface of the villi, amino acids and simple sugars (the end products of protein and carbohydrate digestion) and other nutrients are absorbed by diffusion or active transport into the blood. Some fat molecules pass into the lymph vessels of the villi. Most of the fatty acids and glycerol recombine during absorption to form fat, which then passes into the lymph vessels; very small amounts of fatty acids are absorbed into both the lymph vessels and the blood vessels.

chyme [kīm; Greek: *chymos,* juice]

Can you explain why vomit sometimes tastes sour and sometimes bitter?

pancreatic [păn′krĭ ăt′ĭk; Greek: *pan,* all, + *creas,* flesh]

lymph [lĭmf]. See pages 452–453.

SECRETION	ENZYME	SUBSTANCES ACTED UPON	PRODUCT
saliva	amylase	starch	maltose
gastric juice	gastric proteinase	some protein	polypeptides
	amylases	starch	maltose
pancreatic juice	lipase	fats	*glycerol* and *fatty acids*
	pancreatic proteinases	protein	polypeptides and smaller fragments
	peptidases	polypeptides and smaller fragments	*amino acids*
intestinal juice	disaccharidases	sucrose, maltose, lactose	*simple sugars*
	peptidases	polypeptides	*amino acids*

Figure 14 • 9

Summary of chemical digestion in mammals. Products absorbed are shown in boldface italic type. In what connection were these substances discussed in Chapter 12?

Normally digestion and absorption are completed in four to seven hours, and substances left in the small intestine then pass into the large intestine. There much of the water is absorbed. Undigested foods and indigestible substances, together with mucus, dead cells from the lining of the digestive tube, and bacteria, make up the *feces,* which leave the digestive tube through the *anus.*

feces [fē′sēz]

anus [ā′nəs]

Investigation 14.2

THE ACTION OF A DIGESTIVE ENZYME

INTRODUCTION

In Chapter 12 the discussion of enzymes centers on those involved in energy release and in syntheses. Now you will study an enzyme that acts in digestion. Review the action of salivary amylase shown in Figure 14·9. Because this enzyme is secreted into your mouth cavity, it is easily available for study.

MATERIALS AND EQUIPMENT

(for each team)

For Procedure A

unsweetened cracker

test tubes, 4

thermometer (−10°C to +110°C)

funnel and support

filter paper, 2 sheets

iodine–potassium-iodide solution

Benedict's solution

test-tube holder

bunsen burner

paraffin

For Procedure B

test tubes, 7

paraffin

glass rod

pH test paper

beakers, 7

starch solution

ring stand

bunsen burner

test-tube holder

Benedict's solution

thermometers (−10°C to +110°C)

ice

hydrochloric acid solution, pH 6

hydrochloric acid solution, pH 3

sodium hydroxide solution, pH 8

sodium hydroxide solution, pH 11

PROCEDURE A

Your teacher will first demonstrate the action of maltose, a disaccharide, on warm Benedict's solution.

Crush a piece of cracker (about 1 cm²) into a test tube. Add warm water (about 37°C) to a depth of about 5 cm. Shake and then pour into a funnel lined with filter paper. Collect part of the filtrate (the liquid that seeps through the filter paper) to a depth of about 1 cm in a 2nd test tube. Collect another part to a depth of about 2 cm in a 3rd test tube. Test the 1st portion of the filtrate for starch and the 2nd portion for maltose.

Now one student should chew a piece of paraffin and spit the accumulated saliva into a 4th test tube. When a few milliliters have been collected, test for maltose. If the test is positive, have another student try.

A student who has saliva testing negative for maltose should then chew a piece of cracker (about 9 cm²) testing negative for maltose. After thorough chewing (2 or 3 minutes), deposit the mass of cracker and saliva into a funnel lined with filter paper. Add about 5 ml of warm water (37°C) and collect about 3 ml of the filtrate in a test tube. Test the filtrate for maltose. • Considering the procedure used, what conclusion can you draw from a negative test? From a positive test?(1)

PROCEDURE B

In Procedure A the enzyme action occurred *in vivo* (Latin: in a live [condition]) in its normal situation in the mouth. To test the action of the enzyme under other conditions, it is convenient to work *in vitro* (Latin: in glass —that is, in a test tube, beaker, etc.).

Using paraffin, collect saliva from a student whose saliva gives a negative result with Benedict's solution. You will need 7 test tubes, each containing saliva to a depth of about 2 cm. Using a wide-range pH test paper, determine the approximate pH of the collected saliva.

1. Add a few drops of starch solution to Tube 1. Shake. Place the test tube in a beaker containing water at 37°C and allow it to remain there 10 minutes. Then remove and test for maltose.

2. Add a few drops of starch solution to Tube 2. Shake. Place the test tube in a beaker containing boiling water and allow it to remain there 10 minutes. Then remove and test for maltose.

3. Add a few drops of starch solution to Tube 3. Shake. Place the test tube in a beaker containing crushed ice and allow it to remain there 10 minutes. Then remove and test for maltose.

4. To Tube 4 add a volume of pH 6 hydrochloric acid solution equal to the volume of saliva. Mix by rolling the tube between the palms of your hands. Add a few drops of starch solution and again mix. Place the tube in a beaker containing water at 37°C and allow the tube to remain there 10 minutes. Then remove and test for maltose.

5. To Tube 5 add an equal volume of pH 3 hydrochloric acid solution. Mix. Add a few drops of starch solution and again mix. Place the tube in a beaker containing water at 37°C and allow the tube to remain there 10 minutes. Then remove and test for maltose.

6. To Tube 6 add an equal volume of pH 8 sodium hydroxide solution. Mix. Add a few drops of starch solution and again mix. Place the tube in a beaker containing water at 37°C and allow the tube to remain there 10 minutes. Then remove and test for maltose.

7. To Tube 7 add an equal volume of pH 11 sodium hydroxide solution. Mix. Add a few drops of starch solution and again mix. Place the tube in a beaker containing water at 37°C and allow the tube to remain there 10 minutes. Then remove and test for maltose.

STUDYING THE DATA

If the work has been divided among teams, assemble the data on the chalkboard. • Under what conditions of temperature and pH did the enzyme act *in vivo*?(2) • Under which of the experimental temperature conditions did the enzyme act *in vitro*?(3) • Under which of the experimental pH conditions did the enzyme act *in vitro*?(4)

CONCLUSIONS

• Use the data to work out a general statement concerning the effect of temperature variation on the action of the enzyme.(5) • Use the data to work out a general statement concerning the effect of pH variation on the action of the enzyme.(6) • Would you expect intracellular enzymes to be more sensitive or less sensitive to variations in temperature and pH than are extracellular enzymes? Why or why not?(7)

OBTAINING OXYGEN

For short periods animal cells may release energy by anaerobic methods, but eventually they depend upon cellular respiration. Therefore animals must live in environments where oxygen occurs, and they must be able to transport environmental oxygen to all their cells. Likewise, they must be able to rid themselves of carbon dioxide.

In very small animals—such as rotifers and many planktonic

See Problem 3, page 396.

crustaceans—uptake of oxygen and release of carbon dioxide can occur entirely through the body surface. This is because the body surface is large compared with the volume of living substance that requires oxygen and produces carbon dioxide. As size increases, the ratio of surface area to volume becomes smaller, though in very flat bodies or in very long, cylindrical ones, the change in ratio remains relatively slight. In general, then, larger animals do not have external body surfaces large enough to allow a sufficient exchange of gases with their environment. Thus, all except very small or slim animals have organs that increase the surface area through which respiration may occur.

Why is *movement* important?

In aquatic animals such organs are usually feathery or platelike structures called **gills.** These may be waved through the water, or water may pass over them as the animal moves. Dissolved oxygen then diffuses in and carbon dioxide diffuses out through the membranes of the outmost gill cells. Gills are remarkably similar in a wide variety of water animals.

Is this important for aquatic animals? Consider the gills of a fish living in fresh water.

Any surface through which the respiratory gases can diffuse is also a surface through which water can diffuse. Therefore, animals that live on land may lose a great deal of water through their respiratory organs. For this reason, terrestrial animals that breathe through gills (sow bugs, for example) or through the body surface (slugs, earthworms, and salamanders, for example) must live in places where air is moist—that is, where evaporation is slow.

Figure 14 • 10

Gills in three aquatic animals. The body of the marine annelid is enclosed in a mud tube; only the gills are exposed.

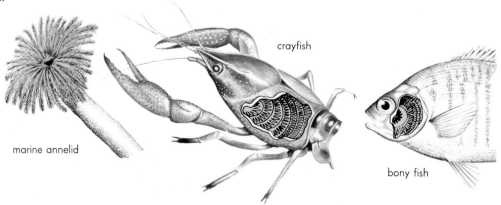

marine annelid

crayfish

bony fish

For terrestrial animals that live where the air is dry, an extensive surface is needed within the body where air can be kept moist. Two principal ways of meeting this requirement have evolved. In insects and some other arthropods, a complicated system of air tubes extends to all parts of the body, bringing oxygen directly to most cells. Movements of the body help move air through the tube system. In air-breathing vertebrates air passes into lungs that are divided into such a large number of tiny air sacs that they have a spongy appear-

Do you know of any terrestrial vertebrate that normally has only one lung?

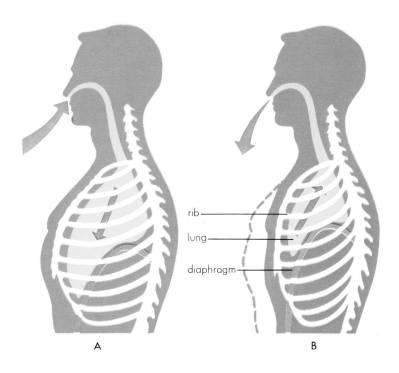

Figure 14 · 11
Movements of breathing in
man.

ance. Through the enormous moist surface area provided by these sacs, respiratory gases diffuse.

Again we take man as an example. Upward and outward movement of the ribs and downward movement of the *diaphragm*—a muscular wall that separates the body cavity into parts—enlarges the chest cavity. This lowers the pressure in the lungs so that external air pressure pushes air inward. As the air passes through nostrils

Why can you "see your breath" on a cold day?

diaphragm [dī'ə frăm'; Greek: *dia-*, through, + *phragma*, fence]. Did you see a diaphragm in your frog?

Why is this method of breathing impossible for a frog?

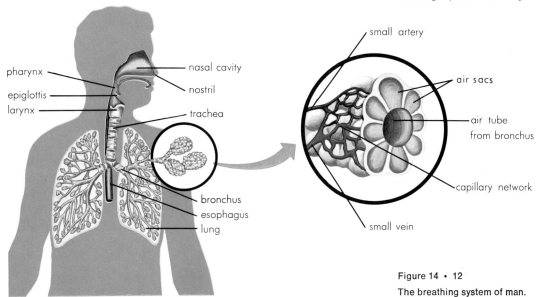

Figure 14 · 12
The breathing system of man.

pharynx [făr'ĭngks; Greek: the throat]. Compare this with "pharyngeal," page 103.

epiglottis [ĕp'ə glŏt'ĭs; Greek: epi, upon, + glotta, tongue]

trachea [trā'kĭ ə; Latin: tracheia, windpipe]

bronchi [brŏng'kī; Greek: bronchos, windpipe]; singular, bronchus

and nasal cavities, it is warmed and moistened. Into the *pharynx* pass both the stream of air from the nasal cavities and food from the mouth. The opening that leads to the lungs is protected by a flap of tissue called the *epiglottis.* It is usually open, admitting air; it closes when food passes by on the way to the esophagus.

The *trachea,* the air passage that extends through the neck ventral to the esophagus, divides in the upper chest into two *bronchi.* Each bronchus leads to a lung, where it branches and rebranches, the smallest divisions ending in almost microscopic air sacs. The walls of these sacs are extremely thin and contain a dense network of tiny blood vessels. Respiratory gases diffuse into and out of the blood through the thin membranes of blood vessels and air sacs.

Historical Pictures Service

Figure 14 • 13
William Harvey: 1578–1657.

TRANSPORTING SUBSTANCES

An early milestone in the development of biological science was the discovery of the circulation of blood. This occurred in the early part of the 17th century through the research of an English physician, William Harvey. As a physician, Harvey was interested in the physiology of man; but as a scientist, his curiosity pushed his investigations in many other directions. In his book, *On the Motion of the Heart and Blood,* he wrote:

> I have also observed, that almost all animals have truly a heart, not the larger creatures only, and those that have red blood but the smaller and seemingly bloodless ones also, such as slugs, snails, scallops, shrimps, crabs, crayfish, and many others; nay even in wasps, hornets **and flies.** I have with the aid of a magnifying glass, and at the upper part of what is called the tail, both seen the heart pulsating myself, and shown it to many others.

pulsating: moving rhythmically, beating

However, Harvey did not know that many animals have much simpler transport systems—lacking not only hearts but even a circulating fluid.

SIMPLE TRANSPORT SYSTEMS

cyclosis. See page 356.

In a single-celled organism, cyclosis is an adequate transportation system. In some multicellular organisms—sponges and coelenterates, for example—almost every cell has some part of its surface exposed to the environment; each cell can obtain its own oxygen and get rid of its own wastes. Though not all cells in these animals take in food, no cell is very far from those that do; so diffusion and active transport are sufficient for the transportation of substances to cells.

Approximately the same situation exists in free-living flatworms.

In roundworms, however, there is a fluid-filled body cavity surrounding the digestive tube. As the worm wriggles, the fluid is squeezed about from place to place, and in this way substances dissolved in it are eventually carried to and from the body cells.

CIRCULATORY SYSTEMS

In most cases, however, an animal that has a body fluid also has a system of tubes through which the fluid flows. Muscular pumps (usually called hearts) propel the fluid (usually called blood), and the direction of flow is controlled by valves within the tubes. Regardless

COELENTERATE

ROUNDWORM

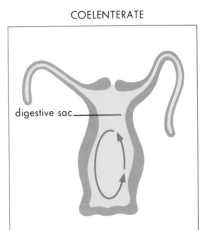

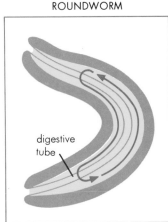

CRUSTACEAN

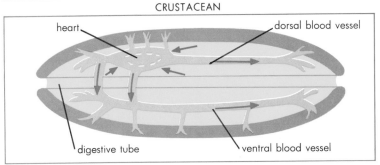

ANNELID

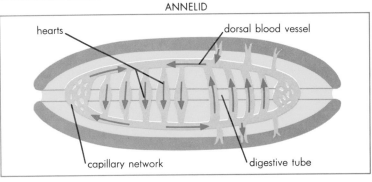

Figure 14 • 14

Diagrams of fluid transport in four invertebrate animals.

It is also referred to as a vascular system. Why?

of detailed anatomical arrangements, the basic function performed by such a circulatory system is always the same: At a place where blood flows slowly, in contact with thin membranes, substances move in or out by diffusion or active transport. The blood then moves rather rapidly to another place where it again flows slowly, in contact with thin membranes, and substances again move in or out.

Invertebrate systems. In arthropods and most mollusks blood is pumped through tubes (blood vessels) that empty into body spaces. Through these spaces the blood moves about sluggishly, in close contact with the tissues. Eventually it gets back into another set of tubes, which carry it back to the pumping point. Such an incomplete vascular system is called an open circulatory system.

You can easily see the movement of blood in the dorsal vessel of an earthworm.

Annelids, on the other hand, have a closed circulatory system—blood flows within vessels throughout its course. In an earthworm the system consists of five pairs of hearts and a complicated set of more and more finely branched vessels; these vessels eventually link up again and empty into a large dorsal vessel. This vessel returns the blood to the hearts. Valves along the walls of the vessel keep the blood flowing in one direction throughout the system.

Figure 14 · 15

Diagrams of circulation in three vertebrate classes. Red indicates oxygenated blood; blue, deoxygenated blood. A = atrium; V = ventricle.

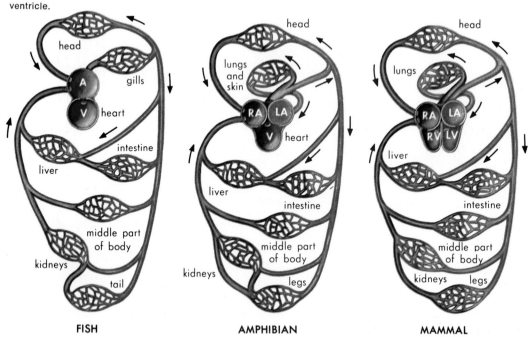

FISH

AMPHIBIAN

MAMMAL

Vertebrate systems. In vertebrates circulation also occurs in a closed system. Vessels of this system are of four kinds. A single, very muscular heart, consisting of two or more chambers, keeps blood moving through the system. *Arteries* have rather thick, muscular walls and carry blood away from the heart. *Veins* have relatively thin walls that contain little muscle tissue; they carry blood toward the heart.

By ingenious experiments, Harvey showed that blood leaves a vertebrate heart through arteries and returns to the heart through veins. Therefore, he reasoned that blood circulates. But he never actually saw blood passing from arteries to veins. Harvey lived before the use of the microscope became widespread. Later in the century Marcello Malpighi first observed *capillaries*—very thin-walled vessels that connect arteries and veins. His observations confirmed Harvey's reasoning.

In all mammals and birds the heart is a double pump. It has right and left sides and each side is connected with its own veins and arteries. In mammals the right side receives blood from almost all parts of the body and sends it to the lungs. The left side receives blood from the lungs and sends it to all other parts of the body. Each of the pumps has two chambers. One, an *atrium,* receives incoming blood. When the heart muscle relaxes, this blood passes into another, a ventricle. When the heart contracts, the walls of the ventricle give the blood a strong push. This forces tissue flaps together; they act as valves that prevent backflow into the atrium. So the blood is forced out through an artery.

arteries [Latin: *arteria,* windpipe or blood vessel. (Ancient anatomists could not determine whether vessels in dissected animals had contained air or blood.)]

Marcello Malpighi [mäl pē′gī]: 1628–1694. Italian anatomist

atrium [ā′trĭ əm; Latin: central court of an ancient Roman house]; plural, atria

ventricle [vĕn′trə kəl; Latin: *ventriculus,* little stomach]

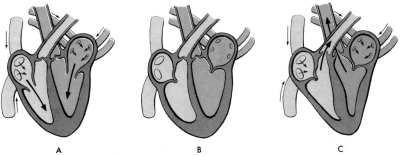

A   **B**   **C**

Figure 14 • 16

Three steps (*A* to *C*) in the pumping action of a mammalian heart. Why does the blood not flow back into the atria when the ventricles contract?

Near the heart, arteries also contain valves. When blood is being pushed by contraction of the ventricles, the flaps are forced against the artery wall and blood flows away from the heart. When the ventricles relax between heartbeats, back pressure of the blood forces the flaps away from the artery wall, preventing the blood from flowing back toward the heart. Similar valves occur in veins.

Capillaries have walls only a single cell thick. As blood flows slowly through the capillaries, substances move from the blood through the thin walls into the cells of the body tissues, and other substances move from the tissues into the blood.

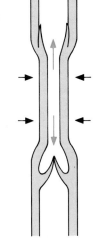

Figure 14 • 17

Movement of blood in veins is brought about by pressure from adjacent muscles. Compression forces blood in both directions, but valves prevent blood from flowing backward—away from the heart.

BLOOD

In many marine animals, there is little difference between the body fluids and the environmental seawater. But in land animals the body fluids are complex mixtures of substances in water, and the environment is a mixture of gases. These two examples are extremes; there are many intermediate degrees of difference between the fluids within animals and the substances in their environments. In general, organisms with circulatory systems have blood that is more or less different from fluids in their environments.

There is great variation in composition of blood among different animal groups. Some bloods are red; others are greenish, brownish, or colorless. Some contain cells; others do not. But all bloods are made up largely of water in which many substances are dissolved or suspended.

Plasma. When you watch human blood flow from a small wound, it appears to be a uniform red liquid. When you examine a thin layer of it under the microscope, you can see many faintly reddish cells. But other cells show up when the smear is stained. By means of a centrifuge, all these cells can be concentrated and a clear yellowish liquid—*plasma*—obtained.

plasma [Greek: *plassein*, tô form]

Figure 14 • 18

A centrifuge (*right*). Liquids that contain tiny solid particles (as does blood) are placed in the tubes. Rapid whirling separates the particles from the liquid, as shown in Figure 14 • 19.

Arthur M. Siegelman from Alpha

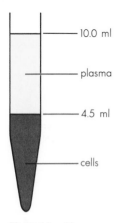

10.0 ml

plasma

4.5 ml

cells

Figure 14 • 19

Centrifuged human blood. What percent of the sample was plasma?

About 91 percent of human plasma is water. The rest is made up of substances dissolved or suspended in the water—about 8 percent proteins and close to 0.9 percent minerals, especially ions of calcium, potassium, sodium, and phosphate. There are also small amounts of amino acids, simple sugars, and wastes from metabolism.

Among blood proteins are the antibodies that protect against infections. And there are many inherited blood proteins. Research during recent years has shown that the more closely animals are related taxonomically, the more blood proteins they have in common. However, even individuals within a single species have some protein differences.

Cells. Human blood contains *red blood cells* and *white blood cells.* Usually considered with them are *platelets,* which are fragments of cells.

The oxygen-carrying ability and color of human blood results primarily from *hemoglobin,* an iron-containing pigment in the red cells. When oxygen is abundant around a red cell (as it is in lung capillaries), it combines with the hemoglobin in the cell, forming bright red *oxyhemoglobin.* When oxygen is scarce around a red cell (as it is likely to be in active muscle tissue), oxygen is released, leaving dull red hemoglobin. In the condition called *anemia* there is either an abnormally low number of red cells or an abnormally low hemoglobin content per cell.

Human red cells live 110–120 days; then they are removed from circulation and destroyed in the liver and spleen. The liver salvages iron ions from these cells, and cells in bone marrow use these ions in making new red cells.

White cells have no hemoglobin and are therefore colorless. Unlike red cells, they do not merely float along in the plasma; a white cell can move about very much like an ameba, even slipping through the thin walls of capillaries and wandering about among the cells of muscle and other tissues. There are several varieties of white cells, which differ in size, function, and reaction to stains. Primarily, however, white cells serve to destroy invading particles, such as pathogenic organisms. They do this by engulfing and digesting the particles much as an ameba does. Some white cells also seem to aid in the repair of wounds.

platelets [plăt′lĭts; Greek: *platys,* broad, flat]

hemoglobin [hē′mə glō′bĭn]

anemia [ə nē′mĭ ə; Greek: *an-,* without, + *haima,* blood]. Why is an anemic individual less active than a normal individual?

A human spleen is not shaped like a frog spleen but generally functions similarly in all vertebrates.

ELEMENT	DIAMETER (in microns)	NUMBER (per cu. mm)	MAIN FUNCTION
red blood cells	7-8	4,500,000-5,500,000	oxygen transport
white blood cells	9-12	7,000-10,000	defense against microorganisms
platelets	2-4	300,000 (much variation)	blood-clotting

Figure 14 · 20
A comparison of some characteristics of blood "elements," a term used by those who wish to emphasize that platelets are only fragments of cells.

Platelets are colorless, usually spherical, and—like red cells—without nuclei. Their life-span is estimated to be four days.

Clotting. Normally when a vertebrate animal suffers a small wound, the blood at the surface clots. But if blood is gently drawn into a paraffin-lined vessel, it does not clot. Therefore, mere exposure to air cannot be the cause of clotting. The process of clotting illustrates the complexity that research sometimes reveals behind apparently simple biological processes.

Clotting begins with platelets. Whenever they are exposed to a rough surface—almost any surface other than the smooth lining of the blood vessels—they tend to stick to it and then to break up. As they do so, they release a substance called thromboplastin. The thromboplastin acts as an enzyme to bring about a change in prothrombin, one of the plasma proteins. This reaction, which does not occur unless calcium is present (as it always is in normal blood), converts prothrombin to thrombin. Thrombin then acts as an enzyme to convert fibrinogen, another blood protein, into fibrin, an insoluble substance that forms threads within the plasma. Blood cells are trapped in a network of fibrin threads, thus building up a clot.

thromboplastin
[thräm'bō'plǎs'tən; Greek: *thrombos*, a lump, clot, + *plassein*]

prothrombin [prō thrŏm'bĭn; Greek: *pro*, before, + *thrombos*]

fibrinogen [fī brĭn'ə jən; Latin: *fibra*, fiber, + *genitus*, born]

Emil Bernstein and Ella Kairinen

Figure 14 · 21

Scanning electron micrograph of a red blood cell caught in threads of fibrin. × 10,250

LYMPH

Some plasma readily passes through capillary walls, though little of its protein content does so. White cells may also escape from the closed vascular system; red cells do not. Thus the tissue fluid that bathes cells, though somewhat like blood, is nearly colorless and is lower in protein content.

Some of this fluid may ooze back into the blood capillaries; the remainder of it collects in another set of vessels, where it is called *lymph.* These vessels join to form larger vessels. Contractions of the muscles that surround the lymph vessels move the lymph along. In the walls of the small intestine, lymph vessels absorb fats; and many of the metabolic wastes of cells pass into the tissue fluid. Thus lymph has a higher fat content and a higher waste content than does blood.

Eventually all lymph vessels join, forming a duct that carries the lymph to the region of the left shoulder; there the lymph is emptied into a vein. Thus the fluids that leave the blood at the capillaries are brought back into the blood again.

At many points in the lymphatic system there are enlargements in which the vessels divide into tiny twisted passages. As a result, the lymph flows slowly through them. Here pathogenic organisms and other foreign materials that may have entered the body are engulfed by white blood cells, much as amebas engulf food particles. Thus the lymphatic system acts as a defense.

Have you ever had "swollen glands" in your armpits or neck during a severe cold? On the basis of this paragraph, explain this condition.

Investigation 14.3

A HEART AT WORK

BACKGROUND INFORMATION

Crustaceans of the genus *Daphnia* are abundant in small bodies of fresh water. Individuals are just large enough to be seen with the naked eye in good light. But when magnified even 20 times, many of the internal organs—including the heart—can be seen through the body wall. Before you begin the procedure of this investigation, become familiar with the appearance of the animals. Look carefully for the beating heart. Do not confuse its motion with that of the legs, which also move rhythmically.

MATERIALS AND EQUIPMENT

(for each team)
Daphnia, in a small beaker of aquarium water, 6 to 8
thermometer ($-10°$ to $+110°C$)
medicine dropper
microscope slide with depression
stereomicroscope
watch with second hand
beaker large enough to hold *Daphnia* beaker
crushed ice

hot water
graph paper, 1 sheet per student

PROCEDURE

Read through the whole procedure. • State a hypothesis that is appropriate to it.(1)

Check the temperature of the water in which the *Daphnia* are living. It should be at room temperature before you begin the experiment. With a medicine dropper, transfer 1 *Daphnia* to the depression in the slide. Soak up excess water with a piece of paper towel. By keeping the amount of water at a minimum, you increase the likelihood that the animal will lie on its side, in which position heart action can best be seen.

One member of the team keeps time with a watch, while another observes the specimen through the stereomicroscope and counts the heartbeats. It may be difficult to count as rapidly as the heart pulsates. If so, try tapping with a pencil on a piece of paper at the speed of the heartbeat; then count the dots. When the observer is ready, the timer says "Go!" At the end of 15 seconds, he says "Stop!" Multiply

Figure 14 · 22

Daphnia. × 60

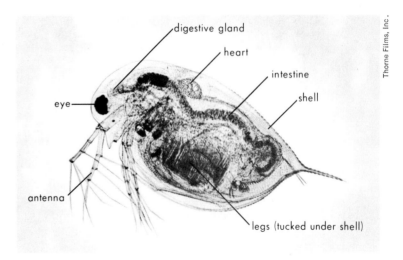

the count by 4 to obtain the number of heart-beats per minute. Make at least 3 timed counts, allowing each member of the team to take a turn as an observer or timer. Return the *Daphnia* to the beaker.

Place the beaker of *Daphnia* in a larger beaker containing water and crushed ice. Stir the water in the *Daphnia* beaker gently with the thermometer. When the water temperature reaches the point assigned to your team by your teacher, quickly transfer a *Daphnia* to the slide and make at least 3 counts as quickly as possible.

As soon as the *Daphnia* is removed from the beaker, members of the team who are not timing or counting should remove the *Daphnia* beaker from the large beaker, pour out the ice water, and replace it with hot water (50° to 70°C).

Place the *Daphnia* beaker in the larger beaker again. Stir the water in the *Daphnia* beaker gently with the thermometer. By the time the water temperature reaches the 2nd point assigned to your team, counting at the lower temperature should be finished. Quickly transfer a *Daphnia* from the warm water to the slide and make at least 3 counts as quickly as possible.

STUDYING THE DATA

Consider the heartbeat data obtained

from *Daphnia* at room temperature. • Why were several counts made by each team?(2) • What factors might account for the variability in these data?(3)

Assemble on the chalkboard the room-temperature data from all teams. Compare the variability in the data from all teams with the variability in the data from your own team. • How can you account for any differences?(4) • Calculate the average rate of heartbeat from the assembled class data.(5)   • Which is likely to be more reliable—the average obtained by your team or the average obtained by the entire class? Explain.(6)

Assemble the data on heartbeat at different temperatures. If 2 or more teams obtained data at the same temperature, calculate a general average for that temperature. Graph the data, placing rate of heartbeat on the vertical axis and temperature on the horizontal axis.

CONCLUSIONS

• On the basis of your graph, make a general statement concerning the effects of variation in environmental temperature on the rate of heartbeat in *Daphnia*.(7)   • Does your graph support your hypothesis? Explain.(8) • Would you expect similar effects of temperature on the heartbeat rate of a frog? Of a dog? Explain.(9)

1. Young pond snails have thin shells through which the heart can be seen, just as in *Daphnia.* Make a study of snail heartbeat for comparison with that of *Daphnia.* Try to account for any differences you observe.

2. The easily observed heart of *Daphnia* can lead to some understanding of the way in which drugs affect heartbeat rate. Investigate the effects of alcohol (about 5%) and of a stimulant (such as dexedrine sulfate) on *Daphnia* heartbeat.

REMOVING SUBSTANCES

EXCRETION, SECRETION, ELIMINATION

The process by which *waste* substances are removed from cells is called **excretion.** But if a substance that passes out of a cell is one that is in some way useful to the organism, then the process is called **secretion.** Because carbon dioxide is a metabolic waste formed in every living animal cell, it is an excretion from each cell. Gastric juice, which passes through the membranes of cells that line the stomach, is a secretion because substances in it are useful in digesting food.

excretion [ĭk skrē'shən; Latin: *ex*, out of, + *cernere*, to sift]

secretion [sĭ krē'shən; Latin: *se-*, aside, + *cernere*]

Both secretion and excretion involve the passage of substances through cell membranes. This may occur by diffusion. Frequently, however, a substance is more abundant outside a cell than it is within. Then energy is required to "pump" the substance out of the cell by the process of active transport.

Once a substance has passed outward through a cell membrane, it has been excreted or secreted. But in multicellular animals it may not be outside the body as a whole. For example, liquid from certain cells above the eyes of many terrestrial vertebrates enters into ducts that empty onto the surface of their eyeballs. The liquid in these tear ducts is no longer in cells, but it is still within the body—at least in the usual sense. The process by which substances are forced out of body cavities—either small ones, such as tear ducts, or large ones, such as the digestive tube—is called **elimination.**

elimination [Latin: *ex*, out of, + *limen*, threshold]

Now consider a little more carefully what we mean by "wastes." Some products of metabolism are, in one way or another, toxic (poisonous). Such a substance is clearly a waste. One example is ammonia, which is formed in the breakdown of proteins. Some substances, however, are toxic only if large amounts accumulate—for example, sodium chloride, which is a normal cell substance. This salt is constantly diffusing into cells from their environments. Therefore, only by continuous excretion can the normal proportion of sodium chloride be maintained in cells. In general, then, any substance can be called a waste if an organism has too much of it.

toxic [Greek: *toxikon*, a poison]

Can you show how this definition of "waste" involves circular reasoning?

EXCRETIONS

In small aquatic animals wastes may simply diffuse out through cell membranes, in the same way that respiratory gases are exchanged with an environment. Sponges and coelenterates—though not always small—also excrete wastes directly through their body surfaces, since all their cells are close to a water environment. Most animals, however, have special devices for ridding their bodies of wastes.

See Figure 12·5.

Water. By the process of cellular respiration, water is constantly being produced by animal cells. What happens to this water depends upon the kind of environment in which an animal lives. Consider a jellyfish living in the ocean. Its cells contain a complex mixture of substances in water. Outside the cell membranes is another complex mixture—the salty seawater. If the concentrations of the water molecules in the two mixtures differ, water molecules move from one to the other by diffusion. But in jellyfish—and a great many other marine invertebrates—the concentrations inside and outside are normally almost equal. As fast as metabolic water is produced, it diffuses into the environment.

Now consider a planarian living in a freshwater stream. There are very few dissolved substances in fresh water; the concentration of water molecules is high. But in a planarian's cells the concentration of dissolved substances is high and the water concentration is relatively low. Therefore, water is always diffusing into a planarian's cells. And metabolic water is constantly added to this excess. We might expect that water would accumulate within a cell, increase its volume, and produce such pressure that it would eventually burst. When drugs that interfere with the mechanism of active transport are used experimentally on planarians, this is exactly what happens. For freshwater animals, then, excretion of water is necessary for survival.

Terrestrial animals are in a similar physiological situation. You, for example, take in a great deal of fresh water; and, of course, your cells also produce water by metabolic processes. As a land animal you are always in danger of drying out, but you are also in danger of swelling up with excess water. In the condition called dropsy this swelling actually occurs. All through your life, you and every other land animal walk a very thin tightrope, balanced between having too much water and too little.

dropsy [Greek: *hydrops* (from *hydor*, water)]

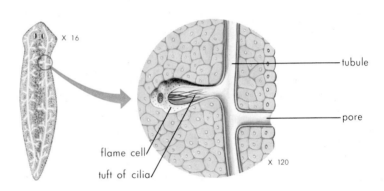

Figure 14 · 23
Excretory structure in a planarian.

Animals maintain water balance within their cells through a variety of structures. In planarians this function is performed by a system of *flame cells* spread throughout the body and connected by tubules. Each flame cell has a tuft of cilia that projects into a tubule. The waving of the tuft (to early microscopists, this action resembled the flickering of a flame) creates a slight negative pressure (suction) within the tubule. This tends to draw water from the surrounding tissues and push it along the tubule. The many tubules join and eventually empty into the environment through a pore. Variations of the flame-cell system are found in some other invertebrates.

tubule [tōō′būl; Latin: *tubulus*, little tube]

Most annelids (including earthworms), as well as mollusks and crustaceans, have quite different excretory systems. In these animals the functional unit is a tubule around which there may be a network of capillaries. In many cases fluid from the body cavity is modified as it passes through the tubule to the outside—more wastes are added and useful materials are absorbed back into the blood or body fluid. In other cases the tubule does not connect with the body cavity; therefore, all substances to be excreted must be diffused or transported into it. In vertebrates somewhat similar tubules are found in the kidneys.

Nitrogenous wastes. The organs usually called excretory—from flame cells in flatworms to kidneys in vertebrates—seem to have evolved chiefly as water-regulating devices. They still regulate water, but in most animals they also function in the excretion of other wastes, particularly nitrogen-bearing ones.

Amino acids are used by cells to build proteins. But often an animal takes in more amino acids than it can use. And some proteins in an animal's body are constantly being broken down into amino acids. Therefore, a surplus of amino acids usually exists. Unlike carbohydrates and fats, amino acids (or proteins formed from them) cannot be stored in large quantities. And they cannot be used for the release of energy until the amino group ($-NH_2$) is removed.

During what part of your life do you think amino-acid requirements might be greatest?

In vertebrates the removal of amino groups occurs chiefly in the liver. The ammonia (NH_3) that results from this process is quite toxic. It is also quite soluble, and if a large supply of water is available, the ammonia can be carried out of the body in solution. If a freshwater fish is placed through a hole in a tight-fitting rubber partition so that the anterior end with the gills is on one side and the posterior end with the opening from the kidneys is on the other, ammonia accumulates in the water on the anterior side of the partition. In such fishes, then, nitrogenous wastes are excreted through the gills.

In other vertebrates the kidneys are the main avenue through which nitrogenous wastes are excreted. But the wastes are not in the form of ammonia. In birds, reptiles, and insects amino groups are incorporated into uric acid. This rather complex substance is almost insoluble and can be excreted with the loss of only a small amount of water. In most adult amphibians and mammals, however, the amino groups are converted to *urea*. Unlike uric acid, urea is soluble. It

uric [yŏor′ĭk; Greek: *ouron*, urine]

urea [yŏo rē′ə]

Figure 14 · 24

Urea. (*A*) Structural formula. (*B*) Model. How many molecules of urea must a mammal excrete to rid itself of the same amount of nitrogen as does a fish excreting 100 molecules of ammonia?

A

B

diffuses into the blood, from which it is removed by the kidneys.

Other substances. Excretion involves many salts in addition to sodium chloride. These enter from the environment faster than they are needed, especially in vertebrates that live in seawater or on land. In land animals, kidneys are the chief excretory organs for salt as well as for nitrogenous wastes. But many seabirds—which are physiologically land animals that take in much salt water—have special salt-excreting glands located in their nostrils. And your tears contain salt.

Do you think that human beings could drink seawater if their tear glands produced saltier tears? Why or why not?

Further, water, small amounts of nitrogenous wastes, and salts are excreted through your sweat glands; the remains of dead red blood cells are excreted through your liver; and almost all the carbon dioxide produced during the release of energy from your cells (along

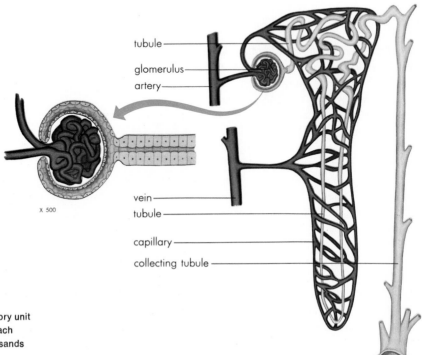

tubule

glomerulus

artery

vein

tubule

capillary

collecting tubule

x 500

Figure 14 · 25

Diagram of an excretory unit in a human kidney. Each kidney contains thousands of such units.

with a considerable amount of water) is excreted through your lungs. There is, then, no one organ that performs all excretory functions in the body of a vertebrate. Nevertheless, loss of function in both kidneys is always fatal.

HUMAN KIDNEY FUNCTION

Three distinct processes, all of which require the expenditure of energy, occur in a human kidney. The first step is filtration of blood. This occurs through a *glomerulus,* a ball of capillary-like blood vessels surrounded by the expanded end of a tubule. Each kidney contains many thousand glomeruli. Blood pressure (which represents energy expended by the ventricle in pumping blood) forces some of the fluid of the blood through the walls of the blood vessels and through the thin walls of the expanded ends of the tubules. This fluid (filtrate) contains no blood cells or proteins, but otherwise it has the same composition as blood. As the filtrate moves down the tubules, useful substances—such as sugar, amino acids, water, some salts—are reabsorbed by cells in the walls of the tubules. These substances are then transferred to the blood in capillaries that surround the tubules. Urea and some other wastes are left behind in the tubules. Thus, as the original filtrate moves along the tubules, it is gradually converted—by removal of useful materials and concentration of waste materials—to *urine.*

fatal: here, causing death. But in humans death can be prevented by two surgical methods. What are they?

glomerulus [glō měr′yŏŏ ləs; Latin: little ball]; plural, glomeruli

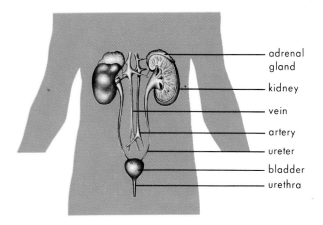

adrenal gland

kidney

vein

artery

ureter

bladder

urethra

Figure 14 • 26
Urinary system in man. Adrenal glands are attached to the kidneys but are not a part of this system.

Constantly, day and night throughout life, urine trickles from each kidney into a urinary bladder. From time to time the urine is eliminated from the urinary bladder through a *urethra.* It has been estimated that a healthy pair of human kidneys filters 135–150 liters of fluid every 24 hours, while only about 1.5 liters of urine are eliminated from the bladder during the same period. In other words, only about 1 percent of the fluid filtered by the kidneys is eliminated.

urethra [yŏŏ rē′thrə]

Kidneys are often described as homeostatic organs. Explain this.

MAINTAINING A STEADY STATE

ENVIRONMENTS: INTERNAL AND EXTERNAL

One of the first concepts you encountered in this book was that of steady state—an always teetering balance held within narrow limits by homeostatic mechanisms. We can observe steady state within an individual organism as well as outside it. From the viewpoint of any one cell within a multicellular organism, the other cells of that body are outside—they are part of that cell's environment. In this view, a cell can be likened to an individual; a tissue, to a species population; an organ, perhaps, to a community. This analogy can help us to understand some of the things that go on within an organism. The environment of a cell within the body of a multicellular organism is, then, external to the cell, but it is internal to the multicellular organism as a whole. Thus we get the rather paradoxical but useful concept of an *internal environment.*

And, like all analogies, it can be carried too far.

The internal environment of an individual cell consists not only of neighboring cells but also of body fluids. These fluids are to a cell what the sea is to an individual sea animal: the source of its requirements, the place to which its wastes are returned. In freshwater and land animals the primary function of homeostatic mechanisms is to keep body fluids as favorable and stable an environment for each cell as seawater usually is for each marine organism.

Consider, for example, the homeostatic regulation of the glucose content of human blood. After a heavy meal, digestion leaves a large amount of glucose in your small intestine. This is absorbed into your blood, but it does not stay there long. Figure 14·15 shows that a vessel carries blood (and glucose) from capillaries in your digestive system directly to capillaries in your liver. Here glucose in excess of 0.1 percent is removed and changed to the polysaccharide glycogen, which is then stored in your liver cells. If the meal produces a very large amount of glucose (as it may if it contains many carbohydrates), your liver cannot take in all the excess. In this case, glucose is excreted through your kidneys.

glycogen [glī′kə jən; Greek: *glykys,* sweet, + *genea,* birth]

Now suppose you take part in some kind of exercise, such as basketball or tennis. Muscle cells must use a great deal of glucose for energy release. This glucose is drawn from the environment of your muscle cells—from your body fluids. Reduction of glucose in your body fluids leads to reduction of glucose in your blood. Under these circumstances glycogen in your liver is changed to glucose, which enters the blood. In this manner your liver and your circulatory and excretory systems provide the homeostatic mechanisms that maintain glucose in steady state in the internal environment of your cells.

Review page 58.

A steady state results from the coordination of the parts of a living system. This coordination results from homeostasis, which requires some means of communication among the cells within an organism. In most animals this communication occurs in two ways: by chemicals that travel through body fluids and by specialized nerve

coordination [kō ôr′də nā′shən; Latin: *cum,* with, + *ordinare,* to arrange]: adjustment of one part of a system to other parts

cells. Chemical and nervous communication act together, but it is convenient to separate them for discussion.

CHEMICAL COORDINATION

Knowledge of the chemical system of coordination has accumulated only within the last century. Just as knowledge of microscopic organisms was dependent upon the development of microscopes, so knowledge of chemical systems in organisms has been dependent upon the development of chemistry.

Hormones. In all multicellular organisms some cells probably secrete chemical substances that in various ways influence the growth, development, or behavior of other cells. We discussed one of these —auxin—in Chapter 13. In general, such substances are called *hormones.* As yet, rather little is known about hormones in most animal phyla. They have been studied chiefly in mollusks, arthropods, and chordates.

hormones [Greek: *hormaein,* to stimulate]

Hormones may be secreted by individual cells scattered among other cells of an animal's body, but usually the secreting cells are grouped into tissues and often into distinct organs—glands. Unlike the glands that secrete tears, sweat, and saliva, those that secrete

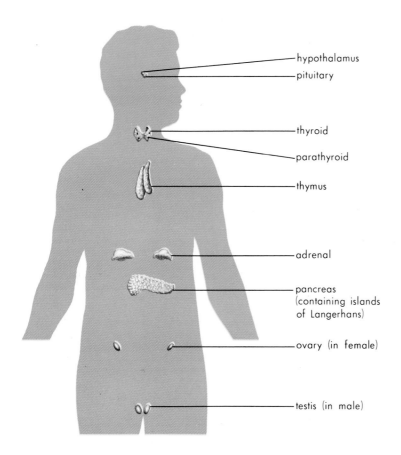

hypothalamus
pituitary
thyroid
parathyroid
thymus
adrenal
pancreas (containing islands of Langerhans)
ovary (in female)
testis (in male)

Figure 14 · 27

Location of the principal endocrine glands in a human body.

endocrine [ĕn′dō krīn′, ĕn′dō krĭn; Greek: *endon*, within, + *krinein*, to separate]

What experimental procedure could be used to demonstrate this?

hypothalamus [hī′pə thăl′ə məs; Greek: *hypo*, below, + *thalamos*, a chamber (here, a part of the brain)]

pituitary [pĭ tū′ə tĕr′ĭ]

thyroid [Greek: *thyreos*, a shield, + *eidos*, form]

hormones do not empty their products into a tubule or duct; their secretions pass directly into the circulatory system and are carried in blood. Because these *endocrine,* or ductless, glands interact with each other, we can say that there is an endocrine system, even though its parts are scattered throughout an animal's body.

Endocrine glands of vertebrates. With some relatively minor variations, all groups of vertebrates have similar hormones. However, the same hormone may have quite different functions in animals of different vertebrate classes. For example, the hormone that causes the mammary glands of mammals to secrete milk causes hens to incubate their eggs. Hormones that cause changes in skin color in certain fishes and amphibians are present in you. But your skin does not contain the special color cells that would enable you to match the colors of your surroundings. Within any one vertebrate class, however, a particular hormone has approximately the same effects in most species. The discussion that follows applies for the most part to mammals.

The *hypothalamus* is in the ventral part of the brain and is a part of the nervous system. But special cells of the hypothalamus produce hormones that pass through the blood in special vessels to the anterior part of the *pituitary* gland, which lies just below the brain. These hormones cause the anterior part of the pituitary gland to release hormones that control the rate at which some of the other endocrine glands function. Thus the hypothalamus is a major link between the nervous and endocrine systems. The posterior part of the pituitary secretes several hormones that regulate such things as blood pressure and the flow of urine.

All vertebrates have *thyroid* glands. The thyroid hormone regulates the rate of cellular respiration. Too little of the hormone brings

Figure 14 · 28

A patient with an enlarged thyroid gland that is secreting an excess of thyroxin. One of the symptoms of this condition is seen in the eyes (*left*). Same patient after treatment (*right*).

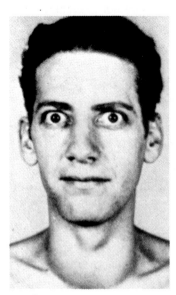

Photos from Lisser, H., and Escamilla, R. F.; ATLAS OF CLINICAL ENDOCRINOLOGY, 1962, The C. V. Mosby Co.; courtesy Dr. W. A. Reilly, Dir., Radioisotope Unit, VA Hosp., San Francisco

about an increase in weight, since food is stored rather than used in energy release. There are other results, such as slow movement, sleepiness, and lowered body temperature. Too much thyroid hormone increases the rate of cellular respiration, so very little food is stored. The individual loses weight, but he has an excess of energy, so he is very active.

Parathyroid glands are present in all vertebrates except fishes, but only in mammals are they embedded in the thyroid glands. Parathyroid hormone controls the metabolism of calcium, which plays a part in the contraction of muscles. It is interference with muscle contraction that brings about death if the parathyroid glands are injured or removed.

Embedded in the pancreas (see Figure 14 • 7) are bits of endocrine tissue that produce *insulin.* This hormone controls the metabolism of glucose. A lack of insulin results in a lack of cellular energy, and the unmetabolized glucose is excreted in the urine.

Adrenal glands are found in amphibians, reptiles, birds, and mammals. Hormones similar to those produced by these glands are secreted by fishes, but the secreting tissues are not organized into glands. The best-known adrenal hormone is *adrenalin.* Adrenalin raises blood pressure, speeds up heartbeat, increases the rate of blood clotting, and raises the percentage of glucose in the blood. All these effects increase the chances of survival when an individual is faced with an emergency—particularly one that is likely to result in wounding.

During the early development of an individual, adrenal glands are formed from two different tissues. The part of an adrenal gland that secretes adrenalin develops from nerve tissue; most of the rest develops from tissue that also gives rise to the reproductive system. Hormones of this latter part of the adrenal gland affect many functions. Among them are: the depositing of fats, the synthesis of proteins, the formation of glucose from amino acids, and the excretion of salt. This part of the adrenal gland is controlled by a pituitary hormone. Obviously, adrenal glands are of vital importance to the biochemical functioning of an organism.

Ovaries and testes are organs in which reproductive cells are formed, but embedded in them are endocrine cells. Hormones from these cells control growth, development, and reproductive behavior.

Sometimes included in the endocrine system are small glands in the walls of the intestine, just below the pyloric valve. When food passes through the pyloric valve, these glands produce *secretin.* This hormone travels through the bloodstream to the pancreas, where it stimulates the production of pancreatic juice.

Other kinds of chemical coordination. Many kinds of substances that cannot be called hormones aid in coordination of physiological processes. No biologist, for example, would call carbon dioxide a hormone. It is obviously a waste product—an excretion rather than a secretion. But CO_2 in the blood plays a part in the coordination of

parathyroid [păr′ə thī′roid; Greek: *para,* beside, + thyroid]

What other functions might be affected by the control of calcium metabolism?

insulin [Latin: *insula,* island]. Can you find the origin of this name?

The disease is called diabetes mellitus. How does it originate and how is it controlled?

adrenal [ə drē′nəl; Latin: *ad,* to, at, + *renes,* kidneys]. Note their position in Figure 14 · 26.

adrenalin [ə drĕn′əl ĭn]

ovaries, testes [tĕs′tēz]. See pages 537–538.

secretin [sĭ krē′tĭn]. This was the first substance to be called a hormone—in 1902.

What can you find out about the thymus gland?

breathing. Numerous experiments have shown that the movements of muscles in breathing are regulated by the nervous system—specifically, by a part of the brain that lies near the base of the skull.

But what determines whether your breathing movements are slow or rapid? Within limits you can voluntarily control your breathing. For a short time you can breathe deeply and quickly—or the reverse, as you may choose. If, however, you hold your breath, the concentration of CO_2 in your blood becomes greater and greater. Eventually the increased concentration of CO_2 stimulates nerves to reactivate the breathing motions in your chest. This chemical control of breathing operates whether you are conscious or unconscious.

NERVOUS COORDINATION

The control of breathing illustrates again how closely nervous and chemical coordination are associated. In general, however, the more rapid adjustments in animals are brought about by nervous systems.

Kinds of nervous systems. Sponges have no nervous systems. Indeed, they have nothing that we can call nerve cells. Yet, just as do other organisms without nerve cells (protists and plants), sponges adjust to changes in their environment—they react to stimuli.

stimuli [stĭm′yə lī]; singular, stimulus. See page 58.

Coelenterates do have nerve cells, some of which are even specialized to receive only certain kinds of stimuli. Their nerve cells are connected in a network that permits local responses as well as some coordinated responses, such as ingestion of food.

Flatworms also have nerve networks. But in addition a flatworm possesses a more centralized system consisting of two cords that extend, with interconnecting branches, along the length of its body. At the anterior end is a rather large mass of nerve tissue, a *ganglion,* a center in which nerve impulses are exchanged. Moreover, a flatworm has cells specialized for receiving stimuli. The eyespots of planarians cannot form images, but they can detect the direction and intensity of light.

ganglion [găng′glĭ ən]

Recall Investigation 4.3. You may be able to devise some experiments to test an earthworm's ability to detect various kinds of stimuli.

Annelids have well-developed nervous systems. A main nerve cord extends along the ventral side of the body. Numerous ganglia occur along the nerve cord, and a large ganglion, sometimes called a brain, is found at the anterior end of the body. Although earthworms have no obvious sense organs, they are able to detect many kinds of stimuli. Other annelids have several specialized sense organs, including eyes.

How many kinds of sense organs can you find in a grasshopper? In a crayfish?

Among mollusks and arthropods there is a great variety of nervous systems. All are basically of the annelid type; however, the sense organs of most mollusks and arthropods are more numerous and more varied than those of annelids.

A dorsal, tubular nerve cord is a distinctive characteristic of the chordate phylum. In vertebrate chordates an anterior enlargement of this nerve cord—the brain—dominates all the rest of the nervous system.

COELENTERATE

FLATWORM

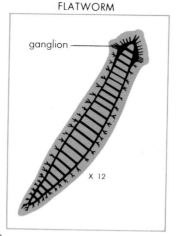

ganglion

X 20

X 12

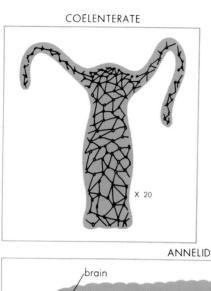

ANNELID

brain

ventral nerve cord

ganglion

X 1

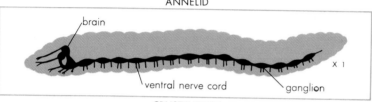

CRUSTACEAN

brain

X 1/2

ganglion

ventral nerve cord

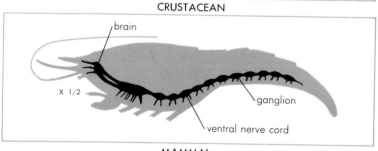

MAMMAL

dorsal nerve cord

brain

ganglion

X 1/6

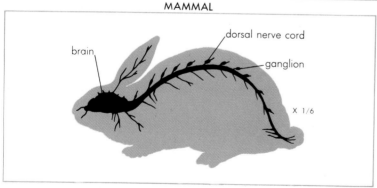

Figure 14 · 29
Nervous systems in five
diverse kinds of animals.

Nerve cells. The basic structural unit in all nervous systems is a
neuron, a nerve cell. Neurons do not occur singly. The nerves that are
visible in a dissected vertebrate are bundles of fibers. In man the
fibers of some neurons are almost a meter long. The cell bodies of

neuron [nŏŏr'ŏn, nyŏŏr'ŏn;
Greek: nerve]

neurons are mostly in the brain, in the spinal cord, or in the ganglia that occur in pairs along the length of the spinal cord.

Functionally neurons transmit nerve *impulses.* Impulses are short in duration—usually only a few ten-thousandths of a second long. Just what a nerve impulse is, physiologists do not completely understand. Electrical changes occur along a neuron during transmission of an impulse, but an impulse is not simply an electric current. For one thing, nerve impulses travel more slowly than electrical currents.

In mammals three kinds of neurons can be distinguished on the basis of their functional specialization. *Sensory* neurons receive impulses from a *receptor* (such as the part of the eye that reacts to light) and transmit impulses to another neuron. *Motor* neurons carry impulses to an *effector*—that is, to a muscle or a gland. *Associative* neurons transmit impulses from one neuron to another.

Neurons do not directly touch each other. When an impulse reaches the end of a neuron, it causes the release of a chemical that starts an impulse in the next neuron. The very narrow space between two neurons through which this chemical passes is called a *synapse.* Transmission across a synapse can take place only in one direction. Therefore impulses are conducted only in one direction by neurons.

synapse [sĭn′ăps; Greek: *syn-*, with, + *apsis*, a fastening]

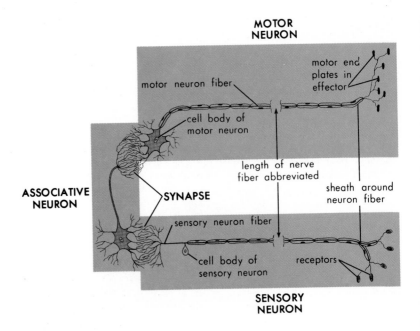

Figure 14 · 30
Kinds of neurons.

Nerves and internal coordination. The activities that you can consciously control are coordinated by your *central nervous system*—your brain, spinal cord, and the nerves that lead directly into and out of them. Thinking and related activities, such as reading and speaking, are functions that involve the *cerebrum* part of your brain. The

Consider speaking: What you say is cerebral, but saying it is cerebellar. Explain.

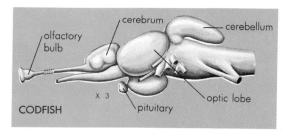

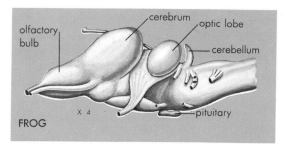

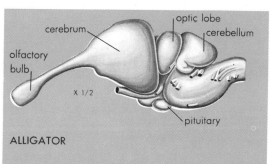

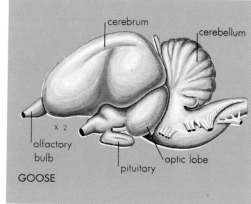

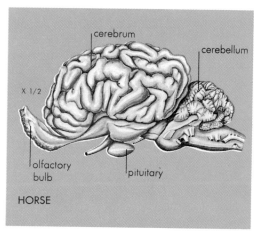

Figure 14 · 31

Brains of animals in five vertebrate classes. Olfactory bulbs are concerned with odor; optic lobes, with sight. The pituitary is not part of the brain. From these examples, what generalizations about brains in vertebrates can you make?

coordination of muscles involves your *cerebellum.* Your central nervous system also coordinates some activities that you can control in part but do not usually think about—such as your rate of breathing.

Much activity in your nervous system occurs without your being aware of it. Some of this is controlled by your central nervous system. But the control of reabsorption of water in your kidneys, the movements of your stomach, the secretion of bile by your liver—these are activities that are under the control of your *autonomic* nervous system, which in turn is controlled through your hypothalamus. Your autonomic system consists of interconnecting neurons that operate, for the most part, independently of your external environment but that coordinate activities in your internal environment.

For example, a steady supply of blood to all tissues is one of the principal requirements for maintaining a favorable internal environ-

autonomic [ô'tə nŏm'ĭk; Greek: *autos,* self, + *nomos,* law] ment. Suppose that after sitting on the sidelines for the first quarter, you are put into a basketball game. The sudden muscular activity forces blood into the right atrium of your heart much faster than blood is being pumped out, because (for the moment) your heart continues to beat at the normal rate—the rate it maintained while you were sitting on the bench. The walls of the atrium are stretched by the blood that is (so to speak) dammed up. Within the atrial walls are the tips of sensory neurons. They are stimulated by the stretching, and impulses pass over their fibers to your brain. These impulses start other impulses in motor neurons that go to your heart and speed up its contractions. This description is somewhat simplified. However, it illustrates the basic functional unit of the nervous system, the *reflex.*

Describe what happens when you go out of the game to the bench.

Figure 14 • 32

Diagram of a reflex. The bending of the leg involves neurons in leg and spinal cord only. *Feeling* involves the brain, but this is not necessary for the reflex.

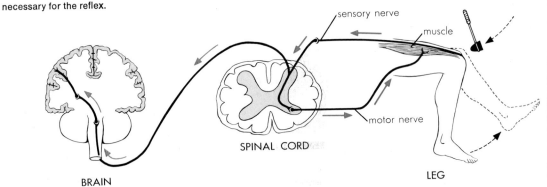

sensory nerve

muscle

motor nerve

SPINAL CORD

BRAIN

LEG

ADJUSTMENT TO EXTERNAL ENVIRONMENT

A need for adjustments in the internal environment of an animal usually arises from events outside its body. Such events may result in changes throughout the whole organism. And, in turn, some of these changes may influence the outside environment through movements that the animal makes.

Ability to move is one of the most obvious characteristics of animals. Of course, not all animals move rapidly, and some remain through much of their lives as firmly anchored as any plant—oysters and sponges, for example. But in looking at movement as part of an organism's ability to react to environment, we are not concerned merely with rapid motion or with locomotion. Any motion that helps an individual adjust to stimuli from its environment is important.

Senses. An athlete's heart beats faster when he enters into the game, but the endings of the sensory nerves are in the walls of the heart—and they cannot receive direct stimulation from the basketball game. Usually we do not think of internal sensory neurons when we speak of the senses; we consider only the sensory endings that receive stimuli from the external environment. The player hears the whistle and the order of the coach. As a whole organism, he reacts to these stimuli.

Ability to receive and to react to stimuli from the environment is one of the basic characteristics of living things, but the ability is developed to different degrees in different organisms. In most animals different kinds of stimuli are detected by specialized receptors. In man, for example, receptors in the skin of the fingertips are sensitive to pressure but not to light. Receptors in the nose are sensitive to chemical substances but not to light. Only receptors in the eyes are light sensitive, but they are not sensitive to sound waves.

In most animals at least some of the receptors are concentrated in special organs. The principal ones in man are well known—eyes, ears, nose. Other kinds of receptors, such as those sensitive to pressure and heat, are distributed widely in skin.

No organism has specialized receptors for all possible stimuli in the environment. Many cave-dwelling animals have no receptors for light, and you have no receptors for the electromagnetic waves that carry radio and television signals. Lack of ability to detect light is ordinarily no handicap to cave animals. You overcome your handicap by using instruments that change electromagnetic waves to sound and light waves, for which you *do* have receptors. Lack of ability to see might result in disaster for a cave animal that leaves its cave environment. And you can suffer fatal damage from nuclear radiation without being aware of your exposure, unless you have an instrument to detect it.

Muscles. In animals, motion usually involves specialized cells— muscle tissue. As in so many other matters, sponges are an exception: they have no muscle tissues, although individual cells are capable of movement. The larvae swim by means of cilia, just as many protists do.

In coelenterates some of the cells—especially those in the outer layer—have a degree of specialization that enables the animals to elongate and move their tentacles. In flatworms many cells are further specialized; they are organized into definite muscle tissues, though locomotion is accomplished largely by cilia. In all other animal phyla, muscle tissues are organized into bundles (muscles) and controlled by nervous systems.

There are two general types of muscle tissue, *striated* and *smooth*. Striated muscle is best developed in arthropods and vertebrates; it moves the parts of the skeleton and, in general, is capable of more rapid contraction than is smooth muscle. In these phyla smooth muscle is found in such places as the walls of blood vessels, of various ducts, and of the alimentary canal. Smooth muscle is usually involved in the regulation of the internal environment; striated muscle, on the other hand, is usually involved in adjustments to the external environment.

The chemistry of muscular contraction is a very active field of biological investigation. In some recent experiments proteins were extracted from muscle, and an artificial fiber was made from them.

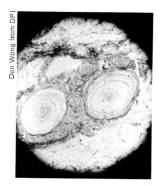

Figure 14 • 33

Touch receptors in a human fingertip.

Can you give any explanation for the lack of these receptors in both cave animals and man?

striated [strī′ă təd; Latin: *stria*, a furrow]

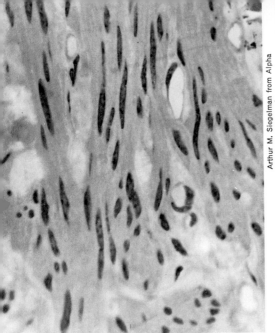

A X 350 B X 490

Figure 14 • 34

Kinds of vertebrate muscle tissue: (A) Smooth muscle. (B) Striated muscle.

This fiber was placed in a water bath. When ATP was added, the fiber contracted. Moreover, tests showed that the ATP was changed to ADP in the fiber during contraction. This and many other experiments indicate that proteins make up the contraction apparatus of muscles and that the energy for this action comes from ATP.

Even when an animal appears to be at rest, its muscles are not completely relaxed. The muscles of a healthy organism are always in a state of partial contraction called *muscle tone.* This produces the firmness that can be felt even in "relaxed" muscles.

Skeletons. The skeleton of a sponge consists of small, more or less rigid parts scattered through the soft, living tissues; it probably serves chiefly to support the softer tissues. Among coelenterates the stony skeletons built up by corals support the animals and also protect them from predators. In mollusks the skeletons (shells) are chiefly protective.

See Figure 2 · 1.

Support and protection are functions of arthropod and chordate skeletons also. But in these phyla skeletons also function in the movements of the animals, particularly in locomotion. Of course, a skeleton is not necessary for movement. An earthworm not only wiggles but also locomotes very well entirely without the aid of a skeleton. In our own bodies, muscles that have no connection to our bones move food along the alimentary canal.

Arthropod skeletons are external, with the muscles attached to the inner surfaces. These exoskeletons are composed of chitin, which is rather flexible when thin. In many arthropods, calcium compounds, deposited along with the chitin, make the exoskeleton quite hard and strong. It is all one piece, but it is rigid only in sections; thin, flexible chitin joints allow bending.

chitin [kīt′ən]: substance structurally similar to a polysaccharide but containing nitrogen

Chordate skeletons are inside the muscles. They consist of one or both of two kinds of tissue: cartilage and bone. The hardness of bone is, in part, a result of calcium and magnesium compounds. Both cartilage and bone contain cells that secrete these compounds; thus the skeleton can grow as the animal grows. Though the skeleton begins as cartilage, in the majority of vertebrate chordates most of this cartilage is gradually replaced by bone. At your age this process is well advanced. But it will never be completed—the tip of your nose and the external parts of your ears will never become hard bone.

Skeletal movement. The parts of a vertebrate or arthropod skeleton act together as levers. Muscles supply the force to move them, and joints act as fulcrums. A muscle attached to a bone is like a rope attached to a wagon: with a rope you can pull a wagon, but you cannot push it. If you want to move the wagon back to its original position, you must attach a rope to the other end and again move it by pulling. Muscles act in the same way—in pairs. While sitting, you can raise and straighten your leg by contracting one set of muscles, and gravity will pull it back to a bent position. But if you stand and then wish to bend your knee, you will have to use another set of muscles—muscles with an action opposite to that of the ones you used to straighten the leg. By the contraction of opposing sets of muscles, all skeletal movements are performed.

PHYSIOLOGICAL STEADY STATE AS A WHOLE

To summarize much of your understanding of animal physiology, consider a case of homeostasis—the regulation of body temperature in warm-blooded animals. Like all chemical reactions, those of metabolism are influenced by changes in temperature; they slow down at low temperatures and speed up at high temperatures. Therefore, warm-bloodedness is an advantage because it permits an animal to be active when environmental temperatures are low.

In warm-blooded animals—birds and mammals—the temperature of the skin and even of tissues some distance beneath the skin may fluctuate. It is only internal body temperature that is held constant. This deep body temperature can remain constant only if the rate of heat loss is the same as the rate of heat production. For a control system that can maintain this balance, receptors that respond to changes in temperature are necessary. The skin has such receptors; they detect changes in environmental temperature. Through nerve impulses these receptors give the hypothalamus notice that adjustments are necessary if the deep body temperature is to remain unchanged. Within the hypothalamus itself are other receptors that detect changes in blood temperature. The hypothalamus, with its mixture of nervous and endocrine functions, is the regulator in the homeostasis of temperature control.

What does a warm-blooded animal do when the environmental temperature becomes cooler than the body temperature? The first adjustments are usually those that conserve heat. Impulses pass

cartilage. See page 116.

What function does the skeleton in ears and nose have? What function does the skull have?

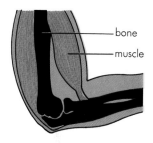

VERTEBRATE

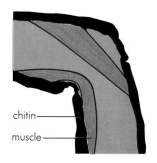

ARTHROPOD

Figure 14 • 35
Relation of muscles to skeletons. Why are two muscles shown in each example?

Can you think of some *disadvantages* of being warm-blooded?

What happens to the coloration of your lips when you become cold?

You have the skin muscles but very little of the hair. How, then, does this nerve action affect you?

along neurons of the autonomic nervous system, constricting the small arteries in the skin. This reduces the flow of blood to the skin, which, in turn, reduces the amount of heat lost through the skin.

At the same time, other impulses along the autonomic nervous system contract the small muscles that control the position of each hair or feather in the skin of the animal. This erects the individual hairs, thus increasing the amount of air space between them. And this in turn improves the insulation provided by fur or feathers.

If these actions are insufficient, the rate of heat production can be increased. For example, an involuntary increase in muscle activity—shivering—helps to increase the metabolic rate in cells. This in turn increases the release of energy from food. Much of the released energy is lost from cells in the form of heat. But this heat energy is useful to the organism as a whole in maintaining a constant body temperature.

In addition to making these internal adjustments, most birds and mammals behave in ways that conserve heat. When cold, a cat curls up in a ball and covers its nose with its tail. This reduces the amount of surface exposed to the cold air; it also covers an uninsulated surface (the nose), through which heat loss is very rapid. A bird tucks its legs up under its feathers and puts its head under its wing. Many birds can thus cut their heat losses in half. How often do you put on a sweater almost without thinking, when the air becomes cool?

Figure 14 · 36
What does the position of the cat probably indicate about the environmental temperature?

What happens when environmental temperature becomes warmer than body temperature? Then maintenance of a constant body temperature requires a reduction of heat production, an increase of heat loss, or both. Again impulses on autonomic neurons originating in the hypothalamus activate the mechanisms. The walls of the small arteries in the skin relax and more blood circulates to the skin; thus more heat is lost from the body surface. In some mammals, such as men and horses, the activity of the sweat glands increases. This provides more water on the skin surface. Evaporation of water always requires heat; heat for the evaporation of sweat comes from the body. Dogs have sweat glands only in their footpads. But a dog can increase the rate of heat loss by increasing the flow of air over the moist surfaces of the upper part of the respiratory system—by panting.

Heat production through metabolism is reduced by inactivity. In hot weather many mammals and birds are quite inactive during the warmer part of a day. And they seek the coolness of shade, where heat can be lost rather rapidly. Bathing, wading, or standing in water also increases heat loss. This is because water conducts heat much more rapidly than air, and because during the day the temperature in natural bodies of water is usually lower than air temperature.

Thus many homeostatic mechanisms are involved in maintaining the steady state of body temperature in warm-blooded animals. We would find equally extensive mechanisms if we were to examine the maintenance of water content of the body, glycogen content of the liver, salt content of the blood, or any other aspect of internal steady state.

Compare this mechanism of homeostasis with the description on pages 58–59.

Investigation 14.4

YOUR CHEMICAL SENSES

INTRODUCTION

Nerve endings with specialized sensitivity to chemical substances are common among animals that have well-defined nervous systems. Among arthropods such receptors are often found in the antennae. Among vertebrates they are found mostly in the mouth and nasal passages and are involved in the senses called taste and smell.

The study of these senses in animals other than man is complicated by a lack of communication. In man, we can at least obtain descriptions of particular stimuli. But then there are difficulties in interpreting such reports, so that a complete understanding—even in man—is not easy.

MATERIALS AND EQUIPMENT

For Procedure A

(for each pair of students)
watch glass, Syracuse form
salt solution (10%), 2 ml

applicators, 4
waste jar, 1 for every 6 students
beakers, filled with water, 2
sucrose solution (5%), 2 ml
acetic acid solution (1%), 2 ml
quinine sulfate solution (0.1%), 2 ml

For Procedure B

(for teams of 3 students)
handkerchief (for blindfold)
paper cups, 3 to 6
solutions of orange juice, milk, onion
   juice, vinegar (2%), sugar, dill-
   pickle juice—any 3 or all 6

PROCEDURE A

During Procedure A, in which you will work in pairs, you will determine the location on your tongue of taste receptors for 4 kinds of chemical substances.

Student A: Pour about 2 ml of 10% salt

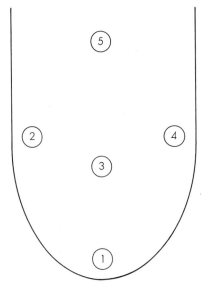

Figure 14 • 37

solution into a watch glass.

Student B: Make a copy of Figure 14 • 37 and label it *Salt*.

Student A: Dip an applicator—a toothpick with a small ball of cotton wrapped around one end—into the solution. Drain excess solution from the applicator. Touch the applicator to the tongue of Student B at the point marked *1* in Figure 14 • 37.

Student B: At Point 1 in your drawing, place a minus sign (−) if you sense no taste of salt, a plus sign (+) if you sense a mild taste of salt, and a double plus (++) if you sense a strong taste of salt.

Student A: As soon as Student B has recorded his sensation, touch the applicator to his tongue at Point 2.

Student B: Record your sensation, using the appropriate symbol.

Continue until sensation has been recorded at all 5 points on the tongue.

Student B: Rinse your mouth with water.

Student A: Break the applicator and discard it. Pour the salt solution from the watch glass into the waste jar. Rinse the watch glass.

Student B: Pour about 2 ml of 5% sucrose solution into the watch glass.

Student A: Make a copy of Figure 14 • 37. Label it *Sweet*.

Student B: Dip an applicator into the sucrose solution, drain off excess solution, and touch the applicator to the tongue of Student A at Point 1.

Student A: Record your sensation.

Continue until sensation has been recorded at all 5 points.

Student A: Rinse your mouth with water.

Student B: Break the applicator and discard it. Pour the glucose solution from the watch glass into the waste jar. Rinse the watch glass.

Student A: Pour about 2 ml of 1% acetic acid solution into the watch glass.

Student B: Make another copy of Figure 14 • 37 and label it *Sour*.

Student A: Dip a new applicator into the acid solution and proceed to test Student B, following the procedure described above.

Student B: Record sensation, as above.

Following the same procedure for changing solutions and students, test the effects of a 0.1% solution of quinine sulfate. Label the diagram *Bitter*.

PROCEDURE B

During Procedure B, in which you will work in teams of 3, you will investigate the relationship between taste and smell. It is important that the student being tested be unaware of the identity of the substance.

Student B: Blindfold Student A. Obtain a paper cup, labeled *A*, containing a few milliliters of Test Solution A.

Student C: In your data book, copy the chart shown below. Write the letter *A* in the first space under the heading "Solution Presented."

SUBJECT	SOLUTION PRESENTED	NOSE CLOSED		NOSE OPEN	
		Taste	Identity	Taste	Identity

Student A: *Holding your nose tightly,* sip the solution; report its taste, and try to identify the substance in the solution.

Student C: Record these reports on the chart.

Student A: Without holding your nose, sip the same solution; again report its taste, and try to identify the substance.

Student C: Record these reports.

Now repeat the procedure, with Student B as the subject. Student C obtains Test Solution B, and Student A records the reports. When tests with Solution B are completed, repeat the procedure, with Student C as the subject. Student A obtains Test Solution C, and Student B becomes the recorder.

If time permits a second round of testing, use Solutions D, E, and F.

STUDYING THE DATA

On the chalkboard make 4 large diagrams, as in Figure 14 · 37. Label them *Salt, Sweet, Sour,* and *Bitter.* Assemble from all students the data obtained in Procedure A. At each test point on the diagrams, record the total number of minus, plus, and double-plus responses. • What are some of the possible causes for variability in the data?(1) • Which kinds of variability are the result of "errors of observation"? Which kinds are the result of physiological variability?(2)

On the chalkboard list the solutions (A, B, C, etc.) used in Procedure B. Tally separately the tastes reported with nose closed and with nose open; also tally the identifications of solutions. • In general, are the kinds of tastes reported with nose open more varied than those reported with nose closed? Less varied? Neither?(3) • In general, are the

identifications made with nose open more accurate than those made with nose closed? Less accurate? Neither?(4) • What assumption is involved in holding the nose closed?(5)

CONCLUSIONS

• Do the data from Procedure A support the hypothesis that receptors of the 4 kinds of taste are equally distributed on the surface of the tongue? Explain.(6) • If the data fail to support this hypothesis, where on the tongue is each kind of taste receptor located?(7)

• On the basis of the data from Procedure B, write a brief statement concerning the relationship of the sense of taste to the sense of smell.(8)

FOR FURTHER INVESTIGATION

1. Hold a bottle containing oil of cloves about 1.5 cm from your nose and vigorously and continuously inhale, exhaling through your mouth. How much time passes before you can no longer clearly detect the smell of cloves? You now have "olfactory fatigue." Immediately smell oil of peppermint through the same nostril. Can you detect its odor?

2. Stick your tongue out and keep it out during the following procedure: Dry your tongue with a piece of gauze or paper toweling. Place a few crystals of sugar on your tongue, and note the time. How much time passes before you can taste the sugar? Rinse your mouth with water. Again stick your tongue out, but do not dry it before placing sugar crystals on it. How much time passes before you can taste the sugar? Try the same procedure with salt crystals. Again measure the time. What conclusion can you draw from your results?

GUIDE QUESTIONS

1. Why is eating such an important animal activity?

2. How do the various food-getting devices of animals illustrate structural diversity?

3. Distinguish between ingestion and digestion.

4. In what ways do digestive cavities differ among animals?

5. How is chemical digestion related to the chemical syntheses carried on by cells?

6. As food passes through a human digestive system, how does its pH change?

7. In what part of the human digestive system does most of the chemical digestion occur?

8. Where does most of the absorption of digested foods occur?

9. Chyme in the small intestine is semi-liquid, yet feces are normally semisolid. Explain this.

10. What are the principal gases exchanged with the environment by animal breathing systems?

11. Why does a very small aquatic animal require no breathing system?

12. Some salamanders have neither gills nor lungs. Why is it necessary for them to live in a moist environment?

13. How is air moved into and out of human lungs?

14. For what functions do animals require the transportation of substances through their bodies?

15. Distinguish between open and closed circulatory systems.

16. What are the differences among arteries, veins, and capillaries?

17. What are some differences among the circulatory systems of a fish, an amphibian, and a mammal?

18. How is blood in mammals kept flowing in one direction?

19. How does human blood plasma differ from whole blood?

20. What substances are contained in human plasma?

21. What are the "elements" in human blood?

22. How does hemoglobin function in transporting oxygen?

23. In what structural and functional characteristics do white blood cells differ from red blood cells?

24. Draw a diagram to show how blood clots.

25. In what ways does lymph differ from blood?

26. Distinguish among excretion, secretion, and elimination.

27. What is meant by a "waste" in an animal?

28. For what reasons can the liver be considered a part of the excretory system of a vertebrate?

29. What are the principal kinds of excreted substances?

30. Describe the functioning of a mammalian kidney.

31. List places in a human body where excreted substances are eliminated.

32. What is meant by the internal environment of an animal?

33. In what two ways does the internal communication necessary for maintaining homeostasis occur?

34. What are hormones?

35. How do endocrine glands differ from other glands?

36. What are the principal glands of a mammalian endocrine system?

37. What evidence supports the idea that the endocrine and nervous systems are closely associated?

38. Compare the nervous system of a vertebrate with the nervous systems of animals in other phyla.

39. How do sensory neurons differ from motor neurons?

40. How does a synapse function in the transmission of a nerve impulse?

41. What are the principal ways in which the brain of a mammal differs from the brains of other vertebrates?

42. Describe the functioning of the autonomic nervous system.

43. What is a reflex?

44. In what ways is the internal steady state of an animal related to its external environment?

45. What are the principal kinds of information that vertebrates obtain through their receptors?

46. Distinguish between striated and smooth muscle.

47. What are three principal functions of animal skeletons?

48. Describe the differences between the locomotion of vertebrates and that of arthropods.

49. Why must skeletal muscles occur in pairs?

50. Using the regulation of internal temperature as an example, describe the manner in which muscular, skeletal, nervous, and chemical systems interact in a warm-blooded vertebrate.

PROBLEMS

1. How might you proceed experimentally to show that (a) secretin causes the pancreas to secrete digestive enzymes, (b) *diabetes mellitus* is caused by lack of insulin, and (c) hormones secreted by the pituitary gland affect thyroid and adrenal glands?

2. Antibodies from horse blood can produce some kinds of immunity in man (Chapter 7). Insulin from a cow pancreas can be used in treating human diabetes. Why cannot whole blood of horses and cows be transfused to man?

3. We have implied that excretion is a general biological process essential for maintenance of life in all organisms. Yet we did not discuss the process in Chapter 13, and it is seldom mentioned in botany textbooks. Explain.

4. Blood transports many substances dissolved in plasma. It can be shown, however, that in mammals less than 10 percent of the carbon dioxide in the blood is dissolved in plasma. How is the remainder of the CO_2 transported?

5. Describe in detail the route followed by a molecule of oxygen as it moves from the air of your external environment to a mitochondrion in one of your muscle cells.

6. A thyroxin molecule contains 4 atoms of iodine. What effects would an iodine-free diet have upon a mammal?

7. Hemoglobin acts as a respiratory pigment in animals of several phyla, but there are other such pigments in the animal kingdom. Investigate this matter, considering the following questions: (a) Do all respiratory pigments act in the same way? (b) What are the chemical similarities and differences among respiratory pigments? (c) Do respiratory pigments provide any clues to the evolutionary relationships among animal phyla? (d) Is there any significance to the chemical relationship between hemoglobin and chlorophyll? Is there any significance to the fact that hemoglobin occurs in the nodules formed by *Rhizobium* on the roots of legumes?

8. A temporary reddening of the skin surface is sometimes called a "flush" and sometimes a "blush." The first term is often used in cases of fever; the second is usually used to describe a reaction to some situation in the external environment. Is the body mechanism the same in both cases? If it is, how does it operate? If it is not, what are the differences?

9. You eat a lettuce and cheese sandwich. Describe what happens to the sandwich from the moment you take the first bite until its remains are passed from the anus. First, you must decide what classes of substances are in the sandwich.

10. In some cases of slow blood clotting, physicians prescribe calcium compounds. Explain. In other cases they prescribe vitamin K. What part does this vitamin play in the clotting process?

SUGGESTED READINGS

ADOLPH, E. F. "The Heart's Pacemaker," *Scientific American,* March, 1967. Pp. 32–37.

D'AMOUR, F. E. *Basic Physiology.* Chicago: University of Chicago Press, 1961. (With many anecdotes of physiological discovery and a breezy, sometimes jocular style, this book presents more than basic human physiology.)

BAKER, P. F. "The Nerve Axon," *Scientific American,* March, 1966. Pp. 74–82.

COMFORT, A. *The Process of Aging.* New York: New American Library, 1964. (Considers aging as a physiological process in animals and its bearing on life-span in man. Fairly easy.)

COMROE, J. H. "The Lung," *Scientific American,* February, 1966. Pp. 56–66.

GORDON, A. S. *Blood Cell Physiology.* (BSCS Pamphlet 8). Boulder, Colo.: EPIC, 1963.

GRAUBARD, M. *Circulation and Respiration: The Evolution of an Idea.* New York: Harcourt, Brace & World, Inc., 1964. (A book of quotations from original investigators, with a commentary that shows how physiologists came to understand these processes. Fairly advanced.)

HUNGATE, R. E. *Cellulose in Animal Nutrition.* (BSCS Pamphlet 22). Boulder, Colo.: EPIC, 1965.

LAKI, K. "The Clotting of Fibrinogen," *Scientific American,* March, 1962. Pp. 60–66.

MERTON, P. A. "How We Control the Contraction of Our Muscles," *Scientific American,* May,

1972. Pp. 30–37.

MOFFAT, D. B. *The Control of Water Balance by the Kidney.* London: Oxford University Press, 1971. (Detailed description relating structure and function. Advanced.)

MUIR, A. R. *The Mammalian Heart.* London: Oxford University Press, 1971. (A short but detailed account of the muscular structure and the physiology of a heart. Fairly advanced.)

NEISSER, U. "The Processes of Vision," *Scientific American,* September, 1968. Pp. 204–214.

PETTIGREW, J. D. "The Neurophysiology of Binocular Vision," *Scientific American,* August, 1972. Pp. 84–95.

RIEDMAN, S. R. *Our Hormones and How They Work.* New York: Collier Books, 1962. (A small book that explains endocrine function, primarily in man. Easy.)

SCHMIDT-NIELSEN, K. *Animal Physiology.* 3rd ed. Englewood Cliffs, N.J.: Prentice-Hall, Inc., 1970. (Concentrates on steady state and the relations of animals to environments. Lightly written but authoritative. Fairly easy.)

SIMPSON, G. G., and W. S. BECK: *Life: An Introduction to Biology.* Shorter ed. New York: Harcourt, Brace & World, Inc., 1969. Chapters 10 and 11. (Maintenance and coordination in organisms considered as general biological processes. All organisms—plants, animals, and protists—are discussed. Advanced.)

STENT, G. S. "Cellular Communication," *Scientific American,* September, 1972. Pp. 42–51.

WIGGLESWORTH, V. *Insect Respiration.* London: Oxford University Press, 1972. (The breathing anatomy and the physiology of insects. Advanced.)

WOOD, J. E. "The Venous System," *Scientific American,* January, 1968. Pp. 86–96.

Behavior

THE STUDY OF BEHAVIOR

It is morning on a vacant city lot. Two dogs arrive simultaneously and dash toward one another—heads up, tails wagging. One snaps up a stick and off both dash, chasing and tumbling. We might guess they are playing a game called "Stick! Stick! Who has the stick?" They disappear down the street.

A bit later two other dogs visit the lot. They also approach one another—but somewhat slowly, heads up, their tails stiffened. They stand side to side for a moment, each with its head toward the other's tail. Then they move quietly away from each other. One urinates on a fence post before leaving the lot.

urinate. See page 459.

Robert C. Frampton

Figure 15 • 1
Dogs interacting. How would you describe this behavior?

Still later a large dog appears. It sniffs about and lies down to doze. Suddenly a puppy comes gamboling by. The older dog jumps up, barks, and rushes at the puppy. The puppy rolls over on its back, legs folded, belly and throat open to the teeth of its attacker. The larger dog hesitates, growls, and stalks off.

What is the basis of these diverse actions?

479

WHAT IS BEHAVIOR?

In varying degrees, all living organisms are continuously *doing* something. They are reacting to stimuli from their environment. Not all these reactions are covered by the term **behavior.** When light is directed to a green plant, the plant begins to split water molecules in photosynthesis. This is a reaction to a stimulus, but it is not behavior. If the light is directed at the plant from one side, the plant turns its leaves and growing tip toward the light, a visible reaction. This is behavior. A cat lies in the sun; muscles move its latest meal through its intestines. This is not behavior. A bird chirps nearby. Unless the cat is deaf, the receptors of its ears react, sending an impulse to the brain. This is not behavior. The cat opens its drooping eyelids, raises its ears, and twitches its tail. This is behavior.

Behavior involves more than the reaction of a cell (unless the individual is a single cell) or of an organ or even of an organ system. It involves the whole individual, and it is directed toward the external environment of the individual. In the two previous chapters it has become clear that what an organism does as a whole depends upon its internal functioning—its physiology. Therefore, both physiologists and ecologists contribute to the study of behavior.

DIFFICULTIES IN BEHAVIORAL STUDIES

Observation and experiment. We all see the behavior of our pets and of other animals, though few of us notice the behavior of plants or protists. But merely watching something is not necessarily scientific observation. And because behavior is action, observing it is especially difficult. It often occurs so quickly that it is difficult for the observer to determine just what he has seen; paradoxically, in plants it may occur so slowly that the observer may have difficulty determining whether it has occurred at all. Motion pictures have helped to solve these difficulties and, at the same time, have provided a basis for the verification that is essential in science.

Where should behavior be observed—in the field or in the laboratory? Study in the field can be very difficult. The organisms that the biologist wishes to study may be hard to find. Even when they have been found, they may be difficult to study because they may be difficult to approach and keep under observation.

In the laboratory organisms can be more easily watched, and the watching can be arranged so that they are unaware of the observer. In the laboratory a biologist can learn much about what an organism *can* do. But a laboratory biologist may still remain ignorant of what an organism *will* do as a part of its ecosystem. And for some purposes such information is important—for example, to an understanding of population structure.

As in other branches of science, a behavioral biologist attempts whenever possible to test hypotheses by making observations under controlled conditions. Experiments may be performed in either laboratory or field, but in field experiments the control of conditions is

Figure 15 • 2

Behavioral study in the field. Recording the voice of an arctic seal.

Sovfoto

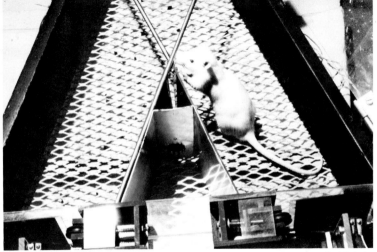

Paul Knipping

Figure 15 • 3
Behavioral study in the laboratory. White rat in a Y-maze—entrance at upper end.

usually more difficult.

Behavioral scientists called **psychologists** usually do most of their experiments in laboratories. Many are interested primarily in the behavior of man. But experimental study of human behavior is difficult, so they may use other organisms also—frequently white rats. Psychologists have a tendency to emphasize the physiological side of behavior.

psychologists [sī kŏl′ə jĭsts; Greek: *psyche*, spirit, soul, + *logos*, speech, reason]

In the past four decades biologists with an ecological viewpoint have turned their attention to behavior. These **ethologists** tend to prefer working in the field. They study a wide array of organisms in natural ecosystems. Psychologists and ethologists have sometimes disagreed about their conclusions and concepts, but—as has happened before in the history of biology—with increase of knowledge, differences in viewpoint are lessening.

ethologists [ĕ thŏl′ə jĭsts; Greek: *ethos*, character, habit, + *logos*]

Interpretation. At times all biologists have difficulties drawing conclusions from their data and fitting their conclusions together with those of other investigators. This is the job of interpretation—giving meaning to observations. Behavioral scientists have some special difficulties.

Consider a laboratory experiment. We place on the side of a frog's body some substance that we think unpleasant. Immediately the frog's hind foot rubs at the spot where the substance was placed. Aha!, we think, the frog doesn't like the substance and is trying to rub it off. But how do we know that the frog isn't trying to rub it *in* because it enjoys the stuff? Interpretation of this behavior becomes even more perplexing if we destroy the frog's brain. The frog continues to bring its hind foot up to rub at its side. Can we use either "liking" or "not liking" to interpret the behavior of a frog without a brain?

In observing behavior, we tend to put ourselves in the organism's place. We tend to explain its behavior in human terms. We commonly say that a barking dog is "angry," that a purring cat is "contented," or even that the roots of a cactus are "searching" for water. This is **anthropomorphism**, the interpretation of the behavior of other orga-

anthropomorphism [ăn′thrə pō môr′fĭz əm; Greek: *anthropos*, man, + *morphe*, form] nisms as if they were human. But we don't know that other organisms have any of these human emotions.

Behavioral biologists must constantly beware of anthropomorphic interpretations. This is especially difficult because they must discuss their findings in a human language. Language is a product of the human brain and therefore reflects human ways of reacting to the environment. Therefore, to describe and interpret the behavior of other species without introducing human viewpoints is probably impossible. But behavioral scientists try to minimize the difficulty—and, as a result, their language often seems strange and obscure to non-scientists.

Another difficulty. Take a walk with a dog along a street. You notice a few odors from automobile exhaust or from freshly cut grass. But the dog goes sniffing along from one odor to the next. And most of these are completely unnoticed by you. You have great difficulty imagining the ability of a bloodhound to follow the "smell trail" of an animal or man that passed an hour or a day before. Man lives in a world that is primarily visual. What we perceive in our environment— our *perceptual world*—is made up mostly of colors, shapes, and movements. Dogs lack color vision and do not distinguish shapes nearly as well as we do. And dogs hear sounds that we don't; this can be shown with dog whistles, which will call dogs home though we hear nothing.

If it is difficult to understand the perceptual world of a dog, a fellow mammal with which we live closely, how much more difficult it is to understand the world of a bird, fish, bee, or octopus. Yet, if we are going to understand the behavior of any organism, we have to know what it perceives in its environment. We must determine what kinds of receptors it has and how sensitive they are. Since man does not perceive all stimuli that affect other organisms, a biologist must frequently depend upon instruments that can translate things he can't perceive into things he can. Flowers that look white to him may have patterns of color to bees, because bees see by ultraviolet light—light of a wavelength that is invisible to human eyes. He can "see" what the bee sees only by taking photographs with film sensitive to such wavelengths.

How did you interpret the behavior of the dogs described on page 479?

perceptual [pər sĕp′chōō əl; Latin: *per,* through, + *capere,* to grasp]

Why do dogs often howl when musical instruments such as violins and flutes are played?

See Figure 1·15.

Photos by Thomas Eisner

Figure 15 • 4

Marsh marigolds. Photographed on film that records light much as man sees it (*left*). Photographed on film that records ultraviolet light as bees see it (*right*).

LEVELS OF BEHAVIOR

The ability to respond to stimuli, *irritability*, seems to be one of the fundamental characteristics of living substance. This ability allows even the simplest organism to adapt to changes in its environment. Many organisms have cells, tissues, or organs in which irritability is specialized. In general, the greater this specialization, the more complex the behavior is.

irritability [ĭr′ə tə bĭl′ə tĭ]

BEHAVIOR INVOLVING NO NERVOUS SYSTEM

A slime mold engulfs food particles but flows around inorganic particles; that is, it responds differentially to objects in its environment, just as you respond differentially to a doughnut and a rubber

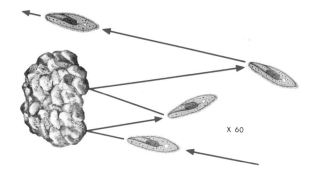

X 60

Figure 15 • 5
A *Paramecium* meets an obstacle. How would you describe this behavior?

band. But the protist accomplishes this behavior without any receptors or brain or muscles.

If a ciliate of the genus *Vorticella* is touched lightly, it usually contracts its stalk. If the stimulus is continued, however, the organism seems to become accustomed to it. If a *Vorticella* is repeatedly touched, it responds in a variety of ways: it may bend away; it may reverse the direction in which its cilia are beating; it may contract; it may even swim away.

Vorticella [vôr′tĭ sĕl′ə]

These protists have no nerve cells or any other cellular differentiation, but they show two characteristics of behavior—selectivity and variability.

Plants also lack nerve cells, but they, too, show some basic behavioral characteristics. In general, reactions of plants are slower than those of protists.

In bryophytes and tracheophytes most behavior is closely associated with growth. You have already studied the behavior called phototropism. There are many such *tropisms*, but in each of them a plant part turns toward (positive) or away from (negative) a stimulus. Though tropisms represent a somewhat fixed kind of behavior, they are not entirely invariable. The responses sometimes vary with differences in the intensity of the stimulus. Bermuda grass is positively phototropic to weak light but negatively phototropic to strong light.

Tropisms are responses in sessile organisms. In motile organisms, similar responses are called *taxes* (singular, "taxis"). In a

X 600

Figure 15 • 6
Vorticella. An individual in feeding position (*left*); same individual after a light touch (*right*).

484

Paul Knipping

Figure 15 • 7

Leaves of a plant (*Mimosa*) as they normally appear (*above*) and a short time after being touched (*below*). How do you think an organism without muscles can perform this response?

taxes [tăk'sēz; Greek: *tassein*, to arrange]

taxis the whole organism moves toward or away from the source of a stimulus. The kinds of stimuli are quite similar for tropisms and taxes. A *Euglena*, for example, is positively phototactic. Near its anterior end is a spot of pigment sensitive to light—a kind of receptor. As *Euglena* swims, its body rotates so that the pigment spot detects the direction of illumination. Somehow this information is transmitted to the flagellum, which then directs the organism toward the light.

A — Reaction to a drop of 0.5% salt
    solution.

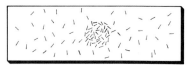

B — Reaction to a drop of weak
    acetic acid.

Figure 15 • 8

Behavior of small populations of *Paramecium* in response to five environmental stimuli. Using the terms in the text, describe the behavior in each case.

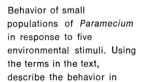

C — Reaction to a piece of filter
    paper.

D — Reactions to a bubble of air
    and a bubble of CO_2.

Investigation 15.1

TROPIC RESPONSES IN PLANTS

MATERIALS AND EQUIPMENT

(for each team)

Part A

soaked corn grains, 4

petri dish

cotton

scissors

heavy blotting paper

scotch tape

glass-marking crayon

Part B

flowerpots, about 8 cm in diameter, 4

cardboard boxes, at least 5 cm higher
than flowerpots, 4

scissors

red cellophane

paste

blue cellophane

scotch tape

soil

radish seeds, 40

Part C

test tubes, 25 × 200 mm, 4

1-hole stoppers, to fit test tubes, 4

shoots of *Zebrina,* about 20 cm long, 4

melted paraffin in a beaker

small brush

glass-marking crayon

ring stand

burette clamps, 4

PROCEDURE

• Study the procedure; then state a hypothesis appropriate for each part.(1)

Part A. Place 4 soaked corn grains in the bottom half of a petri dish. Arrange them cotyledon side down, as shown in Figure 15 • 9. Fill the spaces between the corn grains with wads of cotton to a depth slightly greater than the thickness of the grains. Cut a piece of heavy blotting paper slightly larger than the bottom of the petri dish. Fit it snugly over the grains and the cotton. Hold the dish on its edge and observe the grains through the bot-

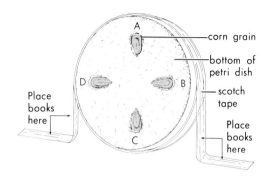

Figure 15 • 9

tom. If they do not stay in place, repack with more cotton. When the grains are secure in the dish, wet the blotting paper thoroughly. Seal the two halves of the petri dish together with strips of scotch tape.

Place the dish on edge in a location that receives dim light. Rotate the dish until one of the corn grains is at the top. Using a glass-marking crayon, write an *A* on the dish beside the topmost grain; then, proceeding clockwise, label the other grains *B, C,* and *D.* Fasten the dish with a long strip of tape, as shown in Figure 15 • 9. If further support is needed, stack books on top of the tape and against the edges of the dish. Do not change the position of the dish until the experiment is completed.

When the grains begin to germinate, make sketches daily for 5 days, showing the directions in which the root and the shoot grow from each grain.

Part B. Number 4 cardboard boxes *1* to *4* and label each with your team symbol. Turn the boxes bottom side up. Cut a rectangular hole in one side of each of 3 boxes; use the dimensions shown in Figure 15 • 10. Tape a strip of red cellophane over the hole in Box 1. Tape a strip of blue cellophane over the hole in Box 2. Leave the hole in Box 3 uncovered. Do not cut a hole in Box 4.

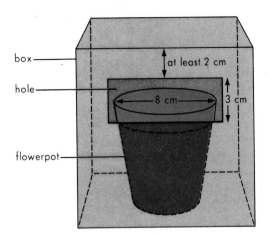

Figure 15 • 10

Using a pencil, number 4 flowerpots *1* to *4* and label each with your team symbol. Fill the pots with soil. In each pot, plant 10 radish seeds about 0.5 cm deep and 2 cm apart. Press the soil down firmly over the seeds and water the pots. Place the pots in a location that receives strong light but not direct sunlight. Cover each pot with the box bearing its number. Turn the boxes so the sides with the holes face the light. Once each day remove the boxes and water the pots. (Caution: Do not move the pots; be sure to place the boxes back in the same position after each time you water them!)

When most of the radish seedlings have been above ground for 2 or 3 days, record the direction of stem growth in each pot: upright, curved slightly, or curved greatly—and if curved, tell in what direction with respect to the hole in the box.

Part C. Fill 4 test tubes with water and insert a 1-hole stopper firmly into each tube. Remove all leaves within 8 cm of the cut ends of 4 *Zebrina* shoots. Push the cut end of each shoot through a stopper until about 5 cm of the shoot is in water. Seal tubes, stoppers, and shoots by applying melted paraffin with a brush. (Caution: The paraffin should be no warmer than is necessary to keep it liquid.) Using a glass-marking crayon, label the tubes *A, B, C,* and *D.* Attach a burette clamp to each tube. Fasten the tubes to a ring stand in the

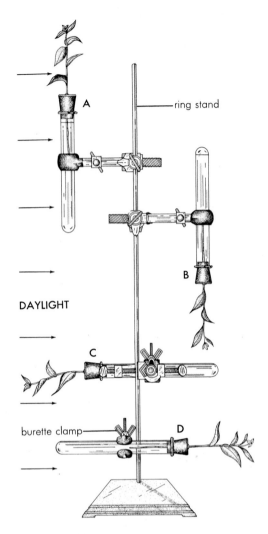

Figure 15 • 11

positions shown in Figure 15 • 11. Place the entire assembly in a location that receives bright light from one side. Observe the shoots daily for about a week.

STUDYING THE DATA

Consider first the data from Part A. • From which end of the grains did the roots grow?(2) • Did the roots of all grains eventually turn in one direction? If so, what was the direction?(3) • From which end of the grains did the shoots grow?(4) • Did the shoots of all 4 grains eventually turn in one direction?(5) • To what stimulus did the corn roots seem to be responding? Was the response positive or negative?(6)   • To what stimulus did the corn shoots seem to be responding? Was the response positive or negative?(7)

Now consider the data from Part B.   • In which pot were the stems most nearly perpendicular?(8) · • Were the stems curved in one direction in any pot?(9)   • If so, in which pot, and in what direction? If not, in what direction did *most* of the stems curve?(10)

Finally, consider the data from Part C. • Did any shoots grow without bending? If so, which ones?(11)   • Did any shoots bend as they grew? If so, which ones bent?(12)   • If you noticed any bending, in what direction did it occur in each case?(13)

CONCLUSIONS

• For each of the hypotheses that you formed at the beginning of the investigation, state as precise a conclusion as your data will allow.(14)

FOR FURTHER INVESTIGATION

Will centrifugal force overcome the response of plant parts to gravity? To test this idea, you may mount the setup used in Part A on the turntable of a phonograph.

BEHAVIOR INVOLVING NERVOUS SYSTEMS

Except for the sponges, all animals have nerve cells that are differentiated. Organisms that have nerve cells also have differentiated muscle cells that have specialized ability to contract and so bring about movement. The combination of specialized nerve and muscle cells so greatly supplements the responses possible through general irritability and hormones that some biologists restrict use of the term "behavior" to animals that possess such cells.

See pages 464–466.

Innate behavior. When a male moth emerges from its cocoon and detects the odor produced by a female of its species, it flies unhesitantly upwind toward the source of the odor. The first time that a tree squirrel encounters a nut, it attempts to bury it—even if it has never seen another squirrel do so and if the nut is lying on the floor of a cage rather than on the ground. Young spiders without any previous experience weave webs as well constructed as those of older spiders.

These are examples of *innate* behavior. Behavior is considered to be innate if it is brought forth by a particular stimulus in individuals that have had no previous experience with the stimulus. Innate behavior is thought to be the result of something that is inherited. To test for innate behavior, animals are hatched in isolation so that whatever they do, they do without following another animal's example. With mammals it is perhaps impossible to determine what behavior is innate, because there is always some chance of learning from the mother. And even mother birds are now known to communicate with their unhatched chicks. So a convincing test of innate behavior is difficult to achieve for many vertebrates.

innate [ĭn āt'; Latin: *in,* in, + *natus,* born]

In some organisms innate behavior is simply a matter of reflex. But the behavior of a newly emerged male moth is more complex than a reflex, because many muscles must work in coordination

See page 468.

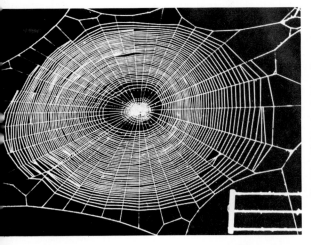

Photos by Peter N. Witt

Figure 15 • 12

Web woven by a normal spider (*left*). Web woven by a spider that had been given the drug amphetamine (*right*). Compare the two.

A. Devaney, Inc.

Figure 15 • 13

Any light tap on the side of the nest causes nestlings of many birds to react in the way shown here. This behavior seems to be innate.

to produce flight. This behavior might be called a taxis, though it is certainly more complex than the taxes in protists.

The behavior of the squirrel with a nut is still more complex; certain muscles must be used in digging, others in pushing the nut into a hole, and others in covering it. Moreover, these actions must be performed in a certain sequence. The construction of a spider web also requires very complex behavior. Yet the existing evidence indicates that all these are innate behaviors. Such complex innate behaviors have been called instincts or *fixed-action* patterns. The first term, according to most behavioral scientists, is no longer useful because too many false ideas have grown up around it. But the second term —the best we have at present—is also somewhat misleading. The behavior is not entirely "fixed," that is, invariable, because the behavior depends upon the organism's physiology as well as upon a stimulus. A sick squirrel or one that is merely tired may pay no attention to a nut.

Many ethologists have been interested in the stimuli that start the chains of physiological reactions in the more complex innate behaviors, the fixed-action patterns. They have found that the required stimulus is often very simple. Such a stimulus—called a *releaser*—acts like a key that unlocks the whole physiological sequence. Like a key, a releaser is specific; only a particular releaser stimulus starts a particular behavior pattern.

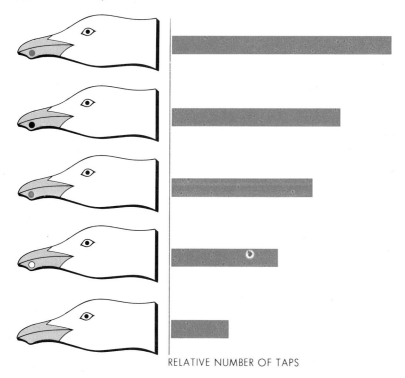

RELATIVE NUMBER OF TAPS

Figure 15 • 14
Herring-gull nestlings tap at a red spot on the bill of the parent; the parent then feeds them. An ethologist presented different cardboard models (*left*) to newly hatched chicks and recorded the results (*right*). Can you draw any conclusion about this behavior?

X 1/3

Figure 15 • 15
During the nesting season a male European robin raises his head and puffs out his breast whenever he encounters another male. Here an ethologist has placed a tuft of breast feathers in a tree. Without anthropomorphism can you explain the reaction of the bird?

X 1/4

Figure 15 · 16
Chaffinch. This is a
European species that has
been much used in behavior
studies.

precisely [prĭ sĭs'lē; Latin: *prae*,
before, + *caedere*, to cut]:
sharply defined, not vague

Konrad Lorenz [lōr'ənz]:
1903 —. Austrian biologist and
one of the first ethologists

Much of the behavior of invertebrates can be classed as innate. But this, of course, does not *explain* the behavior. It is necessary for physiologists to explore the nervous and hormonal mechanisms that control such behavior. And psychologists analyze such behavior experimentally by varying stimuli and by interrupting the sequence of steps in the complete behavior.

Learned behavior. The nut-burying behavior of a squirrel seems to be innate; so, too, is nut opening. A young squirrel opens a nut satisfactorily; but as he becomes older and more experienced, his efficiency at opening nuts increases greatly. Chaffinches reared from hatching in soundproof rooms develop a song pattern basically like that of wild chaffinches. But their songs never include all of the notes of the wild song unless the birds are allowed to hear the wild song. Evidently the song pattern is innate, but something is added to the innate behavior during the life of the birds. In both squirrels and birds *learning* occurs.

Learning is not easy to describe precisely. It depends upon the experiences of an individual, and usually it brings about a lasting change in behavior. We must say a "lasting" rather than a "permanent" change in behavior, because forgetting occurs in learned behavior—as every student knows!

There is another difficulty in describing learning. Some kinds of lasting changes in behavior occur simply as a part of development. When a tadpole's legs develop and its tail disappears, the change in behavior (from tail swimming to leg swimming) is clearly associated with a change in structure. In other cases it is extremely difficult to determine whether changes in behavior depend upon learning or merely upon structural development. Isn't experience, practice—that is, learning—necessary before a child can climb stairs? An experiment was tried with identical twins (twins with exactly the same heredity) in whom the rate of development should be the same. At an early age one twin was allowed much practice on stairs; the other was kept on flat surfaces and given no experience with stairs. Yet, when the second was finally allowed to climb stairs, his performance was about as good as that of his experienced twin.

Most learning requires more than a single experience. In the 1930's, however, Konrad Lorenz discovered a kind of learning that depends upon just one experience. Geese follow the first moving object they see after hatching. Normally this is their mother. But geese hatched in an incubator first saw Dr. Lorenz. Afterward they behaved toward him as though he were the female goose. He was *imprinted* in the experience of the goslings as "mother."

Imprinting resembles the action of a releaser, but the particular stimulus is not recognized innately—it must be learned. In imprinting, however, the learning is the result of just one experience that must come at a particular time in the development of the individual. Experimentation has shown that in many cases, the *first* moving object that a young bird or fish sees will later release many reactions that nor-

Nina Leen

Figure 15 • 17
Konrad Lorenz and some of
his imprinted geese.

mally are released by the presence of a parent. This is particularly
true if the object also gives appropriate sounds—quacking, in the
case of ducks, for instance. If imprinting can be called learning, it is
a very simple kind, closely related to innate behavior.

Imprinting was discovered by an ethologist. *Conditioning* was
discovered much earlier by a physiologist. Ivan P. Pavlov was interested in the physiology of mammalian nervous systems. He began to
study the reflex involved in the production of saliva in dogs and soon
found that the odor or sight of meat was sufficient to start salivation.
Pavlov wondered whether other stimuli would produce the salivation
response. Just before presenting meat to a dog, he rang a bell. This
procedure was repeated many times with the same dog. Before long
the dog was beginning to secrete saliva as soon as the bell was rung,
before the meat was presented. Eventually Pavlov found that the dog
could be made to salivate merely by the ringing of the bell, entirely
without the stimulus of the meat. This kind of learning—the transfer
of a reflex response from one stimulus to another—is referred to as
conditioning.

Pavlov extended his research in many directions. He showed that

Ivan P. Pavlov [ĭ văn′ păv′lôf]:
1849–1936. Russian
physiologist

the substitute stimulus must come *before* the original stimulus if the response is to be transferred. He also showed that the shorter the time interval between the two stimuli, the quicker the reaction becomes associated with the substitute stimulus. Later biologists have extended Pavlov's principles to other animals, including man.

In conditioning, the learner is passive. More complicated kinds of learning require movement by the learner. Animals make many kinds of movements. *Trial-and-error* learning begins when an animal associates certain movements with favorable or unfavorable results. Thus, experimentally, this kind of learning involves either "rewards" or "punishments," or both.

B. F. Skinner has devised a box for investigating trial-and-error learning. A bar in the box releases a pellet of food when pressed. A hungry rat, placed in the box, moves about at random and sooner or later strikes the bar. Before long most rats associate pressing the bar with the reward of food. This device has been used to investigate many questions about learning. For example, what happens if the food pellet is not released after the rat has learned to obtain it by pressing the bar? What happens if the pellet is released sometimes but not always? If you are curious, refer to Scott's *Animal Behavior* (listed on page 516).

With any animal that is capable of locomotion, learning can be studied by means of a maze. Basically, a maze is a route with one or more choices of turns leading to a goal that is favorable or unfavorable to the animal. The simplest form is the T-maze. How can we know that learning has occurred in a maze? With a T-maze we expect that by chance 50 percent of the turns will be to the right and 50 per-

B. F. Skinner: 1904 —.
American psychologist

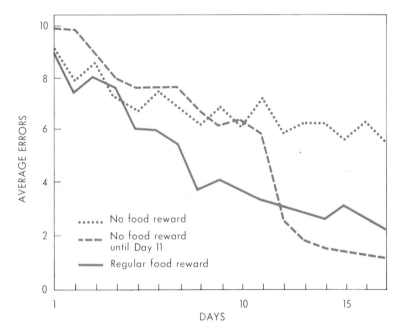

Figure 15 • 18

A learning experiment. Three groups of rats were tested daily in a maze. The route through the maze forked 14 times, and none of the choices could be repeated. The number of errors in choice was counted for each rat, and an average obtained for each group. How do you interpret the results?

AVERAGE ERRORS

...... No food reward

- - - No food reward until Day 11

——— Regular food reward

DAYS

cent to the left. If, after several trials, an animal turns to the right (where food is located) 90 percent of the time and to the left only 10 percent of the time, we might conclude that it has learned.

There is wide diversity in learning abilities among the kinds of animals. Thus far, in all experiments with sponges, coelenterates, and echinoderms, it seems possible to explain their behavior without assuming that learning has occurred. But in flatworms there is no doubt that a simple kind of learning does occur. Unlike the other animals mentioned, a flatworm has an anterior end and a posterior end, with a bilaterally symmetrical nervous system and an anterior ganglion (Figure 14 · 29). There may be something about such a structural development that favors the learning process. But even in organisms with well-developed nervous systems, very little learning may occur. Many kinds of beetles, if put on a tabletop, will crawl to the edge and fall off; and no matter how many times this happens, they never learn about the edge of the table. On the other hand, learning predominates in the behavior of vertebrates—and particularly of primate mammals.

Reasoning. If it is difficult to describe what we mean by learning, it is even more difficult to describe **reasoning.** Perhaps it is best described in an example. The raccoon in Figure 15 · 19 cannot quite reach the food by going directly toward it. First it must go back around Stake B. Given enough time, almost any active animal accomplishes the task by trial and error. Raccoons learn quickly in this way. But the test of reasoning hinges not on how *quickly* the animal learns by trial and error but on what the animal does on the *first* exposure to the problem.

But suppose it went 80 percent leftward, what would your conclusion be? 70 percent? 60 percent? Must we expect the proportion to be 50:50 as the text implies?

Just because it is *possible,* is it *necessary* to do so? Look up "Lloyd Morgan's canon" in Simpson and Beck.

Compare the beetle's behavior with that of the frog and the "unpleasant" substance (page 481). What assumption is made about the beetle's "desires"?

Figure 15 · 19
A problem.

Put in the raccoon's place, what would you do? You would immediately "size up the situation," walk back around Stake B, and reach the food. Raccoons do not do this. Chimpanzees and most monkeys behave in this situation as you would. Many primates apparently do not see A, B, C, and the rope as separate items but as

Figure 15 • 20
Another problem—and its
solution by a primate. How
would you describe this
behavior?

U.S. Navy.

Figure 15 • 21
Porpoises learn many
things very easily. Is this
what we mean by
intelligence?

parts of a whole situation—the meaning is in the situation, not in the items. This behavior is often described as resulting from *insight.*

In another kind of experiment, an animal is allowed to watch the experimenter place food under one of two identical cups. After a delay, the animal is released to find the food. (Of course, odor must be controlled in such an experiment.) Animals such as rats, cats, and dogs fix their attention on the cup covering the food and go directly to it. But if their attention is temporarily diverted, they do no better than would be expected on the basis of chance. Most primates, however, do not seem to fix their attention on the cup under which the food is placed. Even if they are removed from the situation and then brought back later, they still go immediately to the correct cup. Does the nonhuman primate mind form some lasting image, such as "food under right-hand cup"? If so, this behavior closely approaches the language-based behavior of man.

Non-primates apparently do not have insight. Some, such as raccoons, learn quickly, and even an octopus can learn to go around barriers. Often observations of wild animals reveal behavior that seems to demonstrate insight, but of course such behavior may be merely the result of past experience.

Investigation 15.2

BEHAVIOR OF AN INVERTEBRATE ANIMAL

BACKGROUND INFORMATION

Sow bugs and pill bugs are crustaceans —relatives of crabs and shrimp. Unlike most crustaceans they are terrestrial. However, they breathe by gills, as do other crustaceans. They are found in many biomes, though different species may be found in different places. Any species may be used for this investigation.

MATERIALS AND EQUIPMENT

(for a team of four)

Part A
coffee can, with plastic lid
mixture of moist soil and leaf litter
sponge, a cube 2 cm on a side
carrot or potato
sow bugs or pill bugs, 10–12
nail, 8-penny
glass or metal tray, about 20 × 30 cm
blotting paper, about 20 × 15 cm
laboratory desk lamps, 2
masking tape

Part B
small vials with plastic lids, 4
mixture of moist soil and leaf litter
paper towel
carrot or potato
glass-marking crayon
sow bugs or pill bugs, 4
box, about 10 × 15 × 2 cm, all plastic
    or with plastic cover
cardboard, about 12 × 12 cm
scissors
masking tape
laboratory desk lamp
forceps

PROCEDURE

Part A. Pour a mixture of moist soil and leaf litter into a coffee can until it is ⅔ full. Place a few dead leaves on the surface. Add a small piece of moistened sponge and a slice (about 2 × 5 × 1 cm) of carrot or potato. Put in 10 to 12 sow bugs or pill bugs and cover with a plastic lid into which 6–8 holes have been punched with a nail. The animals can be kept in the container indefinitely if the sponge is kept moist and the carrot or potato slice is changed every few days.

In subdued light, place all the sow bugs in the center of a large tray. • Do the animals tend to remain together? If not, do they wander about aimlessly, or do they move in one direction?(1)

Remove the animals gently and place some moist blotting paper at one end of the tray so that half the bottom is dry and the other half is covered by the moist paper. Place all the animals in the center of the dry end of the tray. Observe the animals for several minutes. • What percentage of the animals remain at the dry half of the tray?(2) • If some animals move to the moist end, do they climb on top of the blotter or move underneath it?(3) • When individuals move, do they move faster in the dry half or in the moist half of the tray?(4)   If some animals move under the blotter, wait about 5 minutes and then pick the blotter up. Observe the distribution of animals on its underside. • Do they tend to be uniformly distributed, or are they clustered in groups?(5)   Make note of any other behavior that you observe.

Set 2 lamps of equal intensity about 50 cm apart. Place a sow bug or pill bug equidistant from the 2 lamps and about 20 cm from the imaginary line running between them. • If the animal moves, sketch its route in relation to the 2 lamps.(6)   Repeat this several times. Now cover the animal's right eye with a tiny piece of masking tape and repeat the procedure. Again sketch the route in several trials. • Is there any consistent difference in the routes under the 2 conditions?(7) • To what stimulus is the animal reacting?(8)

Part B. Mark 4 vials *A, B, C,* and *D;* add your team symbol to each. Place a mixture of moist soil and leaf litter into a vial until it is about half full. Add a spiraled strip of moist paper toweling and a small piece of potato or carrot. Into each vial place 1 sow bug or pill

bug. Perforate the lids and cover the vials. Using a plastic-topped cardboard (or all-plastic) box, prepare a T-maze as shown in Figure 15 • 22. Use strips of cardboard for the inner

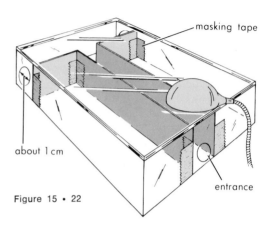

Figure 15 • 22

walls, holding them in place with masking tape. Cut one hole in the box wall at the base of the T and one at the end of each T arm. Place a lamp directly above the T base but do not turn it on.

Place Animal A in the entrance of the maze and cover the hole with masking tape. Turn on the lamp. • How does the animal react?(9)   When the animal reaches the crossarm of the T, it usually will turn in one direction or the other. Note the direction. When it reaches an end of the T arm, remove it immediately and repeat the "test run." Make a total of 5 "test runs," recording the direction of turn each time. Return the animal to its vial. Follow the same procedure with Animal B, Animal C, and Animal D. While you are working with the latter animals, Animal A is "resting." Now make 5 more "trial runs" with each animal, in the same order.

Next day repeat the whole procedure. You now have the results of 20 trials for each animal. Tabulate the results for each animal, and record on its vial *L* (for consistent left-turner), *R* (for consistent right-turner), or *B* (for an animal that turns in either direction without consistency).

You are now ready to train your animals.

Use only the L and R animals. Start with any one of them. Place a lamp at the end of the T arm down which it consistently turned. Do not turn the lamp on yet. Place the animal in the maze as before; but when it reaches the end of the T base, turn on the light. • What is the animal's reaction?(10) Remove the animal from the maze and replace it in its vial. Carry out this procedure with each individual, shifting the location of the light so that it is always at the side of the T arm down which that individual consistently turned during the "trial runs." Then go back to the first individual and repeat the procedure. Continue until each individual has been given 10 runs.

Repeat the whole training procedure each day for at least 3 days. When training has been completed, test each individual in the maze once *without using a light.* Record the direction in which each animal turned.

DISCUSSION

Part A. • Can the behavior of your animals with respect to moisture be related to their survival? If so, how?(11) • Can the behavior of your animals with respect to light be related to their survival? If so, how?(12) In Chapter 4 a term was used to describe a structure that seemed to fit an organism to its environment. • What term might you use to describe the behavior you have observed in this investigation?(13)

Review the discussion of levels of behavior. • Which term best fits the observed behavior?(14) • What information would increase your confidence in your decision?(15)

Part B. • What kind of learning was the procedure used in this investigation designed to produce?(16) • Did you obtain any evidence of learning in the animals with which you worked? If so, what was the evidence?(17) • If you obtained evidence of learning in the species, did all individuals learn equally well?(18) • Do you think that individual differences in ability to learn would have any effect on a population of the animals?(19)

FOR FURTHER INVESTIGATION

In Chapter 8 it was pointed out that a biologist investigating tolerances has difficulty separating the effects of one factor from the effects of another. In Part A of this investigation you encountered the same problem with respect to stimuli. Criticize the procedure and then try to design one that would better separate effects of the stimuli involved.

SOME PATTERNS OF ANIMAL BEHAVIOR

We have been discussing behavior from the viewpoint of its mechanisms—how it is started and how it is performed. To many biologists another viewpoint is more important: how behavior functions in the survival of individuals and of species. From this viewpoint the kinds of behavior are so varied that they are difficult to classify. There is behavior associated with adjustment to factors in the abiotic environment—heat, humidity, salinity, for example. There is behavior associated with food-getting, with escape from enemies, with reproduction. Rather than attempt a brief glance at many parts of behavioral science, we will give somewhat longer consideration to a few, leaving others for you to explore if you wish.

PERIODICITY

Almost everyone has observed that many activities of plants and animals do not occur continuously but rather at regular times in each

Figure 15 • 23

White-crowned sparrow. This species breeds in the northwestern part of North America and in winter may be found throughout much of the United States.

Erwin Bünning [bœ'nĭng]: 1906—

24-hour day. Many birds sing mostly around sunrise. Flowers of some species of plants open in the morning and close at night; those of other species open in the evening. Most species of moths fly at night and rest in the daytime; most butterflies behave in just the opposite way.

Are these daily cycles in activities the direct result of alternating daylight and darkness? In 1729 a French scientist took plants deep into a mine. He discovered that for several days (while the plants were still healthy) the leaf movements were similar to those under natural conditions of day and night. These observations strongly indicated that something within the plant, not just something in the environment, was causing these movements to take place.

As has so often happened in history, scientists of the time failed to recognize the importance of these observations. It was 200 years later that a German botanist, Erwin Bünning, on the basis of his own investigations and those of others, convincingly showed that in many organisms—not only plants but animals and protists also—some behavior occurs periodically without regard to changes of light and dark—a kind of innate rhythm of behavior.

Are all of these activities behaviors?

Figure 15 • 24 shows the feeding activity of a white-crowned sparrow held under constant conditions (continuous light and uniform temperature). In each 24-hour period (a natural day) the bird began to eat about one hour earlier. It therefore had a periodicity in feeding behavior of about 23 hours. Similar experiments have been done with a large variety of organisms and a large variety of activities—for example: leaf movements in plants; cell division in some protists; change in human body temperatures; time of activity in birds, mammals, and insects. Almost all these periodicities turn out to be only approximately 24 hours long. They are therefore now referred to as *circadian rhythms.*

circadian [sûr'kā'dĭ ən; Latin: *circum,* around, + *dies,* day]

Figure 15 • 24

Feeding activity of a white-crowned sparrow. Shading shows dark periods before the experiment under continuous lighting began. Heights of bars indicate amounts of food consumed each time the bird ate.

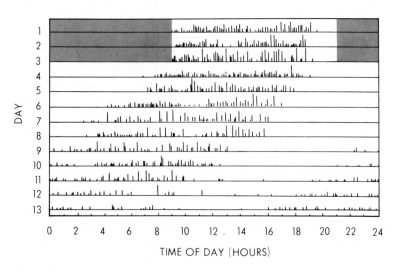

Circadian rhythms are innate. But under environmental conditions that provide a light-dark cycle, the rhythms conform to the cycle —the innate mechanism is reset each day by stimuli from the environment. Thus, under a 24-hour light-dark cycle, the feeding rhythm of a white-crowned sparrow becomes a 24-hour feeding rhythm. This rhythm can be adjusted to changes of proportions of light and dark within a 24-hour period—as with seasonal changes.

Although details differ in different species, most organisms can readjust circadian periodicities to a new light-dark cycle in a few days. In this era of jet-airplane travel, the problem of adjustment is quite important to man. Consider a traveler who flies from San Francisco to London. At first his circadian rhythm—his "biological clock" —tends to retain San Francisco time. When he appears at a meeting in London at 10:00 A.M., his "biological clock" is still very close to 2:00 A.M. San Francisco time, and he is likely to be an extremely sleepy participant in the meeting. Therefore, persons attending important meetings at places many degrees of longitude distant frequently plan to arrive a day or two in advance to permit their "biological clocks" to reset.

How might the existence of circadian rhythms in man affect the development of faster methods of air travel?

Would readjustment of the "biological clock" be necessary on a trip from New York to Santiago, Chile?

TERRITORIALITY

It is spring in Alaska. A male white-crowned sparrow is perched in a low tree. He sings. Again and again he sings. Another male appears. Immediately the first male leaves his perch and flies to the bush in which the second sits. If the second does not leave, the first approaches more closely, and there may be a brief fight. Almost always the newcomer loses and leaves. The first bird then returns to his perch and resumes singing.

After repeated observation we begin to see that this behavior occurs only when a second male bird approaches within certain limits. Usually other males avoid the vicinity of a conspicuous singing male. The presence of a female does not stimulate the same behavior from the singing male.

Alaskan white-crowned sparrows spend the winter in California. There males and females flock together. There is little or no singing. At night two males may sit side by side on a roosting perch.

In 1920 Eliot Howard published a book in which he described his observations of birds nesting in his garden and orchard. By carefully watching the movements of individual birds, Howard discovered that each male tended to remain within a limited area that was strongly defended against intrusions by other males of the same species. He interpreted the constant singing as a way of warning other males that particular areas—territories—were already occupied.

Eliot Howard: 1873–1940. British naturalist

Are "defended" and "warning" anthropomorphic terms? If you think so, can you suggest better ones?

territoriality [těr′ə tör′ĭ ăl′ə tĭ; Latin: terra, land]

Since 1920 many studies of **territoriality** have been made. Most of the early studies were made on birds, and one of the first problems that arose was: How can we explain the change in behavior between summer and winter? Experiments with captive birds and investigations in the field have resulted in some progress toward understanding this problem.

First, consider a male white-crowned sparrow in late winter. The days are becoming longer. The lengthening hours of daylight somehow affect the bird's hypothalamus, which, in turn, causes the anterior pituitary to begin releasing the hormones that cause gradual growth and development of the testes. At the same time the hypothalamus stimulates the production of other hormones. These increase the bird's appetite, and he takes in more calories than are required

Figure 15 • 25
In herring gulls, only the immediate vicinity of the nest is defended. This territorial dispute does not affect birds nesting only a few meters away.

Gordon S. Smith

for his daily activities in the wintering flock; the excess calories are stored as fat. The combination of these (and perhaps other) hormonal activities brings about nocturnal migratory flights northward. When the reserve of fat is used up, the bird interrupts his migration and restores it.

By the time the male reaches the breeding ground, his testes are producing male sex hormones. One effect of these hormones—together with the sight of the breeding area—is to cause territorial behavior. The response of the bird to another male is completely different from his response a few weeks earlier in the wintering flock.

As the year proceeds, the days cease to lengthen. The internal mechanism that responded to the lengthening days of spring is insensitive to the long days of June and the shortened days that follow. The hypothalamus no longer causes the anterior pituitary to release hormones affecting the testes. The testes thus shrink in size and discontinue the production of male sex hormones. Without the effect of male sex hormones on the central nervous system, the territorial reaction to other males disappears. Males abandon their territories and assemble with females and young in flocks that move southward.

Territorial behavior is important for the survival of organisms. An animal placed in unfamiliar surroundings has a poor chance of avoiding predators. A territory becomes a familiar area. After territories are established, little actual fighting usually occurs. Hence individuals have more time and energy to devote to other aspects of daily life. In the kind of territoriality shown by white-crowned sparrows, the conspicuous singing by males may increase the chances that unmated females will locate mates. In this kind of territory, also, an area is reserved from which food may be gathered to feed the young. Thus, territorial behavior may restrict the size of a breeding population to the number of pairs whose young can be adequately supported by the available food supply.

The territory described for white-crowned sparrows is only one of many kinds now recognized: some are places for mating, some are for nesting, some are for feeding, and others are for various combinations of these activities. The essential fact about a territory is that it is defended—most often by males, sometimes by females, sometimes by mated pairs, and sometimes even by a whole flock.

The study of territoriality is a meeting place for many kinds of biologists. Both nervous and endocrine systems are involved in the physiology of territorial behavior. The interactions of individuals are of interest to ethologists, and the function of territoriality in community structure and in the homeostasis of ecosystems greatly concerns ecologists. Territorial behavior of one kind or another has been found among mammals, reptiles, amphibians, fish, and even some invertebrate animals.

Can you describe observations of your own that indicate any kind of territoriality in man?

Investigation 15.3

A METHOD FOR STUDYING TERRITORIALITY

BACKGROUND INFORMATION

To determine the nesting territories of breeding birds, the investigator first prepares a field map of the area to be studied. Then he makes a series of trips through the area. He marks on the map the location of each singing male of each species encountered, plus the location of any nests found. Females and young birds may also be indicated, but a singing male is assumed to indicate the presence of a mate and a nest, though this is not always true. Special symbols are often used to indicate such helpful information as 2 males of the same species heard singing simultaneously, or the locations of fights between males. After the investigator has collected data, he plots on individual-species maps the locations of birds noted on each field trip. From study of the data on the species maps, he can determine the territories.

You will work with actual, though simplified, field data from a breeding-bird study made on a 30-hectare area in Colorado. Most of the vegetation is composed of shrubs, but there are some pine groves, some deciduous trees, and some small grassy areas. Sixteen species of breeding birds were found here, but you will work with only 5 of them. Twenty-seven field trips were made to the area; you will consider data from only 6—those made at the height of. the nesting season.

MATERIALS

graph paper, 5 sheets

sharp pencil with hard lead (about 4H)

PROCEDURE

On each sheet of graph paper outline a plot 40 × 40 squares. Number the horizontal graph lines upward from *0* at the bottom through *40* at the top. Letter the vertical lines from left to right *A* through *Z,* then *a* through *o.* At the top of each sheet, place the name of one of the species being studied.

In the table of data on page 503, the six dates of observation are represented by numerals 1 through 6. Beside each date (except for 6) is the location of an individual bird on each of the first 5 dates. Each location is designated by a number and a letter. For example, 37/c is located at the intersection of line 37 with line c. For Date 6 use the data in Figure 15 • 27, which is given as a simplified example of field data. Also listed is the location

flicker	solitary vireo	robin	scrub jay	rufous-sided towhee
X 1/3	X 1/2	X 1/3	X 1/3	X 1/2
(98)	(160)	(144)	(127)	(205)

Figure 15 • 26

The five birds of this study. Numbers are used instead of names in presenting data.

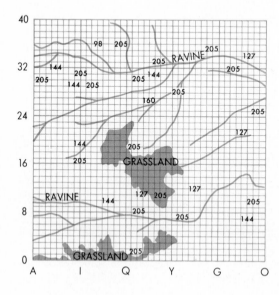

Figure 15 • 27

Location of birds on Date 6.
(See Figure 15 • 26 for key
to numbers.)

of each nest that was found. Many nests were probably not found.

Use a separate sheet of graph paper for each species. Plot the location of each bird and nest on the appropriate sheet. Mark the location of a bird by placing the date number (1 through 6) at the appropriate intersection of lines. Mark the location of a nest with a check (√).

STUDYING THE DATA

Compare the 5 territory maps. • What generalization can you make about the sizes of breeding territories from species to species? Suggest an explanation for this.(1) • Do territories of different species overlap, or is each portion of the study area used only by one species of bird?(2) Red-tailed hawks are frequently seen in this area, but no nest has ever been discovered. • What may be the relation of the size of a red-tailed hawk's territory to the size of this study area?(3) In the region where this study was made, robins have a tendency to nest in deciduous trees along ravines, solitary vireos in pine groves, and scrub jays and rufous-sided towhees in brushland. • From your examination of the distribution and population density of these 4 species, which of the habitats mentioned is most widespread in this 30-hectare plot?(4) Flickers nest in holes in trees but feed on the ground, mainly on ants. • What might explain the low population density of this species here?(5) • What appears to be the approximate carrying capacity (page 56) of this area for *adult* rufous-sided towhees during the breeding season?(6) • Why might this same area not have as great a carrying capacity for towhees in the winter season?(7) Compare the population density of scrub jays with that of rufous-sided towhees. • Is the carrying capacity of the area the same for these 2 species, or are you unable to tell? Explain your answer.(8) • What does the distribution of some of these territories suggest about the habitats in surrounding areas?(9) There is a single record of a rufous-sided towhee at 11/G and a single record of a red-shafted

Red-shafted Flicker (males)	**Solitary Vireo (singing males)**
Date 1: 37/H; 21/F	Date 1: 36/B; 29/V
Date 2: 39/J	Date 2: 30/B; 29/U
Date 3: 38/K	Date 3: 30/U
Date 4: 35/M	Date 4: 37/B; 29/X
Date 5: 34/L	Date 5: 32/A; 30/a
Date 6: See Figure 15 • 27	Date 6: See Figure 15 • 27
Nest: 35/K	*Nest:* 31/a

Robin (singing males)	**Scrub Jay (males or females)**
Date 1: 4/F; 17/S; 33/Q; 29/b; 33/j	Date 1: 33/A; 17/J; 1/Z; 23/f; 37/i
Date 2: 9/D; 22/Q; 29/Q; 32/Z; 30/i; 10/o	Date 2: 29/G; 17/R; 5/Z; 26/g; 39/j
Date 3: 9/M; 17/U; 32/S; 33/c; 30/k	Date 3: 35/M; 18/N; 10/b; 23/l
Date 4: 3/M; 21/N; 33/V; 32/Y; 35/j	Date 4: 38/D; 13/S; 4/c; 26/h; 39/l
Date 5: 2/G; 14/R; 28/R; 27/f; 29/j	Date 5: 35/L; 23/R; 6/Z; 27/d; 36/o
Date 6: See Figure 15 • 27	Date 6: See Figure 15 • 27
Nest: 29/S; 32/i	*Nest:* 9/c; 25/i; 38/n

Rufous-sided Towhee (singing males)

Date 1: 40/A; 28/F; 37/H; 22/F; 25/I; 28/K; 37/P; 31/S; 25/P; 34/Y; 38/c; 12/Y; 11/G; 39/g; 34/j; 27/l; 31/e; 25/b; 4/I; 2/Q; 9/N; 15/L; 7/g; 11/m; 17/h; 21/W

Date 2: 36/C; 37/G; 22/I; 28/I; 36/S; 30/R; 24/R; 32/X; 36/d; 37/I; 8/c; 26/I; 12/j; 30/m; 30/d; 28/z; 12/e; 4/M; 20/Z; 3/S; 14/X; 11/P; 14/P

Date 3: 35/B; 28/A; 33/J; 25/K; 28/M; 33/R; 29/R; 27/V; 31/W; 35/a; 12/X; 37/h; 31/i; 5/d; 24/j; 29/c; 11/j; 15/f; 27/a; 7/G; 19/U; 4/V; 9/Q; 14/R

Date 4: 32/L; 19/E; 26/M; 27/N; 34/R; 25/S; 30/W; 30/k; 7/e; 25/i; 30/b; 13/h; 2/L; 18/U; 7/W; 9/S

Date 5: 36/D; 20/G; 34/d; 26/I; 10/Y; 27/K; 36/T; 30/T; 26/U; 33/W; 36/n; 29/j; 24/h; 32/c; 5/a; 13/d; 28/b; 5/S; 18/Y; 9/O; 17/P

Date 6: See Figure 15 • 27

Nest: 27/U

flicker at 21/F. • What could account for these single records during the breeding season?(10) There may be some doubt that in a particular area during the breeding season the day-after-day presence of individual birds or the regular occurrence of a singing male indicates a nesting territory. • Is there evidence from these territory data that these *are* indicators for nesting territories? If so, what is it?(11)

FOR FURTHER INVESTIGATION

You can try some actual fieldwork in your own area, preparing field maps and working out territories of local nesting birds. Such studies can usually be started in late April and ideally should continue into midsummer. The National Audubon Society, 1130 Fifth Avenue, New York, N.Y., 10028, has a leaflet on how to carry out breeding-bird studies.

COMMUNICATION

In anthropomorphic terms, a singing male bird is telling other males that he will defend the area around him; he is telling females that the area is available for nesting. Communication among individuals is part of territorial behavior.

Any activity of one organism that causes a reaction in another can be regarded as **communication**. In this broad and basic sense, communication must occur in all ecological relationships—among plants and protists as well as among animals. Most biologists, however, use the term in a narrower sense, though they do not always agree on the limits. In this discussion, communication is restricted to animals.

Figure 15 • 28

Long observation led one investigator to interpret the positions of wolves' tails in this way. To what extent does your observation of the ways dogs act indicate similarity with wolves in "tail communication"?

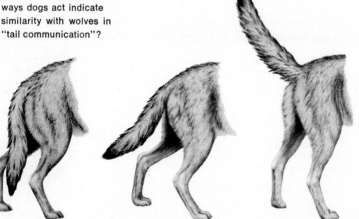

Submissive attitude   Normal position   Self-confidence   Confident threat

To be of value for communication, each kind of stimulus must have a "meaning." A biologist can find out what this meaning is only by observing what organisms do when the stimulus is given. Repeatedly, when a male white-crowned sparrow sings, biologists observe that most other males avoid the vicinity of the singer and that females may approach the vicinity of the singer. In this case the stimulus has one meaning for the males, another for the females. And apparently it has no meaning for the caribou that are grazing nearby, because they show no signs of reacting to it.

Anything that can be sensed by another organism—any kind of stimulus—may serve for communication. Sounds, scents, and sights are the most commonly used stimuli. We have discussed sounds in connection with territoriality, but they have many other functions.

Scent is used as a means of communication, particularly by mammals and insects. By leaving their scents at various places, some mammals mark the limits of their territories. An ant lays down a trail of formic acid from a food source back to its anthill. The formic acid seems to mean, "This is the way." Ants returning empty-handed after the food disappears do not mark the trail. When the formic acid evaporates, the ants no longer go to the old food source.

Man, having a poor sense of smell, makes little use of communication by scent, but, in addition to sound, he uses sight extensively. Most animals in which the sense of sight is present use it for communication. Usually visual stimuli consist of movements. Often movements are made more conspicuous by some structure of the body. A startled white-tailed deer communicates its alarm to the rest of the herd by raising its tail, which flashes conspicuously white in contrast to its dark upper side.

The giver of a visual stimulus need not necessarily have good vision, because communication may be interspecific—directed toward another species. Some caterpillars have spots that superficially resemble large eyes. The true eyes of a caterpillar are small and probably cannot see the spots on another caterpillar's back. But a food-seeking bird may be frightened sufficiently by the large "eyes" to allow the caterpillar to escape.

Might a caribou respond to the note that a sparrow makes when it sees a predator? If so, would this be communication?

What examples of scent as a means of communication were given earlier in this chapter?

See Figure 8·28 for a somewhat similar action in a startled pronghorn.

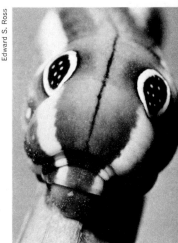

Edward S. Ross

Figure 15 • 29
Hornworm, a caterpillar that has false "eyes." × 3

Figure 15 • 30
"Songs" of two species of field crickets: *Gryllus pennsylvanicus (above)* and *G. rubens (below).* Ethologists can now transform air vibrations into visible form, making possible clear comparison of animal sounds.

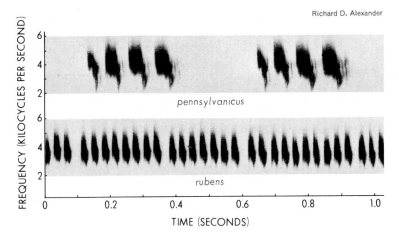

Richard D. Alexander

pennsylvanicus

rubens

FREQUENCY (KILOCYCLES PER SECOND)

TIME (SECONDS)

SOCIAL BEHAVIOR

When the fruit is ripening, large numbers of birds may come together in a cherry tree. The assemblage may last for several days. While it lasts, communication occurs. By voice and movements individual birds interact with one another. This is a simple kind of social system, and it is temporary, but it contains the basic requirements of a social organization.

The assemblage of birds in a fruit tree may be composed of several species. The study of interspecific social relationships is an important matter for ecologists. But in the remainder of this discussion, we shall deal only with groups that contain individuals of a single species.

Fish schools. Many species of fishes are usually found moving about in compact groups. Such a *school* is usually made up of fish not only of the same species but also of the same size. At any particular instant, all individuals in the school swim in one direction; and when one changes direction, all do. A school of fish represents a fairly simple aggregation.

Many species that behave in this way have sleek bodies that glitter as they move. A school's movements seem to be controlled in part by visual stimuli releasers; fish that cannot see do not school. In other cases, pressure receptors along the sides of the fish may receive stimuli that tend to keep each fish at a certain distance from the others.

Part of schooling behavior involves fixed-action patterns, but learning is also definitely involved. Contacts between very young fish increase their ability to swim together in schools. Older fish, when separated from each other over a period of time, tend to "forget" how to school.

Douglas P. Wilson

Figure 15 · 31

A school of mackerel. Can you think of any ways in which this behavior might be an advantage to the fish?

Insect societies. If you look through the animal kingdom for something comparable to human societies, you may find the greatest similarities when you observe certain insects. Among ants, bees, and termites, large numbers of individuals carry on many kinds of special tasks and seem to work closely together for the good of the group. Within a species we find individuals that specialize in different kinds of work: food collectors, fighters, "baby-sitters," even living "food bins." Some species cultivate fungi. Some species wage war and make slaves. Some species construct complicated housing projects. You can easily see the anthropomorphism in this paragraph.

Man has long been interested in the behavior of honeybees, one of the few kinds of insects he has domesticated. So the use of anthropomorphic language has been especially common in describing the activities of bees. But bee societies are very different from those of man. For one thing, the inhabitants of a beehive are really one gigantic family. All are offspring of the queen; all the workers are sisters;

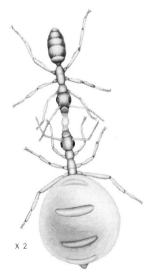

X 2

Figure 15 • 32
In some ant species specialized workers serve as storage bins for food. What environmental conditions might favor such behavior?

worker   drone   queen

all the drones are brothers. Modern human societies, however, are groupings of many families.

Further, repeated experiments show that highly organized insect societies are based on innate behavior. A fungus-cultivating ant automatically goes through the necessary actions. Each generation of men, on the other hand, has to learn how to care for crops.

Neal A. Weber

Figure 15 • 33
Honeybees. Each of these kinds of individuals has specialized behavior. Drones are males; workers are non-reproductive females; queens are egg-layers.

What advantages can you see in innate behavior compared with learned behavior and vice versa? Robins are solitary birds, but crows congregate in flocks. Which should be easier to tame? Why?

Figure 15 • 34
A high degree of social behavior is required in these ants that cultivate a fungus on bits of leaves (Panama).

John Kohout from Root Resources

Figure 15 • 35
Some species of ants feed upon a substance secreted by aphids. They care for the aphids much as man cares for his cows. Why, then, are the behavior of man and the behavior of ants not comparable?

Paul Knipping

Figure 15 • 36
Presented with several mother substitutes, this infant monkey clings to an object that is soft and warm and gives milk. What conclusion can be drawn from such an experiment?

Clarence R. Carpenter: 1905—. American psychologist and anthropologist

Primate societies. An outstanding development in biology during recent years has been increased interest in primates—the animals usually placed in the same taxonomic order with man. Especially active has been the study of primate behavior, in which there has been an unusual degree of coordination between investigations in the laboratory and in the field.

One of the first field studies was made by C. R. Carpenter, who spent almost a year observing howler monkeys on Barro Colorado Island. Carpenter was especially interested in social organization. He found that there were about 400 howlers on the island, organized into 23 clans that varied in size from 4 to 35 individuals. The clans were strictly territorial. When two clans came near each other along a territorial border, vigorous howling started—a vocal battle that continued until one band or the other retreated. There were a few solitary "bachelor" males. These, when they tried to join a clan, were shouted off—though Carpenter watched one "bachelor" who, after persistent attempts over several weeks, was finally accepted into a clan.

persistent [pər sĭs′tənt]: occurring again and again

Carpenter could not find that the clans had leaders. A male was usually in the lead when a clan moved, but sometimes it would be one male, sometimes another. Moreover, males seemed to show no jealousy with respect to females, and no instances of fighting within a clan were observed. Among other kinds of monkeys, particularly Indian rhesus monkeys and African baboons, there is evidence that one of the males is the recognized leader.

jealousy [jĕl′ə sĭ]: intolerance of rivals

Having been successful with his earlier studies, Carpenter turned to gibbons, which are not monkeys but apes—pongids, the group of animals that are structurally and physiologically most like man. More recently other biologists have closely studied other apes —orangutans, chimpanzees, and gorillas. These studies have shown that the social behavior of the larger primates varies greatly.

T. S. Satyan from Black Star

Figure 15 • 37

In India ethologists easily study wild rhesus monkeys and then correlate their findings with psychologists' study of captives and with anatomists' and physiologists' studies in the laboratory.

Orangutans seem to be the least social of the apes, though this conclusion may result from the fact that they have been least studied. Gibbons live in small family groups consisting of male and female with their young. Gorilla bands contain several adult males and females dominated by one older male that rules the band more by threats than by punishment. Chimpanzees also live in groups containing several adults and young.

Are these studies of primate social organization of any help to psychologists who are attempting to understand the social organization of man? Man's social organization varies greatly today and has apparently varied in the past, also. Moreover, man's use of language and of symbols makes his societies vastly more complex than any other primate society. Therefore, even though facts are becoming more abundant, statements concerning the social behavior of both men and apes are still opinions rather than conclusions. But primate behavior continues to fascinate. If you visit the primate house in a zoo and watch what occurs on *both* sides of the bars, you will find that not only biologists are interested in primate behavior.

CONTROL OF BEHAVIOR

What an organism as a whole does depends upon the stimuli it receives and upon its internal functioning—its physiology. If, then, we wish to control the behavior of an organism, we can modify either of these factors.

Can you give some other examples of control by modification of stimuli?

Man modifies both in controlling the behavior of himself as well as that of other organisms. The sight stimulus of a ball rolling across the street causes a child to follow. You employ the sound stimulus "Stop!" and the behavior is changed—maybe. Such behavior control by change of stimulus is the particular concern of psychologists.

PHYSIOLOGICAL CONTROL

We now turn to behavior control by modification of physiology. An organism's physiology depends upon the substances of which it is composed and upon the chemical reactions involving these substances. The substances within an organism can be thought of as playing three basic roles in the organism's body. First, structural molecules maintain shape and form—from the overall appearance of a whale or redwood tree to the microscopic details of organelles in cells. Second, other kinds of molecules are primarily involved in the storage and transmission of energy. Many of these were encountered in Chapter 12. Third, still other kinds of molecules are involved in the storage and transfer of information.

Among informational molecules are DNA and RNA, substances that are involved in heredity—the passage of information from cell to cell and from generation to generation. Other informational molecules are the hormones that were discussed in Chapter 14. Still others are molecules that are involved in the functioning of the nervous system —especially in the transmission of nerve impulses from one neuron to another.

All organized systems can be damaged or destroyed. In a biochemical system an alien molecule that behaves much like a normal one but lacks the ability to carry out the normal function can wreck the physiological machinery. Consider, for example, carbon monoxide, a gas produced by incomplete combustion in such things as cigarettes and auto engines. Carbon monoxide combines with hemoglobin much more readily than does oxygen. But, of course, it cannot substitute for oxygen in cellular respiration. Consequently, even a low concentration of carbon monoxide in the air is deadly if breathed for some minutes.

Physicians—who are, to a large degree, practicing biologists— use knowledge of the physiological effects of many substances. Antibiotics, for example, are chemical substances that physicians use to disrupt the physiological machinery of bacterial cells. Penicillin interferes with the synthesis of new cell walls; streptomycin and other antibiotics interfere with the synthesis of proteins.

CHEMISTRY OF A SYNAPSE

In nervous systems neurons shuttle messages back and forth. Though some neurons are quite long, messages must usually be passed from one neuron to another—that is, across synapses. The precise ways in which nerve impulses are transmitted across synapses differ in different parts of the nervous system and are not completely understood at present. However, we can piece together an explanation that will be reasonably accurate.

A neuron operates on an all-or-none basis. Either it sends an impulse along its fiber or it does not. The individual impulses do not vary in strength, only in frequency (number of impulses per second). At any given moment a nerve cell either "fires" or it does not.

Whether a particular neuron (let's call it Neuron X) fires or not is determined by "vote." Some fibers leading to the body of Neuron X cast negative votes; others, affirmative. Impulses arriving from the negative fibers tend to inhibit (prevent) Neuron X from firing; impulses from affirmative fibers tend to excite (cause) it to fire. Whether X fires or not is determined at each moment by tallying the vote. The majority wins.

Chemicals secreted by synaptical nerve endings are the means by which the votes are cast. In at least one part of the brain, **serotonin** inhibits firing and **norepinephrine** encourages it. Both are rapidly destroyed after they are formed, so their action depends upon constant production by the nerve endings. In Figure 15 · 38 a motor neuron receives input from seven other neurons. Action by Neuron 1, 3, 4, or 6 causes its synaptical endings to secrete norepinephrine (+), to excite firing. Action by Neuron 2, 5, or 7 causes its endings to secrete

serotonin [sĕr′ə tō′nĭn]

norepinephrine
[nôr ĕp′ə nĕf′rēn′]

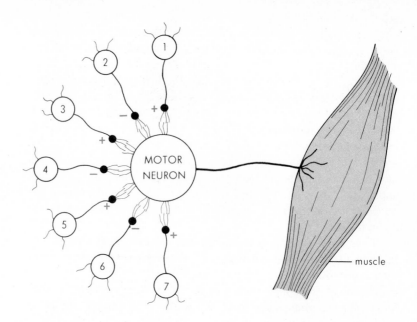

Figure 15 • 38
Will this muscle contract?

serotonin (−), to inhibit firing. Whether or not the motor neuron fires (causes the muscle to contract) depends upon the relative numbers of "+" and "−" impulses it receives. You can see that the motor neuron would be most likely to move the muscle if Neurons 1, 3, 4, and 6 secrete norepinephrine and if 2, 5, and 7 do *not* secrete serotonin.

Name some of the plus and minus factors that might determine whether a boy eats a piece of cake he has found on the kitchen table.

If the synthesis of serotonin is stopped, or if serotonin is destroyed as fast as it is formed, or if the receptor sites for serotonin on the motor neuron are blocked, there is a strong bias in favor of firing. On the contrary, if the synthesis of norepinephrine ceases, or if this substance is destroyed as fast as it is formed, or if its receptor sites on the motor neuron are blocked, the motor neuron receives only inhibitory impulses and does not fire.

DRUG ACTION

Over several thousand years man has discovered hundreds of substances that affect physiology—*drugs.* Some drugs—penicillin, for example—are used because they interfere with the physiology of parasitic organisms and so help a host to overcome a disease that the parasites cause. Others are used to change the physiology of the host itself; many of these do so by affecting nerve endings. Particularly important are those that physicians use in treating human nervous disorders.

tranquilizers [trăng′kwə lĭz′ərz; Latin: *trans*, across, + *quies*, quiet]

chlorpromazine [klōr präm′ə zēn′]

reserpine [rĕs′ər pĭn]

Some persons are overactive and continually agitated. Their neurons are firing too often, and they need calming. *Tranquilizers* are effective treatment, but different ones act in different ways. One, chlorpromazine, blocks norepinephrine receptors. Another, reserpine, increases the rate at which norepinephrine is destroyed at nerve end-

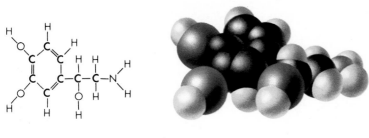

norepinephrine

mescaline

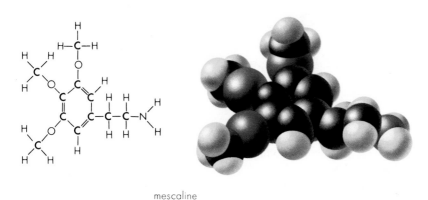

Figure 15 • 39
Molecular structures of
nervous-system chemicals
and a drug. Try to form a
hypothesis for the action
of mescaline on neuron
action.

serotonin

ings. Lithium compounds, long known for their tranquilizing action,
prevent the formation of norepinephrine.

Some persons are underactive; they tend to be sleepy and lethar-
gic. They respond to *stimulants.* One such drug, amphetamine, increases the release of norepinephrine from nerve endings. Iproniazid
slows the breakdown of norepinephrine. Another stimulant drug
causes norepinephrine to remain on its receptor sites on the motor
neuron; this represents a standing order to fire. Still others interfere
with the synthesis or release of serotonin.

amphetamine [ăm fĕt′ə mēn′]

iproniazid [ī prŏ nī′ə zĭd]

Photos by Sidney Cohen

Figure 15 • 40

Under the influence of LSD, a drug that produces hallucinations, the artist made the copy (*right*) of one of his original works (*left*). Which do you think is better?

hallucinations
[hə lo͞o′sə nā′shənz]: perceptions of objects that have no real existence

lysergic [lə sər′jĭk]

In the hands of physicians, tranquilizers and stimulants are valuable tools with which to treat nervous disorders. Unfortunately, these drugs are frequently available to persons who have no medical supervision. They use the drugs to fit events—as stimulants for business conferences, examinations, or evening parties and as tranquilizers for sleep. And, of course, older drugs, such as caffeine and alcohol, have been in common use since long before there were physicians. From widespread, socially accepted use, many drugs have passed on to what might be called "thrill" use. With older drugs this has long been a social problem; newer drugs have worsened the problem.

Still other kinds of substances are used to create mental hallucinations. Most of these have little present use for treating disease. Further, their physiological actions are not well known. One that has received much study, lysergic acid (LSD), seems to attach to serotonin receptors and in this way interferes with all negative votes. Therefore, all neurons affected by it are continuously set to fire—armed with hair triggers, so to speak. As a result, even very minor stimuli have very large effects. An organism under the effect of LSD seems to act in ways unrelated to its environment.

DANGERS

The human brain and its associated nervous system is by far the most complex network in the animal kingdom. It is so complex that it knows itself that it is complex! To tamper with such a mechanism is dangerous. And this is what a person does when he prescribes for himself the drugs that alter neural pathways. These pathways have been established through innate design of the nervous system and through lifelong experiences. They are the means by which a person is capable of coping with the outside world.

Some drugs, particularly those that are related to opium, can lead

Nerve impulses, except for their frequency, are the same in all nerves. Interpretation of nerve impulses occurs in the brain. What might happen if impulses from the ear or tongue were shunted erroneously to the part of the brain normally responsible for sight?

to *dependence.* Frequent use of such a drug causes new metabolic pathways to form. Then the constant presence of the drug is needed to keep these pathways functioning. When such a physiological dependence has been established, withdrawal from the drug upsets the new physiological reactions and death sometimes results. Yet drugs of this kind, when carefully prescribed by a physician, are a powerful medical tool for relieving great pain.

Dependence upon a drug need not be physiological; it may be psychological. In this case, the world seen through the drugged mind seems better than the one seen when the mind is functioning normally. But to survive, every organism must cope with—must adapt to—the stimuli that come from the real environment. It is difficult enough to do this when our nervous systems are functioning normally —when we see things more or less as others do. A drug-created world that does not exist is dangerous at best. Very often it is fatal.

GUIDE QUESTIONS

1. What is behavior?
2. Why is the field study of behavior important?
3. How do the viewpoints of ethologists differ from those of psychologists?
4. Why is anthropomorphism a danger in studying the behavior of animals?
5. What other difficulties does a behavioral scientist encounter?
6. How is irritability related to behavior?
7. Distinguish a tropism from a taxis.
8. What is innate behavior?
9. Compare the terms "instinct" and "fixed-action pattern."
10. What is a releaser stimulus?
11. What evidence shows that much behavior results from both fixed-action patterns and learning?
12. What difficulties are involved in defining "learning"?
13. How does imprinting differ from other kinds of learning?
14. What do we mean by conditioning?
15. In what way is trial-and-error learning studied?
16. How does insight differ from learning?
17. In what ways do organisms show periodic behavior?
18. What are circadian rhythms?
19. What functions may territorial behavior have in the ecology of an organism?
20. How can a biologist determine the "meaning" of a communication stimulus?
21. What kinds of stimuli are used in communication between animals?
22. What factors are usually present in social behavior?
23. What kinds of behavior can be recognized in the schooling of fish?
24. Biologists regard insect societies as only superficially like human societies. Why?
25. Why are studies of the behavior of other primates difficult to apply to an understanding of human behavior?
26. What factors are involved in attempts to control behavior?
27. Why is knowledge of nerve physiology necessary for understanding behavior?
28. What is meant when we say a substance is a drug?
29. How do tranquilizers differ in their action from stimulants?
30. What is meant by dependence upon drugs?

PROBLEMS

1. A human infant clutches at anything that touches its hands, and the strength of its grasp is great enough to support its weight. This grasping reaction appears to be innate. Would you call it a reflex or an instinct? Explain. What adaptive value might this be-

havior have had in the past? Do you think it has any adaptive value now?

2. The following are examples of behaviors that have been called instinctive: (a) the web-building of spiders; (b) the nest-building of birds; (c) the comb-building of bees; (d) the dam-building of beavers. How might it be possible to obtain evidence showing to what extent these activities are innate and to what extent they are learned?

3. Make a list of animals from a number of phyla and arrange it in order of the care given the young—from least to most. List the same animals in order of numbers of young produced—from most to least. Explain any relationships you can find between the two lists.

4. In mammalian embryos movements of the diaphragm and muscles attached to the ribs do not occur. At birth, however, these movements begin immediately. Does the young mammal *learn* this behavior, or are there other ways to explain it?

5. Biologists have found evidence of organization even in apparently simple groupings of animals—for example, in herds of domestic cattle. What is a social hierarchy? How is it formed? How is it maintained? What is the effect on the hierarchy of introducing new individuals into the group? What effect do hormones have on hierarchal behavior?

6. Describe how you might test the hypothesis that unhatched chicks detect and remember sounds, using the following equipment: some fertilized chicken eggs, one or two incubators, a metronome (a clockwork device that beats time for music).

SUGGESTED READINGS

BROWN, F. A., JR. *Biological Clocks.* (BSCS Pamphlet 2). Boulder, Colo.: EPIC, 1962.

COLLIAS, N. E. *Animal Language.* (BSCS Pamphlet 20). Boulder, Colo.: EPIC, 1964.

DAVIS, D. E. *Integral Animal Behavior.* New York: Macmillan, 1966. (Summarizes psysiological foundations and then describes effects of behavior on populations. Advanced.)

DETHIER, V. G., and E. STELLAR. *Animal Behavior, Its Evolutionary and Neurological Basis.* 3rd ed. Englewood Cliffs, N.J.: Prentice-Hall, Inc., 1970. (Considers animal behavior primarily as an expression of the organization of the nervous system. Rather advanced.)

FARNER, D. S. *Photoperiodism in Animals.* (BSCS Pamphlet 15). Boulder, Colo.: EPIC, 1964.

GRINSPOON, L. "Marihuana," *Scientific American,* December, 1969. Pp. 17–25.

HAILMAN, J. P. "How an Instinct Is Learned," *Scientific American,* December, 1969. Pp. 98–106.

HESS, E. H. "Imprinting in a Natural Laboratory," *Scientific American,* August, 1972. Pp. 24–31.

KUMMER, H. *Primate Societies.* Chicago: Aldine-Atherton, 1971. (Uses information from studies of many kinds of primates. Rather advanced.)

LORENZ, K. Z. *King Solomon's Ring.* New York: The Thomas Y. Crowell Co., 1952. (Excellent scientific research lies behind this book, but the material is not presented in textbook style. Easy.)

PALMER, J. D. "How a Bird Tells the Time of Day," *Natural History,* March, 1966. Pp. 48–53.

SCOTT, J. P. *Animal Behavior.* New York: Doubleday and Co., Inc., 1963. (Old—originally published in 1958—but still a good introduction.)

SHAW, E. "The Schooling of Fishes," *Scientific American,* June, 1962. Pp. 128–134.

SIMPSON, G. G., and W. S. BECK. *Life: An Introduction to Biology.* 2nd ed. New York: Harcourt, Brace and World, 1965. Chapter 14. (Considers behavior from a wide viewpoint. Somewhat advanced.)

SPARKS, J. *Bird Behavior.* New York: Grosset and Dunlap, 1970. (Many color illustrations make the book an easy introduction to the behavior of a much-studied group of animals.)

STOKES, A. W., and C. R. WATTS. "The Social Order of Turkeys," *Scientific American,* June, 1971. Pp. 112–118.

TINBERGEN, N. *Curious Naturalists.* New York: Doubleday and Co., Inc., 1968. (An informal account of 25 years of study by a foremost ethologist. Easy.)

————, and EDITORS of LIFE. *Animal Behavior.* New York: Time, Inc., Book Division, 1965. (A well-illustrated discussion of behavior.)

VAN LAWICK–GOODALL, J. *In the Shadow of Man.* Boston: Houghton Mifflin Co., 1971. (A nontechnical account of chimpanzee behavior by a scientist who lived with the animals in Africa.)

WENNER, A. M. *The Bee Language Controversy.* Boulder, Colo.: Educational Programs Improvement Corp., 1971. (Shows how hypotheses about animal behavior are originated and tested and how alternative hypotheses arise.)

CONTINUITY
OF THE BIOSPHERE

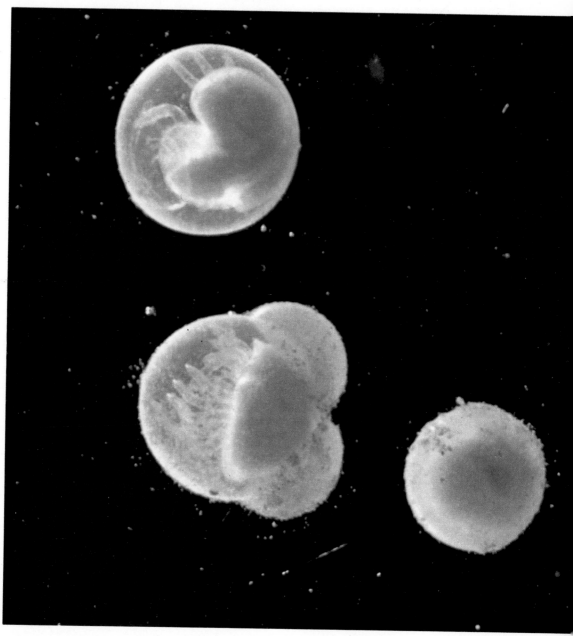

CONTINUITY OF THE BIOSPHERE

We have been looking into organisms. We have been concerned with the way in which a living individual is constructed and with the internal chemical and physical processes that distinguish living from nonliving matter. Much current research centers on problems of this "inner" biology—anatomy, physiology, biophysics, biochemistry. What biologists learn about such matters is of importance to all of us. But its importance becomes evident only when internal processes show up in external actions—behavior. So even in Section Four we had to return to the whole organism, with its internal homeostasis, maintaining a steady state in an unsteady environment.

Individual organisms exist in populations. Through natality and mortality individuals come and go, but populations of organisms exist for ages. And, as we saw in Chapter 10, the evidence from fossils indicates that the biosphere itself has endured perhaps 3 billion years. Thus there is continuity in the biosphere. There is continuity, but there is also change. Again the fossil record is the evidence; it indicates that change has been slow and, in general, orderly. In other words, there is homeostasis between populations of organisms and their abiotic environment.

How do populations achieve continuity? How are individuals replaced? How are characteristics maintained generation after generation? And, on the other hand, how do characteristics change over many generations, so that ecosystems of today are recognizably different from those of past ages? These are some of the questions we shall consider in Section Five.

To start the discussion, we shall have to look again at cell units, at "inner" biology. But we shall soon return to individual units, to "outer" biology. As you have come to appreciate the continuity of the biosphere, so now you may recognize the continuity between "inner" and "outer" biology.

Reproduction

WHY REPRODUCTION?

One statement about living things that has no exception is: They die. An organism may be eaten, may be killed by parasites, may starve, or may be destroyed by natural events—frozen in a blizzard, boiled in lava, or crushed in an avalanche. Very few die of old age.

Since individuals die, life on Earth would obviously cease unless new individuals were continually being formed. There are two possibilities: nonliving substances may somehow come alive spontaneously, or bits of organisms may detach themselves and become new individual living things. The first possibility is referred to as spontaneous generation. The second is called *reproduction.*

Consider first the possibility of spontaneous generation. Many people in many lands at many times have believed that living things can arise from nonliving substances. For example, some have thought that in spring the mud in marshes turns into frogs. Suddenly, after a warm spring rain, the marshes—frozen and apparently lifeless in winter—swarm with frogs, which make their presence known with unmistakable loud calls. The observations are accurate; the conclusion is wrong, mainly because the observations are not carried far enough. Some winter digging in the mud beneath the frozen marsh would reveal that dormant frogs were present from the previous autumn.

Such beliefs, based on insufficient investigation, are still held by some people. Biologists, however, have not believed in the spontaneous generation of larger organisms since the 17th century, when Francesco Redi performed the experiment illustrated in Figure 16 · 1. The discovery of microorganisms revived interest in spontaneous generation—until Pasteur's experiments showed that these organisms, too, come only from others of their kind. Reproduction remained, then, the only way to account for the appearance of new individuals.

For a species, reproduction answers the problem of death. For an individual, there is no answer to death. And for an individual, there is no need for reproduction. Therefore reproduction is a life process

Francesco Redi [frăn chěs'kō rě'dĭ]: 1626?–1698. Italian poet and naturalist

But Oparin's theory (page 315) involves a kind of spontaneous generation. Why is this not relevant to the discussion here?

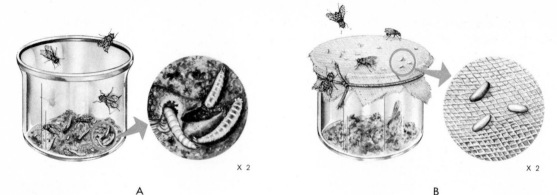

X 2

A   B

Figure 16 • 1

Redi's experiment: (A) Maggots developed in meat left in a vessel. (B) Another vessel was covered with cloth, and no maggots developed in the meat. However, on the cloth, flies' eggs were found—from which maggots hatched.

somewhat different from the life processes discussed in Section Four. Reproduction concerns not the maintenance of individuals, but the continuity of species.

KINDS OF REPRODUCTION

ASEXUAL REPRODUCTION

Why is asexual reproduction of a plant desirable if you want to be sure that the offspring will have certain desirable characteristics that the parent possesses — for example, flavor in apples or flower color in tulips?

It is easier to describe *asexual* reproductive processes than to define asexual reproduction. But we can say that when one or more new individuals are produced by a single parent, the process—with a few exceptions—is asexual. Most organisms that reproduce asexually have *sexual* methods also. But in deuteromycetes sexual reproduction is unknown, and in a few other groups it is rare.

Figure 16 • 2

Vegetative reproduction of a strawberry. Each young plant will eventually lose its connection with its parent.   × 1/4

Walter Chandoha

Vegetative reproduction. In spring, potato farmers in Maine or Idaho prepare for planting. They cut potatoes into pieces, each with an "eye" (actually, a bud). After planting, the bud develops into a leafy shoot, drawing upon the foods stored within the piece. Roots appear, and before long a new plant is established. From one potato a number of new individuals have developed.

In plants a bud or a branch may take root, or a piece of a root may sprout a stem. In either case, a whole new plant may eventually be formed. Many plants reproduce in this way without aid from man. This is *vegetative* reproduction.

See Figure 13·28.

Because starfish eat oysters, it was once a common practice among oystermen to chop up starfish that they caught and throw the pieces back into the water. But each arm that was attached to a piece of the center portion grew into a whole new starfish. The oystermen were actually multiplying starfish! However, starfish do not of their own accord break themselves up into separate pieces; in other words, they do not reproduce vegetatively. In fact, few animals do. However, exceptions occur among some species of freshwater annelids. They reproduce by simply breaking in half; then the anterior piece grows a new posterior section, and the posterior piece grows a new anterior section.

Vegetative reproduction arises from the ability of multicellular organisms to replace lost parts—the process of *regeneration.* This is one aspect of the general process of growth. You have the ability to regenerate lost pieces of skin. In the cases described above, this ability is simply developed to an extreme degree: a small part, separated from one individual, can grow into a completely independent new individual.

X 1

Figure 16 • 3
Vegetative reproduction of *Bryophyllum.* Small new plants develop in notches of the leaf.

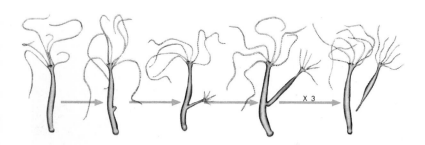

X 3

Figure 16 • 4
Hydra: This kind of vegetative reproduction is called budding.

Fission. Among single-celled organisms—diatoms, many green algae, and most protists—reproduction is often merely a matter of cell division. Two offspring result, and the parent loses its identity in the process. This kind of reproduction is called *fission.* It may occur at a certain stage in the life history of an organism that at another

fission [fĭsh′ən; Latin: *findere*, to split, cleave]

Figure 16 · 5
Fission of paramecium as
seen in a stained
specimen. × 600

stage reproduces by some other means. But some organisms apparently always reproduce by fission.

Fission usually involves the process of mitosis, but among ciliates, bacteria, and blue-green algae there are exceptions. It was long
thought that bacteria had no organized nuclear material. Now the
electron microscope has revealed a structure that is at least similar
to a nucleus, and studies of heredity indicate that each bacterium has
a single chromosome. However, mitosis (at least as described in
Chapter 11) does not occur. In the blue-green algae nothing even
resembling a nucleus has yet been demonstrated.

Reproduction by spores. Vegetative reproduction produces a new
individual that is simply an outgrowth of tissues that normally function
in the nonreproductive life of the parent organism. In fission, also,
there is no differentiated reproductive structure. But in most multicellular organisms (and some unicellular ones, also) there are specialized reproductive parts.

sporangium [spō răn′jĭ əm;
Greek: *spora*, a seed, +
angeion, a small container].
The derivation is misleading;
for distinction between spore
and seed see page 159.

One kind of reproductive structure is called a *sporangium* (spore
case). Within a sporangium many spores are produced, each consisting of a single thick-walled cell. When the sporangium breaks
open, the tiny spores may be carried long distances by currents of
air or water. They can survive long periods of time in dry air with little
loss of water. If a spore reaches a favorable environment, it germinates and develops into a new organism. Though spore formation
does not occur among animals, it is common in the plant and protist
kingdoms.

Investigation 16.1

VEGETATIVE REPRODUCTION

INTRODUCTION

Coleus is a plant that does not usually
reproduce vegetatively. However, gardeners
often cause it to do so. The problem in this

investigation is to explore the conditions under which vegetative reproduction in coleus is
successful.

MATERIALS AND EQUIPMENT

(for each team)

flowerpot (shallow form), 15- to 20-cm
  diameter
stone or piece of broken pot
sand, enough to fill flowerpot
saucer or shallow pan
pot labels, 4
live coleus plant
scalpel
plastic bag
string

PROCEDURE

Place a large stone or a piece of broken
pot over the drainage hole in the empty flowerpot. Pour sand into the pot to a level within
2 cm of the rim. Place the pot in a saucer or
shallow pan and water the sand thoroughly.
Pour excess water from the saucer. Using a
pencil, divide the surface of the sand into
quarter sections. Mark 4 pot labels *A, B, C,*
and *D,* and place one along the outer edge of
each section (see Figure 16 • 6).

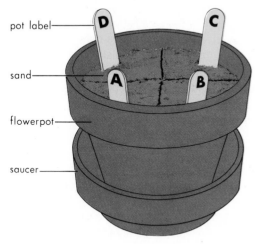

pot label

sand

flowerpot

saucer

Figure 16 • 6

Using a scalpel, take 4 cuttings from the
coleus plant. Three of these (A, B, C) must
each have 3 pairs of leaves and a terminal
bud; the 4th cutting (D) must be at least 5 cm
long and must be taken from *between* pairs of
leaves. (If possible, obtain D and one of the
other cuttings from the same branch.)

From Cutting A remove the bottom pair of
leaves. With a pencil, make a hole in the center of Section A in the pot. The depth of this
hole should be about 1 cm less than the distance from the base of Cutting A to the lower
pair of remaining leaves. Insert Cutting A into
the hole so that the lower pair of leaves is just
above the sand. Press the sand together
around the cutting.

From Cutting B remove the tip of the
branch and all but the uppermost pair of
leaves. Make a hole in the center of Section B
and plant as you did Cutting A.

Prepare Cutting C just as you did B, and
plant it in Section C. Then remove its remaining pair of leaves.

Plant Cutting D, placing it so that at least
5 mm project above the level of the sand.

Cover the cuttings with a plastic bag, and
close the bag's open end around the rim of
the pot with string. Set the pot containing the
coleus plant and the cuttings in a place where
it will receive abundant light. Add water to
the saucer whenever necessary.

After about three weeks, examine the
plant from which the cuttings were taken.
• What, if anything, has happened at the points
where cuttings were removed?(1)   Remove
the plastic cover from the pot containing the
cuttings and examine them.   • Which ones
seem to be alive? In each case, what is the
evidence for your decision?(2)

Loosen the sand and remove Cutting A.
• Have roots developed? If so, at what points
on the cutting?(3)   • What, if anything, has
happened to the cut surface?(4)   • What, if
anything, has happened to the tip of the cutting?(5)

Loosen the sand and remove Cutting B.
• Have roots developed? If so, at what
points?(6)   • What, if anything, has happened
to the end that was in the sand?(7)   • What,
if anything, has happened to the exposed
end?(8)

Loosen the sand and remove Cutting C.
• Have roots developed? If so, at what

points?(9)   • What, if anything, has happened to the end that was in the sand?(10)   • What, if anything, has happened to the exposed end?(11)

Loosen the sand and remove Cutting D. • Have roots developed? If so, at what points?(12)   • What, if anything, has happened to the end that was in the sand?(13) • What, if anything, has happened to the exposed end?(14)

CONCLUSIONS

First consider only the plant from which the cuttings were taken.   • What evidence do you have that coleus has the ability to regenerate parts lost by injury?(15)

Now consider the evidence from the cut-

tings.   • To what extent might the accidental breaking up of a coleus plant (by a hailstorm, for example) result in the reproduction of coleus plants?(16)

FOR FURTHER INVESTIGATION

1. Use this procedure to investigate and compare the abilities of other plant species—tomato, household geranium, begonia, bean, pepper, marigold, zinnia, for example—to reproduce vegetatively.

2. Among animals, planarians have considerable ability to regenerate. To what extent is it possible to obtain vegetative reproduction in planarians? For methods consult F. Moog, *A Laboratory Block on Animal Growth and Development* (Boston: D. C. Heath & Co., 1963).

SEXUAL REPRODUCTION

The main point in sexual reproduction is quite simple: A new individual begins with the union of two cells—*fertilization.* But the consequences of this event are great. They affect heredity, the mechanisms of evolution, and much of the behavior of organisms.

gametes [gə mēts′; Greek: *gamos*, marriage]

Gametes and zygotes. Only specialized cells called *gametes* can unite in the process of fertilization. In some unicellular organisms, gametes look just like other cells of the same species. In some multicellular organisms, gametes differ from other cells only in number of chromosomes. In such cases, gametes can be distinguished only by what they do—their uniting to form new individuals. In most cases, however, gametes are both specialized in function and visibly differentiated from other cells.

Furthermore, the two gametes of any uniting pair are usually different from each other. One kind, the *sperm* cell, is usually relatively small, carries very little reserve food, and is motile. The other kind, the *ovum* (egg cell), is usually larger, carries a reserve food supply, and is nonmotile. The differences between sperms and ova are somewhat variable, but they are the basis for defining sexes. An organism (or any part of an organism) that produces ova is called *female;* an organism (or any part) that produces sperms is called *male.*

In some organisms that have no visible differences between uniting gametes there is evidence that biochemical differences may exist. For example, in one kind of common mold the hyphae that unite in sexual reproduction are not just any two hyphae; they must be from two different varieties (strains). However, because the two strains appear alike, they cannot be called male and female; they are simply referred to as plus ($+$) and minus ($-$).

A cell produced by the union of gametes—by fertilization—is a

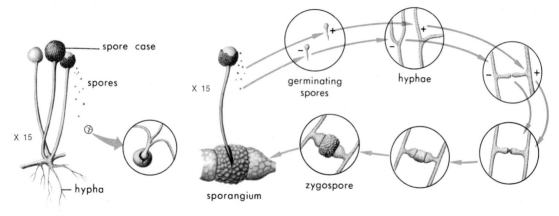

ASEXUAL REPRODUCTION   SEXUAL REPRODUCTION

zygote. After zygote formation there are many pathways of development. In a unicellular organism a zygote is itself a complete new individual, but in a multicellular organism a zygote is merely a beginning. From this beginning a new individual develops by repeated mitotic cell divisions. But these divisions may not occur immediately. In some species a zygote produces a thick covering that is resistant to heat and drying; in this form it may remain dormant for months or

Figure 16 • 7
Comparison of asexual and sexual reproduction in black bread mold, *Rhizopus nigricans.*

zygote [zī'gōt; Greek: *zygon,* a yoke]

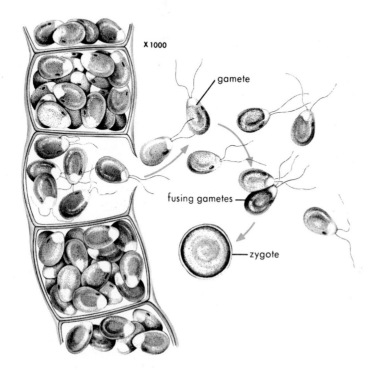

Figure 16 • 8
In the algal genus *Ulothrix* gametes have flagella. Are these sperm cells?

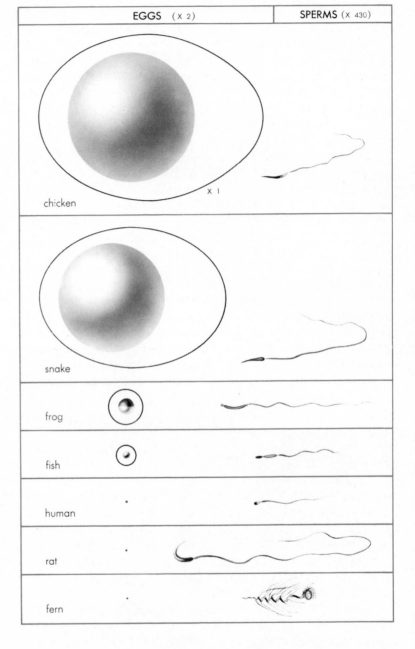

EGGS (x 2)		SPERMS (x 430)

chicken

x 1

snake

frog

fish

human

rat

fern

Figure 16 • 9

Comparison of some eggs (ova) and sperms. Notice the very different magnifications. In chicken, snake, frog, and fish, the ova are surrounded by other materials (*shown in outline*).

even years. In some species a zygote develops into an embryo, which then becomes dormant. In still other species a zygote develops without pause, though often with recognizable embryo and other stages, to adulthood.

Chromosome numbers. Suppose each gamete contains 4 chromosomes. Then the resulting zygote must have 8 chromosomes. A new individual develops from a zygote by means of mitotic cell divisions, and each of these results in daughter cells with the same number of chromosomes as the parent cell. Therefore, in our example, all the cells of the individual that develops from the zygote must contain 8 chromosomes. Continuing our reasoning, we might predict that when the individual matures and forms gametes, each of them will contain 8 chromosomes. When two of these gametes unite, the number of chromosomes in the new zygote will be 16. Would not *every* following generation redouble the number of chromosomes? Clearly there is something wrong with our reasoning.

There is nothing wrong with our idea that cells contain definite numbers of chromosomes. By 1890 cell biologists had shown this. Counting chromosomes is a difficult and tedious job, but chromosome number has now been determined for many species. For example, in corn the number is 20; in the housefly, 12; and in man, 46. Obviously something happens that we did not include in our reasoning: at some step in the life cycle of a sexually reproducing organism, the number of chromosomes must be reduced to compensate for their doubling at fertilization.

tedious [tĕd′ē əs; Latin: *taedet*, to be disgusted with]: here, monotonous but requiring close attention

How and when does this occur? Most of the solution to this problem was worked out just prior to the beginning of the 20th century. Answers to the "how" part of the question turn out to be rather similar for all sexually reproducing organisms—a process called *meiosis.* But the answers to the "when" part vary a great deal.

compensate [kŏm′pən sāt′; Latin: *cum*, with, together, + *pendere*, to hang]: to weigh one thing against another

Meiosis. The process of meiosis consists of two nuclear divisions. As you read the following description, refer often to Figure 16 · 10.

meiosis [mī ō′sĭs; Greek: *meioun*, to make smaller]

The first division begins somewhat like a mitotic division. A spindle forms. Chromosomes become visible as double threads, each pair of chromatids held together by a centromere. However, before moving toward the equator of the spindle, each chromosome pairs with its *homologue*—another that is visibly similar to it. Since each chromosome consists of two chromatids, a pair appears as four strands—often twisted together. Further, at the equator the centromeres do not divide. As a result, whole double-chromatid chromosomes move to the poles of the spindle—one member of each pair to one pole, the other member of each pair to the other pole. Therefore, the number of chromosomes gathering at each pole is *half* the number present in the original cell.

Review mitosis, pages 357–359.

homologue [hŏm′ə lôg′; Greek: *homos*, the same, + *logos*, speech]

The cytoplast may now begin to divide, but the chromosomes do not fade from view as they do at the end of mitosis. Instead, another division begins in each chromosome group. This division is much like mitotic division. The chromosomes gather at the equator of the new spindle, the centromeres divide, and the chromatids (now chromosomes) move to the poles of the spindle. New nuclei are formed, and usually the cytoplast divides. The result of the whole process is four new nuclei, each with half the number of chromosomes that the original cell possessed. The number of chromosomes before meiosis is called the *diploid* number; the number after meiosis is called the *monoploid* number. Gametes contain the monoploid number for a

diploid [dĭp′loid; Greek: *diploos*, double, + *eidos*, form, shape]

monoploid [măn′ə ploid; Greek: *monos*, single, + *eidos*]. A synonym is "haploid" [Greek: *haploos*, single, simple].

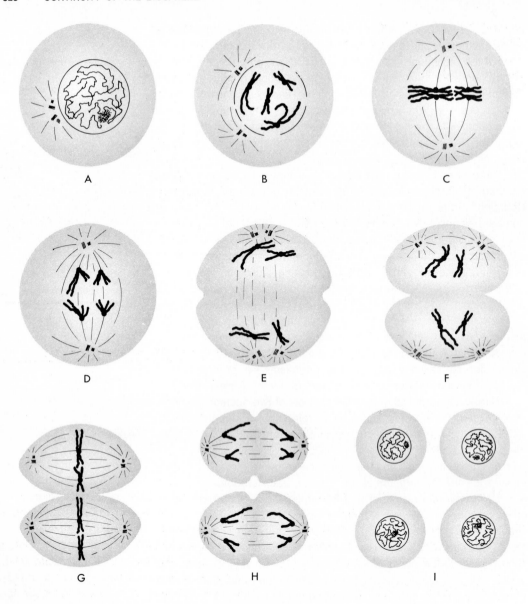

Figure 16 · 10

Diagrammatic representation of meiosis. In this case what is the diploid number of chromosomes?

The numbers of chromosomes mentioned on page 527, paragraph 2, are diploid. What is the monoploid number for each of these organisms?

particular species; union of gametes restores the diploid number.

To simplify the description, one important feature of the first meiotic division was neglected. The photograph in Figure 16 · 11 shows that when chromosomes are paired, more than twisting is involved. The four chromatid strands actually exchange partners, much as a tangle of zippers might. Precisely what is happening to the four chromatids in the photograph cannot be determined visually. Two possibilities are shown in the drawings beside the photograph. Which is the correct interpretation? The answer must await evidence presented in Chapter 17. At present we can only say that for many organisms this complex pairing pattern is necessary to orient chromosomes properly on the spindle, so that one chromosome of each pair will move to each pole.

Figure 16 · 11

Photograph of chromosomes in meiosis (A).   × 500 Drawings of two possible interpretations (B and C).

James Kezer

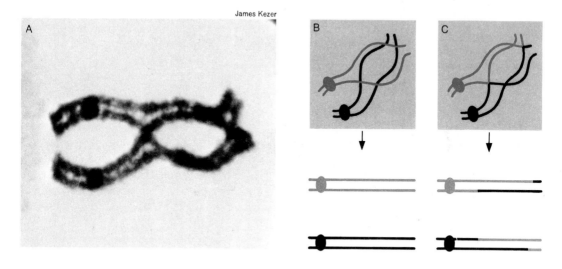

Investigation 16.2

A MODEL OF MEIOSIS

INTRODUCTION

Many biological events are easier to understand when they are explained by means of models. By duplicating the nuclear events of meiosis in a model, this investigation will help you to understand the process.

MATERIALS AND EQUIPMENT

(for each team)

beads, 2 colors, 36 of each
pipe cleaners, 2
scissors
wrapping paper, 2 pieces
crayon

PROCEDURE

Begin the construction of the meiosis model by making up 8 strands of beads as follows:

8-bead strands, all of the first color, 2
8-bead strands, all of the second color, 2
10-bead strands, all of the first color, 2
10-bead strands, all of the second color, 2

Each strand of beads represents a chromatid. Using short pieces of pipe cleaner to represent centromeres, fasten like chromatids together to form chromosomes:

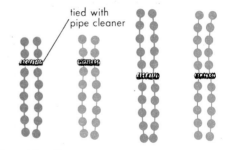

tied with pipe cleaner

Figure 16 · 12

On a large sheet of wrapping paper, draw a spindle large enough to contain the chromosomes you have made. Assume that the early events of the first division have already occurred—the formation of the spindle, the disappearance of the nuclear membrane, the formation of the chromosomes from the nuclear material.

Arrange the 4 chromosomes along the equator of the spindle in pairs. Since gametes contain only half the number of chromosomes characteristic of a species, you can assume that any individual received 1 chromosome of each pair from its male parent and its homologue from its female parent. Though chromosomes of a homologous pair cannot be distinguished from each other under the microscope, you are using colors to distinguish between the chromosomes from the male parent and those from the female parent.

Show the overlapping of chromatids by overlapping the strands of beads representing the chromatids of each homologous pair. To show the possible exchange of chromatid parts (Figure 16 · 11), break the strands at the points where they cross and exchange beads from 1 chromosome with an equal number of beads from its homologue. The colors make the exchange visible throughout the rest of the investigation.

Now begin to move chromosomes of each homologous pair toward opposite poles of the spindle. Move them by grasping the centromeres and pulling. As the strands of beads trail behind, each moving chromosome will have a distinctive shape, resulting from both its length and the position of its centromere.

When the chromosomes of each pair reach the 2 poles, draw 2 more spindles. These spindles should be centered on the poles of the first division, and their axes should be perpendicular to the axis of the first. The model is now ready for the second division of meiosis.

Place the chromosomes along the equators of the 2 new spindles. Unfasten the centromere of each chromosome. Grasping each chromatid at the centromere, pull the chromatids to opposite poles of their spindles. If there are 4 members of your team, all the chromatids can be made to move at once, as they do in a living cell.

Discard the wrapping paper and reassemble the chromosomes as they are shown in Figure 16 · 12. Using a new sheet of paper, repeat the process of meiosis without referring to the directions printed here.

SUMMARY

• How would a mitosis model differ from this one?(1)

• What are some advantages of using a model to visualize a process?(2)

• What are some disadvantages?(3)

PATTERNS OF REPRODUCTION AMONG PLANTS

Thus far we have been considering basic similarities in the reproductive processes of all organisms. But there are also some well-defined differences among organisms. These differences are most conspicuous in multicellular plants and in animals.

CHARACTERISTICS OF PLANT REPRODUCTION

In the plant kingdom asexual methods of reproduction are more frequent than in the animal kingdom. In most plant species both asexual and sexual methods occur. In some species sexual reproduction is rarely observed, however. In some species of algae and fungi, for example, zygotes are formed only under unfavorable environmental

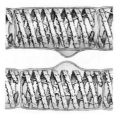 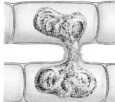 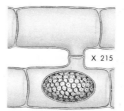

X 215

BEGINNING OF
CONJUGATION

UNION OF GAMETES

ZYGOTE FORMED

Figure 16 · 13
Nonmotile gametes develop
from undifferentiated cells
in the algal genus *Spirogyra.*
This kind of sexual process
is referred to as conjugation.

conditions—such as the approach of winter.

In bryophytes and tracheophytes (and often in the red and brown algae) there is a regular alternation of sexual and asexual methods —one generation reproducing sexually and the next, asexually. Such *alternation of generations* occurs in all the familiar plants; but it is not easily observed, for the sexual generation is microscopic.

Where sexual methods occur in the plant kingdom, the gametes may be alike and motile (Figure 16 · 8). Or they may be alike and not motile. But most often the two gametes are unlike.

One major difference between sexual reproduction in plants and in animals is the timing of meiosis—the "when" part of the question on page 527. In animals meiosis occurs during the formation of gametes; in plants it often occurs much earlier.

EXAMPLES OF PLANT REPRODUCTION

Several times in this chapter we have referred to reproductive processes of fungi and algae. Now we shall look at bryophytes and tracheophytes, which are often linked together as the subkingdom Embryophyta because in these plants an individual that develops from a zygote is dependent—at least for a time—upon its parents.

A moss. In looking at the life cycle of a moss (Figure 16 · 14), we may start with spores. If a spore reaches a favorable environment— usually a moist soil surface—the wall bursts open. The cell within begins to divide by mitosis, and a set of long green threads is formed. From this arises the familiar moss plant, which has a stalk, tiny leaflike structures, and rootlike threads that gather water and nutrients.

At the tips of such plants, *antheridia* (sperm-producing structures) and *archegonia* (ovum-producing structures) are formed. In some species a single plant produces both kinds of gametes; in other species the sexes are separate. During wet weather, sperm cells swim to an ovum and fertilization occurs in an archegonium.

The resulting zygote begins to divide immediately, forming an embryo within the archegonium. The embryo eventually grows out of the archegonium and may become taller than its parent. It often forms chlorophyll and produces food, but it must obtain water and dissolved minerals from its parent, to which it remains attached. Eventually a

Why might asexual reproduction be abandoned at the onset of unfavorable environmental conditions?

Embryophyta [ĕm′brĭ ŏf′ĭ tə; embryo + Greek: *phyton,* plant]. Refer to page 154.

antheridia [ăn′thə rĭd′ĭ ə; Greek: *anthos,* flower, + *idion,* little]
archegonia [är kə gō′nĭ ə; Greek: *archos,* first, chief, + *gonos,* offspring]

How might the kind of sexual reproduction discussed in the above paragraph affect the number of spores produced by the sporophyte?

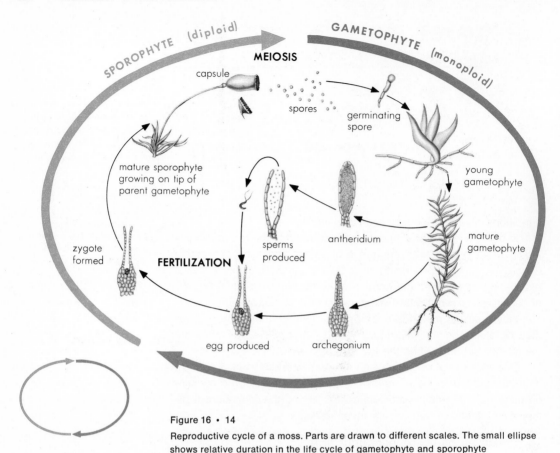

Figure 16 · 14

Reproductive cycle of a moss. Parts are drawn to different scales. The small ellipse shows relative duration in the life cycle of gametophyte and sporophyte generations. Compare with Figures 16 · 15 and 16 · 19.

spore case develops at its tip. Within this case meiosis occurs, and cells with the monoploid number of chromosomes develop into spores. This completes the cycle.

Two points are useful for comparing this life cycle with cycles of other plants. First, the cycle involves two generations. Because meiosis occurs when spores are formed, the "leafy" plant developed directly from a spore must be composed entirely of monoploid cells. This monoploid organism is called a **gametophyte** because it produces gametes. When the gametes unite, a diploid zygote is formed; and the plant developed from it is called a **sporophyte** because it bears spores. Second, fertilization requires a liquid in which the sperms may swim; in terrestrial mosses it can only occur when there is rain or dew.

A lycopsid. The genus *Selaginella* is composed of small plants that are often found competing with grass in moist and shaded lawns. They look somewhat like mosses; but, being tracheophytes, they have vascular systems and, therefore, true roots, stems, and leaves.

gametophyte [gə mē′tə fīt′]

sporophyte [spŏr′ə fīt′]

Selaginella [sə lăj′ə nĕl′ə]

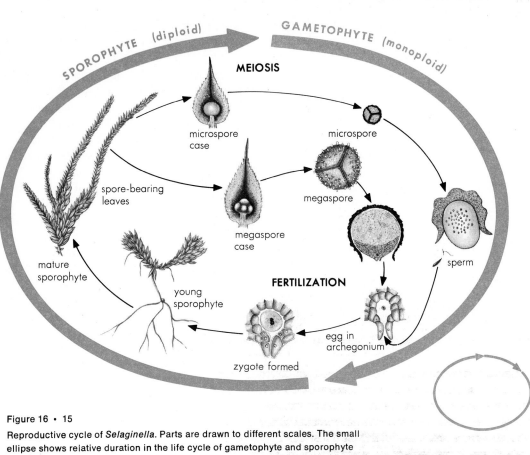

SPOROPHYTE (diploid)   GAMETOPHYTE (monoploid)

MEIOSIS

microspore
case

microspore

spore-bearing
leaves

megaspore

megaspore
case

mature
sporophyte

FERTILIZATION

young
sporophyte

egg in
archegonium

zygote formed

sperm

Figure 16 • 15

Reproductive cycle of *Selaginella*. Parts are drawn to different scales. The small
ellipse shows relative duration in the life cycle of gametophyte and sporophyte
generations.

At the tips of some of the branches, many tiny overlapping leaves
are produced. On the inner surfaces of these leaves are spore cases.
As in the mosses, meiosis occurs during spore formation, which
means that the spores have the monoploid number of chromosomes.
There are two kinds of spore cases. One kind produces small spores
and the other larger spores, though both are nearly invisible.

In the smaller kind of spore, the single cell divides without breaking from the spore wall. The structure that develops in this tiny space
may be thought of as a minute gametophyte. It forms a single antheridium; indeed, the whole male gametophyte is scarcely anything more
than an antheridium. By the time the spore leaves the parent plant, it
contains within its antheridium many flagellated sperms.

The larger kind of spore develops into a female gametophyte,
which forms several archegonia, each with an egg cell. Fertilization
depends on dew or rainwater, through which sperm cells are able to
swim to the eggs. As the resulting zygote develops into a young plant,
the female gametophyte nourishes it with food originally stored in the

spore. Eventually the new sporophyte forms roots and chlorophyll-bearing leaves and so becomes independent.

In the life cycle of *Selaginella* are several similarities to the life cycle of a moss: First, meiosis occurs just before spore formation; second, there is an alternation of generations; third, water is necessary for fertilization. On the other hand, the spores of *Selaginella* are of two kinds, one producing a male gametophyte and the other a female gametophyte. Also, the gametophytes are tiny in comparison with the sporophytes. Keep these points in mind as you consider reproduction in a flowering plant.

For explanation of a number of terms in this section, look back to page 152.

An angiosperm. Think of the pistils and stamens of an angiosperm flower as highly modified leaves that produce spores (just as do the slightly modified leaves of *Selaginella*). The pistils produce the larger spores and the stamens produce the smaller spores; thus we can call the pistil a female structure and the stamen a male structure.

In many angiosperms, male and female structures occur in the same flower. In some—the oak family, for example—they occur in separate flowers on the same individual plant. In a few angiosperms, such as holly, individual plants are either entirely male (bearing flowers with stamens but no pistils) or entirely female (bearing flowers with pistils but no stamens).

How does this statement relate to the explanation of "male" and "female" given on page 524?

Meiosis occurs in cells within the pistil, but a spore does not separate from the sporophyte, as it does in *Selaginella*. Instead it develops right within the pistil of the flower into a gametophyte that consists of only a few cells. This, together with some enclosing tissues, is called an *ovule.* Within an ovule several nuclei form in a single cytoplast. One of these nuclei is the egg nucleus.

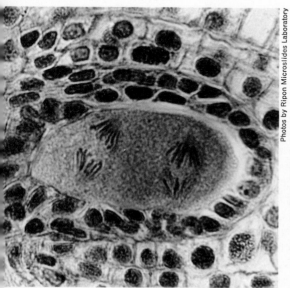
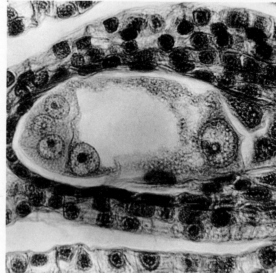

Photos by Ripon Microslides Laboratory

A   X 225

Figure 16 · 16   B   X 225

The gametophyte of an angiosperm (a lily). *(A)* Meiosis in the developing ovule. *(B)* Mature ovule ready to be fertilized; the egg nucleus is one of those on the left.

In the tip of the stamen many spores are produced by meiosis. Each spore divides into two cells; then the spore wall around them thickens, and the result is a pollen grain.

If fertilization is to occur, a whole pollen grain must be transported to a pistil of a flower of the same species. Because most flowers have both stamens and pistils, it might seem that this would be an easy matter—the pollen has only to fall from the stamen onto the pistil of the same flower. Such *self-pollination* does occur, but in many plants various devices prevent it. Though pollen may be transported from flower to flower by wind, a large proportion of angiosperms are pollinated by insects.

On the pistil there is usually a sticky area to which pollen grains adhere. Each pollen grain begins to grow a *pollen tube,* which penetrates into the pistil. The pollen grain and its tube can be considered the male gametophyte. It produces two sperm nuclei, which are carried along in the pollen tube as it grows (Figure 16 • 17). Thus angiosperms (and gymnosperms, which also have pollen grains) are not dependent upon water for fertilization.

Eventually a pollen tube reaches an ovule, where one of the sperm nuclei unites with the egg nucleus, forming a zygote. The second sperm nucleus unites with another nucleus in the ovule. Unlike the monoploid egg nucleus, this nucleus is diploid; by uniting with a sperm nucleus, it forms a *triploid* nucleus—one with *three* sets of chromosomes. In most plants this triploid nucleus gives rise to a mass of food-storing cells, the endosperm.

The zygote develops into a small plant, an embryo. Unlike an embryo of *Selaginella,* an angiosperm embryo becomes dormant. With

What structures in angiosperms might correspond to antheridia and archegonia?

Investigate means by which self-pollination is prevented.

A pollen tube may be surprisingly long—for example, in corn as long as the silk.

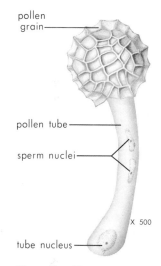

pollen grain

pollen tube

sperm nuclei

X 500

tube nucleus

Figure 16 • 17

Male gametophyte of an angiosperm.

triploid [trĭp′loid; Latin: *triplus,* threefold, + Greek: *eidos,* form]

Figure 16 • 18

Stages (*A to D*) in fertilization and embryo development of an angiosperm.

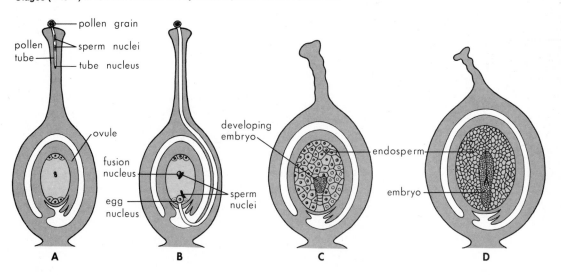

pollen grain

pollen tube

sperm nuclei

tube nucleus

ovule

fusion nucleus

egg nucleus

developing embryo

sperm nuclei

endosperm

embryo

A   B   C   D

In what ways may seed
dormancy be of adaptive
value?

its food supply and a coat formed from ovule tissues, it is a seed. The
pistil, sometimes along with other parts of the flower, develops into
a fruit.

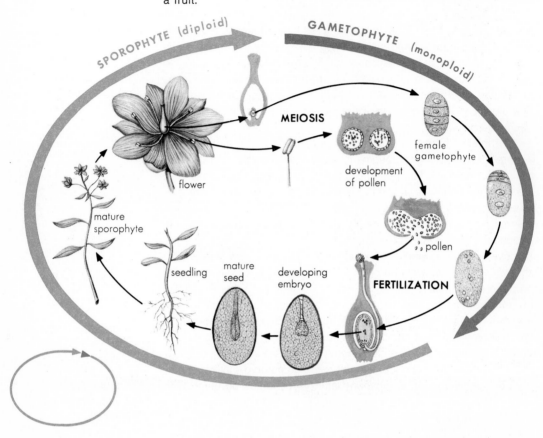

Figure 16 • 19

Reproductive cycle of an angiosperm. The parts are drawn to different scales. The small ellipse shows
relative duration in the life cycle of gametophyte and sporophyte generations.

PATTERNS OF REPRODUCTION AMONG ANIMALS

CHARACTERISTICS OF ANIMAL REPRODUCTION

In the animal kingdom reproduction is primarily sexual. Even in
species that have asexual methods, as do many coelenterates, sexual
reproduction takes place frequently. In animals alternation of monoploid with diploid generations is unknown. In coelenterates there is an
alternation of a sexual generation with an asexual generation, but
both are diploid. Furthermore, in animals gametes are always of two
kinds, and meiosis occurs just before or during gamete formation.

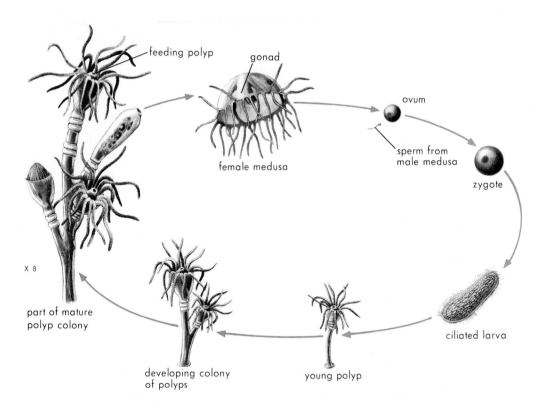

feeding polyp

gonad

ovum

sperm from
male medusa

female medusa

zygote

X 8

part of mature
polyp colony

ciliated larva

developing colony
of polyps

young polyp

Figure 16 · 20

Reproduction in a coelenterate, *Obelia*. Polyps reproduce asexually, forming medusae, which then reproduce sexually. Only sperm cells and ova are monoploid.

Gamete formation. In all animals except sponges, meiosis and gamete formation occur in special structures called *gonads*. Gonads that produce ova are *ovaries;* those that produce sperm cells are *testes.* The two kinds of gonads are usually distinct, though in American oysters gonads produce ova during one year and sperms during the following year.

gonads [gŏn′ădz; Greek: *gonos*, offspring]

How would you describe the sex of an oyster?

In animals nuclear divisions during meiosis are accompanied by divisions of the cytoplast. In the testes each of the resulting four cells becomes a sperm cell. Because there is no period of growth between the two meiotic divisions, only a small cytoplast surrounds the nucleus in each sperm cell. Most of the cytoplast is in the form of a tail by which the sperm cell swims; the head consists mainly of the cell's nucleus.

See Figure 16·9.

In egg formation the substance of the cytoplast is distributed somewhat differently during meiosis. In the first meiotic division almost all of this substance goes to one cell, resulting in one large and one small cell. In the second meiotic division the same thing happens to the larger cell. The outcome is the formation of one large cell, which has almost all of the cytoplast of the original cell, and three

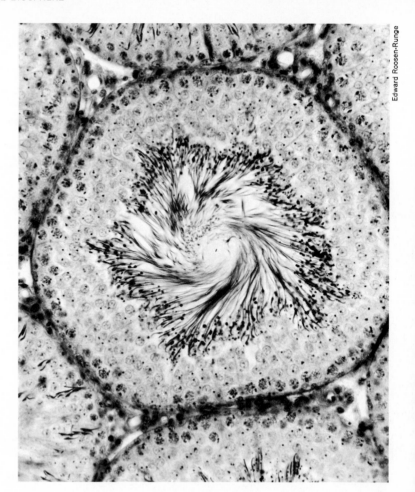

Edward Roosen-Runge

Figure 16 • 21

Photomicrograph of a section through a rat testis. Sperm cells are formed in the walls of tubules. Cells between tubules secrete hormones.   × 375

small cells. The one large cell becomes an ovum; the others usually die. In many species egg cells increase in size after they are formed, but there is enormous variation in the size of fully developed animal egg cells. For an idea of this variation, refer to Figure 16 • 9. A chicken egg is many times larger than a human egg, which may seem surprising in view of the difference in size between a newly hatched chick and a newborn baby.

Sex in animals. In most animals any one individual has either ovaries or testes, not both. Often this difference in the gonads is reflected by differences in other characteristics—secondary sexual characteristics. These may be differences in appearance or differences in voice or behavior. But in a few cases only differences in the gonads distinguish the sexes from each other; otherwise, the males and females appear identical.

In some animals an individual has both ovaries and testes. This is true of earthworms. It is also true of many other annelids, most flatworms, and some crustaceans. An individual animal that has both

Figure 16 • 22
Some secondary sexual
characteristics in animals.

ovaries and testes is called a *hermaphrodite*. Even among vertebrates, hermaphroditic individuals occasionally occur, though they
are not normal in any vertebrate species.

Fertilization. The tails of sperm cells make it possible for them to
swim, but of course there must be some liquid in which to swim. Animals that live in water can release eggs and sperms directly into their
environment. But sperms contain only a very small amount of stored
food. Hence, they can survive only a short time after being released
from the parent. Obviously, then, if there is to be any reasonable
chance that a sperm will unite with an ovum, both must be released
at approximately the same time and place.

Consider the striped bass (Class Osteichthyes) that annually as-
cend all the large rivers of the Atlantic coast and some of the Pacific.
The trip upriver brings the fish into shallow pools, where females lay
eggs and males deposit sperms simultaneously. What factors bring

hermaphrodite [hûr măf′rə dīt′;
Greek: Hermes, a god, +
Aphrodite, a goddess]. This
word is not used by botanists,
but essentially the same
condition is very frequent
among angiosperms. Can you
give examples?

striped bass. See Figure
16·28.

Figure 16 · 23
Specialized behavior called courtship precedes copulation in many animals.

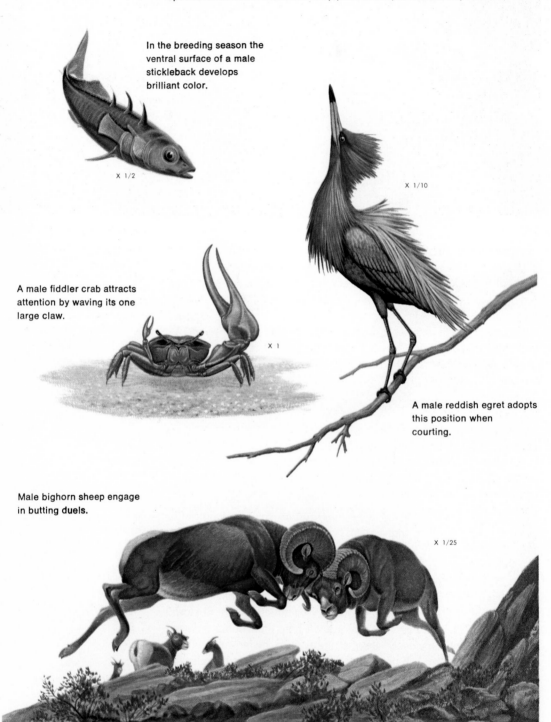

In the breeding season the ventral surface of a male stickleback develops brilliant color.

X 1/2

X 1/10

A male fiddler crab attracts attention by waving its one large claw.

X 1

A male reddish egret adopts this position when courting.

Male bighorn sheep engage in butting duels.

X 1/25

Figure 16 · 24
From March to July, always a day or two after full moon, grunions come to the beaches of southern California, where their eggs are laid and fertilized. What may time this meeting of the sexes?   × ⅓

male and female bass to the same place at the same time, with eggs and sperms ready to be released? This is a question that involves study of hormonal systems of behavior, and of environmental factors. Biologists have investigated these matters in detail but have not yet fully answered the basic question.

In many phyla the meeting of gametes is still further ensured by internal fertilization. The male places sperms into the body of the female, where they meet the ova at some point between the ovary and the opening to the environment. Internal fertilization is not necessary for aquatic animals, but it occurs among many crustaceans and all cartilaginous fishes.

Among terrestrial animals internal fertilization is a necessity because sperm cells cannot swim through air. But there is still the matter of timing. If, when sperms arrive, the ova have not yet reached a proper stage of development, fertilization will not usually occur, because sperms are short-lived. There are exceptions to this, however. For example, in some insects the sperms are stored in a special sac after they have been deposited within the reproductive system of the female. There they remain alive and are released as eggs are laid—in bees, sometimes several years later!

Parthenogenesis. In some animals, and under certain conditions, an ovum may develop into a new individual without fertilization by a sperm cell. Such reproduction by *parthenogenesis* occurs, for example, among aphids. During summer, generation after generation of aphids are produced in this manner. But there is a problem here. Fertilization restores the diploid number of chromosomes that has been reduced to monoploid by meiosis. What happens when there are successive generations without fertilization?

Research has revealed several answers to this question. Meiosis may be bypassed. Or after meiosis, two of the four resulting cells may unite within the ovary. Or after the first meiotic division, the cytoplast may fail to divide. In all these cases a diploid egg results, and there-

parthenogenesis
[pär'the nō jĕn'ə sĭs; Greek: *parthenos*, maiden, + *genesis*, origin]

Do you consider parthenogenesis a sexual method of reproduction? Why or why not?

embryology [ĕm'brĭ ŏl'ə jĭ; embryo + Greek: *logos*, speech, reason]

How many parents may a sexually reproduced hydra have?

fore offspring are diploid without fertilization. In some species of bees and ants, parthenogenetically produced individuals are indeed mono-ploid as expected—and these individuals are always male.

EXAMPLES OF ANIMAL REPRODUCTION

In multicellular organisms fertilization is merely the beginning of reproduction. Only when a zygote has developed into an embryo and the embryo has become an individual capable of feeding and main-taining itself—only then has reproduction been accomplished. *Embryology* is, therefore, a basic part of the study of reproduction.

Hydra. Through much of the year, hydras reproduce asexually by budding. But under certain conditions they produce ovaries and tes-tes. Most species are hermaphroditic. The testis is a conical elevation on the outer body wall, and sperms are released from it through a small pore at its tip. The ovary is a rounded, swollen structure, also on the outer body wall. Only one ovum is formed in each ovary; at maturity it bursts the ovary wall but remains attached to the parent hydra.

If an ovum is fertilized, the zygote splits into two cells of equal size. Each of these splits, forming four cells; the four form eight, and

Figure 16 • 25

Stages in the embryology of a hydra.

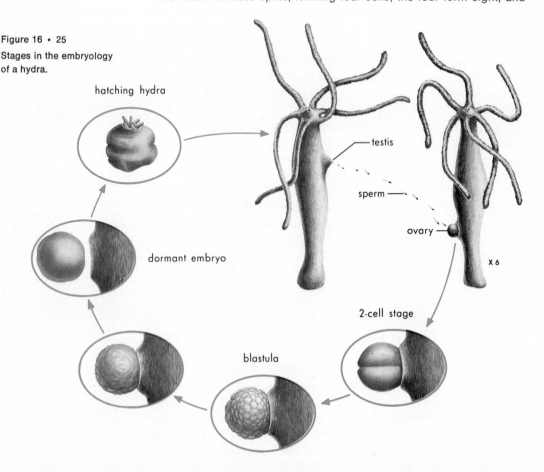

hatching hydra

testis

sperm

ovary

X 6

dormant embryo

2-cell stage

blastula

so on. This process is called **cleavage**. As the number of cells increases, a hollow ball, the *blastula,* is formed. Further divisions inside the blastula fill the hollow space with cells. Thus the embryo includes an outer layer of cells and an inner mass of cells.

blastula [blăs′chŏŏ lə; Greek: *blastos,* a sprout]

At this point the embryo separates from the parent and sinks to the bottom of the pond, where it remains in a dormant condition, protected by a thick wall secreted by its outer cells. Eventually the protective wall breaks away and the embryo elongates. The body of a hydra consists of only two layers of cells: an (outer) **ectoderm** and an (inner) **endoderm.** These two layers develop from the two groups of cells in the early embryo. A hollow space appears among the inner cells, tentacles develop at one end, and in their midst a mouth appears. Development of the new hydra has been completed.

ectoderm [ĕk′tə dûrm′; Greek: *ektos,* outside, + *derma,* skin]
endoderm [ĕn′dō dûrm′; Greek: *endon,* within, + *derma*]

Earthworm. Earthworms are hermaphroditic, but the ova in an individual are not fertilized by sperms of the same individual because tubes from the ovaries lead to the surface of one segment, while those from the testes lead to openings in an adjoining segment. Fertilization is internal. Two earthworms **copulate;** sperms of one individual are deposited in a special sac of the other individual, and likewise, sperms from the second individual are deposited in the sac of the first individual. Later, as ova move from the ovary, they pass the sperm-storage sac; from it sperm cells are released, and the ova are fertilized.

copulate [kŏp′yə lāt; Latin: *copulare,* to unite, couple]

How many parents must an earthworm have?

Earthworm zygotes are enclosed in a tough case secreted by the parent worm. Within this case cleavage occurs. The first cells formed are not of equal size. As a result, the cells of the blastula have a kind of spiral arrangement; this is characteristic in many animal phyla,

Figure 16 • 26

Section through a gastrula (stage following the blastula) of an earthworm embryo.

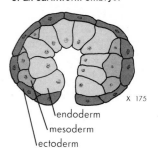

X 175

endoderm
mesoderm
ectoderm

Figure 16 • 27
Earthworms copulating. The thickened bands aid in the transfer of sperms and later secrete a protective coating around the developing embryos.

X 1

from flatworms to arthropods, but not in echinoderms or chordates.

An earthworm embryo also differs from a hydra embryo in having a third layer of cells, a **mesoderm,** between the other two. From the three layers all the organ systems of the body are derived. An earthworm embryo requires two or three weeks for development, after which it escapes from its case as a small copy of the adult.

mesoderm [mĕz′ə dûrm′; Greek: *mesos,* middle, + *derma*]. This layer develops in the embryos of most animals except for sponges, coelenterates, and comb jellies.

See pages 539–541.

Striped bass. In the striped bass fertilization occurs externally. Within a few hours after fertilization, two or more cell divisions occur. The cleavage divisions are approximately equal, but they do not involve the whole zygote. As Figure 16 • 28 shows, new cells are formed only on the top. The *yolk* (food supply) remains undivided and nourishes the embryo. Another difference from hydra or earthworm embryology is the presence of a membrane containing a fluid that surrounds the ovum. Thus, the embryo develops in a somewhat protected environment.

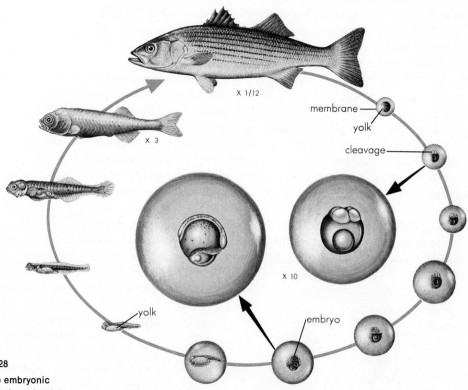

Figure 16 • 28
Stages in the embryonic development of a striped bass.

Three cell layers—ectoderm, mesoderm and endoderm—are formed early in development. Within 36 hours a tadpole-like embryo is visible on top of the yolk; 12 hours later this tiny, undeveloped organism has hatched through the membrane enclosing it and is wriggling about in the water. But the hatchling is not a fully developed fish. It has no mouth, and for many days it lives on the food supply still in the yolk. In about a month the striped bass has gradually developed the appearance of a young fish.

oviduct [ō′vĭ dŭkt; Latin: *ovum*, egg, + *ducere*, to lead]

semen [sē′mən; Latin: *semen*, seed]

Chicken. In a female chicken there is one ovary, with an *oviduct* that leads from the ovary to the outside. Males secrete a fluid, *semen*, in which the sperms swim. During copulation semen is deposited in the oviduct. The sperms swim up the oviduct and meet an ovum in the upper end of the oviduct, where fertilization occurs. Then, as the fertilized egg descends, glands in the wall of the oviduct secrete the various coverings that we find around the yolk of a chicken egg when it is laid. Meanwhile, cleavage occurs. When the egg is laid, the embryo already consists of a few cells on the surface of the yolk. Further development of the embryo is usually delayed until the egg has been incubated by the body heat of the adult bird.

Investigation 16.3

CHICK EMBRYOLOGY

MATERIALS AND EQUIPMENT

(for each team)

Part A. Unincubated Egg
fertilized chicken egg, unincubated
finger bowl
stereomicroscope

Part B. Two-Day Embryo
paper towels
finger bowl
egg incubator
chicken egg, incubated 48 to 52 hours
scissors (fine-pointed)
forceps
medicine dropper
stereomicroscope or hand lens
watch with a second hand
filter paper
Syracuse watch glass
physiological saline solution
heat source
thermometer (−10 to +110°C)
monocular microscope

Part C. Five-Day Embryo
paper towels
finger bowl
egg incubator
chicken egg, incubated 5 to 6 days
scissors (fine-pointed)
forceps
medicine dropper
stereomicroscope or hand lens

Part D. Later Stages of Development
egg incubator
chicken eggs, incubated 10, 14, 18, or 21 days

scissors
forceps
finger bowl
physiological saline solution
heat source
thermometer (−10 to +110°C)
hand lens

PROCEDURE

A. Unincubated egg. Crack a fresh, fertilized chicken egg crosswise. Holding the cracked side up, with your thumbs on each side of the crack, gradually pull apart the two ends and let the contents drop gently into a finger bowl. Observe the *albumen* ("white"), which is made up largely of protein and water. • Where is it most dense?(1) The embryo appears as a white area on the surface of the yolk. • Describe its appearance under the stereomicroscope.(2) Examine the inside of the shell and the membrane that lines it. • At which end of the egg is the membrane not closely attached to the shell?(3) • What occupies this space between membrane and shell?(4) • List in order the structures added around the fertilized ovum as it passes down the hen's oviduct.(5) • Suggest a function for each structure.(6)

B. Two-day embryo. Figure 16·29 shows a chick embryo after 33 hours of incubation at 38°C. At this stage the embryo is still so thin that the parts shown in the drawing can be observed only if stained. *Somites* are

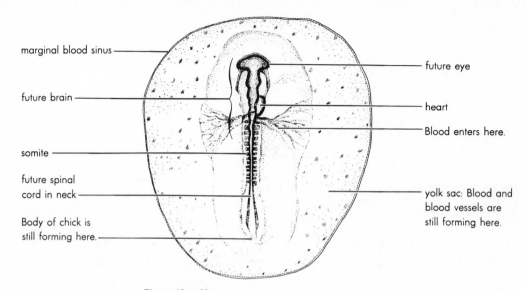

marginal blood sinus

future brain

somite

future spinal
cord in neck

Body of chick is
still forming here.

future eye

heart

Blood enters here.

yolk sac: Blood and
blood vessels are
still forming here.

Figure 16 • 29

Chick embryo after 33 hours of incubation. At this stage the yolk sac is about 1 cm in diameter and is growing along its edge.

blocks of tissue from which vertebrae and muscles develop. Refer to this figure for comparison as you observe a 48- to 52-hour embryo.

Crumple one or two paper towels into a finger bowl and hollow out a space in the center of them to support an egg. Obtain an egg that has been incubated 48 to 52 hours. Before removing it from the incubator, mark a *T* on the top of the egg. Then carry the egg to your work space, holding the marked side up. Keeping that side up, place the egg in the hollow of the paper.

Holding the egg gently but firmly, follow the steps shown in Figure 16 • 30. If you have not rotated the egg since taking it from the incubator, the embryo should be on the top of the yolk. If it is not, *gentle* pushing with the medicine dropper may rotate the yolk until the embryo is on top—but great care must be taken not to break the yolk.

When the embryo is exposed, you can observe the extent of the **yolk sac** by noting the blood vessels on the surface of the yolk. • Approximately what percentage of the yolk is now covered by the yolk sac?(7)   • What do you think is the function of the yolk sac?(8)

Using a stereomicroscope or hand lens, examine the embryo. Locate the heart by looking for pulsating movement. • How fast is the heart beating (pulsations per minute)?(9)

Further observation will be easier if you remove the embryo from the yolk. To do this, follow the steps shown in Figure 16 • 31. Before placing the filter-paper ring on the yolk, make sure that none of the albumen is on the surface of the embryo. If it is, repeat Step C, Figure 16 • 30.

After you have transferred the embryo to the watch glass, the saline solution may become cloudy. If this happens, draw off the saline with a clean medicine dropper and replace it with fresh, warm saline. Place the watch glass on the stage of a monocular microscope and observe under *low* power. • Which of the structures shown in Figure 16 • 29 can you see?(10)   • Compare the general shape of the embryo with that of the 33-hour embryo.(11)   Most of the large mass of tissue adjacent to the heart will become brain. This part of the embryo may have a membrane over it. This is the developing **amnion.** You may be able to see an ear opening, which was not visible in the 33-hour embryo. Examine

A. Carefully insert point of scissors at x, barely penetrating the shell, and slowly clip the shell completely around the egg.

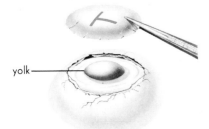

yolk

B. With forceps carefully lift the loose piece of shell and discard.

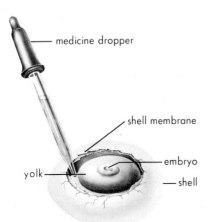

medicine dropper

shell membrane

embryo

yolk

shell

C. Draw off albumen with medicine dropper until yolk is not covered.

D. Remove more of the white and shell until only one half of the egg shell remains.

Figure 16 • 30

Steps in exposing a chick embryo in an early stage of development (*left*).

Figure 16 • 31

Steps in removing a chick embryo from the yolk (*below*).

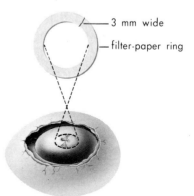

3 mm wide

filter-paper ring

A. Measure diameter of marginal blood sinus. On filter paper, draw a ring that has inner diameter slightly less than diameter of marginal blood sinus. Cut out ring and place over edges of sinus.

B. Grasp ring and edge of membrane. Clip membrane all the way around ring. Slowly lift ring, membrane, and embryo away from yolk.

C. Place ring, membrane, and embryo in Syracuse watch glass containing physiological saline solution (3 mm deep) at 38°C.

Figure 16 • 32

Steps in exposing a chick embryo in a late stage of development.

A. Crack the large end of the egg with scissors or scalpel handle.

the heart carefully. • Can you trace the pathway of the blood through the heart? If so, describe it.(12)

C. Five-day embryo. Using the technique shown in Figure 16 • 30, open an egg that has been incubated 5 days. (Caution: The yolk is quite watery at this stage, and some of the delicate membranes are close to the shell; therefore, it is important that you insert only the *tips* of the scissors beneath the shell.)

Compare the amnion in this embryo with the one in the 2-day embryo. • Describe any differences.(13) Gently probe the surface of the amnion with a blunt pencil. • Is anything besides the embryo inside? If so, what?(14) Next to the amnion and apparently attached to it by a stalk is a bladder-like membrane covered with blood vessels. This is the **allantois.** Through it the embryo obtains oxygen and excretes carbon dioxide. Observe the extent of the blood vessels on the surface of the yolk. • Approximately what percentage of the yolk is now covered by the yolk sac?(15)

B. Use forceps to pick away the shell. Avoid breaking shell membrane if possible.

Using forceps and scissors, carefully cut away the amnion, exposing the embryo. • Compare the size of the eyes with the size of the head.(16) This size relationship is a characteristic of bird embryos in contrast to mammalian embryos. Look for the parts that will become the appendages. • How is it possible to distinguish wings from legs at this stage?(17) • Describe any other differences you can see between a 2-day and a 5-day chick.(18)

D. Later stages of development. Eggs incubated 10, 14, 18, and 21 days are to be opened by different teams. For opening eggs in these later stages of development, use the technique shown in Figure 16 • 32. Try not to break any of the membranes.

When the shell has been removed, you will notice that it is lined with a continuous membrane containing blood vessels. This

C. After part of the shell has been removed, put the egg in finger bowl of physiological saline (at 38°C) and pick off the remainder of the shell.

D. The way the egg will look with all of shell removed.

chorioallantoic membrane results when the allantois is extended and united with another embryonic membrane, the **chorion.** • What substances, then, probably pass through it?(19)

Using scissors and forceps, carefully remove the chorioallantoic membrane. • Can you find the yolk sac? How is it connected to the embryo?(20) • How is the food in the yolk transported to the embryo?(21)

Remove the amnion from around the embryo. • Note all features that indicate the organism is a bird.(22)

After each team has studied its embryo, exchange embryos until all teams have seen each stage of development. • Note (with the day of incubation) features that you were unable to see in your own embryo.(23)

SUMMARY

• List all the structures you have observed, in the order of their first appearance during development.(24)

Using the observations you made in this investigation and supplementing these with any other information you can find, consider the following questions: What characteristics of a chicken egg are adaptations that enable it to develop on land? If the egg developed within the hen instead of outside, what structures would be less important? What explanations can you give for the early development of heart, blood, and blood vessels? How do your observations support the statement (page 119) that chordates show segmentation? What other observations of chordate characteristics did you make (if any)? • Write a summary statement on chick-embryo development that includes your thinking on these questions.(25)

FOR FURTHER INVESTIGATION

1. What effect would incubation at higher or lower temperatures have on the development of a chick embryo? Experiment to test your hypotheses.

2. Pigeon eggs may be incubated artificially, but because the embryos are rather small, handling and observing them are difficult. Even if you cannot make a step-by-step comparison with chicken development, a useful comparison is the state of development at hatching. How do the differences in hatching development relate to parental care? In which bird—chicken or pigeon—is development at hatching most like that of turtles at hatching?

Mammals. Among mammals only monotremes lay eggs. All other mammals retain the fertilized eggs in the body of the female parent, and embryonic development occurs in a **uterus,** a thick-walled part of the tubes that lead from the ovaries to the outside.

uterus [ū′tə rəs]. In nontechnical language this is called the womb.

Most animals reproduce only at certain times of the year. This is true even in a stable climate, such as that of the tropical rain forest. Many animals have a single annual reproductive season. Among domesticated animals such seasonal reproduction is much less clearly marked than in wild ones, but even dogs and cattle breed more frequently at some seasons than at others. Among primates, however, there is a tendency toward continuous breeding. Apes and man reproduce during all months of the year.

In addition to the general seasonal reproductive cycle, which usually affects both sexes, female mammals have a shorter cycle of reproductive activity—the **estrous cycle.** A cycle of physiological activity implies controls. We might expect that we could look to the nervous and endocrine systems for such controls.

estrous [ĕs′trəs; Greek: *oistros*, a gadfly; hence, a frenzy]

Review the discussion of these systems in Chapter 14.

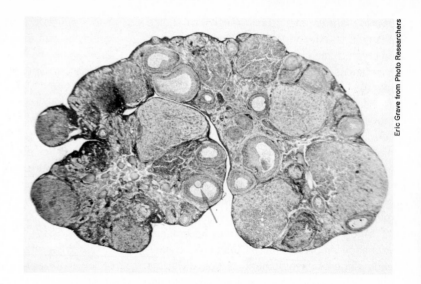

Eric Grave from Photo Researchers

Figure 16 • 33

Cross section of a rat ovary, showing numerous follicles. An egg cell can be seen in the follicle at lower center (*arrow*).   × 26

pituitary gland. See Figure 14·27.

Early efforts of physiologists to explore the control mechanisms indicated that the pituitary gland plays an important part. In experiments with adult female rats, pituitary glands were removed. Development of eggs in the ovaries ceased, and thickening of the lining in the uterus, a usual event in the cycle, failed to occur. These results raised questions: Does the pituitary gland exert a direct effect upon both ovaries and uterus? Or does the pituitary directly influence only the ovaries, which then influence the uterus? Or does the pituitary directly influence only the uterus, which in turn influences the ovaries? And, if removal of the pituitary gland stops the functioning of ovaries and uterus, why are they not continuously active when the pituitary is present?

Other experiments provided information concerning these questions. When rat ovaries are removed, leaving both uterus and pituitary intact, the uterine lining fails to thicken; apparently, then, function of the uterus depends upon the ovaries. But we know from the previous experiments that uterine function depends also upon the pituitary. In still another set of experiments, both pituitaries and ovaries were removed. Then the rats were injected with hormones from ovaries of other rats; thickening of the uterine lining followed. It was concluded that pituitary hormones influence the ovaries and that ovarian hormones influence the uterus.

intact [ĭn tăkt′; Latin: *in-*, not, + *tangere,* to touch]: here, entire or with nothing missing

Man. By many experiments such as these, physiologists have come to understand much about the female reproductive cycle in mammals. As in other studies of physiological processes, much of this understanding can be applied to humans, who have a short-term female cycle even though an annual reproductive cycle is absent. However, in humans (and other primates of the subfamily Hominoidea) the cycle differs enough from that in other mammals to have another name—the *menstrual cycle.*

menstrual [mĕn′strŏŏ əl; Latin: *mensis,* month (because the average length of the cycle is 28 days, the lunar month)]. Do you think this length is accidental?

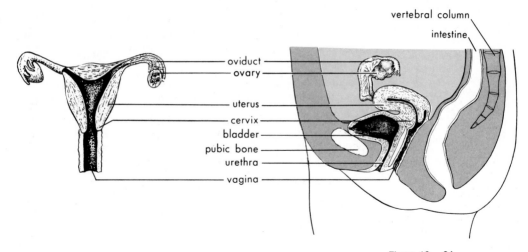

- oviduct
- ovary
- uterus
- cervix
- bladder
- pubic bone
- urethra
- vagina

vertebral column
intestine

Figure 16 • 34
Human female reproductive
system in a sectional view
(*right*), and the principal
organs in a frontal view (*left*).

It is convenient to begin a description of the menstrual cycle at the time when the lining of the uterus is thin. Secretion of *follicle stimulating hormone* (FSH) by the pituitary causes development of a *follicle* in an ovary. Usually one ovum is developed in each cycle. If an ovum is developed in the right ovary during one cycle, then usually during the next an ovum is developed in the left ovary, and so on.

Figure 16 • 35
Hormonal changes in the
human female reproductive
cycle.

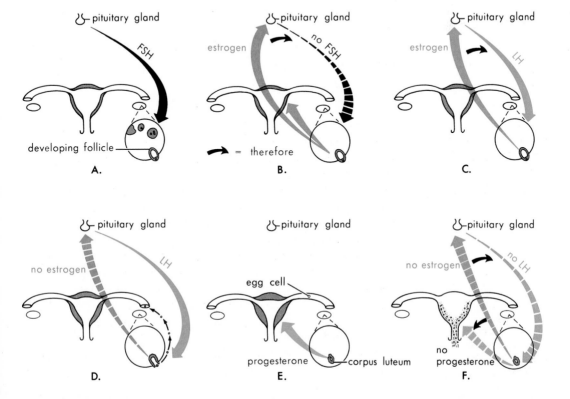

pituitary gland

FSH

developing follicle

A.

pituitary gland

estrogen   no FSH

➤ = therefore

B.

pituitary gland

estrogen   LH

C.

pituitary gland

no estrogen   LH

D.

pituitary gland

egg cell

progesterone   corpus luteum

E.

pituitary gland

no estrogen   no LH

no progesterone

F.

estrogen [ĕs'trə jən; Greek: *oistros*, a gadfly, + *genes*, born]

luteinizing [lōō'tĭ ə nĭ'zĭng; Latin: *luteus*, golden-yellow]

ovulation [ō'vyə lā'shən]

corpus luteum [kôr'pəs lōō'tĭ əm; Latin: *corpus*, body, + *luteus*]. In many mammals this body is yellow.

progesterone [prō jĕs'tə rōn'; Latin: *pro*, before, + *gestare*, to bear young]

slough [slŭf]: cast, shed

vagina [və jī'nə]

Can you recall other physiological processes in which neurohormonal stimulation of the hypothalamus is important?

scrotum [skrō'təm]

penis [pē'nĭs]

Ovum and follicle enlarge and move to the surface of the ovary, and the follicle begins to secrete the hormone *estrogen.* Estrogen does three things. It causes thickening of the uterine lining; it causes the pituitary to cease producing FSH; and it stimulates the pituitary to secrete *luteinizing hormone* (LH). LH brings about *ovulation:* the ovum bursts from the follicle and enters the adjacent oviduct. The follicle then becomes a body called the *corpus luteum.* This, too, secretes a hormone, *progesterone,* which greatly speeds growth of glands and blood vessels in the uterine lining, causing it to become still thicker.

When the follicle bursts at ovulation, its production of estrogen ceases. *If the ovum is not fertilized,* there is no longer estrogen in the blood stimulating the pituitary to produce LH. Without LH, the corpus luteum ceases forming progesterone. And with no more progesterone, the thickened lining of the uterus is no longer maintained; it breaks down. The discharge of blood and the sloughed uterine lining through the *vagina* is called *menstruation.* Meanwhile, decline in concentration of estrogen and progesterone in the blood apparently affects the nervous system, through which the output of neurohormones from the hypothalamus is increased. This, in turn, permits the pituitary to secrete FSH, thus starting a new cycle.

But what happens if the ovum *is* fertilized? This requires the presence of sperm cells, so we turn to the male reproductive system.

In human males, sperm cells are produced continuously in coiled tubules in the two testes, which lie outside the body wall in a sac of skin, the *scrotum.* From the testes, sperms pass through ducts that lead up into the body cavity. Along the way secretions produced by three sets of glands are added to the sperm cells; thus semen is formed. The duct from each testis unites with the urethra, which passes through the *penis.*

As a result of sexual stimuli, veins in the penis contract, slowing the flow of blood, which consequently accumulates in spongy tissue within the penis. This causes stiffening of the penis so that it is able

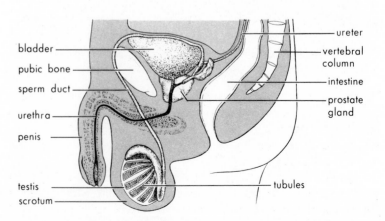

Figure 16 · 36

Human male reproductive system in sectional view.

to penetrate the female vagina. Upon further stimulation semen is discharged. The sperms swim from the vagina through the uterus and into the oviducts; there, if an ovum is present, fertilization occurs.

The pituitary of a male produces both FSH and LH. In a male, LH stimulates endocrine cells in the testes to produce hormones called **androgens**. FSH apparently increases the amount of these hormones, which maintain the functioning of the entire male reproductive system. However, they do not appear to affect the hypothalamus; thus there is no cycle in the reproductive organs of a human male.

androgens [ăn'drə jəns; Greek: *andr*, man, + *genes*, born]

How do you think this might differ in a male white-crowned sparrow? (See page 500.)

Now we can return to the female. If an ovum is fertilized, the menstrual cycle is interrupted. The zygote is moved along the oviduct. When it reaches the uterus, it becomes embedded in the soft, spongy lining, and **pregnancy** begins.

pregnancy [prĕg'nən sĭ; Latin: *pregnans*, heavy with young]

But what prevents the breakdown of the uterine lining and the sloughing of the embryo? The embryo causes glands in the uterine wall to produce estrogen. Uterine estrogen functions just as does follicular estrogen: it prevents production of FSH and stimulates pro-

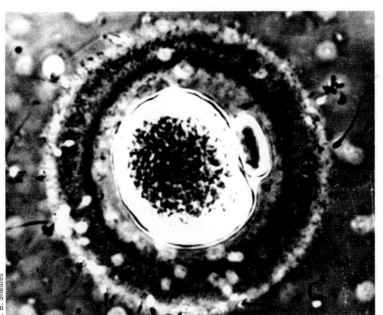

L. B. Shettles

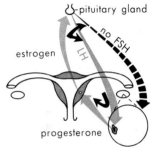

= therefore

Figure 16 · 37
Female hormonal relationships during early part of pregnancy.

Figure 16 · 38
Human ovum surrounded by sperms. In fertilization only one sperm cell penetrates the membrane of an ovum. × 500

duction of LH by the pituitary gland. LH, in turn, causes the corpus luteum to continue to produce progesterone, which maintains the thick lining of the uterus. As long as progesterone is produced, menstruation does not occur, pregnancy is maintained, and no new ova develop in the ovaries.

Very early in pregnancy, embryonic membranes form. A chorion develops against the uterine wall and, together with an outgrowth of the uterine wall itself, forms the **placenta**. A yolk sac appears, but it

placenta [plə sĕnt'ə; Greek: *plax*, anything flat and broad]

In marsupial mammals placentas do not fully form. How might this affect the development of marsupial embryos?

umbilical [əm'bĭl'ĭ kəl; Latin: *umbilicus*, navel]

is not functional; a mammalian egg has very little yolk. An allantois grows out from the embryo, and its blood vessels connect the embryo with the placenta through the **umbilical cord.** The placenta eventually lines much of the uterus. The placenta and umbilical cord together provide the bridge through which, by diffusion, the embryo receives food and oxygen and discharges wastes and carbon dioxide. An amnion develops around a human embryo, just as it does around a chick. It is liquid-filled, protecting the embryo from mechanical shock.

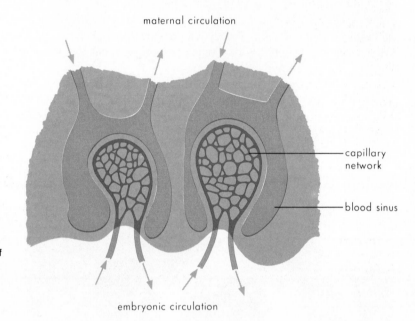

maternal circulation

capillary network

blood sinus

embryonic circulation

Figure 16 • 39

Diagrammatic section through a placenta. The circulations of embryo and mother are separate but close to each other. Blood of the embryo passes through networks of capillaries that are surrounded by small pools of maternal blood.

Hormonal control continues during pregnancy. The developing chorion, for example, secretes a hormone that stimulates the corpus luteum to continue secreting progesterone; this maintains the uterine lining until the placenta begins to secrete both estrogen and progesterone. Eventually the placenta secretes sufficient amounts of hormones to maintain pregnancy even if the ovaries are removed. However, many factors may upset this hormonal control. Or an accident to the mother may injure the embryo even though it is protected by uterus and liquid-filled amnion. In such cases the embryo may be ejected prematurely from the uterus, an event called **abortion.**

By the ninth month (280 days) of human pregnancy, an unborn baby's head is usually turned downward. How the process of birth is initiated is not fully understood. It begins when muscle layers in the wall of the uterus start alternately to contract and relax. At first, the activity is just strong enough to move the baby slowly toward the vagina. At this stage the amnion usually breaks, and its fluid contents are released. Contractions in the muscles of the uterus become

eject [ĭ jĕkt'; Latin: *e*, out, + *jacere*, to throw]: throw or push out

abortion [ə bôr'shən; Latin: *ab*, from, + *oriri*, to rise]

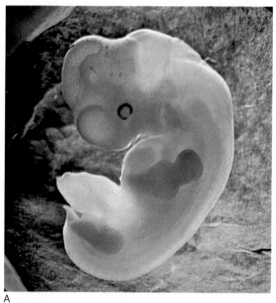

A

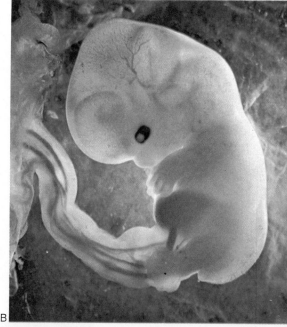

B

Figure 16 • 40

Stages in the development
of a human embryo.
(A) 5 weeks. × 7
(B) 6½ weeks.   × 6
(C) 11 weeks.   × 1/2
(D) 16 weeks.   × 3/4

D

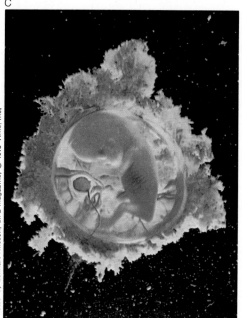

C

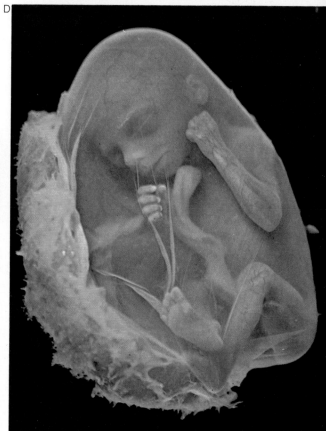

stronger and more frequent, and the baby, still attached to the placenta by the umbilical cord, is pushed out through the vagina. Muscular contractions of the uterus continue until they push out the placenta, commonly called the "afterbirth."

Late in pregnancy the mammary glands undergo changes that prepare them for producing milk after the baby is born. If the baby does not feed from its mother's breasts, the glands soon stop secreting milk. Usually when milk secretion stops, the menstrual cycle begins again.

Figure 16 • 41
The process of human birth.

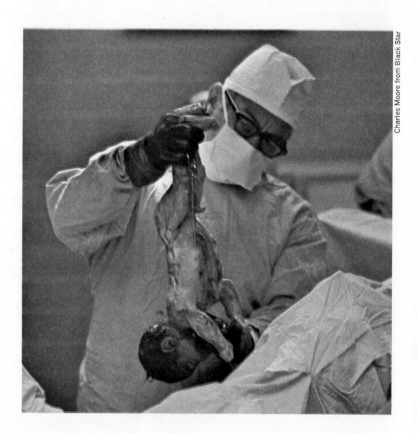

Charles Moore from Black Star

GUIDE QUESTIONS

1. Spontaneous generation and reproduction are two explanations for the production of new life. How do these ideas differ?

2. Which of these ideas did Redi's experiment with meat support? How?

3. From the viewpoint of an individual organism, how does reproduction differ from other life processes?

4. How does vegetative reproduction occur among tracheophytes?

5. How is vegetative reproduction related to regeneration?

6. What is fission? In what groups of organisms does it most frequently occur?

7. What is a sporangium?

8. What is the basic event in the process of sexual reproduction?

9. What is the biological distinction between the terms "male" and "female"?

10. How is a zygote formed?

11. In what ways does meiosis differ from mitosis? Why is meiosis an important event in reproduction?

12. In chickens the diploid chromosome

number is 18. What is the number of chromosomes in the cells that result from meiosis?

13. How is meiosis related to fertilization?

14. What is meant by the phrase "alternation of generations"?

15. In what ways does the reproductive process of a moss differ from that of a primitive tracheophyte as represented by *Selaginella?*

16. Compare the characteristics of the gametophyte generation in mosses, *Selaginella,* and angiosperms. Compare the characteristics of the sporophyte generation, using the same three examples.

17. Why can pollen-bearing plants be considered more completely adapted to life on land than are other terrestrial plants, such as mosses and ferns?

18. What two botanical terms can be considered equivalent to the zoological terms "testis" and "ovary"?

19. How does the formation of sperm cells following meiosis in animals differ from the formation of egg cells?

20. What do we mean when we say that an animal is hermaphroditic?

21. Under what circumstances is internal fertilization necessary? Why?

22. With respect to parentage, how does parthenogenesis differ from the usual methods of sexual reproduction?

23. How is the chromosome number characteristic of a species retained during parthenogenesis?

24. Compare blastula formation in hydras and earthworms.

25. In what major ways does embryological development of a striped bass differ from that of a hydra?

26. From what three embryonic cell layers do the organs of most animals' bodies develop?

27. Where does the food for most animal embryos come from?

28. In chickens where does fertilization occur? How do the sperms reach the ova?

29. What evidence suggests that the pituitary gland plays an important role in the menstrual cycle?

30. When an ovum is not fertilized after it breaks from its follicle, what series of events brings about menstruation in a human female?

31. What is a major difference between the estrous cycle of most mammals and the human menstrual cycle?

32. What is the function of androgens?

33. How is the thick lining of a uterus maintained during pregnancy?

34. What is the function of the estrogen produced by the uterus?

35. Compare protection and nourishment of a developing chick with protection and nourishment of a developing mammal.

36. What is the average length of human pregnancy?

37. How does birth occur?

38. What is the "afterbirth"?

PROBLEMS

1. What experimental procedures could be used to show that progesterone in a particular mammalian species is secreted by the placenta?

2. Testes of vertebrates develop in the body cavity. In man, if they do not descend into the scrotum, they produce no live sperm cells. In some mammals with seasonal breeding, they descend into the scrotum only during the breeding season; during the nonbreeding season they are in the body cavity and produce no sperm cells. If temperatures around the scrotum of an experimental animal are kept the same as the internal body temperature, sperm cells either are not produced or are weak. Yet the testes of birds never leave the

body cavity, and birds have, on the average, a higher internal temperature than most mammals. Can you explain these data?

3. What are the advantages to man of propagating plants by rooting portions of an older plant instead of planting seeds? What is the relation of grafting to this propagation by cuttings?

4. Sexuality is usually discussed in terms of "male" and "female," but we have seen that these terms are not always meaningful—as in some molds. In some protists the situation becomes even more complicated. Investigate "mating types" in the genus *Paramecium* and try to explain the situation as a special case of sexuality.

5. Investigate the ways in which self-pollination is prevented among gymnosperms and angiosperms. Are there, on the other hand, plants in which self-pollination always occurs? Can you see any advantages to a plant species either in self-pollination or in cross-pollination?

6. Describe *apomixis*. To what process in animals is this comparable?

7. From your understanding of plant reproduction, explain each of the following: (*a*) Seeds will not develop in yuccas unless a certain small species of moth lives in the area. (*b*) Berries do not develop on holly trees unless two trees are planted together; even then, berries do not develop on both and may not develop on either. (*c*) In 1839 a single individual of the plant *Alchornea ilicifolia,* bearing only pistillate flowers, produced abundant seeds in the Kew Gardens, near London. The nearest male plant in the species was in Australia. (*d*) Some kinds of flowers open only at night. (*e*) Orchardists often keep apiaries as a sideline. (*f*) Pea plants, even when grown in an insect-free greenhouse, produce seeds. (*g*) At the request of local alfalfa growers, many highways in the American West have signs reading "Slow: Low-flying Bees."

8. Each egg of a bony fish is enclosed in a single membrane. A number of membranes develop during the embryonic life of a bird or mammal. Investigate the development and function of embryonic membranes in all the vertebrate classes.

9. Is human reproduction lacking in seasonality? Record by months the birthdays of the members of your biology class and of as many other classes as possible. If you can obtain the data from all the students in your school, you will have a fairly satisfactory sample. Present the data in the form of a bar graph —one bar for each month. What does the graph indicate about the question?

SUGGESTED READINGS

ALLEN, R. D. "The Moment of Fertilization," *Scientific American,* July, 1959. Pp. 124–130.

EDWARDS, R. G. "Mammalian Eggs in the Laboratory," *Scientific American,* August, 1966. Pp. 10, 72–81.

ETKIN, W. "How a Tadpole Becomes a Frog," *Scientific American,* May, 1966. Pp. 76–80+.

GABRIEL, M. L., and S. FOGEL (eds.). *Great Experiments in Biology.* Englewood Cliffs, N.J.: Prentice-Hall, Inc., 1955. (Reprints of origina' papers in which biological discoveries were announced. Especially recommended: Redi, pp. 187–189; Loeb, pp. 201–203; Driesch, pp. 210–214; and Spemann, pp. 215–219.)

KELLER, D. E. *Sex and the Single Cell.* New York: Pegasus, 1972. (An informative short book that is rather easy to read.)

LEHRMAN, D. S. "The Reproductive Behavior of Ring Doves," *Scientific American,* November 1964. Pp. 48–54.

MICHELMORE, S. *Sexual Reproduction.* New York: The American Museum of Natural History,1965. (Descriptive account of reproduction and embryology in various animal groups. Fairly easy.)

SIMPSON, G. G., and W. S. BECK. *Life: An Introduction to Biology.* Shorter ed: New York: Harcourt, Brace & World, Inc., 1969. Chapters 5 and 8. (An excellent general account of the reproductive process. Advanced.)

SUSSMAN, M. *Growth and Development.* 2nd ed. Englewood Cliffs, N.J.: Prentice-Hall, Inc., 1964. (An excellent discussion of the main features of animal embryology.)

WILSON, C. L., W. E. LOOMIS, and T. A. STEEVES. *Botany.* 5th ed. New York: Holt, Rinehart, and Winston, 1971. (Clear and accurate general accounts of reproduction among plants. Fairly easy.)

WILSON, K. S. "Biology of Reproduction in Ferns," *Natural History,* June, 1965. Pp. 52–59.

Heredity

INHERITANCE

"Who does he look like?" For every infant born, someone asks this question. That a child can be expected to resemble in many ways his parents and his grandparents was certainly one of the first biological ideas developed by man. And still today no biological idea is of more interest.

Man has other interests in the processes by which characteristics are passed from one generation to another—in **inheritance.** He has long worked to improve the characteristics that he finds desirable in his domestic plants and animals. For example, wool-growers have sent sheep that produced poor wool to market as mutton and have selected the best wool-producers as the parents of future flocks. Corn-growers have saved as seed for the next crop ears that contained the largest and most numerous grains. In many cases such **selective breeding** has improved the desired characteristics.

Cindy Rymer from Van Cleve

Figure 17 · 1
Variation in the offspring of
Saluki dogs.

559

Dalmatian [dăl mã′shən]

Frequently, however, very little success has been obtained from selective breeding. Breeders of Dalmatian dogs have wanted animals with many small and distinct black spots. Year after year they have selected for breeding animals that have just the right pattern. But generation after generation, regardless of the pattern of the parents, pups are born with various amounts of spotting. In short, man has long known that many characteristics *are* inherited. But only in the past century has he begun to understand *how* they are inherited.

EVIDENCE FROM A DISEASE

DISCOVERY

Refer to blood cells, page 451, and Figure 14·21.

In 1910 James B. Herrick, a Chicago physician, examined a young man who was suffering from a multitude of ailments, such as muscular aches, swollen joints, dizziness, and shortness of breath. In the course of the examination, he took a blood sample from the patient. Among the red cells in the sample were many nucleated ones —a situation typical of persons with anemia—and many others that were thin, elongated, and crescent- or sickle-shaped. Herrick's was the first description of what is now known as sickle-cell anemia.

Seven years later Victor E. Emmel, a St. Louis physician, found similar sickle-shaped red blood cells while treating a young woman. Dr. Emmel was curious about the source of the odd-shaped cells. Did they have this shape when they were formed in the bone marrow? Apparently not, because the nuclei of new cells are lost rather late in their development and many of the sickle-shaped cells were non-nucleated, just as normal red cells are. In a series of experiments, Dr. Emmel showed that seemingly normal red cells from his patient changed to the abnormal sickle shape when drops of her blood were sealed on slides and kept for a day or more.

abnormal [Latin: *ab*, from, + *norma*, a rule]: unlike the usual

Dr. Emmel also had an opportunity to examine a sample of blood taken from his patient's father. The father's red blood cells appeared to be normal. However, after 24 hours or more on a sealed slide, the father's cells also tended to sickle. Not as many of the father's cells sickled as did his daughter's, nor were the father's cells so abnormal in shape. Looking back from today's vantage point, we would say that the father had the sickle-cell trait, whereas the daughter, like the young man in Chicago, had sickle-cell anemia. Thus we recognize two forms of sickle-cell disease: a major form with severe anemia plus many painful symptoms and a minor form that shows very few physical symptoms.

FAMILY DATA

When two people in the same family are found to have similar rare characteristics, a biologist may hypothesize that the character-

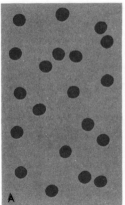

Figure 17 • 2
(A) Normal red blood cells.
(B) Cells of a person who
has the sickle trait. (C) Cells
of a person who has sickle-
cell anemia.

istics are in some way related to one another. So medical biologists began to search out new cases and particularly to examine blood samples of whole families when a case was discovered. During the past half-century medical studies have revealed many families in which various members have shown the sickling abnormality.

Data from such studies can be put in the form of a chart called a **pedigree.** Figure 17 • 3 shows pedigrees of three families in which sickling occurred. You can see that any person who has red cells that sickle has at least one parent whose red cells sickle. Furthermore, any person who has sickle-cell anemia has parents both of whom have sickling cells. On the other hand, persons with the sickle-cell trait, whether married to others like themselves or to normal individuals, may have children with normal red blood cells.

pedigree [pĕd′ə grē′; Latin: *pes*, foot, + *grus*, a crane]: (from the branching lines of such a chart)

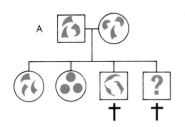
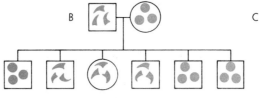

Figure 17 • 3
Pedigrees of red blood cells in three families. Squares = males; circles = females; crosses = deaths. Children listed with oldest on left. For red-blood-cell symbols, see Figure 17 • 2.

These observations from three pedigrees can be supported by observations from many others. They lead us to believe that sickling is indeed a hereditary condition. But the observations are not sufficient to enable us to understand the ways in which the inheritance occurs.

To get extensive data from family pedigrees requires that data on the children produced by similar marriages be **pooled,** that is, added together to form a single set of data. When we pool the data from all families in which both parents have normal (non-sickling) red blood

pooled: summed, put together

cells, we find that *all* the children also have normal red cells. So we can write:

Parents		Offspring
normal × normal	⟶	100% normal

This is a very simple example. To study other examples, you need to know something about the mathematics of **probability.**

probability [prŏb′ə bĭl′ə tĭ; Latin: *probare*, to try]

Investigation 17.1

PROBABILITY

BACKGROUND INFORMATION

The mathematics of probability was originally developed by persons interested in gambling—in games of chance. "Chance" is a term used to describe any situation in which the factors affecting the outcome are so numerous and (taken individually) so weak that we can never hope to determine one cause. The expression "choosing at *random*" means choosing by chance.

The basic question in probability is: How often should we *expect* a particular event in a given number of events? Of course, gamblers would like to know *exactly* when, for example, the ace of spades would appear in a deal of cards. But the best that mathematicians can ever do for either gamblers or scientists is to tell what expectation will *least often* bring disappointment—in the language of gamblers, the "odds."

The simplest way to express probability mathematically is by means of fractions. When a coin is tossed into the air, it may come up either "heads" or "tails." The number of possibilities is the denominator of the fraction —in this example, 2. What is the probability that heads will come up when you toss a coin? In this question you are looking for *1* specific event; this is the numerator of the fraction. Thus, the probability that a coin will land heads up is 1/2. We can also write this as 0.5 or 50%, but the common fraction is the starting point.

Further examples: There are 52 cards in a deck, 13 of each suit. What is the probabil-ity that you will draw a spade from a shuffled deck? There are 52 cards in the deck—52 possibilities—of which 13 meet the conditions of the question. Therefore the probability is 13/52, or 1/4, or 0.25, or 25%. What is the probability that you will draw the ace of diamonds? Again there are 52 possibilities, but this time only 1 meets the conditions of the question; the probability is 1/52.

MATERIALS AND EQUIPMENT

(per pair of students)
pennies, 2 (1 shiny, 1 dull)
cardboard box

PROCEDURE

Tossing a single penny

Student A: Prepare a score sheet containing 2 columns. Label one column *H* ("heads"); label the other *T* ("tails").

Student B: Toss a penny 10 times. Toss into a cardboard box to prevent rolling.

Student A: Use a slash mark (/) to tally the result of each toss in the appropriate column on the score sheet. After the 10th toss, draw a line across the columns of the score sheet and pass the sheet to Student B. Take the penny and make 10 tosses.

Student B: Tally the results of Student A's tosses. Draw a line across the score sheet.

Continue reversing the roles until the re-sults of 100 (10 series of 10) tosses have been tallied.

Tossing 2 pennies together

Student A: Prepare a score sheet containing 4 columns: *Both H, Both T, Dull H / Shiny T, and Dull T / Shiny H* (H = heads; T = tails).

Student B: Obtain 2 pennies—1 dull and 1 shiny. Toss both pennies together 20 times.

Student A: Tally each result in the appropriate column of the score sheet.

Reverse roles once (this will result in a total of 40 tosses).

STUDYING THE DATA

Tossing a single penny. • What does the mathematics of probability lead you to expect in a series of 10 tosses of the coin?(1)

Deviation is a measure of the difference between expected and observed results. It is not the difference itself, however. It is the ratio of the difference to the total number of observations. To calculate deviation, determine the difference between the number of heads you expected and the number of heads you observed. Then determine the difference between the number of tails you expected and the number of tails you observed. Complete the calculation of deviation by dividing the sum of the 2 differences by the total number of tosses.

Calculate the deviation for each set of 10 tosses. Add the 10 sets and calculate the de-viation for your team. Add the data of all teams in your class and calculate the class deviation. If your school has more than 1 biology class, combine the data of all classes and calculate the deviation. Finally, calculate the *average* deviation of sets, teams, classes, and the school. • How does increasing the number of tosses affect the average size of the deviation?(2)   You have just worked out an important principle of probability.

Tossing 2 pennies together. On the chalkboard record the data from all teams and total each column of the chart. • In how many columns do data concerning heads of a dull penny appear?(3) • In what fraction of the total number of tosses did heads of the dull pennies occur?(4) • In how many columns do data concerning heads of a shiny penny occur?(5) • In what fraction of the total number of tosses did heads of the shiny pennies occur?(6) • In how many columns do heads of *both* dull and shiny pennies appear?(7) • In what fraction of the total number of tosses did heads of both pennies appear at the same time?(8) • Is this fraction closest to the *sum*, the *difference*, or the *product* of the 2 fractions for heads on 1 penny at a time?(9)   You have just worked out a 2nd important principle: the relationship between the probabilities of *separate* events and the probability of a *combination* of events.

REASONING FROM FAMILY DATA

Now what do pooled family data show us about sickling? One study was made of families in which one parent had the sickle-cell trait and the other had normal red blood cells. A total of 66 children were born to these parents; 28 had the sickle-cell trait and 38 had normal red blood cells. If you tossed a penny 66 times, you would *expect* 33 heads and 33 tails but you would not be very surprised to get 28 heads and 38 tails. Applying this knowledge of probability to these data on sickling, we might assume that the 28:38 ratio is a chance deviation from an expected 33:33 ratio (or 1:1 or 50%:50%). On this assumption, then, we can write:

Parents   *Offspring*

normal × sickle-cell trait ——————→ 50% normal:50% sickle-cell trait

Remember when you read this that it is based both on a rather small amount of data and on an assumption.

In another study of pooled family data, *both* parents had the sickle-cell trait. Among the children of these parents 146 had normal red cells and 263 had the sickle-cell trait. The best simple ratio that fits these data is 1:2. But in Figure 17 · 3, Pedigree A shows that such parents sometimes have children with sickle-cell anemia. Sickle-cell anemia is such a severe disease that most children who have it die when they are very young. In the families studied there are many records of natural abortions and of children who died too early to be tested by the investigator. In many cases the medical records suggested that the cause of death was severe anemia, though, of course, the investigator could not be sure.

Studies of abortions and deaths from sickle-cell anemia among children both of whose parents have the sickle-cell trait suggest that about 1/4 of these children have sickle-cell anemia. Therefore we can assume that the 146 + 263 children studied were only 3/4 of the total offspring. Consequently, the 1:2 ratio becomes 1/4:2/4; sickle-cell anemia children make up the other 1/4. Assuming this, we can write:

| *Parents* | *Offspring* |
| sickle-cell trait $\times$ $\longrightarrow$ 25% normal:50% sickle-cell trait: |
| sickle-cell trait | 25% sickle-cell anemia |

Remember that this is based on an assumption.

From these studies it becomes clear that normal parents must transmit *something* that causes their children's red cells to be normal. However, a parent with the sickle-cell trait must also transmit *something* that causes red cells to be normal, because normal children appeared both in the families of "trait" $\times$ "normal" parents and "trait" $\times$ "trait" parents. On the other hand, a parent with the sickle-cell trait must also transmit *something* that causes some of his or her children to possess sickled red cells. Geneticists refer to these "somethings" as **genes.**

genes [jēnz; Greek: *genos*, breed, kind]

Why do we not assume two (or more) genes for sickling from each parent?

In Pedigree B of Figure 17 · 3, each child with the sickle-cell trait must have received from his "sickle-cell" parent a gene that causes sickling and from his "normal" parent a gene that causes formation of normal red cells. And these two genes must not unite within the cells of a person who has them because a person with the sickle-cell trait, even when married to another like himself, can produce normal offspring (Figure 17 · 3, Pedigree A). Therefore the "normal" gene must be separate from the "sickling" gene. Further, the data given on page 563 show that parents, one of whom has the sickle-cell trait and the other of whom is normal, produce children in a 1:1 ratio of sickle-cell trait to normal. Therefore, persons with the sickle-cell trait must carry genes of two kinds—in equal proportions (Figure 17 · 4).

If this reasoning is true, then what types of offspring would you expect from the marriage of two persons both of whom have the sickle-cell trait? Because gametes are the only physical bridge between parent and offspring, genes must be carried in gametes. There-

See pages 524–526.

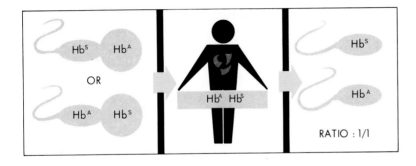

Figure 17 • 4

The union of an egg bearing the "normal" gene (symbol: **HbA**) with a sperm carrying the "sickling" gene (symbol: **HbS**) produces an individual (**HbAHbS**) showing the sickle-cell trait. Half of the gametes produced by this individual carry **HbA**; half, **HbS**.

fore, one way to represent your expectation is shown in Figure 17 • 5. The diagram shows that you would expect a ratio of 1 normal child to 2 with sickle-cell trait to 1 with sickle-cell anemia. This does, indeed, resemble the data shown on page 564. The data support the reasoning.

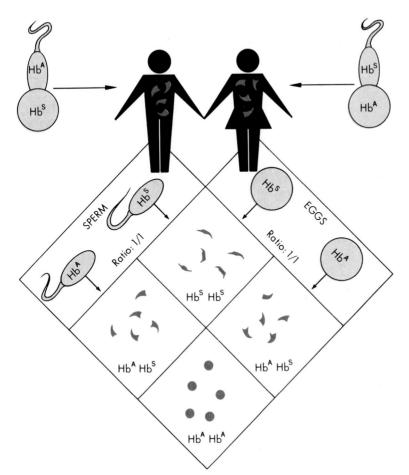

Figure 17 • 5

Children expected from the marriage of two persons both of whom have the sickle-cell trait.

Figure 17 · 6
Gregor Mendel: 1822–1884.
Austrian priest and biologist.

predecessors [prĕd′ə sĕs′ərz, prĕd′ə sĕs′ərz]: those who have gone before in an office, position, etc.

alternative [ôl tûr′nə tĭv; Latin: *alter*, the other]: a choice of two things

axial [ăk′sĭ əl]. See Figure 17 · 7.

terminal [tûr′mə nəl]. See Figure 17 · 7.

hybrid. This word has a special meaning in the study of heredity; the more common meaning is "offspring of parents belonging to different species," as on page 92.

filial [fĭl′ĭ əl; Latin: *filius*, son]

HOW GENETICS BEGAN

You have now studied some data about a human characteristic that seems to be inherited and have reasoned about the way in which inheritance may occur. A century and a half ago, even if the data had existed, no one would have suggested that you reason in that way. That method of reasoning is based on investigations carried out by a 19th-century Austrian monk, Gregor Mendel.

MENDEL'S APPROACH

Through the 18th and early 19th centuries the development of modern science encouraged much experimentation on heredity. But Mendel was the first biologist who was able to make sense from his experimental results. Mendel's success came in large part from the fact that he was trained in mathematics as well as in biology—a combination most unusual for his day. With this background, he planned experiments that differed in three important respects from those of his predecessors.

First, he did not attempt to study everything about the offspring at once; he limited each study to a single characteristic.

Second, instead of studying only the relatively small number of offspring obtainable from a single mating, Mendel used many identical matings. He then pooled the results of these matings.

Third, by working with large numbers of offspring, he was able to apply probability mathematics to the results.

MENDEL'S WORK

Most of Mendel's work was done with garden peas. He used a number of varieties that differed from one another in many **traits**. (As used in studies of heredity, this term refers to a characteristic that occurs in two or more forms, which is different from the medical usage in "sickle-cell trait.") Mendel selected seven traits for study; each trait occurred in two forms (Figure 17 · 7). Mendel's varieties were **true-breeding;** that is, for many generations each variety had consisted of plants that showed only one of the alternative forms of any single trait.

Mendel's crosses. When Mendel used as parents two varieties that differed in respect to any one of the traits—that is, when he crossed the two varieties—he found that all the offspring had the form of the trait shown by one parent and none had the form of the trait shown by the other parent. For example, if he crossed plants that had axial flowers with plants that had terminal flowers, all of the offspring had axial flowers.

It is necessary to have a short way to refer to the generations in such experiments. The original, true-breeding parental plants are called the P_1 (parental) generation. Their *hybrid* offspring are known as the F_1 (first filial) generation. When the F_1 plants are allowed to fertilize themselves (by self-pollination) or each other, they produce the F_2 (second filial) generation.

SEED SHAPE	SEED COLOR	SEED-COAT COLOR	POD SHAPE	POD COLOR	FLOWER POSITION	STEM LENGTH
round	yellow	colored	inflated	green	axial	long
wrinkled	green	white	constricted	yellow	terminal	short

Figure 17 • 7
The seven traits of garden peas studied by Mendel.

When Mendel produced an F_2 generation, he found that *both* alternatives of each parental trait were present among the F_2 plants. For example, from the original P_1 cross of the axial-flowered × terminal-flowered plants, the F_2 generation showed axial-flowered plants *and* terminal-flowered plants. The terminal-flowered form that had disappeared in the F_1 generation reappeared in the F_2 generation.

Consider the facts that Mendel now had. In each trait that he studied, *all* the F_1 hybrid plants had the form of the trait shown by just *one* of the two parental plants. Mendel called this F_1 form of a given trait **dominant.** However, the form that seemed to disappear in the F_1 generation was not eliminated, for it reappeared in the following (F_2) generation. Mendel referred to the form of the trait that seemingly disappeared for a generation as **recessive.**

Mendel's ratios. With his mathematical training, Mendel appreciated the need for precise and abundant data, so he accumulated the data shown in Figure 17 • 8. In each case, the ratios are very nearly 3:1 (or 3/4:1/4).

Notice that plants showing the dominant form were of two kinds: true-breeding (the original varieties) or non-true-breeding (the F_1 plants). Were all of the F_2 individuals that showed the dominant form true-breeding? If not, what was the ratio of true-breeding to non-true-breeding? To answer these questions, Mendel allowed the F_2 plants showing the dominant form of a trait to self-fertilize and then observed the offspring of each plant separately. Parent plants that produced only offspring of the dominant form were counted, and so were those that produced offspring showing both dominant and recessive forms.

dominant [dŏm′ə nənt; Latin: *dominus*, master (of a house, *domus*)]

recessive [rǐ sĕs′ĭv; Latin: *re-*, back, + *cedere*, to yield]

	P_1 CROSS	F_1 PLANTS	F_2 PLANTS	ACTUAL RATIO
1.	round X wrinkled seeds	all round	5,474 round 1,850 wrinkled 7,324 total	2.96:1
2.	yellow X green seeds	all yellow	6,022 yellow 2,001 green 8,023 total	3.01:1
3.	colored X white seed coats	all colored	705 colored 224 white 929 total	3.15:1
4.	inflated X constricted pods	all inflated	882 inflated 299 constricted 1,181 total	2.95:1
5.	green X yellow pods	all green	428 green 152 yellow 580 total	2.82:1
6.	axial X terminal flowers	all axial	651 axial 207 terminal 858 total	3.14:1
7.	long X short stems	all long	787 long 277 short 1,064 total	2.84:1

Figure 17 • 8

Mendel's data from self-pollination of his F_1 plants.

This was a laborious task, but by doing it Mendel found that the ratio of true-breeding to non-true-breeding dominant plants in the F_2 generation was 1:2. Using the example of flower position, this means that of the F_2 plants having axial flowers, about one-third produced only axial-flowered offspring and about two-thirds produced both axial-flowered and terminal-flowered offspring. Therefore, the observed 3:1 ratio among F_2 plants could be rewritten as 1:2:1 or, in fractions, as 1/4 true-breeding dominants, 2/4 non-true-breeding dominants, 1/4 recessive.

At this point Mendel reasoned precisely as you did in the case of sickling. He concluded that parental plants transmit through their gametes "elements" that control the development of certain traits. Clearly, his word "element" is the same as our word "gene." Even though a recessive gene cannot be detected in the F_1 generation, it must be present because the recessive form of the trait reappears in the F_2 generation. Furthermore, when the recessive form reappears, it precisely resembles the original form; wrinkled seeds in the F_2 generation, for example, are no less wrinkled than those of the parental variety.

implied [ĭm plīd'; Latin: in, in, + plicare, to fold]: meant, though not directly stated

segregate [sĕg'rə gāt']

Mendel's reasoning implied that plants possess pairs of genes. Genes of each pair must *segregate* (separate) during gamete formation so that each gamete carries only one member of each pair. Your reasoning about sickling implied the same thing.

Refer now to Figure 17 · 9. The symbols **R** and **r** (differing genes for a single trait) are used to represent the contrasting *alleles* that cause the development of round seeds and wrinkled seeds. If the two members of a gene pair differ, as they do in plants of the F_1 generation, half of their gametes will get one allele and half the other. Then if gametes unite at random during fertilization, the ratio of dominant to recessive individuals in the F_2 generation is

$$3:1 \; [(25\% + 25\% + 25\%) + 25\%].$$

But notice that this ratio concerns the *appearance* of the seeds—their *phenotypes.* If we consider their genes as shown by the symbols— their *genotypes*—the ratio is

$$1:2:1 \; [25\% \; \mathbf{RR}: (25\% \; \mathbf{Rr} + 25\% \; \mathbf{Rr}): 25\% \; \mathbf{rr}].$$

allele [ə lēl′; Greek: *allelon*, of one another]

phenotype [fē′nə tīp′; Greek: *phainein*, to show, + type]

genotype [jĕn′ə tīp′]

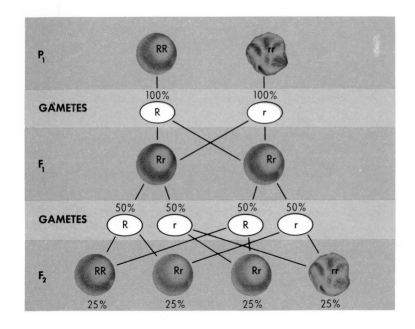

Figure 17 · 9

Mendel's theory illustrated by seed shape in peas.

We refer to genotypes made up of the same alleles (**RR** and **rr,** for example) as *homozygous* and to those made up of two different alleles (**Rr,** for example) as *heterozygous.* Thus, in a cross between two heterozygotes, one-half of the offspring will be homozygous for one allele or the other, and one-half will be heterozygous.

Dihybrid crosses. Mendel went on to consider two traits simultaneously. For example, if plants that are true-breeding for *both* seed shape and seed color are crossed—a *dihybrid* cross—what will be the combinations of shape and color, and in what ratios? In the F_1 generation Mendel found that all the offspring had the same phenotype—the seeds were yellow and round. This was expected, since

homozygous [hō′mə zī′gəs; Greek: *homos,* the same, + *zygon,* a yoke]

heterozygous [hĕt′ər ə zī′gəs; Greek: *heteros,* the other, + *zygon*]

dihybrid [dī hī′brĭd; Greek: *dis,* twice, + hybrid]

these are the dominant forms of the two traits (see Figure 17 • 7). But in the F_2 generation Mendel obtained the following data:

round, yellow	301
round, green	99
wrinkled, yellow	99
wrinkled, green	30
	$\overline{529}$

The closest simple ratio for these numbers is 9:3:3:1. How can this result be explained?

We can say that the genotypes of the true-breeding P_1 generation were **RRYY** for the "round, yellow" and **rryy** for the "wrinkled, green." Reasoning as before, we can say that all the F_1 individuals must have had the genotype **RrYy.** If we assume that when the F_1 plants reproduced, alleles **R** and **r** segregated into gametes *independently* of the alleles **Y** and **y,** then four types of male gametes (1/4 **RY,** 1/4 **Ry,** 1/4 **rY,** 1/4 **ry**) and four types of female gametes (1/4 **RY,** 1/4 **Ry,** 1/4 **rY,** 1/4 **ry**) were formed. And if, as before, we assume that the gametes unite at random, the expected outcome is that shown in Figure 17 • 10.

Compare the formation of gametes with your penny-tossing experiment on pages 562–563.

Figure 17 • 10

Mendel's theory applied to two traits considered together. **R** = gene for round seed; **r** = gene for wrinkled seed; **Y** = gene for yellow seed; **y** = gene for green seed.

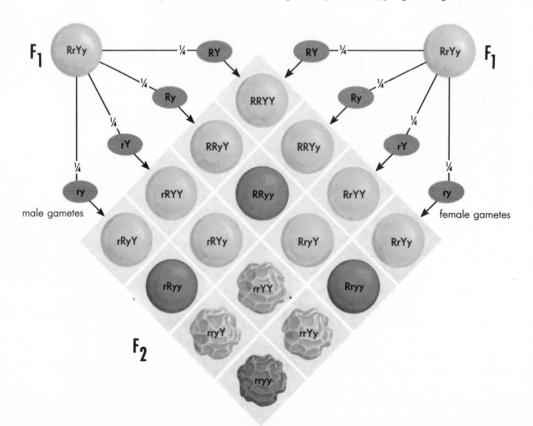

The expectations shown in the figure can be combined as follows:

Fraction	Genotype		Phenotype	Fraction
1/16	**RRYY**	⟶	round, yellow ⎫	
2/16	**RrYY**	⟶	round, yellow ⎪	9/16
2/16	**RRYy**	⟶	round, yellow ⎬	
4/16	**RrYy**	⟶	round, yellow ⎭	
1/16	**RRyy**	⟶	round, green ⎫	3/16
2/16	**Rryy**	⟶	round, green ⎭	
1/16	**rrYY**	⟶	wrinkled, yellow ⎫	3/16
2/16	**rrYy**	⟶	wrinkled, yellow ⎭	
1/16	**rryy**	⟶	wrinkled, green	1/16

The phenotypic fractions, expressed as a ratio, are 9:3:3:1. Mendel's observed ratio (page 570) is close to this. In other dihybrid crosses that he made, the data also came close to this ratio. Therefore, Mendel thought it safe to accept the assumptions that were involved in the reasoning.

What is the ratio for each *individual* trait?

MENDEL'S CONCLUSIONS

From this discussion of Mendel's work three major principles can be drawn.

1. The principle of dominance: when genes controlling a particular trait are different (alleles), the effect of one is observed (dominant) while that of the other one remains hidden (recessive).

Was this true of sickling? Of course, Mendel did not know about that.

2. The principle of segregation: genes controlling a particular trait are separated during gamete formation; therefore, each gamete carries only one gene of each pair.

3. The principle of independent assortment: when two pairs of traits are studied in the same cross, they assort independently of each other.

Investigation 17.2

SEEDLING PHENOTYPES

INTRODUCTION

Mendel had one variety of pea that produced short vines and another that produced tall vines. A little observation shows, however, that the size of plants is affected by the kind of soil in which the plants grow. Mendel sought to control this variable by growing all his plants in the same soil. But we may still raise the question: To what extent is the phenotype of an organism the result of its geno-type, and to what extent is the phenotype influenced by its environment?

MATERIALS AND EQUIPMENT

(for each team)

paper towels

scissors

petri dishes, 2

beaker filled with water

tobacco seeds, 60

forceps, 2

glass-marking crayon

box (large enough to cover half the
     dishes used by the class)

medicine dropper

hand lens

PROCEDURE

Cut 8 disks of paper towel to a size that fits snugly into the bottom of a petri dish. With a pencil write a large *A* on one disk and a large *B* on another. Place 4 disks (with *A* on top) in one petri dish and 4 (with *B* on top) in another. Pour water into each dish. When the paper is thoroughly soaked, pour off the excess water.

Sprinkle 30 tobacco seeds into each dish. Using forceps, arrange the seeds so that each is at least twice its own length from any other. Be sure the *A* and *B* remain visible.

Cover the dishes and label with your team symbol. Put both dishes in a warm place that receives strong light but not in direct sunlight. Cover the B dishes of all teams with boxes that will keep them in darkness. Check the dishes each day to make sure the paper does not dry out. If it begins to do so, add water with a medicine dropper.

When at least half the seeds have germinated, examine them with a hand lens. Each young tobacco plant consists of a colorless root and 2 tiny leaves, the cotyledons (Figure 17 · 11). Usually the root appears first, but in this experiment you are concerned only with the cotyledons. Some seedlings have green cotyledons and some have creamy or yellowish cotyledons. Count the number of each kind in each dish. At least 2 members of the team should make counts; recount if there is disagreement. Using a form like that shown below, record the counts opposite "Day 1." Replace the lids on the dishes; return the dishes to the assigned location, covering the B dishes as before.

	DISH A			DISH B		
DAY	Green	Yellow	% Yellow	Green	Yellow	% Yellow
1						
2						
3						
4						

On the following day (Day 2) make another count. Record the counts. To calculate percentages of yellow seedlings, divide the number of seedlings having yellow cotyledons by the total number of seedlings that have cotyledons. Make this calculation for each dish. Return the dishes to the assigned location, but *do not* cover the B dishes; allow all

Figure 17 · 11

Stages in the germination of a tobacco seed.

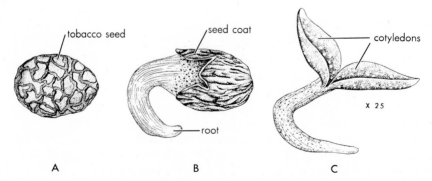

A   B   C

dishes to remain exposed to light.

On Day 3 count the seedlings again. Record the counts and return the dishes to their assigned place, allowing all dishes to remain exposed to the light.

On Day 4 make final counts and calculate the percentage of seedlings with yellow cotyledons in each dish.

STUDYING THE DATA

From the data obtained on Day 2, compare the percentages of yellow seedlings in Dishes A and B. • In what ways are they different?(1) • What experimental variable may be associated with this difference?(2) • Can this variable be considered the cause of yellow color in tobacco seedlings? Why or why not?(3)

Compare the percentage of yellow seedlings in Dish B on Day 4 with the percentage on Day 2. • What change has occurred?(4) • What experimental variable is associated with this change?(5) • Can this variable be considered the cause of yellow coloration in tobacco seedlings? Why or why not?(6) • How can you account for the difference among the seedlings in Dish A?(7)

CONCLUSIONS

• Do any data support the statement "Yellow color of tobacco seedlings is caused by environment"? If so, which data?(8) • Do any data support the statement "Yellow color of tobacco seedlings is caused by heredity"? If so, which data?(9) • Try to formulate a statement that accounts for all the data.(10)

FURTHER DEVELOPMENT OF MENDEL'S PRINCIPLES

Mendel's conclusions fit the results of his experiments. Would the conclusions fit results of other experiments? For a long time this question remained unanswered. In fact, it was not even asked, because the report of Mendel's work, published in 1865, lay neglected on library shelves. The few biologists who had read Mendel's paper either did not understand his mathematics or were unwilling to believe that a biological question could be explained mathematically.

A translation of Mendel's report on his investigations is reprinted in Peters' *Classic Papers in Genetics* ("Suggested Readings," page 604).

Then, some years after Mendel's death, came one of the most striking coincidences in biological history. Three European biologists, working independently on problems of heredity, each found Mendel's paper, each recognized its importance, and each reported it in the same year, 1900. From that year the modern science of *genetics* is dated.

genetics [jĭ nĕt'ĭks; Greek: *gignesthai*, to be born]. Genetics is the branch of biology that deals with heredity.

THE CHROMOSOME THEORY

During the 35 years between 1865 and 1900 much progress was made in the study of cells. In this period biologists developed staining techniques that permitted close observation of the nuclear substance of cells. As a result, chromosomes were discovered, and during the 1870's and 1880's details of mitosis and meiosis became known to biologists. Within two years of the rediscovery of Mendel's work, the close agreement between the events of meiosis and the actions of Mendel's hypothetical genes was being pointed out. One of the first to show this clearly was a young graduate student at Columbia University, Walter S. Sutton.

Sutton's reasoning. The links between parents and offspring in all organisms that reproduce sexually are sperms and eggs. These reproductive cells must, therefore, contain whatever it is that controls heredity. Furthermore, Mendel had found that it makes no difference which parent—male or female—contributes dominant or recessive traits; the ratios among the offspring are the same. Therefore, sperm and egg must contribute equally to the heredity of the offspring. Since only the nuclei of the otherwise dissimilar sperms and eggs resemble one another, it may be concluded that the nuclear material controls heredity.

Now, it is from within the nucleus that the chromosomes appear in both mitosis and meiosis. Sutton continued reasoning as follows:

1. At the conclusion of meiosis, the number of chromosomes going into each sperm or egg is just half the number found in the other cells of an organism's body. This observation corresponds to the idea that one gene of each pair is present in each gamete.

2. The union of sperm and egg, each with its single (monoploid) set of chromosomes, reestablishes in the new individual the double (diploid) set of chromosomes. This observation corresponds to Mendel's idea that each offspring has a pair of each kind of gene—one from each parent.

3. An individual chromosome retains its structure and identity throughout the cell divisions of meiosis and, later, throughout the numerous mitotic cell divisions that occur as a new organism develops. This preservation of the individuality of a chromosome is comparable to the idea that each gene is preserved throughout the growth of an organism.

4. During meiosis each pair of chromosomes separates independently of every other pair. Suppose, in any one pair, we designate one chromosome (of the monoploid set received from the male parent) as *A* and the like chromosome (of the monoploid set received from the female parent) as *A'*. And suppose we designate another pair as *B* (from the male parent) and *B'* (from the female parent). In meiosis we find that *A* does not always go to the pole that *B* goes to, nor does *A'* always end up with *B'*. Instead, there may be at the poles *AB, A'B, AB',* or *A'B'*—and with equal frequency. This chromosome behavior during meiosis corresponds to Mendel's principle of independent assortment.

In summary, then, Sutton reasoned that genes are small particles located in chromosomes. This is the chromosome theory of heredity. But what kind of evidence could be gathered to support the theory?

Meaning of "proof" in science. A theory can do no more than take into consideration all the data that exist *at the time it is formed.* If it does this without any omissions or distortions, it is a good theory. The surest way to test a theory is to use it as the basis of a prediction and then to check (usually by experiment) to see whether the prediction holds true. Thus an important effect of a theory is to spur scientists

distortion [dĭs tôr′shən; Latin: *dis-,* apart, + *torquere,* to twist]: here, twisting facts away from their meaning

to search for new data. When new data are found, the theory must be reexamined. If the new data do not support the theory, then the theory must be revised or discarded.

In science, then, a theory is never proved once and for all. But if it continues to account for new data as they appear, it becomes increasingly convincing. In short, "proof" of a scientific theory means simply this: The theory accounts for new evidence that arises.

EVIDENCE FOR THE CHROMOSOME THEORY

Numbers of genes and chromosomes. In all of Mendel's dihybrid crosses the phenotypic ratios of the F_2 generations were very nearly 9:3:3:1, as predicted by his principle of independent assortment. According to Sutton's reasoning, each of the traits that Mendel studied must have been controlled by genes located on different pairs of chromosomes. But if there were just one gene pair to each pair of chromosomes, the number of traits under genetic control in an organism would be limited to the number of pairs of chromosomes. Some organisms have only two or three pairs of chromosomes, and man has only 23 pairs. When the great number of inheritable traits possessed by an organism is considered, it is clear that many different genes must be located on each chromosome.

So on the basis of the chromosome theory, we can make a prediction: If genes for two different traits are carried on the same pair of chromosomes, they should not be able to assort independently; instead they should always occur together, as if they were a single trait. Therefore, the phenotypic ratio should be 3:1 (3 with both dominant forms of the trait and 1 with both recessive forms) and not 9:3:3:1 (with the two 3's having combinations of dominant and recessive forms). As early as 1906, F_2 dihybrid ratios that differed radically from 9:3:3:1 were found, though none was simply 3:1. For the chromosome theory the new evidence was ambiguous; it raised a new problem: Why were some F_2 ratios neither 9:3:3:1 nor 3:1?

Sex in the fruit fly. Meanwhile, in the laboratory where Sutton had worked, the study of heredity was placed on an entirely new basis when his professor, Thomas Hunt Morgan, began experiments with a fruit fly, *Drosophila melanogaster*. Careful work on the cells of these insects showed that only three of the four pairs of chromosomes are identical in males and females (Figure 17 · 13). In males the fourth

California Institute of Technology

Figure 17 · 12

Thomas Hunt Morgan: 1866–1945. American geneticist.

ambiguous [ăm bĭg′yōō əs; Latin: *amb-*, around, + *agere*, to drive]: explainable in two or more different ways

Drosophila melanogaster [drō sŏf′ə lə mĕl′ə nō găs tər]

x   y

MALE

x   x

FEMALE

Figure 17 · 13

Chromosomes of *Drosophila melanogaster* arranged in pairs.

Construct a diagram for the inheritance of sex that corresponds to the diagram shown in Figure 17·5.

Is white-eye dominant or recessive?

Figure 17 · 14

Inheritance of the white-eye trait in *Drosophila*. Compare this with the results of one of Mendel's crosses diagrammed in Figure 17 · 9.

pair consists of a rod-shaped chromosome, called X, and a hook-shaped one, called Y. In females the fourth pair consists of two X's.

Thus, females can contribute, from the fourth chromosome pair, only an X to each gamete, but males can contribute either X or Y. Thus sex, a clearly visible trait, can be definitely associated with a visible characteristic of an individual's cells: the like or unlike fourth chromosome pair. Here was the best evidence yet that an inherited trait is determined by something involving chromosomes.

Sex-linkage. In *Drosophila melanogaster* the eyes are normally red. But while examining thousands of flies bred in his laboratory, Morgan found one, a male, that had white eyes. He crossed this male with a normal red-eyed female. The resulting F_1 generation consisted entirely of red-eyed flies. Next, he allowed the members of the F_1 generation to mate. Among the F_2 offspring he noted a ratio of 3 red-eyed flies to 1 white-eyed. This, of course, was expected. But *all* the white-eyed flies were males; none were females. Here was a trait related in some way to sex—a *sex-linked* trait.

Since the Y chromosome differs from the X chromosome in appearance, we might assume that it differs in whatever genes (if any) it carries. Suppose, then, we hypothesize that a gene for red eye

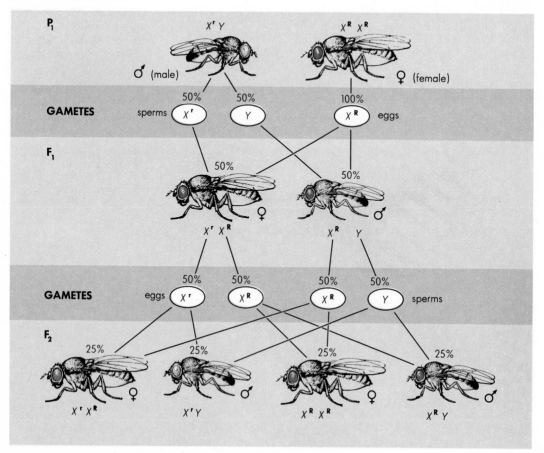

color is located in the X chromosome and has no counterpart in the Y chromosome. What might we expect in a breeding experiment?

Why not hypothesize the opposite?

Let **R** stand for the normal dominant red-eye gene, and let **r** represent the recessive white-eye gene. Since we have hypothesized that these genes occur only on the X chromosome, we can write X^R, X^r and Y for the three kinds of chromosomes. Thus, the genotype of the original white-eyed male found by Morgan must have been X^rY, and that of the normal red-eyed female with which it was mated must have been X^RX^R. With these symbols, Figure 17 • 14 shows the result to be expected according to our hypothesis. Clearly, these are like the results Morgan actually obtained. Hence, the evidence supports our hypothesis that the gene for eye color is on the X chromosome.

Investigation 17.3

MENDELIAN INHERITANCE IN FRUIT FLIES

BACKGROUND INFORMATION

Mendel's experiments have been repeated with many other organisms, most of which (like peas) require long periods of time to produce the necessary generations. But by using fruit flies, you can study Mendelian inheritance in less than 1 month.

There are many species in the fruit-fly genus *Drosophila,* but *D. melanogaster* is especially abundant and widespread. You can easily find the adult flies of this species during the warmer seasons on overripe fruit such as bananas, grapes, and plums.

Morgan found that *D. melanogaster* is an excellent organism for studies of heredity because: (*a*) it has simple food requirements and takes up little space in a laboratory; (*b*) it completes its life cycle in about 12 days at room temperature; (*c*) it produces large numbers of offspring; (*d*) it has many hereditary variations that can be recognized with low-power magnification.

Before using fruit flies in experiments, you must understand their life cycle, practice techniques for handling them, and learn to distinguish males from females.

The eggs are usually laid on the surface of food. They hatch into tiny wormlike creatures (larvae) in about 24 hours. Larvae eat almost continually; in a laboratory culture their black mouthparts can easily be seen moving back and forth in the medium. Mature larvae usually climb up the side of the culture bottle or onto a paper strip in the bottle. There they become *pupae.* During this outwardly inactive stage they change inwardly to adult flies. When the adults emerge from the pupal cases, they are fragile and light in color and do not have fully expanded wings. But within a few hours the body color darkens and wings expand. Females do not mate for about 10 hours after emerging from the pupae. During mating they store considerable quantities of sperms; fertilization occurs later, at the time the eggs are laid.

MATERIALS AND EQUIPMENT

(for each team)

For all parts of the procedure

etherizer (see Figure 17 • 15)
ethyl ether, in dropping bottle
examination plate
water-color brush, small
stereomicroscope
morgue (see Figure 17 • 15C)
glass-marking crayon

For examining fruit flies

    culture of wild-type (W) flies

    culture of laboratory-type (L) flies

For the P$_I$ mating

    culture of W flies

    culture of L flies

    culture vials containing fresh medium, 2

    glass-marking crayon

For the F$_I$ generation

    culture vial containing offspring of P$_I$

        cross

For the test cross

    culture of either W or L flies

    culture of F$_I$ flies

    culture vial containing fresh medium

PROCEDURE

Examining fruit flies. Flies in one culture differ in some conspicuous trait from the flies in the other. One culture (marked *W*) contains flies bearing the form of the trait that is normal in wild populations. The other culture (marked *L*) contains flies bearing the trait in a form that has appeared in laboratory populations. To determine the difference, you must compare the flies in the two cultures.

You can compare flies only when they are quiet. They must be etherized. Refer to Figure 17 • 15 as you watch your teacher demonstrate the following procedure:

1. Place a finger beneath the neck of the funnel of the etherizer. Put several drops of ethyl ether on the string at the upper end of the neck. Avoid using too much ether: you need *vapor* in the etherizer; liquid ether will kill the flies. When the ether trickles down the neck and reaches your finger, place the funnel in the etherizer glass.

2. Gently but rapidly tap against your knee the bottom of the vial containing the flies. This temporarily forces the flies to the bottom of the vial. Quickly remove the cotton plug, invert the vial, and place it firmly in the funnel.

3. Holding vial, funnel, and glass firmly together, tap the bottom of the glass against your hand or knee. This dislodges the flies into the glass.

4. The flies should be quieted within a few seconds. Watch them through the side of the glass. *As soon as* the last fly stops moving, remove the funnel and empty the flies onto the examination plate. (Caution: Flies should not remain in the etherizer more than a minute; over-etherized flies will die.)

5. Use a small brush when moving flies about on the examination plate—they are easily injured. Flies recover activity in about 5 minutes. They may be re-etherized if necessary. Place flies that are accidentally killed into the morgue.

Using the demonstrated procedure, ex-

Figure 17 • 15
Anesthetizing fruit flies.

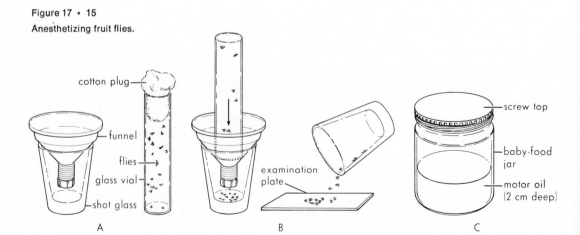

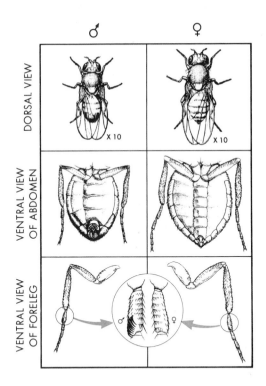

DORSAL VIEW

X 10   X 10

VENTRAL VIEW OF ABDOMEN

VENTRAL VIEW OF FORELEG

♂   ♀

Figure 17 • 16

Comparison of male and female fruit flies.

Now etherize the flies in the other vial (the W culture if you selected females from the L culture and the L culture if you selected females from the W culture). Select 2 or 3 male flies. Place them in the new culture vial containing the female flies. Return the remaining flies to the original vial.

On the new culture vial mark the date, the cross (the sex and the form of the trait in each parent), and your team symbol.

After 7 or 8 days remove the parent flies from the vial containing the crossed flies and place them in the morgue.

The F_1 generation. About 10 or 12 days after the mating, adult flies of the F_1 generation should begin to emerge. Etherize them, examine each for the trait you are studying, and place them in the morgue. For each fly make a tally mark on a chart similar to the one below.

Date of Mating _____

Date Parents Removed _____

P_1 ♂ _____ X ♀ _____

Generation _____

DATE	WILD-TYPE	MUTANT
↕	↕	↕
Total		

amine the flies in the W culture, noting differences between males and females (Figure 17 • 16).

Examine the flies in the L culture. Record the trait in which all these flies differ from all the W flies and the 2 forms in which the trait occurs.

The P_1 mating. Use cultures from which all adults were removed about 8 hours previously. This insures that females will not have previously mated. • Why is this necessary?(1) Using the technique described in the preceding part, etherize the flies in the culture designated by your teacher. Pick out 2 or 3 females. Do not select flies having a very pale color or incompletely expanded wings; these flies have too recently emerged and are easily injured. Using a brush, transfer the selected females into a culture vial that contains a supply of fresh food. Return the other flies to the original vial.

Each day examine the adult flies that have appeared during the previous 24 hours; discard them and tally the counts. Do not count beyond the 9th day after the emergence of the 1st F_1 flies. You might then run into some individuals of the F_2 generation. • With respect to the trait you are studying, how many phenotypes occur among the P_1 flies?(2) Examine your data from the F_1 generation. • How many phenotypes occur among the F_1 flies?(3)

• What Mendelian principle is illustrated by the results of this cross?(4)

The test-cross mating. In a test cross, recessive individuals are mated with individuals of unknown genotypes. From your F_1 results, identify the recessive phenotype. Ask your teacher for a culture of the parental flies with this phenotype. Using the procedure described for the P_1 mating, make a cross between these flies and flies of the F_1 generation. Your teacher will designate from which culture you should take the females and from which the males.

Mark the new culture vial with the date, the phenotype and the sex of the adult flies, and your team symbol.

After 7 or 8 days remove the adult flies and place them in the morgue. When adults begin to emerge, make daily counts and record the results on a chart like the one used before.

STUDYING THE DATA

In the data from the F_1 generation, compare results obtained by teams that used wild-type males with results obtained by teams that used wild-type females in the P_1 mating. • Is the number of F_1 phenotypes the same in both cases? If not, try to explain the difference.(5) • With respect to the trait you are studying, how many phenotypes occur among the test-cross flies?(6) • On the basis of your team's data, calculate the percentage of individuals showing each phenotype in the test-cross generation.(7) • Now combine the data that all the teams have gathered and calculate the class percentages.(8)

Here are some questions that may help you develop a hypothesis appropriate to the procedure you have used. Flies of both the W and L parental cultures were true-breeding. • With respect to the trait you are studying, what types of gametes do you expect males and females of each kind to produce, and in what ratio?(9) • What, then, should be the genotype of the F_1 males?(10) • What types of sperms should these F_1 males produce, and in what ratio?(11) • Now, on the basis of

this reasoning, what ratio of *phenotypes* do you expect in the generation resulting from the test cross?(12) This is your hypothesis for the test cross.

When you have obtained your data, you will need to ask a question: Are the observed percentages of flies in your test-cross generation close enough to those predicted by your hypothesis to give you confidence that your hypothesis may be correct? This question cannot be answered easily. It is similar in form to a question that every scientist repeatedly faces: Are the numbers obtained in my experiment close enough to the numbers expected from my hypothesis to allow a reasonable degree of confidence that only *chance* caused the difference and not some defect in the hypothesis or the procedure? In other words, is the difference between the actually observed numbers and the expected numbers the same kind of difference that occurs when you toss a penny 10 times and observe 4 heads and 6 tails instead of the expected 5 and 5?

Consider an example. A biologist who crossed 2 kinds of tomato plants hypothesized that half the offspring would have green leaves and half yellow. In certain kinds of tomatoes this is a reasonable expectation. In one experiment he obtained 1240 seedlings, 671 with green leaves and 569 with yellow leaves; the expected numbers from a total of 1240 are, of course, 620 of each kind. Is this a minor difference, a matter of chance? Or is it such a large one that the biologist ought to suspect that there is something wrong with his hypothesis?

In Investigation 17.1 you learned one way to express deviation. A better way was invented in 1900 by Karl Pearson (1857–1936), an English mathematician. He called this measure *chi-square* (pronounced "kī square"). It is symbolized by the Greek letter *chi* and the square sign, thus: χ^2. Chi-square is found as follows: For each class of objects, obtain the difference between the number expected and the number observed; square this difference; divide by the expected number; finally, add all the quotients together. The sum is the value of x^2.

In mathematical form this is:

$$x^2 = \Sigma \frac{(O - E)^2}{E}$$

where Σ means "the sum of," O = observed number, and E = expected number. In the example, the difference for the 1st class of objects, green-leaved plants, is $671 - 620 = 51$; squaring this, we get 2601; dividing by the expected. number, 620, we get the quotient 4.2. The difference for the other class of objects, the yellow-leaved plants, is $569 - 620 = -51$; squaring this, we get 2601; dividing by 620, we get 4.2. Added together, the 2 quotients come to 8.4, the value of x^2.

But what does this value mean? By solving an elaborate equation, mathematicians have provided the information needed to judge whether a x^2 value represents the sort of difference that occurs *very probably* by chance alone or *very improbably* by chance alone, or at probabilities between these extremes. A table prepared from the equation allows us to see how often (in 100 cases) a given value of x^2 is expected to arise by chance alone.

For 2 classes of objects, the x^2 value of 8.4 goes beyond the table, which means that there is less than 1 chance in 100 that the difference between the observed and expected numbers could have been caused by chance alone. When the probability that a difference might occur by chance alone is less than 5 in 100, then the difference is said to be *significant*––in other words, we may conclude that

the difference did *not* occur by chance.

In this case, further experimentation showed that the difference from the expected numbers was caused by a loss of yellow-leaved plants. They were less sturdy than the green-leaved plants; fewer of their seeds germinated and lived.

When more than 2 classes occur among the results of an experiment, it is necessary to use other lines in the table. For example, to test the significance of the 9:3:3:1 ratio of a dihybrid cross, x^2 for 4 classes is needed.

Now use the combined data of all teams to calculate chi-square for the test-cross generation of fruit flies.

CONCLUSIONS

• Are the data significantly different from the numbers expected on the basis of your hypothesis?(13)   • If the difference is not significant, what conclusion can you make?(14) • If the difference is significant, how might you explain it?(15)

If you have been sufficiently skillful, you may have found, as dozens of geneticists have, that your hypothesis is supported by your data. Make sure you understand that the ratio of phenotypes in the test-cross offspring is the same as the ratio of gamete types produced by the F_1 males. The test-cross method enables a geneticist to measure the ratio of differing gametes—which he could not do visually with even the most powerful microscope. Just to check your understanding: • Which of the test-cross phenotypes is true-breeding?(16)   • Why not both?(17)

Figure 17 • 17
Table of chi-square values.

x^2 for four classes	.115	.352	.584	2.366	3.665	6.251	7.815	11.341
x^2 for three classes	.020	.103	.211	1.386	2.408	4.605	5.991	9.210
x^2 for two classes	.0002	.004	.016	.455	1.074	2.706	3.841	6.635
Times in 100 that chance alone might give x^2 this large or larger.	99	95	90	50	30	10	5	1

FOR FURTHER INVESTIGATION

Once you have learned the techniques of handling fruit flies and have used chi-square to test the significance of breeding results, you can carry on many genetic experiments. Here are some questions you can investigate: (a) What phenotypic ratios would you expect in the F₂ generation of your experimental crosses? (b) What ratio would you expect if, after they have had an opportunity to mate, you placed 6 or 8 homozygous-recessive females from the test-cross offspring into a fresh culture vial (with no males) and allowed them to produce offspring?

MENDEL'S PRINCIPLES MODIFIED

By 1915 Morgan's fruit flies had become the center of genetic research, but heredity in maize (corn), guinea pigs, mice, and many other organisms was also being investigated. From this research came great quantities of data that did not always agree with Mendel's principles.

Lack of dominance. In all Mendel's experiments, one allele was dominant over the other. Thus, a pea plant with a genotype **YY** (homozygous yellow-seeded) could not be phenotypically distinguished from a **Yy** individual (heterozygous yellow-seeded). But today many cases are known in which neither allele dominates the other, resulting in three phenotypes. In such an instance, hybrid organisms show an intermediate degree of the trait: heterozygous individuals are phenotypically different from both their homozygous parents. The two alleles of the sickle-cell gene are of this sort (Figure 17 · 2).

Figure 17 · 18

Inheritance of flower color in morning glories.

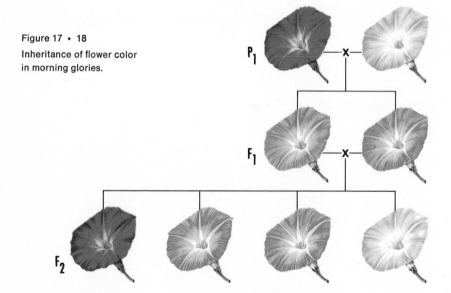

Linkage. Early in the 20th century cases contrary to Mendel's principle of independent assortment had been found (page 575). These cases presented a puzzling problem: Should not the ratios in the F₂ generation of dihybrid crosses be *either* 9:3:3:1 (when the genes are on different chromosomes) *or* 3:1 (when the genes are on the same chromosome)?

A solution to this problem lies in the crossing-over that appears to occur during meiosis (pages 528–529). Suppose we are studying two traits—one of which is determined by alleles **A** (dominant) and **a** (recessive), the other by alleles **B** (dominant) and **b** (recessive). Suppose, further, that the genes for these two traits are on the same chromosome but the *locus* (position) of **A** (or **a**) is near the middle of the chromosome and the locus of **B** (or **b**) is at the end. Figure 17 • 19 shows what happens if crossing-over occurs between the **A** and **B** loci in 20 percent of the cells during meiosis. Instead of 50 percent having **A** linked with **B** and 50 percent **a** linked with **b,** only 45 percent of the gametes have the first linkage and 45 percent the second. Five percent have **A** on the same chromosome with **b,** and 5 percent have **a** linked with **B.** The new linkages are called *recombinations.* If zygotes are formed from such gametes, the two dominant traits are not

locus [lō′kəs; Latin: a place]: plural, loci [lō′sī]

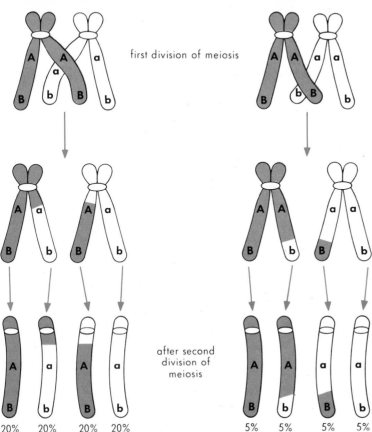

NO CROSSING OVER BETWEEN A AND B IN 80% OF CELLS

CROSSING OVER BETWEEN A AND B IN 20% OF CELLS

first division of meiosis

after second division of meiosis

20%   20%   20%   20%

5%   5%   5%   5%

Figure 17 • 19

Genetic effect of crossing-over. Only the combinations **AB** and **ab** occur before meiosis. Crossing-over between **A** and **B** results in the recombinations **Ab** and **aB** in the gametes. What is the ratio between the percentage of gametes carrying **Ab** and **aB** recombinations and the percentage of cells in which crossing-over occurred during meiosis?

always associated—nor are the two recessive traits. Instead, some zygotes are recombinants of dominant and recessive genes—**Ab** or **aB**—producing two new dihybrid phenotypes. However, because many zygotes may be formed by gametes that were produced by normal meiosis—without crossing-over—the 9:3:3:1 ratio of independent assortment does not occur either.

The chance that crossing-over will occur in the region of a chromosome between two given loci depends largely upon the distance between them. It is unlikely that crossing-over will occur between genes at two loci that are very close together; hence, in experiments we observe phenotypically few recombinations. We say the genes at these loci are closely linked. In general, then, the greater the observed number of recombinants, the farther apart we infer the loci are on the chromosome. By observing the proportions of recombinations that occur between many different pairs of linked loci, a continuous linkage map can be constructed (Figure 17 • 20).

Can you explain why this is so?

recombinants
[rē kăm′bə nəntz]: individuals in which recombination has occurred

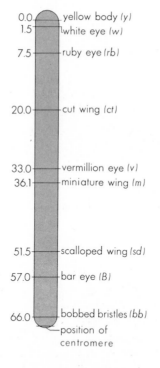

0.0 — yellow body (y)
1.5 — white eye (w)
7.5 — ruby eye (rb)
20.0 — cut wing (ct)
33.0 — vermillion eye (v)
36.1 — miniature wing (m)
51.5 — scalloped wing (sd)
57.0 — bar eye (B)
66.0 — bobbed bristles (bb)
— position of centromere

Figure 17 • 20
Gene loci on one of the chromosomes of *Drosophila*. The numbers at the left are determined by the percentage of recombinations observed in experimental breeding. They indicate, for example, that recombinations between **ct** and **v** are about 13 percent; between **v** and **m**, 3 percent; and between **ct** and **m**, 16 percent—the sum of 13 percent and 3 percent.

Multiple alleles. Mendel never found more than 2 alleles for a given trait. There were **Y** and **y** (yellow-seeded and green-seeded), but there was never a case of **Y, y,** and **Y′** (the **Y′** representing some other color, such as purple)—*3* alleles. Today, however, we know that within a *population* of organisms there may be several (and in some cases, numerous) alleles available to occupy a particular locus in a chromosome. But normally an *individual* has only 2 of these alleles for any trait—one gene derived from its male parent, the other from its female parent.

A good example of multiple alleles is the inheritance of certain blood characteristics in man. When techniques for transfusing blood from one person to another were developed at the end of the 19th century, it was discovered that this could be done safely in some cases and not in others. Karl Landsteiner, an Austrian physician, worked out a system for distinguishing the kinds of human blood that were important in transfusions. These were designated Type A, Type B, Type AB, and Type O. Together they constitute the "ABO" system.

The "ABO" types are determined by 3 alleles available for one locus: I^a, I^b, i. Allele I^a causes the formation of blood factor A, I^b causes the formation of factor B, and i does not cause either of these factors to form. The table shows the genotypes that are responsible for the various phenotypes:

Genotype	Blood Type
$I^a I^a$ or $I^a i$	A
$I^b I^b$ or $I^b i$	B
$I^a I^b$	AB
ii	O

Under what circumstances might an individual have three alleles at a specific gene locus? What plant tissue would *always* have three alleles?

transfusing [Latin: *trans*, across, + *fundere*, to pour]

Karl Landsteiner [lănd′stī′nər]: 1868-1943. Austrian (later, American) physician

Other blood types, resulting from genes at other loci, are known. Many are unimportant medically, but see pages 124–128 in E. P. Volpe, *Human Heredity and Birth Defects* (New York: Pegasus, 1971).

What does this chart show about the dominance relationships of these alleles?

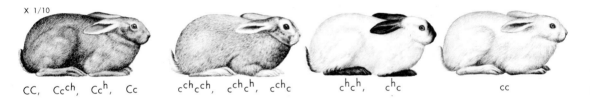

X 1/10

CC, Cc^ch, Cc^h, Cc   c^ch c^ch, c^ch c^h, c^ch c   c^h c^h, c^h c   cc

Figure 17 · 21

Four coat-color phenotypes in domestic rabbits. *From left to right:* normal ("wild type"), chinchilla, Himalayan, white. Genotypes are shown beneath each animal. Explain the dominance relationships of the genes.

Multiple factors. Mendel deliberately chose to work with traits that show only distinct phenotypic alternatives: wrinkled and round seeds, axial and terminal flowers, etc. With lack of dominance and just two kinds of alleles, one locus can yield 3 phenotypes. Cases of more than 3 phenotypes can result from multiple alleles. But multiple alleles cannot account for many characteristics that have continuous variability—human skin coloration, for example. This is obviously in-herited, but there are a great many shades. Human height is also a continuous variable that is at least in part hereditary.

Consider the case of weight in squashes. If you collected a large number of squashes at random, you would certainly find much varia-bility in their weights. Among different varieties of squash, however, there are definite weight characteristics. One true-breeding variety, for example, bears fruits with weights close to 3.5 kg each. Another bears fruits with weights close to 1.5 kg each. If these are crossed,

See Figure 18 · 7.

This is still another example in which dominance is lacking.

Explain why one F₂ plant with fruit weighing about 2 kg is true breeding when self-fertilized whereas a second plant, bearing very similar fruit, produces squashes of highly variable weights when self-fertilized.

nondisjunction [Latin: *non*, not, + *dis-*, apart, + *jungere*, to join]

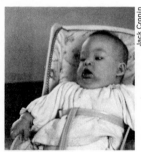

Jack Cronin

Figure 17 · 22

An infant showing characteristic facial features of Down's syndrome.

J. L. H. Down: 1828–1896. British physician

syndrome [sĭn'drōm; Greek: *syn-*, with, + *dramein*, to run]: a group of symptoms that occur together

How does nondisjunction provide evidence supporting the chromosome theory?

Hugo De Vries: 1848–1935. Dutch plant physiologist and hybridizer

each of the F_1 generation plants bears fruits weighing close to 2.5 kg. But in the F_2 generation, plants are obtained that bear fruits not in three weight classes, but in many.

These varieties of squashes seem to have 3 equally important, non-linked loci, each of which has an allele that contributes something to fruit weight (**A, B,** and **C**) and an allele that fails to contribute (**a, b,** and **c**). The two true-breeding varieties mentioned in the example, then, must have genotypes **AABBCC** and **aabbcc.** You should be able to figure the genotype possibilities in the F_1 and F_2 generations. Small environmental differences, in combination with genetic ones, easily produce the impression of continuous variability.

Many human characteristics seem to be inherited in a way similar to that described for squash weight, but many more than 3 loci may be involved. And the interactions between loci may be more complex; for example, skin coloration results from two different pigments, and the amount of each is independently determined by multiple factors.

Nondisjunction. Meiosis is a remarkably exact process. But it is not perfect. Biologists have observed that, very rarely, during the first division both chromosomes of a pair go to one pole of the spindle—an event called *nondisjunction.* When they do, there is, of course, no chromosome representing that pair at the other pole. In a human female, then, one of the new cells would have 24 chromosomes (one each of 22 kinds and two of the 23rd kind) and the other would have only 22 chromosomes (one each of 22 kinds and none of the 23rd). If these abnormal cells complete meiosis and form gametes that are fertilized, abnormal (47-chromosome or 45-chromosome) zygotes are formed. This does indeed happen—though rarely.

Even more rarely, the abnormal zygote survives and develops into a new individual. This happens when nondisjunction occurs in the 21st pair of human chromosomes. The individual that develops when the 24-chromosome gamete is fertilized has a total of 47 chromosomes in his cells. The chromosome abnormality is accompanied by a phenotypic abnormality called Down's syndrome. An individual with this abnormality has a characteristic facial appearance and extreme mental deficiency.

In addition to Down's syndrome, other kinds of nondisjunction effects are known in man. They occur in other organisms and were actually first described in fruit flies.

Mutations. The basic fact of heredity is that offspring resemble their ancestors. But the fossil evidence outlined in Chapter 10 clearly shows that new heritable traits must have appeared from time to time in the past; otherwise, there could have been no changes in organisms through geological time.

Mendel took no notice of this reasoning; he assumed that genes remained the same generation after generation. And he encountered no evidence to make him think otherwise. However, one of the rediscoverers of Mendel's work, Hugo de Vries, did find in plants heritable

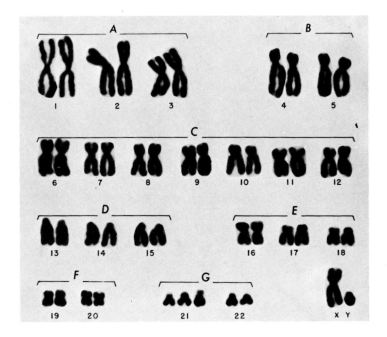

Figure 17 • 23
Chromosomes in Down's
syndrome. To make this
chart, a photomicrograph of
a cell in mitosis was taken;
then the picture was cut
apart and the chromosomes
rearranged in pairs. Was this
a female or a male?

characteristics that he could not trace to their ancestors. De Vries
called these changes *mutations.* The white-eyed male that Morgan
found among his flies was almost certainly a mutation.

mutations [mū tā′shənz; Latin:
mutare, to change]

However, not *all* characteristics that seem new in the ancestry of
an organism are recent mutations. Consider feeblemindedness in
man. For most human families pedigrees that go back more than a
few generations are difficult to construct, and some kinds of feeblemindedness are the result of rare recessive genes that may remain
hidden for many generations. For these reasons, feeblemindedness
may appear to be a new trait in a family when in fact it has been inherited. Feeblemindedness may also occur as a result of lack of oxygen during or shortly after birth. In this case the cause is environmental, not genetic, and the trait cannot be inherited by the next
generation. Finally, feeblemindedness in a particular family might appear at any time by mutation.

How can a recessive gene be
hidden for generations?

Where have you observed an
environmental influence on a
genetic trait?

According to the chromosome theory of heredity, mutations
should result from changes in chromosomes. We might, then, look
for visible changes in the chromosomes and associate the occurrence
of such a change with the appearance of a new trait. And in fact, this
is exactly the case in nondisjunction. In addition to nondisjunction,
other chromosomal changes that result in phenotypic changes have
been discovered. Mutations of this sort are called chromosomal
mutations.

Often, however, mutations occur without any visible change in
the chromosomes. It seems reasonable to assume that such mutations are due to changes in the invisible genes. For example, a gene
that normally controls the formation of a red pigment in a flower might

Figure 17 • 24

Hermann J. Muller: 1890–1967. American geneticist who developed methods of measuring mutation rates by exposing fruit flies to X-rays.

change so that a purple pigment or no pigment at all is formed. Such mutations are called gene mutations.

Genes are quite stable. Any one gene usually replicates itself exactly for hundreds of cell generations. However, if a gamete carries 10,000 different genes, it has been calculated that there may be between one new mutation per 10 gametes and one per 100 gametes. The rate is known to vary somewhat at different loci, but this is a basic rate—a rate that occurs without any known cause.

The gene-mutation rate can be increased, however, by certain environmental factors. First, it can be increased by heat. Within the range of temperature that a given organism can tolerate, the higher the temperature, the greater the mutation rate. Second, it can be increased by certain chemicals, such as formaldehyde. Third, it can be strikingly increased by high-energy radiations, such as X-rays and beta and gamma rays that result from atomic explosions.

Investigation 17.4

RELATIONSHIPS AMONG GENETIC DIFFERENCES

BACKGROUND INFORMATION

An apple or a potato wrinkles as it dries out. Therefore, when you first observe round and wrinkled peas together, it may occur to you that some have simply dried more than others. You can investigate this matter in reverse by determining whether the 2 kinds of peas take up the same amount of water when they are soaked.

But phenotypic characteristics of organisms are not necessarily easily visible ones. Some may be visible, but only with a microscope. Others may be physical or chemical characteristics that can be observed only by applying chemical tests. It is reasonable, therefore, to inquire whether there are relationships between the macroscopic phenotypes of a particular organism and the organism's physical, chemical, and microscopic characteristics.

MATERIALS AND EQUIPMENT

(for each team)

Day 1

    small bottles, 2
    glass-marking crayon
    balance (0.1-g sensitivity)
    round peas, 25
    wrinkled peas, 25

Day 2

    bottles of soaked peas (from Day 1), 2
    paper towels, 2
    balance (0.1-g sensitivity)
    glass-marking crayon
    microscope slide
    medicine dropper
    scalpel
    soaked peas, round and wrinkled, 1 of
        each
    monocular microscope
    dry peas, round and wrinkled, 10 g of
        each
    mortar and pestle
    graduated cylinder
    cheesecloth
    beakers, 250-ml, 2

Day 3

    glass-marking crayon
    petri dish containing glucose agar
    extracts of round and wrinkled peas
        (from Day 2)

medicine droppers, 3

watch

paper towel

forceps

iodine–potassium-iodide solution (I_2KI)

PROCEDURE

Day 1. Label one bottle *R* (round) and the other *W* (wrinkled). Label both bottles with your team symbol. Rinse the bottles and shake out as much water as possible. Weigh each bottle separately and record the weights in a table like the one below. Place 25 round peas in Bottle R and 25 wrinkled peas in Bottle W. Weigh each filled bottle. Record the weights. Fill the bottles with water and allow them to stand overnight.

a. Weight of dried round peas + bottle . .   - g
b. Weight of bottle . . . .   - g
c. Weight of dried round peas (a — b) . .   - g
d. Weight of soaked round peas + bottle .   - g
e. Weight of soaked round peas (d — b) .   - g
f. Water absorbed by round peas (e — c)   - g
g. Weight of dried wrinkled peas + bottle .   - g
h. Weight of bottle . . . .   - g
i. Weight of dried wrinkled peas (g — h) .   - g
j. Weight of soaked peas + bottle . . . .   - g
k. Weight of soaked wrinkled peas (j — h)   - g
l. Water absorbed by wrinkled peas (k — i)   - g

m. % increase in round peas (f ÷ c ✕ 100) ___%
n. % increase in wrinkled peas (l ÷ i ✕ 100)___%

Day 2. Pour the water from each bottle. Place the round peas on one paper towel, the wrinkled peas on another. Shake as much excess water as possible from each bottle. Return each group of peas to its bottle. Weigh each bottle with the peas it contains. Record the weights.

Using a glass-marking crayon, label the left half of a microscope slide *R* and the right half *W* Place a drop of water near each end of the slide. Using a sharp scalpel, cut through a soaked round pea. Scrape the cut surface and mix the scrapings into the drop of water

at the R end of the slide. Clean the scalpel thoroughly. Cut through a soaked wrinkled pea. Scrape the cut surface and mix the scrapings into the drop of water at the W end of the slide.

Using the low power of a monocular microscope, examine the scrapings from both peas. Look for starch grains in each. Carefully compare the starch grains from the 2 kinds of peas. Record the appearance of the starch grains from each kind of pea. The following are some terms you may find useful: "compound," "simple," "divided," "whole," "oval," "spherical." Make sketches of a few grains in each sample.

Weigh out 10 g of dried round peas. Using mortar and pestle, grind the peas in 10 ml of water. Filter the mixture of water and ground peas through 2 layers of cheesecloth into a beaker. Mark the beaker *R* and add your team symbol to it.

Thoroughly wash mortar and pestle. Weigh out 10 g of wrinkled peas. Grind and filter as directed for the round peas, using new cheesecloth. Mark this beaker *W* and add the team symbol. Store both beakers in a refrigerator overnight.

Day 3. Using a glass-marking crayon, draw a line dividing into halves the bottom of a petri dish that contains glucose agar. Mark one half *R* and the other half *W*. The marks should be visible through the agar when you turn the dish right side up. Remove the cover of the dish. Using a medicine dropper, place 4 small drops of the extract from round peas on the R half of the agar surface. Space the drops as widely as possible. Note the time. Using a different medicine dropper, place 4 small drops of the extract from wrinkled peas on the W half. Note the time.

At the end of 10 minutes, use a small piece of paper towel held in forceps to blot up 1 drop of the round-pea extract. (Caution: Do not disturb the other drops!) Using a 3rd medicine dropper, place a drop of I_2KI solution on the spot from which you removed the extract. Immediately carry out the same steps with 1 drop of the wrinkled-pea extract.

Three minutes later, use a piece of paper towel and forceps to blot up both drops of I_2KI solution. Look beneath the surface of the agar for evidence of a positive starch test. Record the time; sketch each of the drops, accurately showing the size and shape of any blue area.

Continuing at 10-minute intervals (20, 30, and 40 minutes after the drops of extract were first placed on the agar), blot another drop of extract on each half of the petri dish and repeat the starch test.

STUDYING THE DATA

Complete the calculations in the table of data obtained from soaking the 2 kinds of peas.

• Do round peas differ from wrinkled peas in ability to absorb water? If so, which kind absorbs more water in proportion to dry weight?(1) • Assuming that the cells in all developing pea seeds have approximately the same water content, which peas—round or wrinkled—lose the greater amount of water as they mature? Or are the amounts equal?(2)

Compare all the data on the shape of starch grains in round and wrinkled peas. • Is there a consistent difference? If so, would it enable you to predict seed shape from starch-grain shape, and vice versa?(3)

Compare the data of all teams on the production of starch from glucose. • Is there a consistent difference between enzyme extracts of round and wrinkled peas in speed of starch production?(4) • In amount of starch produced?(5)

SUMMARY

You have investigated 3 characteristics in round and wrinkled pea seeds. • Which characteristics, if any, were always associated with roundness?(6) • Which characteristics, if any, were always associated with wrinkledness?(7) • Is association between characteristics conclusive evidence that they are effects of 1 gene? Why or why not?(8) • If your answer to the last question is No, what additional evidence might change it?(9)

GENETICS TODAY

WHAT A GENE DOES

Experiments led to the theory that heredity is controlled by some particle—a gene—in the nucleus of a cell. Further experiments showed that genes must be located in chromosomes. Now, *how* does a particle in a chromosome cause a pea plant to develop round rather than wrinkled seeds, or a man to develop Type A rather than Type O blood? In other words, how do genes work?

One gene : one enzyme. Experiments with a mold, *Neurospora crassa,* provided the first clear evidence of how genes act. This mold can be grown easily in a test tube on a medium consisting of a dilute solution of minerals, some table sugar, and a single vitamin. Hyphae of the mold grow beneath the surface of the medium; then tufts of pink or orange spore-bearing threads grow upward through the surface.

If a mature mold plant is analyzed chemically, we find that it is made up of a wide range of proteins, carbohydrates, lipids, a large number of vitamins, nucleic acids, pigments, and so on. The mold must have produced these complex chemical compounds from the simple raw materials in the test tube. These environmental materials

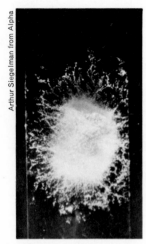

Arthur Siegelman from Alpha

Figure 17 • 25

Neurospora crassa. A colony growing on a slide.   ×1

Neurospora crassa
[nyo͝or ŏ spər'ə krăs'ə]

must have been put together in just the way that would make the new mold plant resemble its parent.

In the early 1940's George W. Beadle and Edward L. Tatum, at Stanford University, treated spores of *Neurospora* with X-rays and then placed them on the simple medium that had supported the growth of their parents. They found that many of the treated spores could not grow at all on the simple medium. Apparently, some kind of mutation had occurred. The two investigators hypothesized that a mutant spore failed to grow because it was unable to make some substance that the parent mold had been able to make for itself from the materials in the medium. Perhaps if that substance were supplied in the medium, the spores would grow. So they devised what they called a complete medium. It contained additional nutrients, particularly many vitamins and all the amino acids known to be required for protein synthesis. When more X-ray–treated spores were placed on this medium, almost all grew—supporting the hypothesis.

The next step was to find which substance (or substances) in the complete medium was required by a particular mutant—that is, which it could not make for itself. Figure 17 · 26 shows the procedure Beadle and Tatum used. They found that the production of almost every substance normally synthesized by *Neurospora* can be blocked by an X-ray–produced mutation.

George W. Beadle: 1903—. American geneticist

Edward L. Tatum: 1909—. American biochemist

Figure 17 · 26

Procedure used by Beadle and Tatum. In this case the *Neurospora* spore has lost the ability to synthesize Substance C.

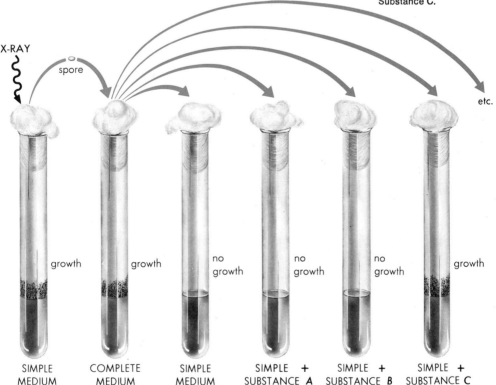

X-RAY spore					etc.
growth	growth	no growth	no growth	no growth	growth
SIMPLE MEDIUM	COMPLETE MEDIUM	SIMPLE MEDIUM	SIMPLE + SUBSTANCE **A**	SIMPLE + SUBSTANCE **B**	SIMPLE + SUBSTANCE **C**

enzymes. See page 372.

How can the synthesis of a substance be blocked? You have seen that syntheses are controlled by enzymes. Beadle and Tatum suggested that each failure by a mutant to synthesize a substance resulted from the lack of a specific enzyme. The mutant was unable to make the enzyme; therefore, it was unable to make the substance.

By this reasoning, each missing enzyme was linked to a gene change—a mutation—and vice versa. Genes do their work by controlling the production of enzymes, which control the formation of chemical substances, which, in turn, determine the characteristics of organisms!

Structure of proteins. More or less simultaneously with the work of Beadle and Tatum, other biochemists decided that all enzymes—not just some—are proteins. Now protein molecules are among the largest and most complex molecules known, and for a long time it seemed that the structure of any particular kind of protein might never be discovered. Fortunately for geneticists, however, chemists did develop laboratory procedures for determining the sequences of amino acids in proteins.

proteins. See pages 382–383.

During digestion of protein molecules any one kind of enzyme always splits a given protein into the same polypeptide fragments. Other kinds of enzymes split the protein into different polypeptide fragments. The sequence of amino acids is discovered by comparing the amino acids in the short polypeptide fragments produced by two different enzymes. Information from these two sets of small fragments is fitted together very much like pieces of a puzzle so that the entire

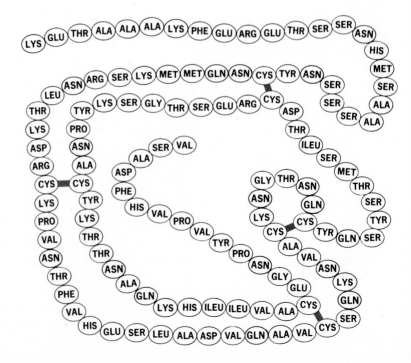

Figure 17 · 27

Sequence of amino acids in a rather small protein molecule —ribonuclease. Biochemists use a system of abbreviations for the names of amino acids. How many different amino acids are in this protein?

amino-acid sequence is discovered. For example, from the following two sets of letters

FBDM	FERO	AGZ	TX

and

EFXT	ROMD	AG	ZFB

How can you explain the FERO and TX sequences?

the original letter sequence from which they were obtained can be reconstructed:

AGZFBDMOREFXT

In 1953 Frederick Sanger completed the analysis of amino-acid sequence in insulin, a rather simple protein. In the years since 1953, the complete amino-acid sequences in many kinds of proteins—enzymes, hormones, hemoglobin, and others—have been determined.

Frederick Sanger: 1918— British biochemist

GENES AND DNA

Genes somehow direct the construction of enzymes—which are proteins. We have concluded that a gene is "something" passed from generation to generation through gametes—that is, a gene is a particle of some substance. And geneticists in the first quarter of the 20th century gathered abundant evidence to show that genes are located in chromosomes. Further, it had been found that chromosomes contain much deoxyribonucleic acid (DNA). And within cells DNA is restricted largely to chromosomes. Do these facts prove that DNA is the genetic material—the substance of genes? Unfortunately, no. Wherever DNA occurs naturally, protein also occurs. And so it is possible that genes are themselves proteins and DNA merely "packing material" around them.

DNA. See pages 383–384.

Identifying the genetic substance. One step in deciding whether DNA or protein is the genetic substance was carried out with a pneumonia bacterium. Dead cells of one type of this organism (say, A cells) can transform living cells of a second type, B, into A. Because *dead* cells can do this, it is possible to take them apart little by little and find out which part or parts cause the transformation. O. T. Avery and his colleagues undertook this work. Again and again they separated proteins from dead bacterial cells, and each time, the proteins were unable to transform living cells but the remaining cell substances could. When the active transforming substance was isolated from everything else, it turned out to be DNA.

O. T. Avery: 1877–1955. American physician and biologist

colleague [kŏl′ēg; Latin: *cum*, with, + *legare*, to choose a lieutenant]: one who works with another

More evidence was obtained from bacteriophages, which consist of a core of DNA surrounded by a protein coat. By labeling the protein with radioactive sulfur, A. D. Hershey showed that the coats do not penetrate bacterial walls, but the DNA does. And once inside a bacterial cell, this DNA, with the help of the bacterial physiological machinery, makes new virus particles like the original ones—including new protein coats. So DNA is capable of performing the function of genes—carrying characteristics (in this case, viral characteristics) from one generation to the next.

bacteriophages. See page 197.

labeling. See page 390.

A. D. Hershey: 1908—. American biologist

Structure of DNA. You may think bacteria rather simple organisms, and viruses, perhaps, not organisms at all. In the 1940's DNA molecules themselves were thought to be rather simple sequences of nucleotides. Perhaps they could function genetically in simple organisms, but how could they carry the complex characteristics of peas and fruit flies and humans? Many biologists, faced with this question, were reluctant to give up the idea that genes are proteins.

James D. Watson: 1928—.
American biochemist

F. H. C. Crick: 1916—.
English biochemist

M. H. F. Wilkins: 1916—.
English biochemist

nucleotides. See page 383.

Most doubts were removed in 1953 when James D. Watson and F. H. C. Crick, using data collected by M. H. F. Wilkins, proposed a structure for DNA that enabled geneticists to imagine how it could act as a gene. They described a DNA molecule as a long, double-stranded structure, like a twisted ladder. The two strands are composed of four kinds of nucleotides. The sugar-phosphate parts of the nucleotides are joined to each other to form the sides of the "ladder." The nitrogenous bases form the "rungs" (Figure 17 · 28). Further-

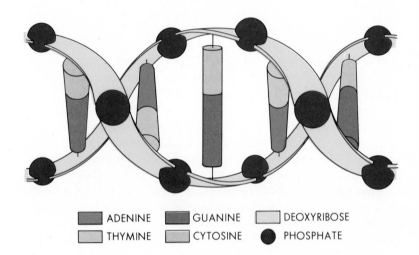

Figure 17 · 28
Diagram of a small part of a DNA molecule.

| ADENINE | GUANINE | DEOXYRIBOSE |
| THYMINE | CYTOSINE | PHOSPHATE |

adenine [ăd′ə nēn]; thymine [thī′mēn]; guanine [gwä′nēn]; cytosine [sīt′ō sēn′].

more, because of the structure of the bases, if a base on one strand is adenine, only thymine can pair with it to form a "rung," or vice versa. If a base is guanine, only cytosine can pair with it.

These base pairs can occur *in any order* along the length of a DNA molecule. The restriction in the possible pairing of the bases enables us to visualize synthesis of a new DNA molecule that faithfully reproduces the order of base pairs on an existing molecule. The chemical bonds that hold the base pairs together are weak; if they are broken, two separate strands result. Then upon each strand a duplicate of the missing strand can be constructed from simple nucleotides. The result is two new molecules of DNA identical to each other and to the original molecule (Figure 17 · 29).

Function of DNA. Geneticists now knew that genes direct the building of protein molecules. How could DNA molecules function as genes? Consider one of the two strands of a DNA molecule. Could each base correspond to an amino acid? Hardly, because there are

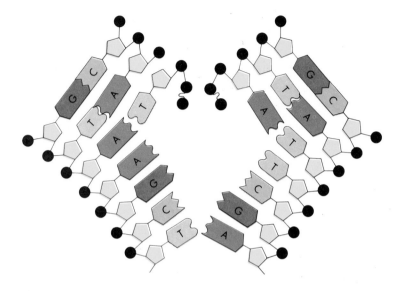

Figure 17 • 29

Replication of DNA. The strands come apart at the bonds between the nucleotides. New nucleotides—which temporarily bear extra phosphates—are added one by one, eventually producing two new DNA molecules.

20 different amino acids—and only 4 bases. Could two adjacent bases correspond to an amino acid? Not quite, because there can be only 16 combinations of 4 different bases—and 20 amino acids. And so geneticists were compelled to decide that a combination of *three* adjacent bases is needed to correspond to each amino acid. Such triplet bases can be thought of as a kind of code for amino acids.

What are the 16 combinations?

Chromosomes with their DNA are in a cell's nucleus. But many experiments, using radioactive amino acids and cellular fragments, showed that ribosomes are the sites of protein synthesis. And ribosomes are in a cell's cytoplast (Figures 11 • 4 and 11 • 7). How can genes direct protein synthesis in the cytoplast from their position in the nucleus?

"Direct" is an anthropomorphic word. Is the use of such a word as dangerous in biochemistry as in the study of behavior?

RNA, the second kind of nucleic acid (page 383), is found in both cytoplasts and nuclei. It is very much like DNA except that its sugar is ribose instead of deoxyribose, and the base uracil is substituted for the thymine found in DNA. Experiments have shown that in most organisms, RNA is synthesized by copying one of the two DNA strands, after which it separates from the DNA strand and passes into the cytoplast.

uracil [yŏo'rə sĭl']. This is the fifth nucleotide base.

Two distinct kinds of RNA are found in cytoplasts. One consists of long strands and is called messenger RNA (mRNA) because it carries the instructions for protein synthesis from the DNA in the nucleus to the ribosomes in the cytoplast. The other consists of short strands and is called transfer RNA (tRNA). Much complex biochemi-

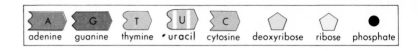

| A adenine | G guanine | T thymine | U uracil | C cytosine | deoxyribose | ribose | phosphate |

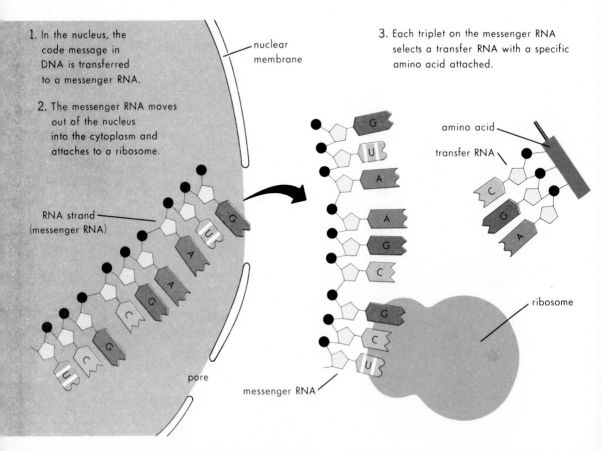

Figure 17 • 30
Formation of part of a strand
of mRNA on one strand of
a DNA molecule.

Figure 17 • 31
How DNA determines the
formation of a protein.

1. In the nucleus, the
   code message in
   DNA is transferred
   to a messenger RNA.

2. The messenger RNA moves
   out of the nucleus
   into the cytoplasm and
   attaches to a ribosome.

RNA strand
(messenger RNA)

nuclear
membrane

3. Each triplet on the messenger RNA
   selects a transfer RNA with a specific
   amino acid attached.

amino acid

transfer RNA

ribosome

pore

messenger RNA

cal evidence indicates that tRNA molecules pick up specific amino acids according to the triplet codes they match. Then they take the amino acids to the ribosomes, where the sequence of triplet codes on a particular mRNA specifies the order for assembling amino acids to make a particular protein.

As this understanding of protein synthesis was being worked out, other investigators were trying to find out which base triplets were codes for the various amino acids. Biochemists had discovered ways to make an artificial RNA consisting of long chains of a single kind of nucleotide. In 1961 Marshall W. Nirenberg placed an artificial RNA consisting entirely of uracil-bearing nucleotides into a test tube containing a mixture of amino acids and substances from bacterial cells. In the mixture, polypeptides consisting of strings of just one amino acid, phenylalanine, were formed. Evidently the triplet UUU (uracil-uracil-uracil) specified phenylalanine. By the end of the 1960's, biochemists had discovered the amino acids that can be specified by most of the possible nucleotide triplets.

Now, in the 1970's, an abundance of genetic problems still remain. But it is clear that DNA satisfies the requirements of Mendel's

Marshall W. Nirenberg: 1927 —. American biochemist

phenylalanine [fĕn′ĭl ăl′ə nēn′]

4. The ribosome moves along the messenger RNA as it "reads" the code. The amino acids are joined to each other in the order coded forming a protein molecule.

5. After delivering its amino acid, transfer RNA can pick up another amino acid molecule.

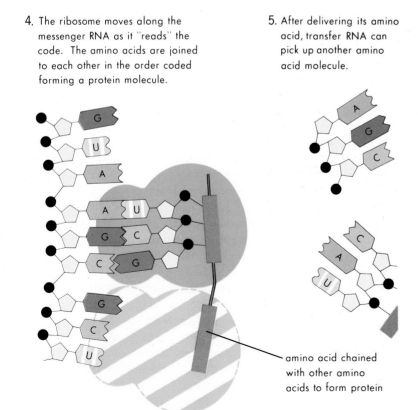

amino acid chained with other amino acids to form protein

"elements" (genes): (1) DNA molecules are distinct particles; (2) DNA can replicate in an exact way; (3) DNA can carry "information." Put very simply, this means that the genetic difference between a pine tree and a worm, or between you and your neighbor, is the sum of the differences in the sequences of bases in the DNA molecules they (or you) contain.

Does this seem unbelievable? The only scientific *way to believe otherwise is to devise an explanation—a theory—that* fits the facts *better.*

GENES AND SICKLE CELLS

Now we can return to sickling, the human trait with which we began this discussion of genetics. In some way red blood cells that sickle differ from normal red blood cells. About one-third of each red blood cell is hemoglobin, and hemoglobin is protein. Therefore, you might hypothesize that the difference in the red cells is a result of a difference in their proteins.

electrophoresis
[ĭ lĕk′trō fə rē′sĭs]

Proteins may be separated from one another by a process called *electrophoresis.* A mixture of proteins is placed in a moist electrical conductor (such as paper containing dilute salt solution) and a current of electricity is passed through the conductor. Some atoms of the protein molecules are ionized. This causes the molecules to become electrically charged so they move through the conductor toward either the positive pole (if the molecule has more negative charges than positive) or the negative pole (if the molecule has more positive charges). The speed of movement of any molecule depends upon its size and its net charge—the difference between the numbers of negative and positive ions. Because different kinds of protein molecules differ in size and net charge, electrophoresis efficiently separates them from one another.

Linus Pauling: 1901 — American chemist

During electrophoresis, normal hemoglobin moves toward the *negative* pole as a single band. Hemoglobin, then, consists of one kind of protein with a net positive charge. In 1949 Linus Pauling and his colleagues found that hemoglobin from a person suffering from sickle-cell anemia moves toward the *positive* pole as a single band. Clearly these persons had a *different* kind of hemoglobin. But when Pauling tested hemoglobin from persons with the sickling trait, he found that approximately half of the hemoglobin moved toward the negative pole just as normal hemoglobin did and the other half moved toward the positive pole. Therefore, persons with the sickling trait must have both normal and sickling hemoglobin.

The kind of hemoglobin in a person's red blood cells depends upon the kind of genes he has. If he has only normal hemoglobin, he must have only genes that direct the formation of that kind. Therefore he must be homozygous for it, and we can write his genotype Hb^AHb^A. If a person has sickle-cell anemia, all of his hemoglobin must be of the sickling type. He also is homozygous, with a genotype Hb^SHb^S. A person with the sickle-cell trait has both kinds of hemoglobin; therefore he has one gene for normal and one for sickling hemoglobin. He is heterozygous, with a genotype Hb^AHb^S. Finally, Hb^A and Hb^S are merely ways to show a difference in DNA.

Investigation 17.5

THE GENETIC CODE AND GENE MUTATION

INTRODUCTION

Knowing now something of the way in which the structure of DNA molecules is related to the structure of protein molecules, it is possible for you to understand more clearly what is meant by gene mutations. You can most easily arrive at such understanding by working out with paper and pencil some hypothetical examples.

sound? Assume that by X-radiation a geneticist deletes (that is, destroys and thus removes) the left-most base pair of the DNA molecule shown above. • To discover the effect of this kind of mutation, construct the mRNA chain indicated by the remaining letters, starting at the new left-hand base.(3) • Again using the chart, construct the chain

Figure 17 • 32

—t—t—a—c—a—t—c—g—a—a—a—g—g—t—c—a—t—g—a—t—c—
—a—a—t—g—t—a—g—c—t—t—t—c—c—a—g—t—a—c—t—a—g—

PROCEDURE

Assume that the above diagram represents a part of a DNA molecule. The whole molecule is much longer, and the strands of deoxyribose and phosphate groups have been omitted. The key to the bases is:

a = adenine,   c = cytosine,
t = thymine,   g = guanine.

Assume that the lower strand is the one from which a messenger RNA strand is copied. • Using paper and pencil, write the sequence of bases in an mRNA strand that would be formed on the DNA strand. (Remember that in RNA, uracil—symbolized by u—replaces thymine.)(1)

Reading from left to right, divide your sequence of mRNA bases into code triplets (codons). • Then, using Figure 17 • 33, construct the protein segment—the chain of amino acids—that is specified by your sequence of mRNA codons.(2)

The dictionary of RNA codons provided here does not include all the amino acids. Even if it did, you would find that there are many more possible codons than there are amino acids. Might there be more than one codon for some of the amino acids—as "cat" and "kat" are different spellings for the same

RNA CODON	AMINO ACID
aag	lysine
auc	isoleucine
aug	methionine
cau	histidine
cga	arginine
gaa	glutamic acid
gga	glycine
guc	valine
uac	tyrosine
uca	serine
uga	none
uua	leucine

Figure 17 • 33
An incomplete chart of codons.

of amino acids specified by the complete codons of the new mRNA.(4) • What has happened to the codon on the right end?(5) The codon that does not appear in the chart specifies arginine. Thus you see that a single amino acid can be specified by more than 1 codon. • Does the deletion in the DNA molecule change the resulting protein? If so, in what way?(6)

One codon (uga) in the altered mRNA

does not specify an amino acid. Codons of this sort specify the ends of protein molecules.

Assume now that X-radiation deleted the first 3 base pairs on the left instead of just the first one. • Would this kind of deletion have more or less effect on an amino-acid sequence than deletion of a single base pair? Explain.(7)

Occasionally, errors in DNA replication occur—apparently without environmental causes. For example, at rare intervals adenine pairs with cytosine instead of thymine. The consequence of this error is as follows:

Figure 17 • 34

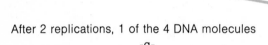

After 2 replications, 1 of the 4 DNA molecules

(IIIb) has the base pair $\begin{matrix} -g- \\ \vdots \\ -c- \end{matrix}$ where the others

have the original $\begin{matrix} -a- \\ \vdots \\ -t- \end{matrix}$. An error of this sort, if

it had occurred in the DNA molecule diagramed at the beginning of this investigation, would substitute c for t at some point in the DNA strand. Assume such a substitution occurs at the 3rd base pair from the right. • Show how this changes the mRNA.(8) • Show how it changes the amino-acid chain.(9)

One of the changes known to occur in this way involves the substitution of glycine for glutamic acid at 1 site within the protein molecule. • Can you deduce an error in the normal DNA molecule that would account for this mutational change? If so, what is it?(10)

SUMMARY

Studies of amino-acid sequences in hemoglobins show that the only difference between normal **Hb**[A] and sickle-cell **Hb**[S] hemoglobins is the substitution of one amino acid (valine) for another (glutamic acid) in a poly-

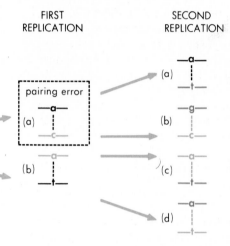

FIRST REPLICATION   SECOND REPLICATION

peptide chain approximately 150 amino acids long! • According to the codon chart above, how many changes in base pairs would be necessary to specify this substitution in amino acids?(11) Because there are 4 codons for valine (guu, guc, gua, gug) and 2 for glutamic acid (gaa, gag), the change can be made by a mutation in only 1 base pair. • What are the possibilities for such a change?(12) • Which possibility is more likely: that the mutation involves changes at 2 base pairs simultaneously or a change at just 1 pair?(13) From such a small genotypic difference arise the great phenotypic differences between persons with and those without sickling disease!

GUIDE QUESTIONS

1. What is selective breeding?
2. How do red blood cells of people with sickle-cell anemia differ from normal red blood cells?
3. What is the difference between a person who has the sickle-cell trait and one who has sickle-cell anemia?
4. What is a pedigree?
5. With what kinds of events does the mathematics of probability deal?
6. Why is probability useful in studying the inheritance of characteristics?

7. What evidence shows that the probability of inheriting the sickle-cell trait is about 50 percent when one parent is normal and the other has the sickle-cell trait?

8. Why might information be missing from pedigrees in which both parents have the sickle-cell trait?

9. What is a gene?

10. Why must we conclude from the evidence that a person with the sickle-cell trait carries a gene for sickling?

11. How did Mendel's experimental methods differ from earlier ones?

12. What does "true breeding" mean?

13. What experimental results caused Mendel to distinguish dominant and recessive forms of a trait?

14. What reasoning leads to the conclusion that organisms have two genes (a pair) for each trait?

15. If you say two genes are alleles, what do you mean?

16. Using sickling as an example, explain the difference between the terms "genotype" and "phenotype."

17. Using one of the traits studied by Mendel as an example, explain the difference between a homozygous and a heterozygous individual.

18. What is a dihybrid cross?

19. What was Mendel's experimental evidence in favor of the principle of independent assortment?

20. What evidence do you have that a genotype and an environment interact to produce a phenotype?

21. How does observed behavior of chromosomes in mitosis and meiosis parallel Mendel's theory about behavior of genes in heredity?

22. What do we mean if we say that the chromosome theory has been "proved"?

23. How did the inheritance of white eye color in fruit flies convincingly link the inheritance of a particular trait with a particular chromosome?

24. Why have fruit flies been used so frequently for experiments in genetics?

25. For what purpose does a scientist use the chi-square test?

26. In the F_2 generation of a dihybrid cross, the ratio of phenotypes often is neither 9:3:3:1 nor 3:1. Why?

27. Which of Mendel's principles has been least modified by later discoveries?

28. How can there be more than two alleles for a given locus?

29. What effect does the existence of multiple alleles for a given trait have on the number of phenotypes?

30. How can the inheritance of traits that show great variability in phenotypes be explained by the gene theory?

31. When nondisjunction occurs during meiosis, what result is visible in the chromosomes of a zygote?

32. How does nondisjunction provide further support for the chromosome theory?

33. What is a mutation?

34. Distinguish between chromosomal and gene mutations.

35. What factors in the environment are known to affect the *rate* of mutation?

36. What biochemical characteristic of peas is associated with one of the traits that Mendel studied?

37. How did the *Neurospora* research of Beadle and Tatum show that genes affect the biochemistry of organisms?

38. Why did this research turn the interest of geneticists to proteins?

39. How does a biochemist determine the order in which amino acids occur in a protein molecule?

40. How did research on dead pneumonia bacteria and bacteriophages provide evidence that DNA rather than protein is the genetic substance?

41. Describe a DNA molecule.

42. Why are three adjacent bases in a DNA molecule needed to specify one amino acid in a protein molecule?

43. How does transfer RNA differ from messenger RNA?

44. What protein is made if an artificial mRNA consisting only of uracil bases is used?

45. How does the Watson-Crick model of DNA structure fit the theory of the gene?

46. How did Pauling show that the hemoglobin proteins from people whose red blood cells sickled differed from normal hemoglobin proteins?

47. According to present evidence, what must happen when a gene mutation occurs?

PROBLEMS

1. The *polled* (hornless) trait in cattle is dominant; the horned trait is recessive. A certain polled bull is mated to three cows. Cow A, which is horned, gives birth to a polled calf. Cow B, also horned, produces a horned calf. Cow C, which is polled, produces a horned calf. What are the genotypes of the four parents?

2. In shorthorn cattle, when a red bull (**RR**) is crossed with a white cow (**rr**), the offspring are *roan* (intermingled red and white hairs). How could a rancher go about establishing a herd of roan cattle?

3. In sheep, white coat is dominant; black is recessive. Occasionally a black sheep appears in a flock. Black wool is worthless. How could a farmer eliminate the genes for black coat from his flock?

4. In summer squash, white fruit color is dominant; yellow is recessive. If a squash plant that is homozygous for white is crossed with a homozygous yellow, predict the appearance of the F_1 generation. Of the F_2. Of the offspring of a cross between an F_1 individual and a homozygous white individual.

5. The storage roots of radishes may be long, round, or oval. In a series of experiments, crosses between long and oval produced 159 long and 156 oval. Crosses between round and oval produced 199 round and 203 oval. Crosses between long and round produced 576 oval. Crosses between oval and oval produced 121 long, 243 oval, and 119 round. Show how root shape is inherited in radishes.

6. What are the possible blood types of children in the following families?
   a. Type A mother, Type A father
   b. Type A mother, Type O father
   c. Type B mother, Type AB father
   d. Type AB mother, Type AB father
   e. Type A mother, Type B father

7. In tomatoes, red fruit color is dominant to yellow; round-shaped fruit is dominant to pear-shaped; and tall vine is dominant to dwarf vine. If you cross a pure-breeding tall plant bearing red, round fruit with a pure-breeding dwarf plant bearing yellow, pear-shaped fruit, predict the appearance of the F_1 generation. Assuming that the gene loci controlling the three traits are in three different pairs of chromosomes, what are the possible genotypes in the F_2 generation? What are the expected ratios of the phenotypes?

8. How would you go about improving the characteristics of the seedless orange?

9. Before Mendel, the chief theory of heredity was "blood-line inheritance." According to this theory, the parents' traits are blended in the offspring, just as two liquids blend when mixed together. Mendel's theory rested on the idea that traits are transmitted by particles (genes) and do not blend. Give evidence in support of the older theory. Then show how the results of Mendel's experiments fail to fit that theory.

10. At the present time there is no such thing as an all-blue tulip. The first one found will be quite valuable. How might a tulip breeder increase his chances of finding a blue tulip in his fields?

11. Emphasis is usually put upon mutations in the cells that produce gametes, because such mutations affect later generations. But mutations can occur in any cell. Suppose that during the development of a human embryo, a mutation that increases the production of pigment occurs in a cell of the right anterior ectoderm. What effect will this have upon the appearance of the infant? Will this trait be inherited by the infant's future offspring?

12. The Himalayan coat pattern in domestic rabbits is influenced by environment. Find out what factor is involved and as much as you can about the way it works. Then write a comparison between this case and your results from Investigation 17.2.

13. How does proof in science differ from proof in mathematics?

14. A die (singular of "dice") has six sides. What is the probability that an even number will come up on one throw of the die?

15. If base pairs in DNA molecules can consist of adenine-thymine or of cytosine-guanine only, what must be the ratio of the amount of adenine to thymine? Of cytosine to guanine? Of adenine to cytosine?

16. The pedigree on the next page shows the descendants of Mohan, a white tiger captured in India. Assuming that whiteness in tigers is a single-locus trait, is it recessive or dominant? What evidence supports your answer?

GENEALOGY OF CAPTIVE WHITE TIGERS

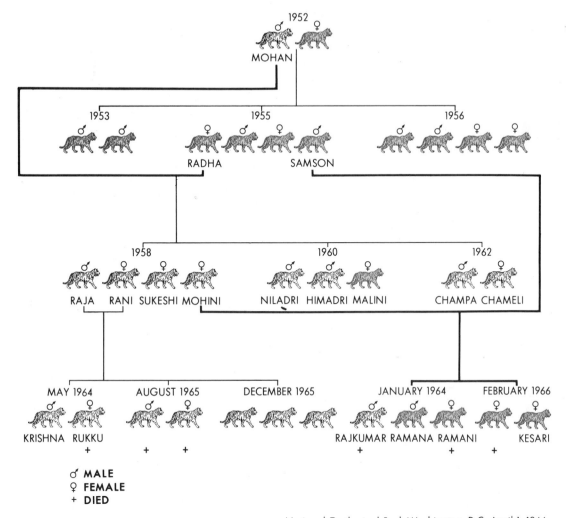

National Zoological Park Washington, D.C. April 1, 1966

Smithsonian Institution

SUGGESTED READINGS

BONNER, D. M., and S. E. MILLS. *Heredity*. 2nd ed. Englewood Cliffs, N.J.: Prentice-Hall, Inc., 1964. (A short book, with heavy emphasis on the molecular and biochemical aspects of heredity. Advanced.)

GOLDSTEIN, P. *Genetics Is Easy*. New York: The Viking Press, Inc., 1961. (Especially written for high school students. Easy.)

GOODENOUGH, U. W., and P. P. LEVINE. "The Genetic Activity of Mitochondria and Chloroplasts," *Scientific American*, November, 1970. Pp. 22–29.

HARTMAN, P. E., and S. R. SUSKIND. *Gene Action*. Englewood Cliffs, N.J.: Prentice-Hall, Inc., 1965. (The relationship of DNA to the gene concept, and the chemical links between gene and organism. Advanced.)

McKUSICK, V. A. "The Mapping of Human Chromosomes," *Scientific American*, April, 1971. Pp. 104–113.

————. *Human Genetics*. Englewood Cliffs, N.J.: Prentice-Hall, Inc., 1964. (This book describes the methods and results of genetic study applied to man. Rather advanced.)

NOMURA, M. "Ribosomes," *Scientific American,* October, 1969. Pp. 28–35.

PETERS, J. A. *Classic Papers in Genetics.* Englewood Cliffs, N.J.: Prentice-Hall, Inc., 1959. (Includes [pages 2–20] a translation of Mendel's report on his experiments and 27 other important reports by geneticists from 1903 to 1955. Advanced.)

REISFELD, R. A., and B. D. KAHAN. "Markers of Biological Individuality," *Scientific American,* June, 1972. Pp. 28–37.

SIGURBJORNSSON, B. "Induced Mutations in Plants," *Scientific American,* January, 1971. Pp. 86–95.

SIMPSON, G. G., and W. S. BECK. *Life: An Introduction to Biology.* Shorter ed. New York: Harcourt, Brace & World, Inc., 1969. Chapters 6 and 7. (A good account of genetics on the college level, with special attention to reasoning from experimental results to principles. Rather advanced.)

SRB, A. M., and R. OWEN. *Facets of Genetics.* San Francisco: W. H. Freeman, 1970. (A collection of articles from *Scientific American.* Somewhat advanced.)

TEMIN, H. M. "RNA-directed DNA Synthesis," *Scientific American,* January, 1972. Pp. 24–33.

VOLPE, E. P. *Human Heredity and Birth Defects.* New York: Pegasus, 1971. (A short book that is rather easy and very important—but not pleasant to read.)

ZOBEL, B. J. "The Genetic Improvement of Southern Pines," *Scientific American,* March, 1971. Pp. 84–103.

Evolution

CHARLES DARWIN AND EVOLUTION

The Galápagos Islands are a bleak volcanic archipelago, straddling the equator in the Pacific Ocean far off the west coast of Ecuador. Their shores are fringed by broken black lava rocks crowded with marine lizards, and behind are arid hills guarded by ranks of towering tree cacti.

Late in the year of 1835 a British exploring vessel, HMS *Beagle,* arrived in the Galápagos. Almost the first person ashore was the ship's naturalist, Charles Darwin. This young Englishman, who had already spent nearly four years in scientific exploration of the lands and waters of South America, was fascinated by the harsh landscape of the islands. For three weeks he roamed the islands, observing and collecting animals and plants. Many things aroused his curiosity—the giant tortoises, one of which he rode at the alarming speed of ''360 yards

Galápagos [gə lä′pə gōs′]

archipelago [är′kə pĕl′ə gō′; Greek: *archos*, chief, + *pelagos*, sea]: a group of islands

X 1/40

Figure 18 • 1
Galápagos tortoise.

Robert I. Bowman

Figure 18 • 2
Cactus forest on Santa Fé Island, Galápagos.

X 1/4

Figure 18 · 3
Galápagos mockingbird.

an hour''; and the mockingbirds, which seemed to differ from island to island. But nothing made a more lasting impression than a group of small, dull-colored finches.

In general these birds reminded Darwin of finches he had seen in Ecuador. But what diversity there was among these in the Galápagos! Finches ordinarily are seed-eaters. Indeed, some of the Galápagos finches did eat seeds; but others fed on the fleshy parts of cacti. There

Figure 18 · 4
The Galápagos finches. Which part of the body varies most?

X 1/2

X 1/2

was even one that used a cactus spine, held in its beak, as a tool to extract insects from under the bark of tree cacti. This was especially interesting, since Darwin noticed that there were no woodpeckers on the islands. Every habitat seemed to contain finches: big and little; ground finches, tree finches; seed-eaters, fruit-eaters, insect-eaters; and a "woodpecker" finch!

In his notebook Darwin jotted down his observations; in his mind he recorded vivid pictures of the island scenes. There in the Galápagos he began to form new ideas. But not for 23 years would the world hear of these ideas—and never would it be the same again!

THE RELUCTANT SCIENTIST

Charles Darwin did not set out to be a scientist. Indeed, as a boy he was an unenthusiastic student who, as his father once commented, cared "for nothing but shooting, dogs, and rat-catching." But he liked to read, enjoyed travel, and collected everything he could get his hands on.

His attempt to follow in his father's footsteps by studying medicine at the University of Edinburgh was a failure. He found the medical lectures as dull as the lecturers themselves and became sick at the two operations he attended. With the idea of becoming a clergyman, Darwin transferred to Cambridge University. At Cambridge he was fortunately befriended by several teachers, especially a botanist named Henslow who enjoyed taking groups of students on field trips.

Through Henslow Darwin received an exciting offer. A British naval expedition, setting out to survey the coast of South America, had room for an unpaid naturalist, who would observe and collect plants, animals, and geological specimens. Charles' father vehemently objected to the invitation—an unpaid naturalist, indeed! Nevertheless, on December 27, 1831, at the age of 22, Darwin put to sea from Plymouth aboard the *Beagle*.

THEORIES FORMING

Five years later, having sailed entirely around the world, the *Beagle* again docked in England. There, as he prepared his official report, Darwin relived the sights and sounds of the trip. He began to see patterns among the queries hastily jotted down during the voyage.

All the tremendous variety of life forms seemed to require some explanation. Those odd finches on the Galápagos, for example—all so similar, yet each with some peculiar characteristic of its own. And the geological problems—the origin of islands in the open ocean, for instance. Could there be any connection between the biological and geological problems? Sir Charles Lyell, whose *Principles of Geology* accompanied Darwin on his voyage, had already gathered evidence showing that the rocks of the earth are subject to change. Darwin had checked this evidence throughout South America. If rocks, islands, and continents could change, might not time also bring about changes in living things?

American Museum of Natural History

Figure 18 • 5
Charles Darwin 18 years after the voyage of the *Beagle*.

Edinburgh [ĕd′ən bûr′ō], Scotland

John S. Henslow: 1796–1861. English botanist

queries [kwĭr′ĭz]: brief questions, especially those expressing doubts

Sir Charles Lyell [lī′əl]: 1797–1875. British geologist

Figure 18 • 6

The red jungle fowl, a bird of Southeast Asia, is thought to be the species from which the many breeds of domestic chickens have been developed. Which of the breeds shown seems to retain the greatest number of the wild bird's traits?

Indeed, domesticated animals and plants *have* changed in the relatively short time that man has been breeding them. How have such changes occurred? Darwin began patiently to collect examples of variation among domesticated animals and plants. He went directly to the sources of information—to seedsmen, to farmers, to animal-breeders. And he undertook experiments of his own.

Figure 18 • 7

Under domestication, species of the genus *Cucurbita* have developed a wide range of fruit forms. Working with domesticated *Cucurbita* nearly a century ago, the French botanist Charles Naudin proposed the biological definition of "species."

Victor Larsen

At the same time, he dug deeper into the accumulated knowledge of geology. He checked the geological evidence that showed many changes in series of fossils taken from older to younger rocks. Could the older fossils be the ancestors of the later forms? Darwin found more and more evidence that made him think so. Moreover, the manner in which present-day plants and animals are distributed over the surface of the earth could be linked to the past distribution of their possible ancestors. So Darwin sifted through reports of exploring expeditions that had charted the geographical distribution of organisms.

See pages 338–339.

The structures of organisms that are now living might hold clues to the structures of their ancestors. Then, too, the ways in which modern organisms develop as individuals might reveal something about how their ancestors had changed. So Darwin, though he had little contact with laboratory biology, studied anatomy and embryology.

As the years went by, from a hill of hypotheses a mountain of facts arose. All pointed to the conclusion that individuals within species vary and that from these variations great changes in the species inhabiting the earth have occurred. Still lacking, however, was a guiding principle. To produce changes that will result in populations adapted to their environment (as species populations are), variations must take some direction. Or if all sorts of variations occur, then some of them must be preserved and others not. What directs change?

If Darwin had known only the peaceful English countryside, he might long have pondered this question. But still fresh in his mind was the teeming life of the Brazilian rain forest. In a variety of ways, the rich plant life of the tropical forest seemed to struggle upward to reach the light. Having seen this, Darwin could detect in all kinds of habitats the struggle among individuals to obtain the necessities of life. Moreover, not long after he returned to England, he chanced to read Malthus' book, *An Essay on the Principle of Population.* Malthus had concluded that man tends to produce more offspring than can be supported. If this were true of all living organisms, wouldn't there be a struggle for existence among them? Under such circumstances, wouldn't the offspring best fitted for survival be the ones most likely to grow up and produce offspring like themselves? So it seemed to Darwin.

Malthus. See page 39.

The breeder of domestic animals selects as parents for the next generations of his flocks and herds those individuals that have the characteristics he desires. In a like manner, Darwin thought, the struggle for existence in nature might remove from each generation the individuals fitted poorly to live in their environment, leaving the fit to produce the next generation. The natural selection, then, might explain how populations arise with characteristics that are fitted to new environments.

See page 559.

THE THEORIES PUBLISHED

It is one thing to convince one's self; it is something else to convince one's fellow scientists and the public. As patiently as he gath-

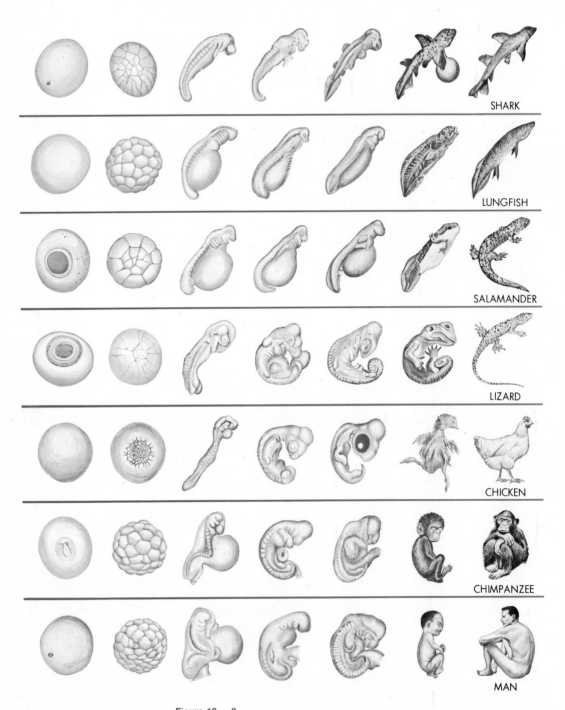

Figure 18 · 8

Comparative embryology of some vertebrates. Zygotes are shown on the left, adult animals on the right, and comparable embryological stages between. Drawings are not on the same scale.

ered evidence supporting his idea, Darwin also gathered objections to it. He examined contrary evidence. He worked over flaws in reasoning. He tried alternative methods of explaining the facts. Nearly a quarter of a century passed.

Then, quite unexpectedly, he received a scientific paper from an unknown young man who had been exploring in Malaya. The explorer, A. R. Wallace, asked Darwin to read it, and if it seemed "sufficiently novel and interesting," to send it on to Lyell for his comment. Imagine Darwin's surprise when he discovered that Wallace had worked out ideas almost identical to his own. Darwin felt that he could not now, in fairness to Wallace, publish his own ideas. But a few of his friends, who knew of his years of work, persuaded him to summarize his theories and make a joint presentation with Wallace. So, on July 1, 1858, the Darwin and Wallace papers were presented before a meeting of the Linnaean Society of London, though neither Wallace nor Darwin was present.

identical [ī děn′tə kəl; Latin: *idem,* the same]: alike in all respects

Linnaean [lĭ nē′ən]. From its name, what do you think may have been the interests of this society?

The next year Darwin assembled his accumulated studies in a book, *The Origin of Species by Means of Natural Selection.* In it he proposed two theories. First was the theory that the living species of today are but modified descendants of species that populated the earth in bygone ages. This idea was far from new. It had been held by some of the ancient Greeks. And during the previous century it had been used to explain the fossil evidence that was then beginning to accumulate. But Darwin was the first to present such an enormous body of carefully sifted evidence to support this theory. Within a decade many of the biologists of the world were convinced that this theory—the ***theory of organic evolution***—was as "true" as any theory can be. The second theory attempted to explain what makes evolution occur. This ***theory of natural selection*** became widely, but not universally, accepted by biologists of Darwin's time.

How true is that?

In 1809 Jean de Lamarck had published a theory based on the idea that a change made in an individual by a factor in its environment could be passed on to the individual's offspring. Thus an animal that browsed on twigs and leaves of trees would stretch its neck to reach food, and, generation after generation, offspring would be born with longer and longer necks. In this manner, said Lamarck, giraffes could have developed from ancestors similar to antelopes.

Lamarck. See pages 345–346.

Figure 18 • 9
Alfred Russell Wallace: 1823–1913. British naturalist.

Darwin tried to reject this idea. He believed that variation is a basic characteristic of living things and that all kinds of variations occur. He maintained that ancestors of giraffes included both shorter-necked and longer-necked individuals. Over a long period, the average neck length increased because, *on the average,* the longer-necked individuals survived in greater numbers (being better able to reach food) and, *on the average,* they therefore produced a larger population of the offspring. But Darwin was still troubled. What made the variations occur in the first place? And how are variations transmitted from one generation to the next?

Darwin was never able to answer these questions. Apparently

Who was this?

he never ran across the work of the Austrian monk who was experimenting with inheritance in garden peas and applying his mathematical training (which Darwin lacked) to the results.

THE PROCESS OF EVOLVING

All the evidence Darwin presented in support of his theory of natural selection was indirect. No person could live long enough to observe directly the processes of evolution—or so it seemed to Darwin and to biologists for more than half a century after him. They were wrong.

AN EXAMPLE

Biston betularia
[bĭs′tən bĕt ū lā′rĭ ə]

Consider the case of *Biston betularia,* the peppered moth, a common inhabitant of English woodlands. To a casual observer all peppered moths look alike; but if you examine a large number of them carefully, you find—as in any population—many individual differences. A few have shorter antennae than most. Some have longer legs. The most noticeable difference, however, is in coloration: some individuals are light and others dark.

For a long time collecting moths has been a popular hobby in Britain. Thus, many specimens from all periods of time during the last two centuries and from all parts of the country are available for study. When biologists examine these specimens, they find that the variations among moths caught in, say, 1850 are mainly the same as those seen among moths collected a hundred years later. But there is one startling difference. Among moths collected in 1950 there are more dark than light ones; in 1850 there were many more light than dark.

When, however, biologists examine specimens taken from rural southern England only, they find the proportion of light to dark moths is still very much like that of 1850. It is when they examine collections from the heavily industrialized Midlands of England that they find very few light moths. Why should light moths predominate in one region, dark moths elsewhere? And why should dark moths have been rarer in the past than now?

Before reading further, can you state a hypothesis of your own?

The biologists who investigated this matter developed a hypothesis, which they proceeded to test. In the Midlands they placed both light and dark moths on smoke-blackened tree trunks in the position moths take during their daytime rest. They soon observed that birds preying on moths ate many more light than dark moths. Then they placed both light and dark moths on trees of the kinds common in southern England—soot-free and encrusted with whitish lichens. Here the birds ate more dark than light moths.

What can we conclude from the experiments? Dark moths survive predation better than white ones on the soot-covered tree trunks that resulted from the industrialization of the Midlands. Coloration is known to be controlled genetically. During the last century, therefore,

Photos from American Museum of Natural History

Figure 18 • 10

The basis for natural selection in the peppered moth (*Biston betularia*). Dark and light forms on a tree blackened by soot (*left*). The two forms of the moth on a tree covered with light-colored lichens (*right*).

Darwin's natural selection favored the moths most protectively colored in the new environment. Meanwhile, the white form survived successfully in rural areas, where tree trunks are not sooty.

CHARACTERISTICS OF THE EVOLUTIONARY PROCESS

Comparing the populations before and after industrialization, we can note three main points.

First: An evolutionary event involves a change in a population. Individuals do not undergo evolutionary changes during their lifetimes. It is the frequency of different kinds of individuals in the population—the makeup of the population—that changes. Dark individuals occurred in the 1850 moth population, but they were more frequent in the 1950 population.

Frequencies can be expressed as fractions, ratios, or percentages. In what investigation did you deal with frequencies?

Second: An evolutionary event involves relatively few characteristics. Because organisms are systems of complex interactions, change in frequency of dark moths may very well have brought about some less obvious changes in moth characteristics. But when we consider all possible moth characteristics, very few changed in frequency. There is a stability factor in the characteristics of populations.

Third: An evolutionary event involves a change in a particular direction. There must, therefore, be some basis for change to work

Figure 18 • 11

Screech owls occur in the two color forms shown here. The red form is common in New England but is less so elsewhere in the East; it is rare or absent in the West. Can you propose a hypothesis to explain this?

Lynwood M. Chace

on—some "raw material." Before the rise in frequency of dark moths, there were already a few dark individuals in the moth population—and their darkness was hereditary. An evolutionary event, then, requires genetic variations as its raw material. Thus there is a change factor in evolution. But an evolutionary event does not involve *all* the raw materials available. There were many hereditary variations in the moths of a century ago, but only one, the dark color, became the basis for a change in the population. Evolution is a selective change, with environmental factors (the soot and the birds, in our example) guiding the selection. Thus there is a guiding factor in evolution.

Investigation 18.1

GENETIC STABILITY

BACKGROUND INFORMATION

In general, people have been more impressed by the stability of the kinds of living things than by changes in them. People have, indeed, seen how new varieties appear in domesticated animals but have apparently not been much impressed by this. And they have been puzzled by fossils but have been inclined to think of them simply as remains of kinds of organisms that failed—that became extinct and left no descendants. The changing of one kind into another has been left for myths and children's tales. For 2500 years there have

been dissenters from this viewpoint, but they have not changed general opinion. Like other common-sense opinions, this one is based on observation—but uncontrolled observation. And in this case, of course, it is hindered by the relative shortness of a human lifetime.

However, scientific evidence for stability seemed to be found when the very exact mechanisms of mitosis and meiosis were linked with the inheritance of characteristics. Since these processes were so precise, it seemed that organisms must conserve their genetic characteristics generation after generation. In this investigation you will see a further development of this line of reasoning.

PROCEDURE

Consider a hypothetical species of squirrel. Assume that among the variations in this hypothetical species are 2 hereditary hair types—one straight and the other curly. Assume that the trait is determined by a single pair of alleles and that straight (S) is dominant over curly (s). Finally, assume that the species population consists of 1000 squirrels, with equal numbers of males and females. Among the 500 squirrels of each sex, 250 are homozygous straight-haired (SS) and 250 are homozygous curly-haired (ss).

• Using the symbols ♂ for male and ♀ for female, diagram all the possible phenotypic matings in this hypothetical population.(1) • Now list all the possible kinds of matings in terms of genotypes—for example, SS × ss. (2) • Beside each kind of mating write all the kinds of genotypes that occur among the offspring.(3) • Does any cross produce more than 1 kind of offspring?(4)

Assume that the offspring generation also consists of 1000 squirrels and that each kind of mating you listed for Item 2 contributes equally to this population. • What is the expected ratio of straight-haired squirrels to curly-haired squirrels in the offspring?(5) • Is this phenotypic ratio the same as that in the 1st generation?(6)

The frequency of any particular characteristic within a group is expressed as a fraction. Thus, in a group of 100 marbles containing 20 red and 80 blue ones, the frequency of red marbles is $20/100 = 1/5 = 20\% = 0.2$. The frequency of blue marbles is $80/100 = 4/5 = 80\% = 0.8$. Regardless of the way the fractions are written, their sum (whether expressing 2 frequencies, as in this case, or more) must always be equal to 1:

$$20/100 + 80/100 = 100/100 = 1$$
$$1/5 + 4/5 = 5/5 = 1$$
$$20\% + 80\% = 100\% = 1$$
$$0.2 + 0.8 = 1.0$$

Now consider the 2 genes S and s. • What were their frequencies (expressed as decimal fractions) in the original population? (7) • What are their frequencies in the offspring generation?(8) • How do the gene frequencies in the original population compare with the frequencies in the offspring generation?(9)

Now make the same calculations for a 3rd generation. You can do this by mating every genotype with every other genotype *in proportion to their frequencies*. But this becomes complicated and tedious. You can obtain the same result by using the **gene-pool** method: Write the frequencies of all the kinds of gametes in the 2nd generation. (In this case, they are equivalent to the frequencies of genes in Item 8.) Then assume random combination of these gametes. The frequency of S plus the frequency of s represents the total sperm population. Likewise, the frequency of S plus the frequency of s represents the total egg population. By algebraic multiplication the 3rd-generation genotypes and their frequencies can be obtained.

Use the gene-pool method to answer the following questions: • What are the frequencies of the genotypes in the 3rd generation? (10) • Assuming that the 3rd-generation population is again 1000, what are the frequencies of S and s in the 3rd generation?(11) • Is the phenotypic ratio the same as that in the 2nd generation?(12) • Are the gene frequencies the same as those in the 2nd generation?(13)

Retaining all other assumptions, change the original population to 400 homozygous straight-haired squirrels and 600 homozygous curly-haired squirrels, each group containing males and females in equal numbers. • What are the frequencies of the 2 genes among males in the population?(14) • Among females?(15) • By algebraic multiplication determine the frequencies of genotypes among the offspring.(16) • What are the frequencies of the 2 genes in the offspring population?(17) • Calculate the frequencies of the genes in a 3rd generation.(18)

CONCLUSION

• In a single sentence try to state a conclusion concerning gene frequencies in populations.(19)

If you have been successful in formulating your sentence, you have stated the basic idea of the *Hardy-Weinberg principle.* In 1908 Godfrey H. Hardy, an English mathematician, and Wilhelm R. Weinberg, a German physician, independently worked out the effects of random mating in successive generations on the frequencies of allelic genes in a population. You have just done the same thing they did.

As you worked, you may have noticed that in many ways the hypothetical population differs from real ones—in other words, there are several unstated assumptions. Nevertheless, the Hardy-Weinberg principle has been important for biologists because it is the basis of hypothetical stability from which to measure real change.

THE CHANGE FACTOR

In the example of evolution that we have been discussing, frequency of black moths could not have changed if there had been *no* black moths in the population—if their frequency had been 0. Evolution is impossible without genetic differences between individuals in a population—without variations. Darwin easily found variations among the individuals of many species. He asked where the variations came from, but he could give no answer.

Review pages 586–588.

An answer came from 20th-century genetics: mutation is the ultimate source of variation. The sickling gene in man originated by mutation. The characteristics of the peas studied by Mendel originated by mutation.

Once mutant genes have arisen, new combinations of them can be formed through independent assortment and crossing-over. The number of combinations increases much more rapidly than the number of mutant genes themselves. Two alleles at one gene locus, **A** and **a,** produce three genotypes: **AA, Aa,** and **aa.** Two alleles at each of two loci, **A** and **a** at one and **B** and **b** at the other, produce nine genotypes.

What are these genotypes? How many genotypes will two alleles at each of three loci produce?

Recombination of two mutations may produce an individual as different from an individual with one mutation as either of these is from an individual with neither mutation. For example, a combination of very big bones and very strong muscles would produce a giant among men, while very big bones with ordinary muscles might produce a cripple, and ordinary bones with very strong muscles might do likewise. Thus, recombination can yield a wide variety of individuals from relatively few mutations.

Does this statement apply to organisms that reproduce asexually? Explain.

Summing up: Mutation supplies the raw material for evolution, and recombination casts mutations into new combinations. But no evidence has been found that mutation supplies needed or desirable changes. Just change—any change.

THE GUIDING FACTOR

Mutation is a random process. But fossils—the evidence for evolution in the past—clearly show that the changes in living things during geological time have *not* been random. On the contrary, the combinations of traits that we find in living things both past and present are in most cases well-organized, well-coordinated *sets* of traits.

How can such order come from the chaos of randomness? The theory devised to answer this question is the most important accomplishment of Charles Darwin. His theory of natural selection supplied reasonable, natural causes for the guiding factor of evolution; it was worked out on the basis of evidence then available to naturalists. And the new evidence of 20th-century genetics has supported it.

chaos [kã′ŏs; Greek: *khaos*, empty space]: total disorder

You have already seen how the idea of natural selection developed; now let us summarize the theory. First, in every species there are many hereditary variations. Indeed, very few individuals of any species are exactly alike genetically. Second, in most cases the process of reproduction operates so that offspring are more numerous than the parents that produce them. If, in any species, all offspring grew up to become parents, the number of individuals after a few generations would be greater than available nutrients could possibly support. Third, it is clear that this increase in numbers *is* checked. The net population of a species does not continue to increase sharply over long periods of time. This means that many members of each generation fail to reproduce. Usually they die from one cause or another before reaching the age of reproduction.

Review Investigation 2.2.

Which ones die? There must be a kind of struggle among individuals of a species for the available food, light, water, or other environmental factors important to their survival. This intraspecific competition takes place among individuals that are genetically different from one another. Often it is these heritable differences that determine which individuals survive and which do not.

On the average, *in any particular environment* individuals having characteristics that improve their ability to survive must more often reach reproductive age than individuals lacking such characteristics. Thus, in each generation we should expect a slight increase in the

Figure 18 • 12

The varying hare (*left*) has a nearly white coat in winter, although it is brown in summer. The coat of the cottontail rabbit (*right*) changes little from summer to winter. Which species is likely to escape predators better in Georgia? In Ontario?   × ⅛

Lynwood M. Chace

Leonard Lee Rue III from Annan

viability [vī′ə bĭl′ə tĭ; Latin: *vivere*, to live, + ability]

proportion of individuals having high ***viability***—that is, having many characteristics favorable to survival. That is what Darwin called "survival of the fittest."

Now let us see how the theory of natural selection worked in the case of the peppered moths. In the clean forests that existed before industrialization, birds ate more dark moths than light ones. So dark moths remained very rare in the population. But after industrialization the dark moths in the sooty woods were eaten less often than the light ones—their darker color fitted them better to withstand predation in the new environment. So more of the dark moths survived to have dark offspring than did light ones to have light offspring. Therefore, generation after generation the ratio of dark moths to light ones in the population increased. Eventually, the light moths became rare, and dark moths—fittest in the new environment—became common.

Note that fitness is not just a characteristic of an organism. It is an ecological characteristic, the interaction of a particular organism and a particular environment. Blackness of the moths does not fit them to live everywhere—only in places where tree trunks are dark. A different example: In most environments the possession of wings is obviously an advantage to a fly. But in the southern Indian Ocean, far from any other land, is an island swept all year by savage winds. Flies are present there, but none have wings. It is easy to imagine what would likely happen to any mutant winged fly on that island.

Many flightless land birds live on islands, but some do not. Look up some examples and try to explain their survival as species.

However, not every characteristic of every organism is adaptive. Natural selection can act only on *whole* organisms. If genes of poor adaptive value and genes of high adaptive value are closely linked, selection can sort them out only after recombination has separated them. And often, since each gene mutation has several or many effects, harmful effects may be inseparable from beneficial. If the *overall* effect is favorable, seemingly harmful effects are carried along.

Now one final important point. Superior ability to survive—viability—is not the only factor in natural selection. Equally important

Figure 18 • 13

Two land animals that get their food from the ocean. Green turtle (*left*) produces a large brood; fairy tern (*right*) produces one off-spring a year. What might you hypothesize about the mortality of the young in these two species?

Russ Kinne from Photo Researchers

Lewis W. Walker from Photo Researchers

is superior *fertility*—the ability to produce offspring. High viability and high fertility do not always go together. The most fertile individuals in a population are not always the biggest, the strongest, or even the healthiest ones. Differences in viability and differences in fertility add up to differential reproduction: On the average, populations whose members produce the most offspring capable of living to maturity tend to survive and increase in numbers.

Do you think nearsightedness was an advantage or a disadvantage to individual survival in a primitive hunting tribe?

Investigation 18.2

SICKLE CELLS AND EVOLUTION

BACKGROUND INFORMATION

Before beginning work on this investigation, review the genetics of sickling in Chapter 17 (pages 560–565 and 598).

PROCEDURE

The **Hb^S** gene, which brings about the formation of hemoglobin associated with sickling, is rare in most human populations. In some parts of Africa, however, the sickle-cell trait (genotype **Hb^{A}Hb^S**) is found in as much as 40% (0.4) of the population. • In such a population, what is the probability that any 1 heterozygous individual will marry another heterozygous individual?(1) • What percentage of their offspring may be expected to be homozygous for the sickle-cell gene?(2) • On the average, then, which would you expect to leave more offspring—individuals with the sickle-cell trait or individuals with normal red blood cells?(3) • How many sickling genes are lost from the gene pool when a child with sickle-cell anemia dies?(4) • What effect would you expect the death of children with sickle-cell anemia to have on the frequency of the gene for sickling in any population?(5) You have described an evolutionary change in terms of modern genetics. • How would Darwin have described this situation?(6)

Actually, there is no evidence that the frequency of the gene for sickling is becoming less in African populations. Therefore, a biological problem arises: How can the frequency of the gene for sickling be maintained at such a high level when selection works so strongly against the gene?

After several months in this course, you know that a scientist begins his attack upon such a problem by devising hypotheses—explanations that may be tested by making suitable observations or by carrying out suitable experiments. Biologists have developed at least 3 hypotheses to account for the high frequency of the sickling gene in African populations. One is based on mutation rates, a 2nd on fertility, a 3rd on resistance to disease. • Using these clues, devise 3 hypotheses to explain the persistently high frequency of the sickling gene in African populations.(7)(8)(9) *Write these down before reading further.*

Through genetic reasoning and mathematical techniques, it is possible to calculate the rate at which genes are lost from the gene pool by natural selection. For the sickling gene, this rate is about 100 times the average rate of mutation at any known locus in human chromosomes. Geographically, mutation rates vary only slightly. • Does this information support or weaken your 1st hypothesis? Explain your answer.(10)

At present there is no evidence that individuals with the sickle-cell trait produce more children than do individuals with normal red blood cells. • Does this information support or weaken your 2nd hypothesis? Explain your answer.(11)

As data on sickling were collected, the frequencies of the sickle-cell trait in various populations were plotted on maps; it became clear that the gene is most common in a belt extending across central Africa. In the same region malaria and hookworm disease are common. • From your knowledge of these 2 diseases and from your knowledge of the part of the body affected by sickling, which of the 2 diseases, if either, would you think more likely to be associated with sickling?(12) • The foregoing question—and its answer— provides new information for your 3rd hypothesis. How might you now word it?(13)

To test this hypothesis, an investigator examined the blood of 290 children of an East African population in which both malaria and sickling were common. The results are given in Figure 18 • 14. • Calculate the percentage of "sicklers" (persons with either the sickle-cell trait or sickle-cell anemia) with malaria and then the percentage of "nonsicklers" with malaria.(14)

	WITH MALARIA	WITHOUT MALARIA	TOTAL
SICKLERS	12	31	43
NONSICKLERS	113	134	247
TOTAL	125	165	290

Figure 18 • 14

The chi-square (χ^2) test can be used to determine whether the difference between "sicklers" and "nonsicklers" with respect to malaria is significant. In this case, however, the method of calculation is somewhat more complex than that in Investigation 17.3. You must consider *four* combinations: (a) "sicklers" with malaria, (b) "sicklers" without malaria, (c) "nonsicklers" with malaria, and (d) "nonsicklers" without malaria. To obtain the expected values for each combination, multiply the totals in the far-right column by a ratio obtained from the totals in the 3rd line. For "sicklers" with malaria, this is $125/290 \times 43$; for "sicklers" without malaria, this is $165/290 \times 43$, etc. • Calculate the chi-square.(15) In the table on page 581 use the χ^2 for 2 classes. • Reasoning from the chi-square re-

sults, do you find that these data tend to support or weaken the hypothesis?(16)

To test the hypothesis further, 30 volunteers were inoculated with malaria parasites. The volunteers were men of approximately the same age and physical condition. A blood examination at the beginning of the experiment showed that none of the 30 had malarial parasites, 15 had the sickle-cell trait, and 15 had normal red blood cells. Two of the "sicklers" and 14 of the "nonsicklers" developed malaria. • Apply the chi-square test to see whether the difference between the "sicklers" and the normal individuals with respect to malaria infection is significant.(17) • Does the result tend to support the hypothesis in Item 13?(18)

The present frequency of the sickle-cell trait in the parts of Africa from which the ancestors of present-day Afro-Americans came indicates that about 22% of those ancestors were "sicklers." • Would genetic mixture with the population of European ancestry and with the Amerind population have caused this frequency to increase, to decrease, or to remain the same?(19)

In the United States, man has almost completely eliminated the vector of malaria, the *Anopheles* mosquito. • Do heterozygotes still have a survival advantage over homozygotes in this country?(20) • Recalling that an individual homozygous for sickling usually dies before reaching reproductive age, and considering your answer to Item 20, what might you predict to happen to the frequency of the **Hb**^{s} gene in the United States?(21)

CONCLUSIONS

• How does sickling illustrate the factors in the evolutionary process?(22) • How does this investigation show that evolution involves interaction between the genetic makeup of an organism and its environment?(23) Hereditary traits (and the genes that determine them) are sometimes described as "beneficial" or "good" and "harmful" or "bad." • Keeping in mind the ideas in this investigation, comment on the use of such terms.(24)

SPECIATION

Darwin called his book *The Origin of Species*. But so far in our description of evolution, no species have originated—there has been no **speciation.** Mutation and natural selection have merely brought about changes in the ratios of different kinds of individuals in a population. At the end of a century, the population of peppered moths in industrial England was composed mostly of dark individuals, but there were some light-colored ones with which they could interbreed. And in the more rural parts of England, populations of *Biston* still had a large percentage of light individuals interbreeding with the few dark ones. We cannot say, then, that any new species has developed, because no population has become reproductively isolated from other populations—that is, no population has developed that cannot interbreed with individuals from other populations. How can **reproductive isolation** of a population develop?

speciation [spē′shǐ ā′shən]

Recall the biological definition of "species," pages 93–94.

isolation [ī′sə lā′shən; Latin: *insula*, island]

ISOLATION IN TIME

Perhaps the most complete fossil record of any evolutionary line is that of the horse family. The oldest fossils that definitely show characteristics of the family came from an Eocene animal that was scarcely larger than a dog. It had a short muzzle and low-crowned teeth and probably browsed on bushes. It had four toes on each front foot and three on each hind foot, each toe with a tiny hoof. A modern horse has a long muzzle, with a wide gap between the front and rear teeth. Its teeth are high-crowned, with ridges of resistant enamel, a fine adaptation for grazing on coarse, dry grasses. On each foot it has only one toe, which ends in a large hoof. There are many other differences, also, between horses that lived in the Eocene and modern horses.

See Investigation 10.1, pages 329–331.

muzzle: the projecting nose and jaws of an animal

The fossil record shows that all these differences are the result of a series of many gradual changes. Each change that became established through natural selection must have been very slight; only when many such changes accumulated did they result in detectable differences. How can this long sequence of horses be divided into species? We cannot breed the extinct species of the family with the modern ones—horse, donkey, and zebra; nor can we breed the extinct ones with each other. Yet the skeletal differences between many of the extinct populations are enormously greater than the differences among horse, donkey, and zebra.

If there are many differences, and if they are large compared with differences among modern species, most paleontologists agree to call populations of two very different times different species. But a population of any one time must have given rise to later populations; these, in turn, gave rise to still later ones—and so on. Thus, over a long period, genetic differences can gradually accumulate until a later population may become so different that it undoubtedly could not have interbred with the earlier, even if the two had existed at the same time.

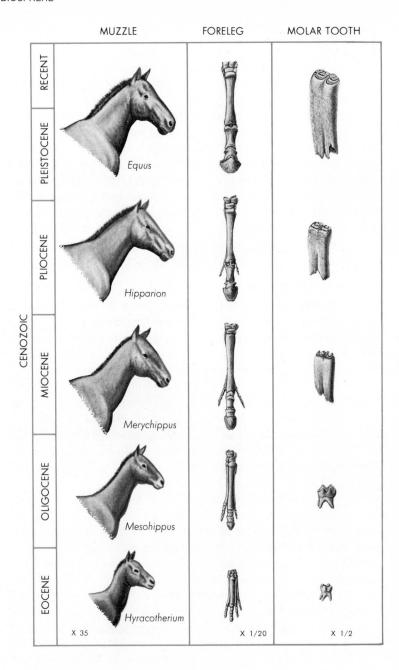

Figure 18 • 15
Some characteristics in five genera of the horse family. For relationships of these genera to others, see Investigation 10.1.

ISOLATION IN SPACE

See Figure 18·4.

Islands. The finches of the Galápagos interested Darwin because they seemed much alike and much like the finches on the distant mainland of Ecuador—yet they had many different forms of beaks.

It is easy to suppose that a few Ecuadorian individuals of Darwin's finches (as the whole group is now called) might have been

Kauai akialoa

iiwi

apapane

Kauai creeper

akepa

palila

Maui parrotbill

X 1/2

Figure 18 • 16
Some of the species of
honeycreepers (Hawaii).
Why doesn't this arrangement
illustrate the same idea as
the arrangement of horses in
Figure 18 • 15? What ideas
does it suggest to you?

For aquatic organisms what
might maintain isolated
populations in the way islands
do for terrestrial organisms?

carried by storms from the mainland to the Galápagos. The islands
are so close to each other that at one time or another local storms
may have carried birds from island to island. Yet the islands are
also far enough apart to make interbreeding between populations on
different islands a rare event. Therefore, mutations and gene recombinations occurring in a population on one island are not likely to be
carried into populations on other islands. And different environments
select differently the traits that do occur. So the isolated populations
have taken separate genetic and ecological paths.

Having diverged in this manner over hundreds of years, the gene
pools of the isolated populations have come to differ greatly. In some
cases, the differences may be so great that gametes from one population may no longer be able to fertilize gametes from another population even if a bird from one population might wander or be blown
into another population. In other cases, the difference in genotype
might not be so great, but phenotypic differences—in mating calls,
in courtship behavior, etc.—might prevent interbreeding. Or if interbreeding were successful, the hybrid offspring might have less viability, less fertility, or less of both than the two parental types. In any
case, the accumulated differences resulting at least in part from
isolation on separate islands have produced species different from the
one (or few) that colonized the archipelago.

Five hundred miles northeast of the Galápagos lies a single
island, Cocos. Its existence serves as a kind of control for what we
might think of as the long "Galápagos experiment." It has but one
species of Darwin's finches—a species unlike those of either Ecuador or the Galápagos.

Variation on continents. It is difficult to believe that evolution of
new species has taken place only on islands. Is there any basis for isolation on continents? In species that have wide geographic ranges,
characteristics often vary among populations in different parts of the
range of the species. The variation may be in the frequency with
which a characteristic occurs, or it may be in both the frequency and

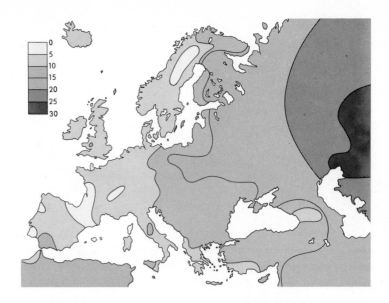

Figure 18 • 17

Cline in the frequency of the
I^b gene (see page 585) in the
human population of western
Asia and Europe.

the intensity of the characteristic. If, by moving in a particular direction
through the range, we find that there is a continuous increase or decrease in the variation, the variation is called a *cline.*

cline [Greek: *klinein,* to slope]

agouti [ə gōo′tĭ]: a hair color
in which each hair has bands
of yellow, black, or brown
pigment; frequent in wild
mammals

    Hamsters, natives of Eurasia, are frequently found in school bi-
ology laboratories. Domesticated hamsters come in many colors, but
in most of their natural geographic range wild hamsters have two
color phases, agouti and black. In southern Russia the frequencies
of the two colors are known from trapping records, for hamster pelts
are economically important there. Figure 18 • 18 summarizes these

Figure 18 • 18

Distribution of two forms of
hamsters in southern Russia.

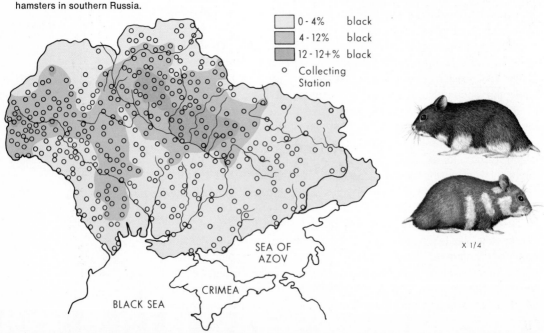

0 - 4%   black
4 - 12%   black
12 - 12+% black
○ Collecting
   Station

X 1/4

SEA OF
AZOV

CRIMEA

BLACK SEA

records. As you can see, the frequency of black hamsters decreases as you go from a central region toward the edges of the hamsters' range.

A cline in the intensity of a characteristic is found in North American white-tailed deer. In general, when deer of populations at more and more northerly localities are measured, the average height of each successive population is greater. The largest white-tailed deer in the Florida Keys measured 53 cm high at the shoulder; in northern Michigan the largest was 104 cm.

A cline is not always gradual. This is shown by a characteristic of the black-racer snake, *Coluber constrictor*. Along the Atlantic coast of the United States, there is a variation in the number of white scales on the ventral surfaces of the snakes' heads. In the New York population the average number of white scales is low; in Florida populations it is high. But the cline is not even. From central Florida to Georgia the decline in the number of white ventral scales is steep, but the change northward from Georgia is slight.

Coluber constrictor
[kăl′yə bər   kən strĭk′tər]

Figure 18 · 19
Cline in a trait of the black racer (*Coluber constrictor*). The areas from which population samples were taken are shown in color. The graph shows the average number of white scales in specimens from each population.

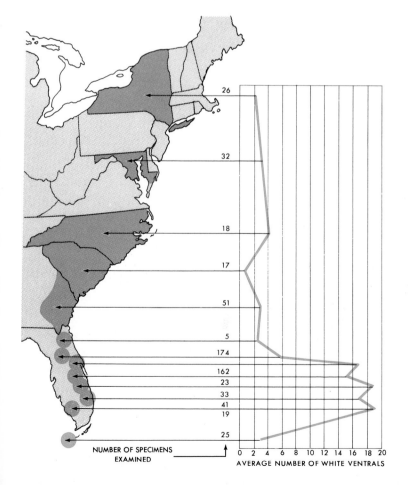

NUMBER OF SPECIMENS EXAMINED

AVERAGE NUMBER OF WHITE VENTRALS
0 2 4 6 8 10 12 14 16 18 20

26
32
18
17
51
5
174
162
23
33
41
19
25

New York

X 1/4

South Carolina

Florida

Subspecies into species? Within the range of a widespread species there may be clines in many traits—but the clines do not necessarily coincide in location, direction, and intensity. When several clines *do* coincide, and when distinct changes occur in several clines at about the same place, it is useful to describe *subspecies* within a species. It is impossible to draw on a map lines that show boundaries between subspecies, because all adjacent populations can interbreed—there are no completely separate gene pools.

coincide [kō′ĭn sīd′]: to occupy the same place

Figure 18 · 20 shows the distribution of some of the subspecies of the black racer in the eastern United States. Using the facts of geographical variation recorded on the map, let us make a supposition. Suppose that the sea invades the Mississippi Valley (as it has in the past, according to geological evidence), destroying all the populations of *Coluber constrictor* intermediate between the subspecies *flaviventris* and the subspecies *constrictor*. At first the two subspecies would still be capable of interbreeding, but they would be prevented from doing so by the water barrier between them. Therefore, new mutations that occurred in *flaviventris* and in *constrictor* could not be exchanged. And with the accumulation of different mutations over a long period of time, wouldn't the two eventually become incapable of interbreeding—that is, separate species? Perhaps so—but let us examine some further evidence.

flaviventris [flā′vĭ vĕn′trəs]

Figure 18 · 20
Distribution of subspecies of *Coluber constrictor* in a part of eastern North America.

Figure 18 · 21
Lazuli bunting (male).

X 1/4

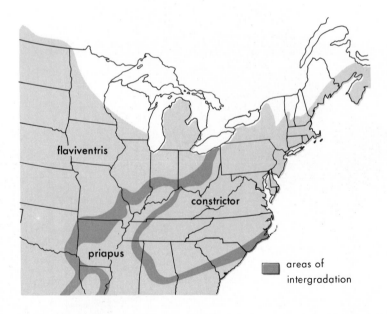

Passerina cyanea [păs′ə rĭn′ə sĭ ā′nē ə]. See Figure 4 · 7.

lazuli [lăz′yŏŏ lĭ′]

Indigo buntings (*Passerina cyanea*) are small birds that breed throughout the eastern United States. Lazuli buntings (*Passerina lazuli*) breed over much of the western United States. Both nest in bushes and small trees. One hundred fifty years ago, both were ap-

red-shafted flicker
Colaptes cafer

X 1/3

many hybrids

red-shafted   yellow-shafted

hybrid flicker

X 1/3

yellow-shafted flicker
Colaptes auratus

X 1/3

Figure 18 • 22

How has the history of the Great Plains affected these species of flickers?

How do the names show this?

parently absent from the Great Plains (between the Mississippi River and the Rocky Mountains), where trees and bushy habitats were rare. The biological names indicate that taxonomists consider these two species to be closely related. At one time there may have been a single bunting species, spread across the United States in the continuous forest environment that probably once existed. Development of the treeless plains—a habitat unsuitable for buntings—would then have separated eastern and western populations. During this separation, visible genetic differences arose—especially in the males.

See Figure 20·5.

Now man has transformed the prairies and plains. Patches of trees and shrubs surround hundreds of farmhouses and line miles of streets in towns. Indigo buntings have spread westward from the deciduous forest, and lazuli buntings have spread eastward from the mountains. With the buntings we have a case much like the last step in the supposed case of the racer: the reunion of two populations that have acquired genetic differences through *geographical isolation.* What is the result? In many places male lazuli buntings mate with female indigo buntings, and vice versa. Hybrids are produced, and they seem to be fertile. But their fertility and their viability may not be as high as those of the parent species. At least there is as yet no evidence that *P. cyanea* and *P. lazuli* are merging.

On the basis of this evidence, do *you* consider these populations to be separate species?

Investigation 18.3

A STEP IN SPECIATION

BACKGROUND INFORMATION

The small salamanders of the genus *Ensatina* are strictly terrestrial; they even lay their eggs on land. Nevertheless these salamanders require a rather moist environment and do not thrive in arid regions. In California *Ensatina eschscholtzii* (ĕn'sə tī'nə ĕs shōlt'zē ī) has been intensively studied by Robert S. Stebbins of the University of California (Berkeley). This investigation is based on his work.

MATERIALS

outline map of California
colored pencils

PROCEDURE A

Imagine that you are working with Stebbins' specimens of salamanders, some of which are pictured below. In the following list, the parentheses after each subspecies name contain a number and a color. The number is

the total number of individuals that Stebbins had available for his study; the color is for you to use in designating the subspecies. Following this is a list of collection localities, indicated by a code that fits the map of California shown in Figure 18·24. For example, 32/R means that one or more *E. e. croceator* specimens were collected at the intersection of Line 32 and Line R.

1. *croceator* (15; brown): 32/R, 32/S, 30/T, 31/T
2. *eschscholtzii* (203; red): 30/M, 32/O, 34/S, 35/V, 36/W, 35/Z, 38/Y, 40/Z
3. *klauberi* (48; blue): 36/Z, 38/a, 40/a, 39/a
4. *oregonensis* (373; pink): 9/B, 7/E, 6/E, 13/C, 10/C, 7/D, 15/D
5. *picta* (230; yellow): 2/B, 2/C, 3/C, 4/C
6. *platensis* (120; green): 8/J, 10/J, 11/M, 13/M, 15/M, 15/O, 17/M, 15/P, 20/Q, 24/S, 21/R, 25/T, 26/U
7. *xanthoptica* (271; orange): 17/G, 17/F, 19/H, 19/O, 20/I, 20/J, 21/I

Figure 18 • 23
Specimens of the salamander species *Ensatina eschscholtzii*.

Plot each collection locality by making a small X mark on an outline map that has a grid like the one in Figure 18 • 24. Use pencils of different colors to indicate the different populations.

STUDYING THE DATA

You now have a distributional map of the subspecies of *Ensatina eschscholtzii* in California. • Is the species uniformly distributed throughout California? Use your knowledge of the species' ecological requirements to offer an explanation for the distribution.(1)   Now consider the physiography of California (Figure 18 • 24). • Does the species seem more characteristic of mountain areas or of large valley areas?(2)   • Do you expect any order in distribution of subspecies? Why or why not?(3)

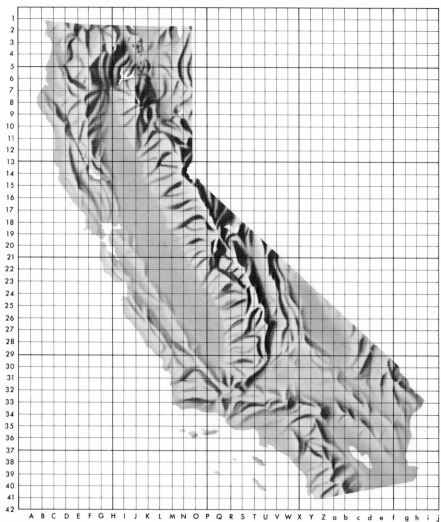

Figure 18 · 24

Map of California, with the grid to be used in plotting distributional data.

Examine the pictures in Figure 18 · 23. Note that some subspecies have yellow or orange spots and bands on a black body; some have fairly plain, brown-orange bodies; one has small orange spots on a black background; etc. There are other differences as well; for example, some of the 7 have white feet. Now refer to your distributional map.   • Does there appear to be any order to the way these color patterns occur in California? For example, do the spotted forms occur only along the coast? Do spotted forms occur in the north and unspotted ones in the south?(4)   • Subspecies *eschscholtzii* and *klauberi* are very different from each other. What relationship is there between their distributions?(5)

PROCEDURE B

Now you may begin to wonder whether there might not be salamanders in some of the areas for which you have no records and whether there might be additional subspecies for which you have no specimens in your collections. A biologist faced with these questions would leave his laboratory and go into the field to collect more specimens. Imagine that you do so, too, and return with the following additional data:

eschscholtzii (16; red): 36/Z, 41/Z, 33/M, 34/W, 34/U
klauberi (23; blue): 40/b, 40/Z, 36/a
Unidentified population #8 (44; black and green): 4/I, 5/H, 7/H, 7/F, 6/J, 9/F
Unidentified population #9 (13; black and red): 28/T, 27/T, 26/T, 28/S, 29/T
Unidentified population #11 (131; black and blue): 23/J, 24/K, 24/I, 29/M, 25/J, 25/I
Unidentified population #12 (31; black and yellow): 6/C, 7/C, 6/B

Mark with a *0* the following places that were searched for *Ensatina* without success:

11/I, 14/I, 17/K, 19/K, 22/N, 26/Q, 5/M, 32/U, 32/a, 35/f.

Specimens of #8 and #9 are shown in Figure 18 • 23; there are no illustrations for #11 and #12.

STUDYING THE DATA

According to Stebbins, the unidentified populations are not additional subspecies. • What, then, is the probable genetic relationship of Populations #8, #9, and #11 to the subspecies already plotted on the map?(6) • On this basis, describe (or, better, make a colored drawing of) the appearance you would expect specimens of Population #11 to have. (7) • Why is it unlikely that you would ever find individuals combining characteristics of *picta* and *xanthoptica*?(8)

Now consider *eschscholtzii* and *klauberi*. Look at the distribution of the original collections. • What reasons were there for making efforts to collect additional specimens from extreme southwestern California?(9) • How

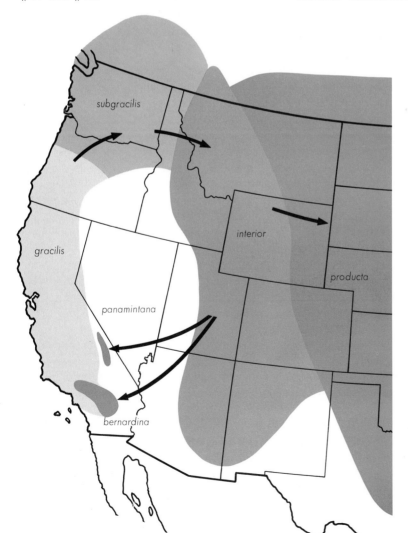

Hoplitis producta

Figure 18 • 25

Ranges of the subspecies of *Hoplitis producta* (a bee). The subspecies *panaminta* and *bernardina* do not interbreed with *gracilis*. Arrows show the way in which the species probably spread from an origin in California. How does this relate to the case of *Ensatina*?

do the results of the additional collections differ from the results in other places where 2 different populations approach each other? (10)   Bear in mind the biological definition of a species and also the appearance and distribution of the named populations of *Ensatina*. • Which one of these populations could best be considered a species separate from *E. eschscholtzii?*(11)   This population was indeed once considered by biologists to be a separate species.

Now imagine that while examining another museum collection, you find the specimen shown in Figure 18 • 23, #10. Compare its characteristics, especially the pattern of spotting, with those of the named populations. Also

consider the distribution of these populations. • Between which 2 is this specimen most likely a hybrid?(12)   On your map draw a line along which you might expect to collect other specimens like this one.

CONCLUSIONS

• In a brief paragraph explain why Stebbins concluded that there is but one species of *Ensatina* in California.(13)

Suppose that the mild volcanic activity that now occurs in northern California should become violent and completely destroy all the salamanders of that region.   • How would this event affect the concept of species in *Ensatina?*(14)

Figure 18 • 26

Deer mouse.

x 1/3

Peromyscus maniculatus
[pĕr ə mĭs′kəs mə nĭk′yə lā′təs]

How might an adult salmon recognize the stream in which it hatched?

But the salmon population of each small stream is not considered a separate species. Can you explain the reasoning of taxonomists in this case?

OTHER KINDS OF ISOLATION

Perhaps geographic isolation is always necessary to get populations started toward the formation of new species. Many biologists think so. But other factors can contribute to reaching permanent reproductive isolation.

In Michigan there are two populations of the deer mouse (*Peromyscus maniculatus*). One of these inhabits the shoreline of the Great Lakes; the other, wooded areas. Between shore and woods is a zone of meadowland that both populations avoid; therefore individuals from the two populations rarely meet. However, there is a good reason to suppose that if they did meet, they could still interbreed. In this case, the two populations are isolated because they live in different habitats—*ecological isolation.*

Pacific salmon spend most of their lives in the ocean. When they mature, they enter rivers and swim upstream toward the headwaters—each individual swimming toward the small stream where it was hatched. When the salmon reach the headwaters, they breed and then die. Because of this behavior, the new generation in each stream obtains its genes from a preceding generation of the *same* stream. Therefore, though the salmon in the ocean have been living together for years, they are not really a freely interbreeding population. They are genetically separated by *behavioral isolation.*

THE OUTCOME OF ISOLATION

Looking at the organisms now living around us, we see many degrees of reproductive isolation—many stages in the evolution of species. Anything that hinders the free exchange of genes between populations—that is, anything that tends to prevent free interbreeding

—sets the stage for speciation. Geographical, ecological, or behavioral isolation may fail; old barriers may fall and mating may resume between individuals of different populations. But the more
complete the isolation and the longer it continues, the greater the
genetic differences between populations will become. Therefore, we
can predict that ultimately genetic differences will become so great
that interbreeding will become impossible.

Where did you read of an
example of this?

Sperms of a duck do not survive in the reproductive system of a
female chicken. Pollen grains from one plant species often burst and
die when placed on the pistil of a second species. Sperms and eggs
may meet but fail to unite. They may unite but the zygote or young
embryo may die. The hybrid may live but be very weak or sterile.
Finally, the hybrid may survive and mate but produce no living offspring. In all of these cases, gene flow between populations has
ceased—gene pools of the two populations have become separated.
Speciation has been completed.

ABRUPT ORIGIN OF NEW SPECIES

We have seen that the process of evolution can be directly observed. But must not speciation—reaching complete reproductive
isolation—require a very long time? Not always.

Sometimes, especially in plants, meiosis is so abnormal that
gametes are formed with two whole sets of chromosomes; the gametes are diploid. If fertilization is accompanied by a normal monoploid gamete, the new individual has three sets of chromosomes—that
is, it is triploid. Occasionally even higher numbers of chromosome
sets may occur; the general term for this situation is *polyploidy*.

triploid [trĭp'loid; Greek:
triploos, triple, + *eidos*, form]

polyploid [pŏl'ĭ ploid'; Greek:
polys, many, + *eidos*]

Dr. Ted Bingham

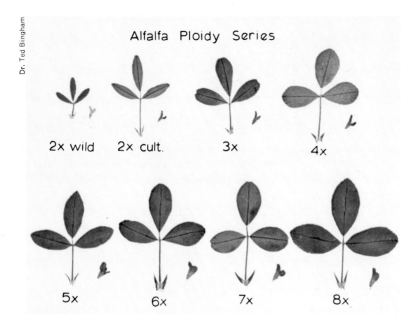

Alfalfa Ploidy Series

2x wild   2x cult.   3x   4x

5x   6x   7x   8x

Figure 18 · 27
Effects of increasing ploidy
on leaves and flowers of
alfalfa. (2X = diploid,
3X = triploid, etc.;
cult. = cultivated)

When an Asiatic species of cotton (in which the monoploid number is 13) is crossed with a wild American species of cotton (monoploid number also 13), the hybrid is sterile. This sterility occurs because the 13 chromosomes from the two parents fail to pair during meiosis; apparently they are very different from each other. If, however, chromosome doubling occurs in the hybrids, each resulting cell has two sets of chromosomes from each of the species—a total of four sets (tetraploid). In such cells, each chromosome from the Asiatic cotton has an identical chromosome to pair with, as does each chromosome from the American cotton. Therefore, normal meiosis can occur. Each gamete formed then receives a complete set of the Asiatic and a complete set of the American chromosomes. By self-fertilization, these gametes can again produce a tetraploid plant. And such a hybrid is completely self-fertile. But if the hybrid is crossed with either ancestral species, only sterile offspring are produced, because a diploid gamete uniting with a monoploid gamete produces a triploid in which normal pairing cannot occur during meiosis. Thus, a new tetraploid species—reproductively isolated from its parents—may arise suddenly, in only two generations. In this case speciation *can* be directly observed.

The fine cultivated cottons of today are all polyploids that have come into existence in this way. So are the cultivated tobaccos and wheats. Many of these originated naturally, as have polyploids in many wild species. But now plant breeders can increase the frequency of polyploidy by the use of chemicals. In a sense, then, they can create new species.

tetraploid [tĕt′rə ploid′; Greek: *tettares*, four-parted, + *eidos*]

Look through seed and nursery catalogues for examples of polyploid plants.

Figure 18 · 28

Changes in the number of listings of selected family names in a small city. What is the source of a new name? What might explain the disappearance of a name? What analogy is intended by this illustration?

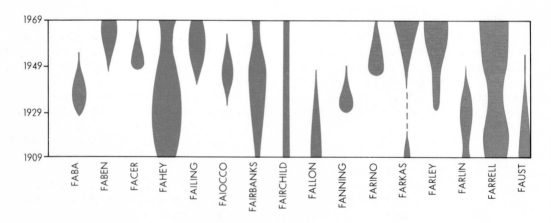

GUIDE QUESTIONS

1. How did Charles Darwin become a biologist?

2. What experiences in Darwin's life helped to form his theories?

3. What kinds of evidence did Darwin gather to develop his theories?

4. How did the ideas of Lyell and Malthus influence Darwin's thinking?

5. What event hastened the publication of Darwin's theories?

6. Which of Darwin's theories merely restated an old idea?

7. How did Lamarck explain the changes that occur in evolution?

8. How did Darwin's ideas differ from those of Lamarck?

9. What important part of Darwin's reasoning remained unexplained during his lifetime?

10. What has been the basis for natural selection in the peppered moth? On what evidence is this conclusion based?

11. Why can a single individual organism not indicate an evolutionary change?

12. What are the characteristics of the evolutionary process?

13. What is the Hardy-Weinberg principle? From your study of the hypothetical squirrel population, try to state the assumptions on which this principle is based.

14. What are the bases for the change factor of evolution?

15. What is the reasoning that leads to the theory of natural selection?

16. Why must environment as well as an organism's characteristics be considered in describing fitness?

17. How can you explain the continued existence of unfavorable characteristics in a population?

18. Why must fertility as well as viability be taken into account when natural selection in a population is studied?

19. What seems to be the explanation for the high frequency of the sickle-cell gene in central-African populations?

20. If we are to recognize that speciation has occurred, what must happen to a population of organisms?

21. How is time a factor in the process of forming new species?

22. How might a small population of one species, carried to an archipelago, develop into a number of separate species?

23. What is meant by a cline?

24. What is the relationship between clines and subspecies?

25. What events may bring about geographical isolation between subspecies?

26. How might geographical isolation of subspecies on a continent lead to speciation?

27. In addition to geographical isolation, what other kinds of isolation may lead toward speciation?

28. How can the process of polyploidy produce new species suddenly?

PROBLEMS

1. Sexually reproducing organisms are most likely to adapt rapidly to changing environments. Self-fertilization and parthenogenesis reduce the adaptability of populations. Explain these statements, using your knowledge of both reproductive and evolutionary mechanisms.

2. How do you explain the much greater variability of domesticated organisms than of similar or the same species in the wild (for example, dogs vs wolves; chickens vs red jungle fowl; pigeons vs rock doves)?

3. Polydactyly (in which more than the normal number of digits are present) is caused by a dominant gene, but it is quite rare phenotypically in the human population. Type O blood results from a recessive gene; yet in some populations of North American Indians, as many as 97 percent of the individuals may have Type O blood. Can you explain these two statements?

4. Look back at the question in the caption to Figure 8·13. Do you recall how you answered the question? Would you answer it differently now?

5. It is sometimes said that an organism that has only asexual reproductive methods (domesticated bananas, for example) has reached the "end of the evolutionary road." To what extent do you think this expression is true?

6. In many species of birds, it has been found that populations living at higher latitudes lay more eggs per clutch than do populations living at lower latitudes. Would you expect the former gradually to replace the latter? Why or why not?

7. What effects may modern medicine have upon the future evolution of man? The facts needed for investigating this problem are to be found in biological science, but the interpretation of the facts lies outside the realm

of verifiable conclusions. Therefore it is necessary to distinguish carefully between the facts and your interpretation of them.

8. The discussion of speciation has centered on terrestrial organisms. The same principles can be applied to speciation in the oceans, but fewer examples of the process are known there. Apply these principles to the oceans, using hypothetical cases—or real ones, if you are able to find them.

9. In Cambrian rocks, brachiopods have been found that are indistinguishable from the modern *Lingula* (page 128). Modern cockroaches are very similar to those of the Carboniferous period. Turtles of the genus *Caretta* occur in Cretaceous rocks and in the modern seas. Yet, during these same long years, other organisms have changed greatly. How can you explain such great differences in *rate* of evolution between species?

10. You are collecting grasshoppers in the vicinity of a canyon. The canyon is 80 km long and averages 800 m deep but in several places is only about 300 m from rim to rim. Along one rim of the canyon, most of the grasshoppers have yellow wings; along the opposite rim, most have orange wings. How can you account for this difference? Where would be the most likely place to look for grasshoppers that have intermediate wing coloration?

11. Deep-sea animals and cave animals both live in lightless environments. Few, if any, deep-sea animals are blind, and a great many are luminescent (Chapter 9). Few, if any, cave animals are luminescent, and most are blind. Try to explain these facts from an evolutionary viewpoint.

12. What might be the evolutionary consequences of a worldwide nuclear war?

SUGGESTED READINGS

ALEXANDER, R. D. *Singing Insects: Four Case Histories in the Study of Animal Species.* Chicago: Rand McNally & Co., 1967. (Steps in the process of speciation are shown by examples of familiar American insects. Fairly easy.)

BROWER, L. P., and J. V. Z. Brower. "Investigation into Mimicry," *Natural History,* April, 1962. Pp. 8–19.

CROW, J. F. "Ionizing Radiation and Evolution," *Scientific American,* September, 1959. Pp. 138–142.

DARWIN, C. *The Origin of Species.* New York: Mentor Books, 1959. (A paperback reprint. Darwin's style is heavy, but his reasoning is clear, and his abundant examples are entertaining. A "must" for every prospective biologist.)

DeBEER, G. *Adaptation.* London: Oxford University Press, 1972. (A pamphlet that considers adaptation from the evolutionary point of view. Rather easy.)

KETTLEWELL, H. B. D. "Darwin's Missing Evidence," *Scientific American,* March, 1959. Pp. 48–53.

MOORE, R., and Editors of LIFE. *Evolution.* New York: Time, Inc., Book Division, 1962. (A book of many striking pictures and a text that stresses history rather than explanation. Fairly easy.)

MOOREHEAD, ALAN. *Darwin and the Beagle.* New York: Harper & Row, Inc., 1969. (A vivid account of Darwin's great adventure. Easy.)

PETERSON, R. T. "The Galapagos; Eerie Cradle of New Species," *National Geographic,* April, 1967. Pp. 540–585.

SHEPPARD, P. M. *Natural Selection and Heredity.* New York: Philosophical Library, Inc., 1959. (Clearly relates genetic principles to evolutionary processes. Advanced.)

SIMPSON, G. G., and W. S. BECK. *Life: An Introduction to Biology.* Shorter ed. New York: Harcourt, Brace & World, Inc., 1969. Chapters 13–15. (Probably the best account of the mechanism of evolution in any college biology textbook. Advanced.)

STEBBINS, G. L. *Processes of Organic Evolution.* Englewood Cliffs, N.J.: Prentice-Hall, Inc., 1966. (Excellent discussion, with many examples and good illustrations. Advanced.)

VILLIERS, A., and J. L. STANFIELD. "In the Wake of Darwin's Beagle," *National Geographic,* October, 1969. Pp. 449–495.

WALLACE, B. *Population Genetics.* (BSCS Pamphlet 12.) Boulder, Colo.: EPIC, 1964. (A discussion of the role of genetics in the modern interpretation of Darwin's theory of natural selection. Rather advanced.)

MAN AND THE BIOSPHERE

MAN AND THE BIOSPHERE

Through all the words and pictures and investigations of the preceding five sections, through all the facts, hypotheses, and theories, have run some ideas that tie them all together:

Each organism—you and every other—continually interacts with its environment. Individual organisms, interacting with each other and with their abiotic environments, form ecosystems. Conditions in ecosystems, in communities, in populations, and within individuals fluctuate. But the tendency everywhere in the biosphere is toward steady state. Steady state is achieved through the homeostatic functioning of each organism, and this is dependent upon its structure. On the other hand, the structure of each organism is meaningful only in relation to its functioning. Function depends upon the experiences of an organism in its environment and upon its heredity. Through the mechanisms of heredity, one generation of organisms is linked to the next. Thus, all organisms of the present have a continuity with organisms of the past. But none is entirely the same in structure and function as its ancestors, for living things have changed through time and are changing today.

These ideas are the result of a long history of observation, experimentation, and thought. And they are continually changing as new knowledge is acquired. They exist only in human minds. So any kind of activity that involves ideas—any kind of study—involves man. Yet mankind is itself a species, functioning as a unit of the biosphere, having a part in all the processes mentioned above. You as a human being, then, have a double role in a biology course: you are both the observer and the observed.

You began your biology course as an observer of human biological problems. In the following pages, the biology of the human species was not neglected, but neither was it emphasized. However, you yourself are human and the problems pictured in Investigation 1.1 are your problems. So it is desirable now in Section Six to devote some special attention to human biology—your biology.

A Biological View of Mankind

THE HUMAN SPECIES

Man is an animal. If you cut open a specimen, you find that the organs—heart, intestines, liver, lungs—differ little from corresponding ones of dogs, cats, or monkeys. If you study human nervous or endocrine coordination, respiration, digestion, reproduction, or muscle contraction, you find the same general chemical and physical processes as in many other animals.

Obviously man is a vertebrate. Among the vertebrates he is a mammal—he has hair, and his young are nursed with milk. To be sure, he has an unusually small amount of hair, but some mammals have even less—whales, for instance. He is also unusual among mammals in his bipedal locomotion, but this is also characteristic of kangaroos. You can best obtain some understanding of important characteristics of man by studying a human skeleton and comparing it with the skeleton of a four-footed mammal.

bipedal [bī′pə dəl]; Latin: *bis*, twice, + *pedes*, feet]

Investigation 19.1

A STUDY OF SKELETONS

INTRODUCTION

Vertebrate skeletons may be thought of as being composed of 2 major divisions—the *axial* skeleton and the *appendicular* skeleton. The axial skeleton consists of the skull and the column of vertebrae (including the ribs that are attached to certain of the vertebrae), arranged along the longitudinal axis of the body. The appendicular skeleton consists of the shoulder girdle, the hip girdle, and the bones in the appendages, which are attached to the girdles.

MATERIALS AND EQUIPMENT

human skeleton, mounted
cat skeleton, mounted
rulers, 2

PROCEDURE

Throughout this procedure you are to make observations on both cat and human skeletons. Thus, when you are directed to examine the skull, examine the skulls of *both* animals.

Begin with the axial skeleton. Examine

the general outline of the skull. • Which occupies the greater volume—the brain case or the bones of the face? In cat? In man?(1) • With respect to the rest of the skull, are the eye sockets directed forward, downward, backward, sideward, or upward? In cat? In man?(2) • What change in the facial bones of the cat would bring its eye sockets into the human position?(3)

Viewing the skeleton from the side, hold a ruler along the axis of the vertebrae in the upper part of the neck. • In which skeleton is the axis of the vertebrae closer to the vertical midline of the skull?(4)   Holding the 1st ruler in position, place another ruler along the base of the teeth. • In which skeleton is the angle formed by the rulers closer to a right angle?(5) The *articulation* (jointing) of the skull with the 1st vertebra occurs around the *foramen magnum* ("big opening"). Through the foramen magnum the spinal cord connects with the brain. • In which skeleton is the foramen magnum closer to the posterior end of the skull?(6)   If you look closely, you will notice roughened areas and ridges on the bones. These mark places where muscles were attached. Examine the back of the skull. • In which skeleton is there a greater area (in proportion to skull size) for muscle attachment?(7)

Examine the vertebral column. • Which skeleton has the greater number of vertebrae? (8) • Where are most of the "extra" vertebrae?(9) • In general, which skeleton (in proportion to its size) has the thicker vertebrae? (10) • How do the vertebrae in the region of the hip girdle differ in man and cat?(11)   Observe the vertebral column from the side. • Ignoring the vertebrae of the neck and tail, tell in which skeleton the vertebral column forms a single arch.(12)

Now consider the appendicular skeleton. The posterior legs are attached to the *pelvis*— a set of bones that, in adults, are grown together. • In proportion to its size, which skeleton has the heavier pelvis?(13) • Is the pelvis articulated with the vertebral column, or are the 2 structures fused together? In cat? In man?(14)

The forelegs (arms, in man) are attached to an anterior girdle that is made up of 2 broad, flat *scapulas,* 2 collarbones, and a *sternum* (breastbone). • In which skeleton are the bones of this girdle more closely associated? (15) • How are these bones attached to the vertebral column? In cat? In man?(16) • With respect to their attachment to each other, how do the bones of the anterior girdle differ from the bones of the pelvis?(17)

Compare the bones of the human hand with the bones of one of the cat's front feet. • In which skeleton are the bones of the *digits* (fingers and toes) longer in proportion to the total length of the appendage?(18) • In which skeleton is the inside digit articulated in such a way that it is opposable to (can be pressed against) the other digits?(19)

Compare the cat's posterior appendages with the legs of man. • In which skeleton is the knee joint in normal standing position closer to a 180° angle?(20)   Consider each leg to be made up of upper leg, lower leg, and foot (including toes). • What fraction of the length of the upper leg does the length of the foot equal? In cat? In man?(21) • Which animal normally stands on its toes, with its heel raised from the ground?(22)

DISCUSSION

The following questions may help you to interpret your observations and to organize your thoughts.

• What non-skeletal human characteristic is implied by your answer to Item 1?(23) Items 2 and 3 related to a visual characteristic found in many primates. • What is the characteristic?(24)   Observations reported in Items 4 to 7 are concerned with structural adaptations that make possible the support of a relatively heavy head in an upright position. Assume that the structure of man's distant ancestors was somewhat like that of the cat. • What mutations in the catlike structure would have brought about changes favorable to the development of both a large brain and an upright posture?(25)

• In a cat, where is most of the weight of

the anterior part of the body supported?(26) • Where is the anterior weight supported in man?(27) • How do Items 10 to 13 relate to Items 26 and 27?(28)

• Judging from the structure of its anterior girdle, do you think a cat could easily support its weight on its forelegs?(29) Can a man? (30) Of course, a man moving in an upright position does not need to support his weight on his arms. But he has the same kind of strong anterior girdle that many primates use in moving about through trees. • How is this structural characteristic an advantage to man, who walks upright on the ground?(31)

• How is the position of the legs in a man who is poised to start a race similar to the normal position of the posterior appendages in a cat?(32) • What advantage does this position have for athlete and cat?(33) Try to stand 5 minutes in this position. • What disadvantage does it have for man?(34)

SUMMARY

• In a paragraph, summarize characteristics of the human skeletal system that are related to man's upright posture.(35)

FOR FURTHER INVESTIGATION

Aristotle described man as a "featherless biped." The adjective was necessary because birds are also entirely bipedal. (Aristotle, of course, knew nothing of the dinosaurs, some of which were also bipeds, or of kangaroos.) Using a mounted skeleton of a pigeon or a chicken, make a comparison similar to the one you made with a cat.

PRIMATE INHERITANCE

Men, monkeys, and apes are very similar in the details of their mammalian anatomy, and they are therefore grouped together in the order Primates. Most primates are arboreal, and all possess structural and behavioral characteristics that relate to the arboreal way of life. Arboreal life is dangerous and demanding, and mistakes are likely to be fatal. Therefore, natural selection of adaptations to this life must be severe.

Primates: See page 108.

The digits of primates are well developed and achieve powerful grasping actions. Epidermal ridges—which are what produce fingerprints in man—help prevent slipping from tree limbs. In addition to being powerful, the digits are very sensitive and can easily distinguish whether a surface is crumbly or slippery.

The eyes of primates are directed forward instead of to the side, as in most mammals. Therefore the two eyes view the same scene from slightly different angles; this enables the brain to derive an impression of three dimensions, which makes accurate distance judgments possible. And in most primates the brains are exceptionally large, compared with the brains of all other mammals except cetaceans.

Why is this an advantage for an arboreal animal?

One young at a time is the rule among primates, though twins are not unusual. An active arboreal animal cannot be burdened with carrying many offspring. To feed these young, a female primate has only two nipples on her mammary glands. Young primates, unlike young horses or jackrabbits, are given intensive and prolonged maternal care. They cannot afford to learn ordinary activities, such as locomotion, by trial and error.

Primates tend to be omnivorous. They consume a varied collection of fruits, seeds, insects, eggs, and young birds. They gather their

omnivorous [ŏm nĭv′ə rəs; Latin: omnis, all, + vorare, to eat]

A. W. Ambler from Photo Researchers

Figure 19 · 1

A potto, primitive primate. What primate characteristics can you see?

food in social groups. Perhaps because they cannot always readily see each other in leafy treetops, they tend to communicate by vocal signals.

HUMAN CHARACTERISTICS

Man shares some characteristics with all other primates. But what he is seems to have resulted both from characteristics that primates developed as they adapted to life in trees and from those that some of the larger primates developed when they began to live mostly on the ground. All the ground-living primates have many characteristics in common, and *anthropologists*—specialists in the study of man—find it difficult to describe conspicuous *biological* differences that distinguish mankind clearly and distinctly from the others.

anthropologists
[ăn′thrə pŏl′ə jĭstz; Greek: *anthropos*, man, + *logos*]

Refer to Figure 4·9 as you read this section.

Structure. Man's outstanding structural distinction is his upright position—his ability to stand, walk, and run on his hind legs. This ability involves many anatomical modifications. Man's legs are longer than his arms. His foot has a high arch, and his big toe is in line with the others. A human foot is well adapted for walking or running, but not for grasping.

The upright position leaves human hands free. While sitting, other primates also have great skill in handling objects. But they cannot carry objects easily because they—even the great apes—use all four appendages in locomotion.

The upright position is also related to the pivoting of a human

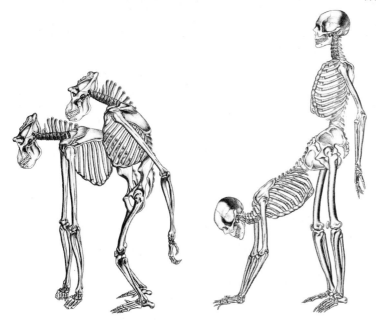

Figure 19 • 2

Skeletal proportions and postures of gorilla and man.

head on the top of the spinal column. This enables a man to look straight ahead when he is standing, and it puts the weight of his large brain directly on his spinal column.

And man has a very large brain. In modern man the volume of the brain case is 1200 to 1500 cc, as compared with 350 to 450 cc in chimpanzees. There is no exact relation between brain size and intelligence—individuals with the largest brains are not necessarily the brightest—but the large human brain undoubtedly reflects great ability to learn.

Other characteristics of the human head are: the vertical face, the reduced projection of the jaws, the distinct chin, the prominent nose with its elongated tip, and the external mucous membrane of the

Figure 19 • 3

Comparison of facial features of man and chimpanzee.

Charles Rogers

Nathan W. Cohen and Ziggi Brashears

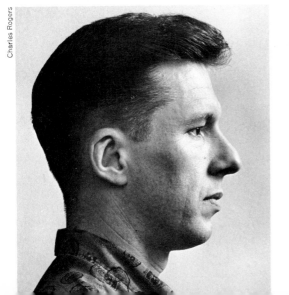

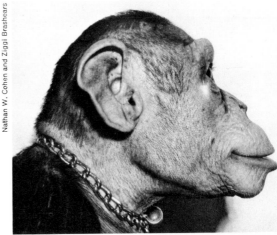

lips. Men also differ from apes in having canine teeth that are no more prominent than the other teeth. The small size of the canine teeth may be related to tool-using. For men with clubs, there is little advantage in having large canine teeth with which to bite enemy or prey.

Then there is the distribution of hair on the human body. This varies somewhat in different human populations. Most human individuals have long hair on the head; males of some populations have heavy beards. There are variable amounts of body hair and special patches of hair at the bases of all four appendages. We can only guess about the adaptive meaning of this hair distribution—and so far the guesses have not made much sense.

Figure 19 • 4

The shoulder muscles characteristic of brachiating animals (Figure 8 • 21) are easily adapted for other uses.

Ernst Haas from Magnum

Why is this an advantage in medical research?

Physiology. Physiologically, man is not very different from other mammals, especially other primates. But some characteristics in the physiology of other mammals are developed to an extreme in man.

Mankind has no definite breeding season; reproductive activity can occur at any time of the year. Monkeys and apes also have a tendency toward lack of seasonality in reproduction. It may be that this tendency is carried to an extreme in man partly because of his artificial shelters from seasonal effects.

Few species of animals have as long a life-span as mankind. In the majority of organisms the weakening of the physiological processes at the onset of old age provides an opportunity for some predator or parasite to finish off an individual. This makes it difficult to determine the natural life-span of most organisms. But from records kept in zoos and aquariums, where animals lead protected lives, some data on possible length of life have been obtained. Only the large tortoises are known to exceed the maximum ages attained by some humans. The *average* life-span of man is probably longer than that of any other animal, and it seems that this only partly results from superior care and protection. In addition, human physiology is adjusted to a long existence.

Not only is man capable of long life; he also takes a long time to grow up. This is true no matter how we define "growing up." Many animals are independent from the time of hatching or birth. Mammals require at least a few weeks or months before they can care for themselves, because they must be nourished by the mothers' milk. A human child is completely dependent upon adults for six to nine years—and partially so (even in primitive societies) for a time after that. The closest approach to this is among the great apes, where the young need perhaps two years to become independent. Man reaches reproductive age at about 14 years; the apes, at about 10 years; most other mammals—even those with life-spans approaching man's—at a much earlier age. Full skeletal development is reached in man at about 22 years; in the apes, at about 12 years.

These physiological characteristics probably define mankind at least as clearly as any structural characteristics. They make possible —and perhaps even necessary—the behavioral characteristics that distinguish man as a most remarkable kind of organism.

Behavior. As a solitary individual, a man is rather helpless—despite his big brain. Imagine his plight in the forests of Europe during one of the ice ages. He would probably not have survived long. Normally, however, a man is not solitary; he is a social animal. Of course, there are other social animals. But insect societies are not really comparable to those of man. And societies in other mammalian species, even in the apes, are not as highly organized as even the simplest human societies.

Much that is characteristic of human societies can be traced to the long period of growing up. Dependency upon parents over many years insures that the young will be woven into the social group. During the period of dependency, the experience of one generation is passed to the next; the same discoveries need not be made anew by each individual. Thus knowledge accumulates within the group.

But what about plants?

tortoises. See Figure 18·1.

Is there a physiological limit to the human life-span? If you think so, can you find any information about it?

But there are cases in which a man has survived for a long period of time as a solitary individual. Can you explain one?

See page 507.

Figure 19 • 5
A primitive family group of the present—Bushmen of southwestern Africa. Social behavior is important to survival in their harsh, arid environment.

The transfer of knowledge depends upon communication among individuals. Human beings may communicate by gestures, but these are usually just a substitute for language or are used for emphasis. Human language is not only more complicated than other means of communication; it is fundamentally different. It involves much more than a system of cries and calls. It is dependent upon the structural organization of the human brain. It is fundamental to being human, to the human achievement. Yet we have no knowledge of when speech began, no definite information concerning how language started. The languages of "primitive" peoples throw little light upon the early stages of language development; many such languages are in some respects more complex than our own. But there can be no doubt that talking is a fundamental human behavioral characteristic.

How might you try to investigate the problem of the origin of speech?

THE UNIQUENESS OF MANKIND

The human species has all the basic characteristics of living things. And you have just seen that structurally and physiologically the species has few characteristics that clearly separate it from other existing species. Yet it is quite obvious that in some ways man is very different from every other living thing. Because of this, you can argue that he is a quite new sort of creature—that he is unique.

unique [ū nēk'; Latin: *unus*, one]: unlike any other

When this uniqueness is investigated, it is found to be primarily based not on anatomy and physiology, but on behavior and accomplishment. The uniqueness lies in man's way of life—his *culture*. The word "culture" is used by anthropologists to cover all human knowledge and all the human ways of doing things that are passed on from generation to generation by teaching and learning. Mankind's uniqueness comes from the vast fund of information (and misinformation) that the species has accumulated and shared among its members.

Man as an animal—physical man—is a proper subject of bio-logical study. But it is far from easy to separate animal man from cultural man. In fact, the separation is impossible, because everything man does is affected by his culture. We eat, for example, because, as animals, we have to have food; but whether we eat oysters, rice, ham, grasshoppers, potatoes, spaghetti, or other things depends not so much upon the nutritional value of these things as upon cultural at-titudes toward them. In the study of man, then, there is a broad overlap between the biological and the social sciences.

Investigation 19.2

HUMAN BLOOD GROUPS

INTRODUCTION

The substances that are the basis for the human ABO blood groups (page 585) are, as a set, a human physiological characteristic. As with other physiological characteristics, however, this one is not clear-cut; blood of apes contains substances that are chemically similar to those in blood of man.

BACKGROUND INFORMATION

The major difficulty in blood transfusion comes from the clumping of red blood cells. The clumps of red cells cannot pass through the capillaries, which therefore become clogged. If many of the capillaries are clogged, the circulatory system is blocked, and death may result.

Karl Landsteiner demonstrated that the clumping of the red blood cells is brought about by a reaction between substances on the red-cell membranes and substances in the plasma. The reacting substances do not occur together in the blood of any one individual. But since different individuals have different sets of the substances, blood from one individual may contain the plasma substance that reacts with the red-cell substance of another individual.

In the ABO system of blood types, there are 2 red-cell substances, "A" and "B," and 2 plasma substances, "anti-A" and "anti-B." The following are the possible combinations: Individuals with A on their red cells have

anti-B in their plasma. Individuals with B on their red cells have anti-A in their plasma. In-dividuals with both A and B on their red cells have neither anti-A nor anti-B in their plasma. Individuals with neither A nor B on their red cells have both anti-A and anti-B in their plasma.

MATERIALS AND EQUIPMENT
(for each team)

glass-marking crayon
microscope slide, 1 per student
paper, white, unlined, 1 sheet
    per student
cotton balls, several per student
alcohol, isopropyl, 70%
forceps, 2
lancet, sterile, disposable,
    1 per student
anti-A serum
anti-B serum
toothpicks, 2 per student
monocular microscope

PROCEDURE

Using a glass-marking crayon, draw a line across the short axis of a microscope slide, dividing it into halves. In the upper left-hand corner of the left half, write A; in the upper right-hand corner of the right half, write B. Place the slide on a sheet of white, unlined paper.

Wash your hands thoroughly. Using a ball of cotton dipped in alcohol and held in forceps, scrub the tip of a finger (on your left hand if you are right-handed; on your right hand if you are left-handed). Allow the alcohol to dry. Using a sterile, disposable lancet, make a small puncture in the tip of your finger. Wipe off the 1st drop of blood with a dry ball of cotton. Place a small drop of blood in the middle of each half of the slide. You can do this by touching the slide to your finger. Cover the puncture with a ball of cotton soaked in alcohol, and continue the procedure. (Hold the cotton in place with the thumb of the same hand for about 5 minutes.)

Immediately place a drop of anti-A *serum* on the drop of blood on the A half of the slide. (Serum is plasma from which fibrinogen has been removed.) Use a toothpick to mix blood and serum; be careful to mix them within as

small an area as possible. Break the toothpick and discard it. Place a drop of anti-B serum on the drop of blood on the B half of the slide. Use a 2nd toothpick to mix the blood and serum. Break the toothpick and discard it.

Compare the material on each side of the slide with Figure 19·6, which shows both clumping and nonclumping reactions. You may check your naked-eye observations by examining the material under the low power of a microscope. Compare your slide with the slides of neighboring students.

STUDYING THE DATA

If cells are clumped on Side A only, your blood type is A.

If cells are clumped on Side B only, your blood type is B.

If cells are clumped on both sides, your blood type is AB.

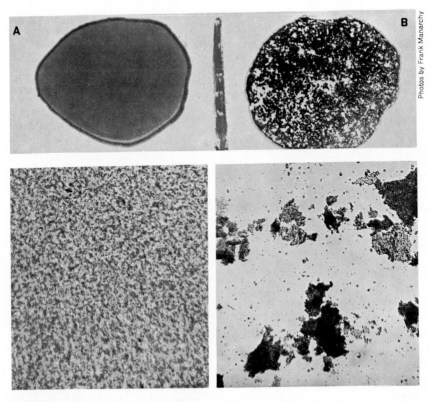

Photos by Frank Manarchy

Figure 19 · 6

Above: Blood-typing slide. The blood is Type B.
Below: The same samples as seen with a microscope.   × 650

If cells are clumped on neither side, your blood type is O.

• What is your blood type?(1) (Caution: There are a number of factors that may produce errors in this test. Only the results obtained by an experienced technician are satisfactory for medical purposes.)

On the chalkboard tally the blood types of all individuals in your class. Other classes will do the same. Total the tallies and calculate the percentage of each type. • Why are individual errors in determining blood type not likely to have much effect on the percentages of blood types when data are reported by a large number of individuals?(2) • In your student population, which type occurs most frequently?(3) • Least frequently?(4)

SUMMARY

• Assuming that your determination is correct, name the red-cell and plasma substances in your blood (see "Background Information"). (5) Large numbers of "foreign" red blood cells are introduced in blood transfusions; on the other hand, the introduced plasma is quickly diluted in the plasma of the recipient.

• Keeping these facts in mind, describe what would happen to your circulation if you were given a transfusion of Type A.(6) • Of Type B.(7) • Of Type AB.(8) • Of Type O.(9) • Describe what would happen to the circulation of individuals of each type if you were the donor.(10)

• With respect to blood types, can your biology classes be considered a random sample of the population of your community? Explain.(11) Regardless of your answer to Item 11, assume that the percentages derived from the pooled class data represent the percentage in your community. Compare them with the percentages in the following samples:

	A	B	AB	O
London, England	43	8	1	48
Paris, France	42	12	6	40
Berlin, Germany	43	14	6	37
Montana (American Indian)	76	0	0	24
Zaire	30	29	10	31
Peking, China	25	34	10	31
Tokyo, Japan	38	22	10	30

• Explain similarities and differences between your percentages and these.(12)

BECOMING HUMAN

When Charles Darwin published *The Descent of Man* in 1871, he based his discussion almost entirely on evidence from living species. Darwin thought that "missing links" between apes (family Pongidae) and men (family Hominidae) might never be found, since it is only by a rare accident that fossils are preserved; and animals of the tropical forest —where much of the evolution of the human line probably took place —are especially rare as fossils.

During the past century, however, paleontologists have uncovered a surprising number of anthropoid fossils. Among fossils from Miocene times are those of the genus *Dryopithecus.* These animals had characteristics that were definitely anthropoid and could have been ancestral to either pongids or hominids. Very few anthropoid fossils have been found in the Pliocene, and these are fragmentary. But some anthropologists place the early Pliocene *Ramapithecus,* mainly on the basis of tooth and jaw structure, in the early hominid line. And when we come to the Pleistocene, all the fossils are clearly either hominid or pongid.

Pongidae [pŏn'jə dē']

Hominidae [hō mĭn'ə dē']

Why do you think fossils are formed only infrequently in tropical forests?

anthropoid [ăn'thrə poid'; Greek: *anthropos,* man, + *eidos,* a shape]. This term refers to both pongids and hominids.

Miocene. See Figure 10·5.

Dryopithecus [drī'ō pĭth'ə kəs]

Ramapithecus [rä'mə pĭth'ə kəs]

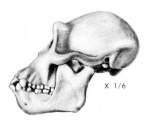

Figure 19 • 7

Skull of *Dryopithecus*, a
Miocene primate.

Australopithecus africanus
[ôs trā'lō pǐth'ə kəs]
ăf'rǐ kä'nəs]

Olduvai [ŏl'də wā']

Louis S. B. Leakey: 1903–1972.
British (born in Kenya)
paleontologist

See page 314.

robustus [rō bŭs'təs]

Figure 19 • 8

Skull of *Australopithecus.*
Hominid fossils are usually
fragments; note the restored
parts of this one.

X 1/6

Smithsonian Institution

PRE-MAN

Thus, the fossil evidence indicates that the pongid and hominid lines have evolved separately for a long time. To call the early hominid fossils "ape-men" or "man-apes," then, is misleading. It might be better to call them "pre-men."

One day in 1924, Raymond Dart, a professor of anatomy at a university in South Africa, began studying a collection of fossil-bearing rocks from a quarry not far from his home in Johannesburg. Embedded in one piece of rock were parts of a skull unlike any he had ever seen before. When finally removed from the rock and assembled, the skull resembled in some respects that of a five- or six-year-old child. In others, it was distinctly apelike. Dart named his find *Australopithecus africanus.* He continued to study it and after four years of work succeeded in separating its jaws so that the teeth were fully revealed. They were remarkably like those of a human child. Moreover, because of the position of the foramen magnum, Dart felt certain that the skull had belonged to a creature that had held its head in a human position and had probably walked erect.

Over the next 40 years, enough fossil materials—skulls, leg bones, and pelvises—were collected to clearly indicate that groups of pre-men had indeed existed in South Africa during the early Pleistocene. Far to the north and east, in the Olduvai Gorge of Tanzania, Louis Leakey and his family have been finding and studying pre-human fossils for many years. The rock strata forming the walls of the gorge are relatively undisturbed, so that accurate dating of fossils included in them is possible by the potassium-argon method. From this site the Leakeys have obtained a group of australopithecine fossils basically similar to those from South Africa. The oldest of them are found between strata believed to have been laid down about 1,759,000 years ago—at the beginning of the Pleistocene.

As more fossils were found, it became clear that there were at least two species of *Australopithecus.* One included individuals weighing perhaps 70 kg and standing about 1.5 m high. This species, now named *Australopithecus robustus,* had very large teeth and powerful jaw muscles, both indicative of a herbivore. Dart's original species—*africanus*—was more slender, weighed about 50 kg, and stood about 1.2 m high. Although the fossil record is still far from complete, there is evidence that these two species of *Australopithecus* lived in Africa for about 750,000 years. During this time *A. africanus* became more and more manlike; *A. robustus,* on the other hand, remained remarkably unchanged.

THE GENUS *HOMO*

The African fossils are hominid, but they are not *Homo;* this means that anthropologists believe they are more manlike than apelike, but not enough like modern man to be placed in the same genus with him.

Back in the days when Darwin was still living, Eugène Dubois

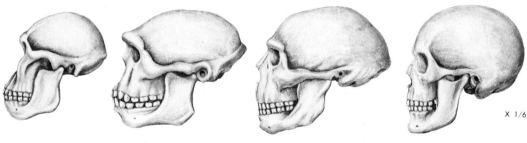

X 1/6

Australopithecus   Homo erectus   Homo sapiens neanderthalensis   Homo sapiens sapiens

Figure 19 • 9

Reconstructions of some hominid skulls. Can you see any characteristics that might distinguish *Homo* from *Australopithecus*? That might distinguish *Homo sapiens* from *H. erectus*?

had a strong conviction that fossil-bearing strata near Trinil, Java, would be a likely place to look for fossil evidence of man. In 1887 he took a job as a surgeon in the Royal Dutch Army and was assigned to a post near the Trinil site. The strata he wanted to examine had been laid down by volcanoes about 500,000 years ago. In two seasons of digging, Dubois unearthed a small piece of human jawbone, several teeth similar to those of apes, and part of a skull that suggested a brain too big for an ape and too small for any known man. In the next year he uncovered a fossil thighbone, and its straightness suggested that it came from an erect primate. Dubois gave this "Java man" the name *Pithecanthropus erectus.* It was the first fossil hominid to get wide public attention.

In 1929, after two years of excavation, Davidson Black and W. C. Pei discovered "Peking man." During the next 12 years, parts of more than 40 individuals were dug up from a cave floor near Peking.

Eugène Dubois [dü′bwä′]: 1858–1940. Dutch physician and paleontologist

Trinil [trē′nĭl]

Pithecanthropus erectus [pĭth′ə kăn′thrə pəs ĭ rĕk′təs]

Davidson Black: 1884–1934. Canadian biologist

W. C. Pei [pā]: 1898—. Chinese paleontologist

X 1/6

Australopithecus   Homo erectus   Homo sapiens neanderthalensis   Homo sapiens sapiens

Figure 19 • 10

Artist's reconstruction of heads of some hominids. What characteristics do you think are directly based upon the skulls shown in Figure 19 • 9?

X 1/2

Figure 19 • 11

A pebble tool. Such crude instruments have been found with the remains of *Homo erectus.* Is the use of tools a distinctively human characteristic?

Neanderthal [nē ănd′ər thäl]

Homo sapiens neanderthalensis [hō′mō′ săp′ē ənz nē ănd′ər thəl ĕn′sĭs]

subspecies. See pages 626–628.

Cro-Magnon [krō măg′nən]: after the Cro-Magnon cave, in France, where remains were discovered

Whereas only a few crude flint tools had been found near the fossils of "Java man," many rough stone tools chipped to an edge on one end (somewhat like modern chisels) were found among the split bones and punctured skulls of "Peking man" and the animals he ate. There is now general agreement that "Peking man" and "Java man" were closely related. Both have been renamed *Homo erectus*—in the same genus as modern man but recognized as a different species. Additional fossils of *Homo erectus* have been found in Tanzania, Algeria, South Africa, and Germany.

The first fossil of a manlike creature had actually been discovered much earlier. It was uncovered in 1856 in the Neanderthal Valley of Germany. Darwin's work had not yet been published, so it is not surprising that at first this fossil was much misunderstood. But during the past hundred years a large amount of fossil material belonging to the same kind of hominid has been found throughout Europe and in North Africa, Asia Minor, and western Siberia. It is now clear that *Homo sapiens neanderthalensis* was not a pre-man; he was a man— though perhaps not one you would like to meet. The biological name indicates placement in the same genus and species as ours—but he was enough different from us to be placed in a different subspecies. Neanderthal man was short and almost chinless and had protruding ridges above his eyes. But he had a brain about as large as that of modern man, and the part of the brain that is known to be involved in speech was well developed. He lived in caves, used fire, buried his dead, and made good stone tools.

MODERN MAN

Neanderthal men flourished for about 100,000 years, during the third interglacial period and into the fourth ice age. At the beginning of this period, they were probably contemporary with *Homo erectus.* Near the end—about 25,000 to 50,000 years ago—they came into contact with another group of hominids, Cro-Magnon men.

Cro-Magnons are unhesitatingly placed in the same species and subspecies (*Homo sapiens sapiens*) as is modern man. They

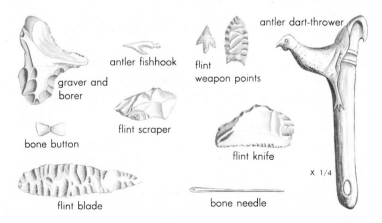

antler dart-thrower

antler fishhook

flint weapon points

graver and borer

flint scraper

bone button

flint knife

X 1/4

Figure 19 • 12

Some tools of primitive *Homo sapiens sapiens*— Stone Age man.

flint blade

bone needle

were tall and straight and had brains as large as the brain of any modern member of the species. These people were excellent tool-makers and fine artists. In addition to stone, they used bone, ivory, and the antlers of reindeer for tools. Some of these materials were engraved with designs or carved into the shapes of recognizable objects.

What do you think happened to Neanderthal man when modern man appeared?

The story of human paleontology is tentative and incomplete—more so than may appear from the account we have given here. The fossils of man are always fragmentary, and they are often difficult to date. But the study of the period from Miocene to Pleistocene, in which most of the evolution of pre-man and man occurred, is progressing rapidly. The immediate future is bound to bring forth much greater scientific understanding of human origins.

tentative [tĕn′tə tĭv; Latin: *tentare*, to try]: uncertain

VARIETIES OF MODERN MAN

It is clear that all living hominids form a single biological species, *Homo sapiens*. There is abundant evidence that the most diverse varieties can and do interbreed and produce fertile offspring. Yet populations of the human species differ considerably in appearance. There is a great range in size, from the tall people of northern Europe and the upper Nile River to the Pygmies of the Congo forest. Skin color ranges from very dark to very pale. There are also wide differences in the texture and distribution of hair on the body, in the shape of the skull, and in facial features, such as the nose and lips. On the basis of such differences, numerous attempts have been made to work out a classification of human populations, but anthropologists have reached no general agreement.

Human varieties show geographical patterns, just as do varieties of other organisms. But mankind is very widely distributed and wanders about extensively, so gene flow among human populations has been much greater than among populations of other organisms. However, before the mass migrations of populations that have occurred during the last 500 years, there was a rough correlation between geographical areas and variations in certain human characteristics.

Europe and western Asia were inhabited by rather light-skinned peoples with thin lips; the males had heavy beards (unless they shaved) and relatively abundant body hair; head hair was either straight or wavy. In eastern Asia the human population had yellowish or yellow-brown skin; brown eyes; very little facial and body hair; straight, black head hair; and a fold in the upper eyelid (Figure 19 • 13). In Africa south of the Sahara, the common traits were dark skins, very curly head hair, relatively thick lips, and wide noses. In Australia, curiously enough, the native peoples were somewhat similar to Europeans: their head hair was curly, and the males had thick beards

Figure 19 • 13

Above: The Mongoloid eye fold. *Below:* An eye without the fold.

Caucasoid [kô'kə soid';
Caucasus, a mountain range in
southeastern Europe, + Greek:
eidos, a shape]

Mongoloid [mŏng'gə loid';
Mongolia, a region in central
Asia, + *eidos*]

Negroid [nē'groid; Spanish and
Portuguese: *negro*, black, +
eidos]

Australoid [ô'strə loid';
Australia + *eidos*]

Amerind [ăm'ər ĭnd]

and abundant body hair; but their skin was generally quite dark. In America the population was similar in some ways to that of eastern Asia, but with the eye fold less developed.

From these sets of traits, some anthropologists have recognized Caucasoid, Mongoloid, Negroid, Australoid, and (sometimes) Amerind populations. But wide transition zones linked each (except the Australoid) to the others. Further, many subdivisions can be made within each of these groups. And there are also many oddities of distribution, such as similar-looking Pygmy peoples in the Congo and the Philippine Islands. So other anthropologists name as many as 30 human varieties.

Amerind (United States).

C. Bruce Hunter

Australoid (Australia).

B. Brander from Photo Researchers

Figure 19 • 14

Examples of variation in some physical characteristics among humans.

Caucasoid (Greece).

Annan

Mongoloid (Mongolia).

Shostal Associates

Negroid (United States).

H. Bergmann from Shostal

The simpler classification of human populations correlates well with geographical distribution, but this does not necessarily mean that the characteristics of populations are adaptations to a region or a climate. From northern Europe through the Mediterranean region and southward into equatorial Africa, there is a cline of average skin pigmentation, from very light to nearly black. Is this because dark skin allows body heat to escape, while light skin reflects it back inward? Is it that unpigmented skin allows the formation of adequate vitamin D in the cloudy north-European climate, while pigmented skin reduces the chance that too much of the same vitamin will be produced by the nearly bare skins of Africans? Or is it that dark skin protects against cancer in equatorial sunlight, while no such protection is required in northern regions? Or might it be a combination of two or more of these? And in the Americas, Indian populations inhabit a similar cline of climates, but there is remarkably little change in skin color throughout this vast area. It is obviously easier to ask questions about the complexities of human characteristics than it is to answer them.

Sometimes discussion of the various human populations gets involved in arguments about the superiority or inferiority of one or of another. From a biological point of view there is no meaning to such arguments. All existing varieties of mankind have been successful in coping with the environments they have encountered; if they had not been successful, they would not exist. We might ask which variety has evolved anatomically farthest from the primitive characteristics of pre-men. Then we could argue that the most advanced are the Mongoloids, because they have the least hair; or the Negroids, because the out-turned lips are most highly developed in them; or the Caucasoids, because they have the lighest skins. Usually, however, it turns out that the argument is cultural, not biological. And to cultural arguments biologists have no special contributions to make.

vitamin D: a substance required for bone formation (Figure 7·5). Some can be synthesized by action of ultraviolet light on substances in skin. Too much can be injurious.

Does this necessarily mean that any one, or all, will cope with future environments? Explain.

Investigation 19.3

BIOLOGICAL DISTANCE

BACKGROUND INFORMATION

In recent years anthropologists have begun to use gene frequencies as a basis for classification of human populations. In doing so, they refer to the degree of similarity in the gene frequencies of 2 or more populations as *biological distance.* In other words, the more similar the gene frequencies of 2 populations, the less the biological distance between them; conversely, the less similar the gene frequencies, the greater the biological distance.

William C. Boyd, an American biochemical anthropologist, has proposed a human classification based on frequencies of the genes that determine blood types. There are several advantages to using blood types for this purpose. First, the ways in which the blood-type genes are inherited are well known (page 585). Second, the blood type of an individual does not change with age or with changes in environment. Third, natural selection does not seem to cause any rapid changes in the frequencies of blood-type genes; therefore, present frequencies indicate to some extent how human populations have mixed with one another in the past. Fourth, blood types are rather easy to determine from blood samples taken for various medical purposes, so data for a large number of individuals representing many human populations are readily available for study.

PROCEDURE

In this investigation you will consider the following questions: To what extent are 3 selected North American populations genetically related to each other? How do the migrations of human populations affect gene frequencies? How can the mixing rate of 2 different populations be calculated?

Recall that the 4 blood types, A, B, AB, and O, are determined by allelic genes, I^a, I^b, and **i**. Figure 19·15 shows the frequencies of these 3 alleles in an Eskimo population of Point Barrow, Alaska; in the Indian population of British Columbia, Canada; and in the Navajo population of New Mexico. These gene frequencies have been calculated from the blood-type frequencies found in samples of the populations. •In your present opinion do you think these 3 human populations should be classified as 1 variety (or "race") or as 3? Explain your answer.(1)

Examine the data. •On the basis of the I^a gene frequencies, which 2 populations are most alike?(2) •On the basis of the I^b frequencies, which 2 populations are most alike? (3) •On the basis of the **i** frequencies, which 2 populations are most alike?(4) •Now would

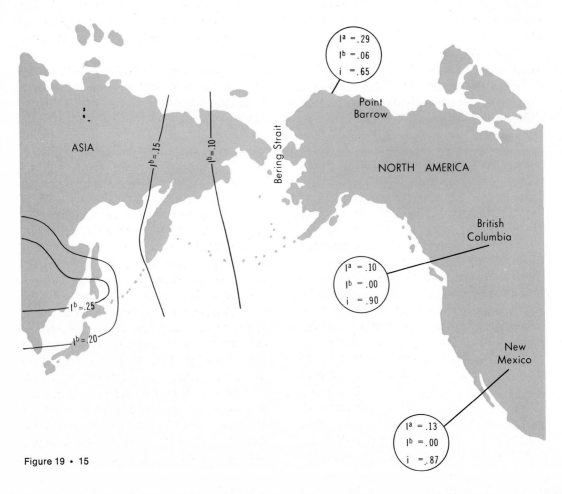

Figure 19 • 15

you classify these 3 populations in a single human variety? Explain your answer.(5)

Look again at Figure 19 • 15. Notice that it shows the frequency of the **I^b** gene in northeastern Asia. • As you move westward and southward into Asia from the Bering Strait, what happens to the frequency of the **I^b** gene? (6) • As you move eastward and southward in North America from the Bering Strait, what happens to the frequency of the **I^b** gene?(7)

Over much of central Asia the frequency of **I^b** is .25 to .30. Westward from central Asia into Europe, the frequency declines (Figure 18 • 17). There are several hypotheses to account for this situation, but we shall consider only one. Briefly, the hypothesis states that the primitive population of Asia had all 3 allelic genes, that Europe and America were populated from central Asia, and that the 1st emigrant populations from the Asian homeland either lacked the **I^b** gene or lost it along the way.

How could an interbreeding population lose a gene? Loss by selection seems highly improbable, since the blood types apparently have neither selective advantages nor selective disadvantages. In *large* interbreeding populations where neither mutation nor selection is involved, the Hardy-Weinberg principle (pages 614–616) states that gene frequencies remain constant. But what about *small* populations— the kind very probably involved in all early human migrations? Consider the following situation:

Suppose that we had a human population with ABO blood-type genes distributed in the following frequencies: 25% **I^a**, 10% **I^b**, and 65% **i**. Suppose that it is a very small population, consisting of only 50 persons per generation. Of course, each individual has 2 genes for the ABO blood type. According to the Hardy-Weinberg principle, therefore, we should expect to find among the 50 children of 1 generation 25 **I^a**, 10 **I^b**, and 65 **i** genes. Yet from experience in penny-flipping, card-dealing, and genetic experiments, you know that you don't always get *exactly* what is expected on the basis of probability. In penny-

flipping, you *expect* to get heads as often as tails; but if you flip a penny only 10 times, you might obtain 9 heads and 1 tail—or even all heads or all tails.

Similarly, in the case of the small, hypothetical population of people, instead of getting expected results, we might find that purely by chance there were 28 **I^a**, 4 **I^b**, and 68 **i** genes —or some other combination of frequencies. If this occurred, what should we expect in the next generation? Not 25 **I^a**, 10 **I^b**, and 65 **i**, but (according to the Hardy-Weinberg principle) a repetition of the *new* frequencies—that is, 28 **I^a**, 4 **I^b**, and 68 **i**. Of course, in a 3rd generation, the frequencies might by chance return toward the original ones, but they might result in a further reduction of the **I^b** gene in the population. This might even happen a number of times, until the **I^b** gene disappears from the population. Then it could never return unless reintroduced by mutation or by immigration of **I^b** genes in individuals from some other population.

Thus, as a result of ***genetic drift,*** as this process was named by the American geneticist Sewall Wright (1889——) the 1st populations of *Homo sapiens* to reach Europe and America may have had genes **I^a** and **i** only. • What blood types could they have had?(8) Later, according to the hypothesis, other emigrating populations carried the **I^b** gene outward from central Asia and, by interbreeding, reintroduced the gene into American and European populations. • Considering the difficulties of primitive travel, where would you expect these later emigrant populations to be most numerous? Least numerous?(9) • On the basis of the frequencies of the **I^b** gene, which of the North American populations shown in Figure 19 • 15 has probably had the more recent genetic contact with populations of Asia?(10) The frequency of the **I^b** gene is .00 in the Basque population of southwestern France. • On the basis of the **I^b** gene only, what can you say about the biological distance between the Basques, natives of central Asia, and Navajos?(11) • Does this mean that the Basques and the Navajos belong to one "race"? Why or why not?(12)

Now, for a study of the *rate* of gene flow from one population to another. Two populations with the following characteristics are needed: Both populations must be large; they must differ markedly in the frequencies of allelic genes at 1 or more loci; the traits determined by these genes must be easily and precisely identifiable; and, of course, the populations must be mixing. All of these characteristics are found in the Caucasoid and Negroid populations that have come into North America during recent centuries.

The genetic trait best suited for this study involves another blood characteristic. In 1940 Landsteiner discovered that material from the blood of rabbits that have been injected with the blood of rhesus monkeys causes the red blood cells of some persons to clump. Such persons are said to be "Rh positive" ("Rh" for "rhesus monkey"); persons whose red blood cells do not clump are "Rh negative." Further study showed that the Rh blood types are, genetically, more complex than the ABO types. Among the genes involved is one that has been symbolized **Rh°**. This gene can be rather easily identified, and its frequency differs markedly in the 2 populations that you are considering.

In Negroid populations of Africa, the frequency of the **Rh°** gene is about .60; in Caucasoid populations of Europe, about .03; and in the American Negroid population, about .44. From these figures the rate of mixing between African and European populations in North America can be computed.

• What is the difference between the frequencies of the **Rh°** gene in the African and European populations?(13) • In the African and American Negroid populations?(14) The amount of mixing between the Caucasoid and Negroid populations in North America may be expressed as a percentage. • Divide your answer to Item 14 by your answer to Item 13 and multiply by 100.(15)

The year 1625 may be taken as the beginning of the genetic mixing between Caucasoid and Negroid populations in America; the frequency of the **Rh°** gene in the American Negroid population was obtained from data gathered about 1950. • Assuming an average generation length of 25 years, how many generations of mixing could have occurred?(16) • On the basis of this number of generations, what was the average amount of mixing per generation?(17)

From calculations like this—crude though they may be—anthropologists can estimate the biological distance between populations, the routes of human migration, and the rates at which genetic differences among populations change. And from these studies, anthropologists can deduce some aspects of the biological history of man.

GUIDE QUESTIONS

1. What bases do taxonomists use to classify mankind as a species in the class Mammalia?

2. What structural characteristics of primates can be related to an arboreal habitat?

3. What are the chief anatomical characteristics that distinguish mankind from apes?

4. With what cultural characteristic of man can the lack of seasonality in human reproduction be linked?

5. How does the life-span of man compare with that of other animals?

6. How is the slow development of a human being related to culture?

7. What kind of communication is apparently dependent upon the organization of the human brain?

8. How can man be most clearly differentiated from all other animals?

9. Why are primate fossils rare?

10. How does the primate genus *Dryopithecus* fit into the paleontological history of hominids?

11. During what division of geological time has most of the development of hominids occurred?

12. On what evidence did Dart base his conclusion that *Australopithecus africanus* was a hominid?

13. What are the relationships of "Java man" and "Peking man" to each other and to modern man?

14. In what ways did Neanderthal man differ from modern man?

15. How is Cro-Magnon man related to existing man?

16. On what basis have biologists made the statement that all existing men are a single species population?

17. What are some of the characteristics used in attempts to distinguish varieties of *Homo sapiens*?

18. How does the simple classification of human populations correlate with ancient geographical distribution?

19. What biological explanations can be given for the pole-to-equator cline in skin coloration among Old World human populations?

20. What is meant by the biological distance between populations?

PROBLEMS

1. In which of the following activities would a man most likely excel over all other species of animals?

running	high jumping
swimming	distance jumping
throwing a ball	climbing a rope
shooting a bow	hitting a tennis ball

Make a statement summarizing the ways in which human physical achievement is superior to that of other animal species.

2. Why are tropical forests poor sources of fossil evidence? Consider both the conditions for fossilization and the conditions for finding fossils.

3. The Pleistocene has been called the *anthropogen* epoch. From the study of word roots in the marginal notes to this book, can you figure out the meaning of this word? Is it appropriate?

4. Language is frequently considered a fundamental human behavioral characteristic. Recently claims have been made that chimpanzees can also learn to communicate with symbols. "Teaching Language to an Ape," by Ann and David Premack (*Scientific American,* October, 1972), reports an experiment. What evidence do the researchers present to indicate that their chimp can use language in the human sense? What evidence remains lacking? Try to design an experiment or experiments to test for parts of the missing evidence.

5. Assume that pre-men resembled *Homo sapiens* in lacking a breeding season. How would their social organization differ from that in a wolf pack in which there is a definite breeding season?

6. In this chapter you read: "The small size of the canine teeth may be related to tool-using." Comment on this quotation in the light of the discussion of evolution in Chapter 18.

7. Make a list of human characteristics that have been used to describe "races" of man. Now assume—as do some anthropologists—that the word "race" is equivalent to "subspecies" (Chapter 18). Which of the characteristics in your list are best suited for describing subspecies of man? Why are blood groupings particularly useful in attempts to define subspecies of man? Why are characteristics of skull shape less useful? Which of the two is easier to use in studying the subspecies of man in past geological time? (You might begin this investigation with William C. Boyd's *Genetics and the Races of Man* [Boston: Little, Brown & Co., 1950].)

8. On September 23, 1789, nine Englishmen and seventeen Tahitians left Tahiti and sailed to Pitcairn, an isolated, uninhabited island in the South Pacific. For 24 years they and their descendants had no visitors, and since then their contacts with the rest of the world have been few. The effects of this isolation on both biological and social evolution are described in Harry L. Shapiro's *The Heritage of the Bounty,* rev. ed. (New York: Doubleday & Co., Inc., 1962). Can you find any evidence of random genetic drift among the Pitcairn Islanders?

9. Consider the factors that bring about death among people in modern urban and suburban environments. Include factors that kill individuals before, during, and after the age of

reproduction; factors that reduce health or impair development; and factors that reduce fertility or the survival rate of offspring. Speculate on the results of these factors in effecting changes in the characteristics of future human populations.

SUGGESTED READINGS

CAVALLI-SFORZA, L. L. "Genetic Drift in an Italian Population," *Scientific American,* August, 1969. Pp. 30–37.

ECKHARDT, R. B. "Population Genetics and Human Origins," *Scientific American,* January, 1972. Pp. 94–103.

EDEY, M. A., and the Editors of LIFE. *The Missing Link.* New York: Time-Life Books, 1972. (Discusses current research on pre-man fossils, on non-human primates, and on methods of analyzing genetic relationships among living species. Rather easy.)

EIMERL, S., I. DeVORE, and Editors of LIFE. *The Primates.* New York: Time, Inc., Book Division, 1965. (Attention is given to the ways in which the study of primate biology throws light on man. Many illustrations.)

HARRISON, R. J. *Man, the Peculiar Animal.* Baltimore: Penguin Books, Inc., 1958. (This is a biology of man that concentrates attention upon his anatomical and physiological peculiarities. Somewhat advanced.)

HOWELL, F. C., and Editors of LIFE. *Early Man.* New York: Time, Inc., Book Division, 1965. (The abundant colorful illustrations included in this book show both evidence and artists' interpretations of evidence. Fairly easy.)

LEAKEY, L. S. B. "Adventures in the Search for Man," *National Geographic,* January, 1963. Pp. 132–153.

LEAKEY, R. E., and G. W. GAHAN. "In Search of Man's Past at Lake Rudolf," *National Geographic,* May, 1970. Pp. 712–733.

MONTAGU, A. *Man: His First Million Years.* New York: New American Library of World Literature, Inc., 1958. (One of the leading anthropologists of the present day discusses both the biological and the cultural development of man.)

NAPIER, J. "The Antiquity of Human Walking," *Scientific American,* April, 1967. Pp. 56–66.

————. "The Evolution of the Hand," *Scientific American,* December, 1962. Pp. 56–62.

PETTIGREW, J. D. "The Neurophysiology of Binocular Vision," *Scientific American,* August, 1972. Pp. 84–95.

PILBEAM, D. *The Ascent of Man.* New York: The Macmillan Co., 1972. (A good recent summary of human characteristics and human paleontology. Moderately difficult.)

SIMONS, E. L. "The Earliest Apes," *Scientific American,* December, 1967. Pp. 28–35.

Man in the Web of Life

ECOLOGICAL HISTORY OF MANKIND

Many chapters ago you began your study of biology by examining a collection of illustrations, each accompanied by questions. The questions linked human activities to environment. Later, the links were made clearer by discussions of energy flow, materials cycles, and ecological relationships in the biosphere. Then, when you looked into the structure and function of the individual organisms that make up a biotic community, you found that they are wholly dependent upon energy and materials that come from outside themselves—from other organisms and from the abiotic environment. Each organism, each organ, each cell, each chromosome—indeed each molecule of DNA—makes sense only in relation to the biosphere as a whole.

Is mankind an exception to all this? In Chapter 19 you looked at man as a species, with characteristics of structure and function that distinguish him from other organisms. But in previous chapters you frequently encountered man as just another example of an organism. Man fitted into the world of living things at every point—yet he always seemed to fit in a little differently. Perhaps this is because we who write and read books are ourselves human. Perhaps we need some historical review to give us some perspective on mankind in relation to the biosphere.

perspective [pər spĕk'tĭv; Latin: *per*, through, + *specere*, to look]: a view of a subject in relation to other things

HUNTING AND GATHERING

When modern men—Cro-Magnon men—appeared 25,000 or more years ago, they were hunters and food-gatherers. They were particularly efficient predators because of their use of tools, their intelligence, and their social organization. The human niche in a biotic community was not unlike that of wolves. Human tribes were able to find food in a variety of communities, just as do wolf packs, but any particular tribe (like any one pack of wolves) was—because of territorial behavior—probably part of a particular community.

Cro-Magnon men. See pages 652–653.

Though primitive men were primarily carnivores, they frequently gathered berries, fruits, and nuts and dug roots; at such times they were herbivores. Studies of the few remaining hunting and food-

Wide World

Figure 20 · 1

A few food-gathering cultures still exist. This is a hunter in the Northern Territory of Australia.

See Figure 7 · 15.

Do you know of any hunting-and-gathering people of the present day?

gathering tribes show that about 5 km² of land are needed to support each person. Therefore, the total human population 25,000 years ago must have been small and it must have been scattered in more or less isolated groups.

Occasionally, *Homo sapiens* became food for other kinds of animals, such as the big cats, wolves, and crocodiles. But man must have been a minor source of food for such animals, because social organization as well as fires and shelters was an efficient defense.

Men were undoubtedly hosts for many kinds of parasites. But because the human population was scattered, conditions were not favorable for the spread of contagious diseases such as measles and small-pox. Therefore, the most common diseases were probably those involving pathogens with alternate hosts. Yellow-fever virus, for example, can live in both man and monkeys, and it is passed between them through forest mosquitoes. Thus, if monkeys are numerous, man can be infected no matter how scattered the human population may be.

Primitive hominids, then, were gatherers of various plants, predators on some animals, occasional prey to other animals, and hosts for parasites. Hominid ecological relationships changed little for perhaps a million years. Indeed, in some remote parts of the world some human populations continued to exist in these ways well into the 20th century.

AGRICULTURE

At some early time—at least 10,000 years ago—hunters formed a mutualistic relationship with one or more species of the genus *Canis:* From this relationship came what is most probably the earliest domesticated organism—the dog. With the help of dogs in hunting and perhaps with the invention of nets for fishing, some human groups began to form more or less permanent settlements.

A by-product of settled life—the garbage dump—must have appeared almost at once. People may have noticed how a discarded portion of a wild plant that had been gathered for food sometimes grew into a mature plant on their dumps. They may then have dug up favorite wild plants and transferred them or their seeds to the dumps. At any rate, sometime before 7000 B.C. men began to cultivate plants—that is, they assisted the growth of the plants and harvested the plant products.

Most such relationships with animals came later. Remains of domesticated animals are found only in association with agricultural communities and never—except for dogs—with the remains of hunters. Perhaps during times of drought wild grazing and browsing animals invaded man's fields and gardens. Such animals man might

In what other way might wild plants appear on dumps?

What kind of ecological relationship is this?

V-DIA Scala

Figure 20 • 2

A primitive digging-stick agriculture can affect the biosphere only slightly (southeastern Asia).

easily capture and pen up until they could be conveniently slaughtered. The step to raising young that happened to be born to the captured animals must have eventually occurred. So domesticated cattle, sheep, and goats may have originated.

husbandry: care and management

Anthropologists have gathered much evidence about the development of agriculture and animal husbandry. Conflicting theories have arisen from such research. However, the principal ecological result of the long period known as the Agricultural Revolution was a shifting of man's position in the biosphere. Man had been merely a *member* of a biotic community; he became now a *maker* of biotic communities. From a biological point of view, the art of agriculture is the art of managing ecosystems. And the principal aim is to establish the simplest possible community: the crop (plant or animal) and man. A wheat field should contain no organisms but wheat, which goes directly to human use. A pasture should contain no organisms but plants that are edible by consumers such as cows or horses, which are useful to man. Of course, mankind has never fully achieved this goal; but since the days of the first farmers, he has been trying.

What ecological principles hinder the achievement of this goal?

This discovery was apparently never fully made in ancient America. What domesticated animals did Amerinds have, and how were they used?

What do you think may have been a source of mechanical energy used even earlier by man?

Well after the beginning of the Agricultural Revolution, some primitive farmers discovered that animals could not only be eaten— some could be put to work. Of course such animals had to be fed. But directed by human intelligence, their biological energy enabled a farmer to grow far more food than the animals ate. Thus another niche was formed in what we may call the "community of the domesticated." And man had taken a long step in applying energy other than that of his own muscles to the modification of his environment.

Agriculture demanded a foresight that was not needed for hunting. A farmer had to adjust his activities to coming seasons. He had to store his produce between harvests. He had to be willing to work without immediate reward. However, agriculture also provided increased leisure time. During planting, cultivating, and harvesting, a

USDA Photo

Figure 20 • 3

Animal-power agriculture (Tennessee). Compare its effects on the biosphere with the effects of the kinds of agriculture shown in Figures 20 • 2 and 20 • 4.

primitive farmer worked longer hours than a primitive hunter. But once the harvest was in and the surplus had been stored, there was usually a period of weeks or months—instead of hours or days, as for a hunter—when a farmer did not need to worry about where his next meal would come from. In the privacy of his own mind, at mealtimes with his family, and in village gatherings, a farmer mulled over his problems, sought to find relationships between noticed events, and tried to foresee future events.

mull: implies a somewhat disorganized kind of thinking

And to ponder problems together, there were greater numbers of farmers in a village than there were hunters in a camp. Because land suitable for agriculture is scarcer than land suitable for hunting, larger numbers of agriculturists tended to gather at each suitable place. And because agriculture makes more efficient use of solar energy than hunting does, a small area of land could support more people. In some favorable places, even ancient methods of agriculture permitted one person to be supported by just one hectare of land instead of the 500 hectares (5 km^2) required to support a hunter. So, by permitting the enlargement of human groups, the Agricultural Revolution gave a big boost to the development of culture.

ponder: [Latin: *pondus*, a weight]: to think deeply

INDUSTRIAL MAN

Crude tools have been discovered with the fossils of australopithecines, and even the most primitive *Homo sapiens* were skillful in tool manufacture. The Agricultural Revolution brought about an increased demand for tools of many new kinds. And it provided the leisure that gave man increased opportunity for experimentation and invention.

What physical characteristic enables man to make more use of tools than do other animals?

Even in hunting cultures a few persons skilled in making tools often specialized in that occupation. They were given food by other members of the tribe in return for the tools they produced. In agricultural tribes this specialization increased. Whole families of artisans came to exist, fed by the farming families of their villages.

artisan: a person trained in some special skill of the hands

For a long time stone was the basic material used by toolmakers. But in many parts of the world they eventually discovered how to use metal. Smelting of metals required large amounts of heat energy. Fuels became important for industry as well as for cooking food. Man began to look upon all the things in his environment as *resources*— things that he could turn to his own use.

As time went on, man exploited more and more resources to satisfy his needs and desires through industry. But all kinds of resources are not found in all places. Even in the Stone Age, flint, an especially desirable kind of stone for toolmaking, was traded from one group of hunters to another. As industry grew so did trading. Tin from Britain was reaching the eastern Mediterranean 3000 years ago; and in America, Indians in Alabama obtained copper from the region of Lake Superior long before the arrival of Europeans.

exploit [ĕk sploit'; Latin: *ex*, out, + *plicare*, to fold]: to treat a thing so that it is made useful

As trade brought resources from distant regions, a tribe was no longer merely a part of a local ecosystem. To hold the new, dis-

Why could not most foods be traded as distantly as metals?

tinctive, and widespread human ecosystems together, trading became a specialized human occupation. Villages grew into towns of artisans and traders. Food for the townspeople came through trade with nearby farmers. Crowding produced excellent conditions for contagious diseases to flourish. And many of the biological wastes of the townspeople were scattered on fields and in water, where they were excellent vectors.

It is not necessary to trace the entire development of trade and industry. You have learned much of these matters in your social studies courses. What must be emphasized is the importance of both economics (from social science) and ecology (from natural science) for understanding the development of the present situation of man in the biosphere.

economics [ē'kə nŏm'ĭks; Greek: *oikos*, house, + *nemein*, to manage]. Compare the derivation with that of "ecology," page 63.

The Industrial Revolution, which is said to have begun in the 18th century, has been a revolution in the human application of energy to reshaping ecosystems. Mankind long used the energy of animal muscle, the energy of wind and water, and the simple heat energy of fire. But it was the discovery of ways to channel heat energy through machinery that increased human ability to change environment in a revolutionary way. And in the 1940's mankind succeeded in putting to use for the first time a source of energy that is independent of the sun—atomic energy.

Figure 20 • 4

Wheat harvesting (Nebraska). How does the energy in this kind of agriculture differ in its ecological effects from that shown in Figure 20 • 3?

USDA Photo

tremendous [Latin: *tremere*, to tremble]: fearfully great

The ecological and economic results of all this have been tremendous. Where once towns were isolated specks on the landscape, now the landscape is covered with concrete and steel. A large percentage of people now dwell in cities—and these cities are utterly unlike anything that bore the name before the Industrial Revolution. For many square kilometers, soil has disappeared under buildings, roadways, airports. Within cities man tends to shut himself indoors,

Bert A. Kempers

Figure 20 • 5
Human activities now change whole landscapes. Man-made "forest" in a town on the naturally treeless Great Plains (Colorado).

where he often manufactures temperature and humidity conditions to suit his preference. And outdoors, man is continually manipulating the homeostatic mechanisms of the biosphere to make life more immediately appealing to himself. As a result, within two centuries industrial man has had a greater impact on Earth than his ancestors had in nearly 200,000 years—indeed, more than all other species of organisms have had in all of Earth's history.

manipulating [mə nĭp′yə lāt′ĭng; Latin: *manus,* hand, + *plere,* to fill]: handling in such a way that changes are made

BIOLOGICAL PROBLEMS: PRESENT AND FUTURE

No man is an Iland, intire of it selfe; every man is a peece of the Continent, a part of the maine; if a Clod be washed away by the Sea, Europe is the lesse, as well as if a Promintorie were, as well as if a Mannor of thy friends or thine owne were; any mans death diminishes me, because I am involved in Mankinde; And therefore never send to know for whom the bell tolls; It tolls for thee.—JOHN DONNE

John Donne [dŭn]: 1573–1631. British clergyman and poet

As we human beings have gravitated into cities, many of us have lost our sense of kinship with each other and with natural ecosystems. In urban surroundings we find it more and more difficult to realize that we are involved in the biosphere, in the web of life. Far from knowing the answers to the problems that assail us, we scarcely know the origin of our difficulties. But now, after a year's study of biology, let us see if the questions encountered at the beginning of this course mean more than they did then.

gravitated [grăv′ə tāt′əd; Latin: *gravis,* heavy]: pulled together as if by a force like gravity

assail [ə sāl′; Latin: *ad,* to, + *salire,* to leap]: to attack

OUR NUMBERS

Before the Industrial Revolution even the largest and most famous cities were scarcely more than what we would call big towns. London,

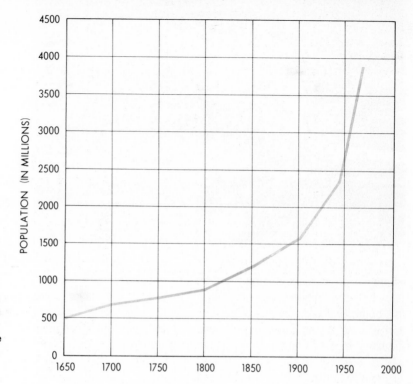

Figure 20 • 6

Estimated world population of *Homo sapiens* during the past three centuries. Compare this graph with the one you drew in Investigation 2.2.

demographers
[dĭ mŏg'rə fûrz; Greek: *demos*, the people, + *graphein*, to write]

Can you estimate the biomass of the living human population?

Paris, Vienna, Rome—each had less than 100,000 people. In 1650 all of England had only 4,000,000—less than half the present population of London alone.

It has been estimated by **demographers** (scientists who study size, density, and distribution of human populations) that the number of individuals of *Homo sapiens* alive today is equal to 10 percent of the total number that have *ever* lived. You are one of about 4,000,000,000 living human beings! We are not only numerous; we are also big. The 4 billion (4×10^9) of us require a large portion of all the food consumed by animal species.

Approximately 187 babies are born every minute, or about 270,000 every day. And about 142,000 people die every day. Since there is neither world immigration nor world emigration, the daily world population increase is about 128,000. Thus, every two weeks the human population increases enough to populate a new city the size of Detroit. In a year the increase adds up to more than 47,000,000 people.

Increase of population is not something happening only in *other* countries. In 1970 the population of the United States was 205,000,000. This was an increase of 25,000,000 since 1960. And though birth rate is declining, population increase continues.

What has happened to the human species? The basis for the present world growth of human population is simply this: Natality exceeds mortality.

Figure 20 • 7

The population meter of the U.S. Bureau of the Census. Each of the lower dials shows one of the four population determiners. The large upper dial shows the algebraic sum of these four rates, and this sets the speed at which the numerals turn in the population estimate. How much has the population grown since this picture was taken in 1967?

Mortality and death control. Mortality was high in the early history of *Homo sapiens*. We still die—but we die later in life and from other causes. There are still occasional victims of sharks, crocodiles, and snakes, but long ago we freed ourselves from most of the dangers of predation. We have almost learned how to free ourselves from pathogens—although this freedom is not enjoyed equally in all parts of the world.

What effect does postponing death to older ages have on population?

Only a century has passed since Pasteur, Koch, and others established the nature of infection. In that time, great progress has been made in the control of infectious diseases, particularly those dangerous to infants. As a result, fewer individuals now die in infancy and youth than formerly. In 1900, 162 out of every 1000 infants born in the United States died in their first year of life; by 1970 this figure had been lowered to 20 out of every 1000.

Figure 20 • 8 shows how the causes of death have changed in the United States. In 1900 the leading causes of death were influenzas and pneumonias, tuberculosis, and diarrheas—all infections. By 1970 they were heart disease, cancer, and cerebral hemorrhage —none infections and all chiefly degenerative diseases of old age. Diseases such as typhoid, diphtheria, and smallpox have practically disappeared.

influenzas [ĭn′flŏŏ ĕn′zəz]; pneumonias [nū mō′nyəz, nŏŏ mō′nyəz]

diarrheas [dī′ə rē′əz; Greek: *dia*, through, + *rheein*, to flow]

hemorrhage [hĕm′ə rĭj; Greek: *haima*, blood, + *rhegnynai*, to burst]

Much of this decrease in fatal infectious disease has come about through the discovery of drugs and antibiotics—chemical agents effective against bacteria and other protists. Equally important in re-

Wide World

	CAUSES OF DEATH	1900	1910	1920	1930	1940	1950	1960	1968
INFECTIOUS DISEASES	influenzas and pneumonias	203	162	208	103	70	31	37	37
	tuberculosis (all forms)	202	160	114	72	46	22	6	3
	diarrheas and intestinal diseases	133	117	54	26	10	5	4	2
	diphtheria	43	21	26	5	1	0.3	0.0	0.0
	typhoid and paratyphoid fevers	36	26	8	5	1	0.0	0.0	0.0
	syphilis	12	14	16	16	14	5	2	0.3
	measles	12	12	9	3	0.5	0.3	0.2	0.0
	whooping cough	12	11	12	5	2	0.7	0.1	0.0
	scarlet fever	10	12	5	2	0.5	0.0	0.0	0.0
	malaria	8	2	4	3	1	0.0	0.0	0.0
	erysipelas	5	4	3	2	0.0	0.0	0.0	0.0
	smallpox	2	0.4	0.6	0.1	0.0	0.0	0.0	0.0
NONINFECTIOUS DISEASES	heart diseases	132	159	159	206	293	300	366	373
	cerebral hemorrhages and thrombosis	72	76	82	81	91	100	107	106
	cancer (all forms)	63	76	83	97	120	140	151	160
	bronchitis	46	23	13	4	3	2	3	3
	cirrhosis of liver	13	14	7	7	9	7	11	15
	appendicitis	10	11	13	15	10	2	1	0.7
	diabetes mellitus	10	15	16	19	27	16	17	19
	kidney diseases	89	99	89	91	82	21	11	5
	senility	—	26	14	10	8	13	12	13
	congenital malformations	92	88	85	61	12	13	10	8
OTHER	suicide and homicide	14	22	17	25	21	18	15	18
	accidents	72	84	70	78	70	61	52	58
	miscellaneous	479	264	202	196	186	205	139	143
	all causes	1770	1498	1310	1132	1078	962	944	966

Figure 20 • 8

Causes of death in the United States (per 100,000 population).

susceptible [sə sĕp′tə bəl; Latin: *sub*, under, + *capere*, to take]: easily affected by

These are not usually pathogens (see *Escherichia coli*, page 209), but where they are present, pathogens, such as those of typhoid fever, may also be present.

ducing infectious disease have been sanitation and public-health practices that prevent the spread of infections. But not all infectious-disease problems have been solved. In many species of pathogens, populations resistant to chemical agents have evolved. The most susceptible individual pathogenic organisms have been killed, but the more resistant ones have survived and have multiplied, producing new resistant populations. This is natural selection.

Figure 20 • 9 shows the sensitivity to antibiotics of bacteria obtained from a person's alimentary canal. Each arm of the paper resting on the culture medium has been treated with a different antibiotic. A clear area around a tip indicates that the bacteria did not grow in the presence of that antibiotic and so are susceptible to it. Without preliminary tests such as these, physicians might waste valuable time using an ineffective antibiotic in treating a spreading bacterial infection.

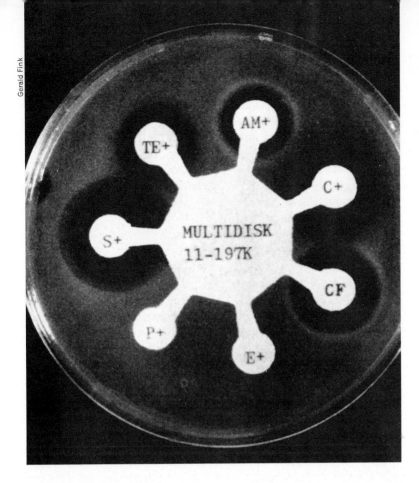

Gerald Fink

Figure 20 • 9

Each small disk contains a different antibiotic. A clear zone around a disk results when bacteria in the plate fail to grow. If an antibiotic had been chosen at random, what is the probability that it would have been effective in treating an infection by this kind of bacterium?

A similar problem exists in the control of vector diseases. For example, control of malaria in the past has been based upon reducing the number of mosquitoes by spraying with poisons. Because of natural selection, however, mosquitoes are developing resistance to many of these substances.

When we turn from infectious disease to other kinds, the outlook is mixed. A great deal has been learned about nutritional diseases, and they can be controlled where foods are sufficiently abundant and people have the money to buy them. Some knowledge of human hereditary diseases and their prevention or treatment has been obtained. Degenerative diseases, which appear chiefly in old age, are receiving more attention as more and more persons live longer. If we succeed in reducing deaths from degenerative diseases, what next will become the leading causes of death? Accidents? Suicide? Mental illness has become an increasing problem as civilization becomes more complex.

For examples, see E. P. Volpe, *Human Heredity and Birth Defects* (reference, page 603).

There are still many medical problems, but one point is clear: Increased ability to cope with disease has resulted in a decrease in mortality. This decrease in death rate has been greatest in the technologically advanced countries. But medicines are easily transported and sanitation is easily taught in even the most remote countries; increasing international medical cooperation is reducing mortality everywhere.

Consequences of death control. In Ceylon in 1947, an intensive campaign to control malaria caused the death rate to drop abruptly from 20 to 13 per 1000 per year—and during the same period there was a slight increase in the birth rate, from 38.4 in 1946 to 40.2 in 1948. In 1962 the introduction of a measles preventative reduced the infant death rate in Upper Volta (Africa) by half; the birth rate there was 48. Elsewhere, especially in industrialized nations, natality has declined. But in very few places has the decline in natality approached the decline in mortality.

Alan Gregg: 1890–1957. American physician

Alan Gregg, formerly medical director of the Rockefeller Foundation, compared present human population growth within the biosphere with the growth of a cancerous tissue within an organism. This tissue somehow escapes growth controls and multiplies at the expense of all the other tissues. Likewise we are multiplying at the expense of the rest of the biosphere. If you could ask the cancer cells, they would surely think they were doing fine—but when at last the organism is killed, they die, too. There is a frightening possibility that we, with our increasing numbers and our increasing power to destroy the rest of the biosphere, may multiply our way to destruction.

A comparison of Figure 20 · 6 with your graph from Investigation 2.2 indicates a possible future. Demographers, using methods similar to yours and projecting the *present* rates of mortality and natality, have calculated that by 2560 A.D. there will be one person for every 5 m² of land surface—forest, desert, tundra, everything. Destruction would probably come long before. But most demographers think this projection is unlikely.

Figure 20 · 10

How many people can Earth's supplies of energy and matter support?

H. Armstrong Roberts

There is a finite amount of substance on Earth; therefore, the size of the human population cannot become infinite. The growth of the human population will cease—at some future time. Of that there can be no doubt. The question is, How?

Consider the possibilities. There is no immigration to Earth, so this cannot be reduced. Emigration from Earth is a possibility, but not even the most imaginative scientist can foresee emigration on a scale that would affect the human population problem. Mortality can rise: disease, starvation, and war are still with us and can increase. Some human societies have deliberately used mortality to control their numbers: in ancient Greece and in Tahiti unwanted infants were left to die in the fields; Eskimos left old people behind when they moved their villages. Few people today would be willing to approve of these or similar practices; indeed, almost everyone is willing to support generously all efforts to reduce mortality still more.

The only population determiner remaining is natality.

Natality and birth control. Following the birth of a child, a woman can again become pregnant within a few weeks, so that having one child per year is not an impossible feat. A woman's child-bearing age extends from approximately 15 to 45 years of age. Therefore, 30 children per woman is biologically possible. In no population, however, does the *average* number of children per woman even approach 20. Several factors reduce the number. Following some illnesses ovulation may not occur for a time. Frequent pregnancies increase the likelihood of abortion of the embryo. And frequent pregnancies also increase the likelihood of the mother's death.

In most societies, however, the principal factors limiting natality are cultural. Most societies have restrictions on marriage, especially with respect to age, and most frown on births that occur outside the ceremonial pattern. Many societies have taboos regarding the times and spacing of copulation (in humans, usually called *coitus*), especially following childbirth and menstruation. In some societies certain persons—usually in religious positions—refrain from coitus throughout life. And in some societies abortions may be brought about by mechanical or chemical means. (It can be argued that the last is actually population control by the increase of mortality, but natality is usually calculated on the basis of live births.)

Biologically, coitus is a means of reproduction, just as eating is a means of nutrition. But just as our eating habits are no longer restricted to the foods that maintain good nutrition, so our sexual habits are no longer restricted to reproduction. The most effective means of birth control would undoubtedly be for large numbers of people to cease coitus. Unlike ceasing to eat, such a practice has no adverse effects on the body, though it may have adverse effects on the mind. However, the biological pressures acting through both hormonal and nervous systems toward sexual activity are very strong; therefore, this means of reducing natality is improbable.

Some years before there was public concern about population

finite [fī′nĭt]: limited

infinite [ĭn′fə nĭt]: without limits

taboos: things strongly forbidden by custom or religion

coitus [kō′ət əs; Latin: *cum*, together, + *ire, to go*]

adverse [ăd vûrs′; Latin: *ad*, to, + *vertere*, to turn]: acting against, unfavorable

growth, the private concern of individuals for the size of their own families stimulated research on means of preventing births even though coitus occurred. One discovery was that ovulation generally occurs about the midpoint between menstrual periods. If coitus is avoided for several days at this time, pregnancy should be avoidable. This rhythm method of birth control fits well into human traditions, but it frequently fails.

Another discovery was the intrauterine device (IUD), a wire and plastic coil that is placed within a woman's uterus, where it may remain for long periods of time. It is effective and simple, is easily made and shipped to all parts of the world, and apparently has only a few possibilities of affecting a woman's health. How it works is not certain, but it probably interferes with the embedding of the fertilized egg in the wall of the uterus. Like abortion, then, this might be considered as producing mortality at a very early stage of development.

effective [ĭ fĕk′tĭv; Latin: *ex*, out, + *facere*, to make]: having a desired result

Devices that prevent sperm cells from reaching egg cells in the upper part of the oviduct can prevent fertilization. Now made of rubber and designed for both male and female, they are inexpensive and effective. The form for the male has the added advantage of providing some hindrance to the spread of the microbes of syphilis, gonorrhea, and other venereal diseases.

device: a thing that has been designed to achieve some purpose

Surgical means of preventing sperm cells from reaching egg cells can also be used. In males the operation is relatively simple and requires no hospitalization. A short piece of each sperm duct is removed and the cut end of each duct is tied with surgical thread. Following the operation, sperms are unable to pass from the testes, though all the other substances in semen are unaffected. In females a similar operation involves cutting and tying the oviducts so that eggs cannot pass through them. This operation requires a stay in a hospital. At present these surgical means of birth control must be regarded as permanent sterilization, because an operation to rejoin the ducts has a poor chance of success. Recently, however, it has become a practice to collect sperm-bearing semen before the male operation and preserve it in a frozen condition. For many years frozen semen has been used successfully in cattle breeding, but as yet there has been little experience in the storage of human semen.

What is the purpose of this in cattle breeding?

Biological knowledge of female hormone cycles has led to the development of hormone-containing pills. Taking them is probably the most widely practiced birth-control method that is presently in use. The pills are of several kinds. The most common one contains a mixture of progesterone and estrogen that imitates a pregnant woman's hormonal condition. This condition suppresses ovulation and thus prevents pregnancy from occurring. Unfortunately, the interference with normal hormonal cycles has had serious effects upon the health of a few of the women who have taken the pills. Therefore, much research on birth-control methods still continues, for in control of natality lies the hope of avoiding much more unpleasant ways of limiting our numbers.

OUR RESOURCES

Every individual organism requires energy and matter from its environment. Therefore the size of any species population has meaning only in relation to the resources of the environment in which that species exists. For the human species, which has spread over the whole world, all of Earth is now a single great resource. And every problem of resource use involves the total world population.

It is customary to classify resources as either *renewable* or *nonrenewable.* Renewable resources are those that can be continuously replaced. Living things belong to this class. Water and air also can be considered renewable resources. Soil is a slowly renewable resource; forming an entirely new soil requires far more time, for example, than does growing a new crop of timber.

We might think of all substances as renewable, since matter is not ordinarily lost from Earth's surface. Nevertheless, the gas, coal, and oil that we burn cannot be used again, even though the carbon remains in the atmosphere or is picked up again by plants. The iron of scattered rusting cans is lost to us even though it remains in the soil. The cycles of these substances are too long for any possible management, so such substances have to be classed as nonrenewable resources.

What are some other nonrenewable resources that are important to industrial culture?

Food. Malthus considered food supply to be the limiting factor for human population. Through most of history it has certainly been an important factor. Famines and starvation have repeatedly struck

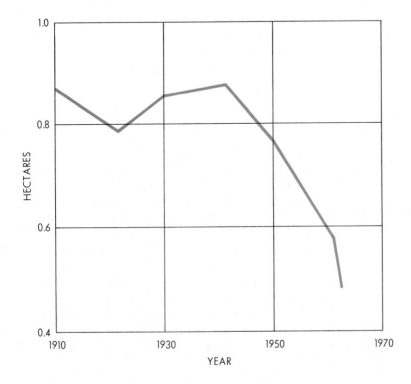

Figure 20 · 11

Amount of agricultural land required to feed one person in the United States.

many nations, though these factors have usually interacted with disease in limiting population.

We who live in an industrial nation are likely to forget famine. In the United States, Canada, Australia, and much of Europe, the application of science to agriculture and the use of machinery to replace the labor of man and animals have so greatly increased the production of food that famine is now unknown and starvation rare. In 1910, when the population of the United States was about 92,000,000, 13,500,000 persons (or 1 person in 7) were employed in agriculture. By 1970 only about 1 person in 67 was employed in this way. Nevertheless, the total agricultural output has increased even faster than the population of the nation has grown.

If we thus restrict our view, the food situation seems excellent. But when we look at many other areas of the world—particularly, much of Asia, Africa, and South America—we find that the number of mouths to feed is increasing more rapidly than is the amount of food with which to feed them. In many places an average of 1800 Calories per day per person is consumed—many individuals get far less. The average daily intake of a person in the United States is over 3000 Calories.

But the number of Calories is not the only factor in judging the adequacy of human nutrition. Even 3000 Calories, if obtained entirely from corn bread or rice, do not nourish a person. Food is the source not only of energy but also of chemical substances. And humans require some specific kinds of such substances—vitamins and, particularly, certain amino acids that are rare in plant proteins. But animal protein is expensive—not simply in money, but in energy. To give an American 3000 Calories of food that supplies the required vitamins and amino acids, a farmer must raise 11,000 Calories in plant substance, most of which goes to feed animals.

World agriculture has indeed improved considerably in recent years. Geneticists have developed varieties of wheat and rice that are particularly well suited to specific parts of the world. In many coun-

adequacy [ăd′ə kwə sĭ]: here, the extent to which a thing meets a need

Figure 20 · 12
Geneticists have contributed greatly to the increase of food production. In two strains of corn (*left*) that have been inbred for several generations, many undesirable recessive traits are homozygous. Crossing these strains makes the traits heterozygous, and the hybrid (*right*) is greatly improved.

Photos from Dekalb AgResearch, Inc.

Figure 20 · 13

Ancient irrigation works (Iran). Why do you think these lands were abandoned?

tries educational programs have provided farmers with information on how to use the new varieties. In Mexico, Pakistan, and the Philippines increased crop yields have caught up—at least temporarily—with increasing population.

Nevertheless, the world food situation is less rosy than it appears at first glance. To obtain large crops from modern agricultural techniques, more industrial energy is required—nonrenewable petroleum fuels and machinery that must be made from other nonrenewable resources. And to use machinery efficiently, single crops are planted over large areas of land. Thus ecosystems are simplified.

In such large, simplified, man-made ecosystems the effects of natural homeostatic mechanisms are reduced or eliminated. A field of corn or cabbage offers a splendid opportunity for consumers that like these plants. For example, the larvae of cabbage butterflies feed only on cabbage and a few closely related plants. Under natural conditions a butterfly must search through scattered vegetation to find the appropriate plants on which to lay its eggs. In a cabbage field it need spend no time in searching; all the plants are suitable. Conditions are ideal for the multiplication of cabbage butterflies. The same principle applies to organisms that cause plant diseases.

Therefore, much use has been made of poisons. The poisons often destroy natural predators, and this increases the need for more poisons. Further, the *pest* organisms—the ones causing damage—often develop new resistant varieties. So new kinds of poisons are required. To develop these, expensive research is needed.

In general, then, the high yield of human food per hectare that is characteristic of industrialized agriculture is achieved only by heavy use of resources—mostly nonrenewable—and, perhaps, through hidden ecological costs.

Of course, food is also produced in the waters of the world. Some human societies have long obtained most—almost all in a few cases —of their food from aquatic ecosystems. Much of this food is from species that are many links along aquatic food chains. This is

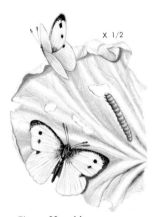

X 1/2

Figure 20 · 14

Cabbage butterflies and their larvae.

Why might predator species be destroyed by poisons before the pests on which they prey?

How does the term "pest" compare with the term "weed"?

Where are some places where people depend to a large extent upon aquatic food resources?

What marine producers are harvested for human food?

because most aquatic producers are microscopic and therefore difficult to harvest. Moreover, the productivity of the vast open oceans is low. Undoubtedly, human use of aquatic food resources will increase, but many oceanographers doubt that improvements in use of these resources can keep pace with the present rate of human population increase.

Soils, forests, and space. The basic resource on which agriculture rests is soil. But from soil comes much more than food. Through agriculture, soil produces fibers such as cotton; through forestry, soil produces a variety of useful items, including paper and lumber.

What are some other important forest products?

It was not until 1891 that the first national forests were established in the United States. These forests have been expanded greatly

Figure 20 • 15
Block harvesting of Douglas firs (Oregon). The bare areas are quickly reseeded by the surrounding forest.

Figure 20 • 16
Another method of harvesting timber: selective logging (Michigan). Though 40 percent of the timber volume was removed here, the forest community was only slightly disturbed.

USDA-SCS Photo

Figure 20 • **17**
Wasting a resource that is
difficult to renew (New
Jersey).

in the present century and have been managed to obtain an approximate balance between harvest and growth. Large lumber companies,
recognizing that their continued existence rests upon a steady supply
of trees, have designed plans to maintain continual reproduction of
the forests they own. Because the life-span of most trees is long in
comparison with human life-span, forest management is almost necessarily a concern of governments and corporations rather than of
individuals.

In addition to producing pulpwood and lumber, forests have
important ecosystem functions. They break the impact of rain on the
ground and promote absorption of water into the soil. Thus they reduce
erosion of soil and the frequency and violence of flooding. Especially
in hilly country, soil may be completely washed away when forests
are absent. When this occurs in forest biomes, trees are difficult to
reestablish. Soil, water, and forests, resources that should be renewable, are lost.

Forests, rangelands, and deserts—all nonurban, nonagricultural
areas—represent another kind of resource, a less tangible resource
than any of those previously mentioned—open space. This has
been a cultural force in the United States throughout its history. Perhaps if you travel across some parts of the country, you may find it
hard to believe that the time is rapidly approaching when open space
may be in short supply. Every day, however, there is less open
countryside—and more cultivated land, more cities, and more
highways.

You have studied effects of crowding on populations of mice and
ponderosa pines, and have examined the concept of territoriality.

tangible [tăn′jə bəl; Latin:
tangere, to touch]: real, in the
sense of being touchable

Figure 20 • 18

Often the search for open recreational space is in vain. Campers are as crowded as at their city or suburban homes. (Assateague Island, Maryland.)

Every organism requires some living space. No one knows what the minimum space for a human being may be or the length of time the minimum can be tolerated. Certainly some people have existed under very crowded conditions for long periods. But there is evidence that, at least in industrial environments, accidents, mental illness, and other undesirable effects result from inability to get away from crowds occasionally.

That a great many people feel a need for open space, even though they may not be able to explain why, is shown by the number of businesses based on outdoor recreation. Each year more than 25,000,000 persons go to forests or other open lands for hunting and fishing. Millions more go for other purposes—to camp, to picnic, to swim, to photograph, or just to look into the distance. To do all this, they spend billions of dollars. And each year the increasing population swells the demand for open space—but the amount per person decreases.

Wildlife. Forests, fields, and other nonurban open lands provide habitats for the many species that have not been domesticated or that have not learned to live in and around man's structures. Upon this wildlife depends the value of such lands for hunters and fishermen.

Figure 20 • 19

Elk are "shot" by photographers as well as by hunters—and many other persons find pleasure in merely watching them.

And much of the value of these lands for other persons who flock to parks, forests, and seashores also depends upon wildlife. The bare face of Death Valley has a certain grandeur, but most persons find even a desert more interesting when it is dotted with living things.

The problem of managing wildlife resources is basically the same as that of managing open space, because wildlife requires such space in which to live. And particular kinds of wildlife require particular kinds of habitat. When a marsh is drained and turned into a wheat field, the area supplies food for people but no longer supports ducks. This is a clear illustration of one consequence of increasing human population. Fortunately, it is an oversimplification. More wheat fields can also result in more pheasants, which find wheat fields a suitable habitat. In the management of wildlife, as in the management of other resources, choices must be made (economists call them "trade-offs"), and these involve the study of many interacting ecological factors.

For some kinds of organisms man-produced changes in lands and waters have been disastrous. On the average, one species of mammal has disappeared from Earth every year since 1900. Zoologists have compiled a list of 600 species of mammals that now seem in danger of extinction. Extinction, of course, is nothing new. But with industrial civilization altering entire ecosystems, extinction is going on at an increasingly rapid rate. And, of course, in addition to mammals many species of birds and other organisms have been driven to extinction.

What difference does it make that passenger pigeons and dodoes have disappeared from Earth? Or that whooping cranes may disappear tomorrow? Cro-Magnon man was probably quite satisfied when the last cave bear was killed. And there is certainly no place for packs of wolves in the vicinity of New York City. It may be difficult to argue a case for *every* threatened species, but there are good biological arguments against extinction in general.

One of these arises from genetics. In breeding specialized populations of domesticated organisms, many genes may be bred out of the gene pool or lost from it by random genetic drift. At some later time characteristics determined by such genes may be desired. Wild populations of the species or of related species may then be used to obtain the desired genes. Moreover, the genetic characteristics of most wild organisms are entirely unknown and might well be useful when further investigated. As long as wild populations exist, therefore, a vast resource of genetic characteristics remains available. But the extinction of each wild population erases its gene pool forever.

Another argument arises from the ecological principle that instability is a characteristic of simplified ecosystems. Although new species are undoubtedly evolving, speciation is usually a very slow process compared with the rate at which man is capable of extinguishing species. So each time a species becomes extinct, the simplification of the world ecosystem, the biosphere, is carried one step further. And the difficulty of maintaining a stable biosphere becomes greater.

Why do you think that speculations concerning life on Mars arouse more interest than descriptions of the chemical composition of the planet?

X 1/14

Figure 20 · 20
Whooping cranes are the tallest of North American birds. Efforts to save the remaining population have received wide publicity.

Is this the *only* way a desired gene might be available?

Why *usually*?

Hawaii oo

X 1/3

X 1/8

passenger
pigeon

X 1/15

great auk

X 1/8

Carolina paroquet

X 1/10

dodo

X 1/34

X 1/18

X 1/34

white-tailed gnu

European lynx

Père David's deer

Figure 20 · 21

Some animals that have been
completely or nearly exter-
minated through the
activities of man.

Power. Food is the source of biotic energy for consumers. Man
as an organism—a consumer—requires food. But to shape his environment, man now directs other kinds of energy besides that in his
own muscles. In doing so, he usually is interested in the rate at which
the energy is used—what physicists call *power.* This term can be
applied to any kind of energy, but today the unit horsepower usually
refers to engines, not animals. And the kilowatt is an even more
familiar unit of power.

Industrial civilization depends upon power, and upon industrial-

Figure 20 • 22

Multiple use of space. Forest products, water-flow control, water for electric power, and boating and fishing recreation are all provided at Norris Lake, Tennessee.

ization depend the new food-production methods that *might* catch up with the food needs of the human population—if population increase can be slowed down. There are, of course, many other human demands for power—from running factories to operating electric toothbrushes. Use of power will undoubtedly continue to increase, both because of increased numbers of people and because of the increased power demands of each person.

Shifts in the sources of power will be required. Some have already occurred in the United States (Figure 20 • 23). Even if the use of coal does not continue to decline, remaining supplies will probably satisfy fuel demands well beyond the end of this century. But before this, if present trends continue, the supplies of readily available oil and natural gas will be low and the cost of removing the remaining supplies

Why do these new food-production methods depend upon industrialization?

How have *your* demands for power increased in the past two years?

demands. As used by economists, this means what a person is willing to pay for.

Figure 20 • 23

The history and probable future of power sources in the United States.

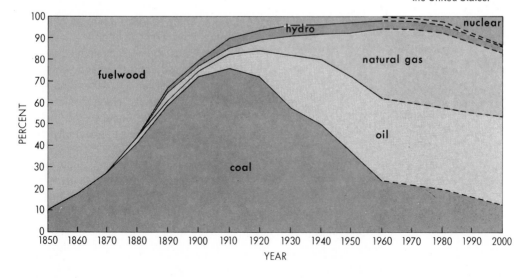

Figure 20 · 24

The Yankee Atomic Power Plant (Connecticut). What advantages and disadvantages does this have compared with a steam-power plant?

from the earth may be very high. Technologists know they must develop other sources of power. Already nuclear energy is supplying some of our power needs. And other power resources, such as solar radiation, are being further explored.

Can you name any other power resources?

The solution to the power problem is not basically biological. But the problem itself is biological, because it is people—living beings—who demand the power.

OUR WASTES

Four hundred years ago an Indian on Cape Cod might have used the shell of a clam that he had just eaten to make a hoe for cultivating his corn. Or he might have thrown it on the shell heap that had grown through the years around his camp. Thus, the shell could be a resource for technology or a waste to be discarded. Four thousand years ago a Chinese farmer carefully collected all his family's feces and spread them as fertilizer on his fields. Today American cities spend millions of dollars to rid themselves of human feces. Because the matter of which Earth consists is finite in amount and can be repeatedly cycled, every waste is an unused resource.

Wastes may accumulate to such an extent that they become harmful; they may then be called pollutants. All organisms produce substances that they discard into their environments. Sometimes these wastes may accumulate in harmful amounts; for example, wastes from seabirds that nest in colonies may kill surrounding vegetation. But mankind is a special kind of organism in this as in other ways.

Humans discard not merely their biological wastes but a great variety of things that result from technology. And both the great number of humans and—in many parts of the world—their highly developed technology produce tremendous amounts of polluting wastes.

These are of many kinds—sewage, garbage, plastic and glass containers, automobile-exhaust gases, chemicals from industry and agriculture, silt, smoke, radioactive substances, even hot water. All have one basic effect; they worsen our environment. Each acts in its own way; each must be studied separately. But most interact with others, so the study of pollution, like all ecological studies, is complex.

Sewage, garbage, and junk. Sewage is composed principally of biological wastes that are usually flushed away in water. This water also contains soaps and detergents that have been used in washing. The disposal of sewage raises two major problems. Disease micro-organisms, which usually are present in sewage, will be spread if the sewage is not treated to remove them. And the high organic content of sewage encourages the growth of decomposers, which use up dissolved oxygen. The oxygen supply in a river or lake highly polluted with sewage may be reduced to such an extent that nearly all animal life dies.

detergents [dĭ tûr′jənts; Latin: *de*, from, + *tergere*, to wipe]: cleaning substances—usually, other than soaps

Garbage once meant the wastes from butchering animals for meat. Later it included solid organic wastes, such as discarded foods from kitchens. Now it often refers to solid household wastes of all kinds, particularly containers—paper, metal cans and wrappers, plastics, glass. These solid household wastes range from quickly decomposable lettuce leaves to slowly decomposable paper to more slowly rusting cans to almost unchangeable plastics and glass. In cities many tons of this mixture must be removed each day. And each day the problem of where to put it and other solid wastes such as old mattresses, broken furniture, worn-out refrigerators—junk—becomes greater.

Henry Monroe from DPI

Figure 20 · 25
Garbage ready to be towed to sea for dumping (New York City).

What other processes add
CO_2 to the atmosphere?

Wastes from fuels. The burning of fossil fuels—coal and oil—has greatly increased the rate at which carbon dioxide is added to the atmosphere. Photosynthetic organisms have not kept pace in removing this CO_2. As a result, atmospheric CO_2 has increased about 20 percent in this century. CO_2 traps infrared radiation—heat rays—reducing the rate at which it escapes from Earth. On the other hand, CO^2 interferes only slightly with radiant energy arriving from the sun. Therefore, some ecologists and physicists believe that the 1.6°C increase in mean world temperature since 1900 may be explained by the increase of atmospheric CO_2.

But effects of atmospheric pollution are not this simple. Offsetting the upward trend of mean world temperature in the early part of the century has been a *decline* of 0.3°C in the years since 1940. This too can be traced to pollution. Besides CO_2, burning fuels release into the atmosphere many tiny particles—often visible at first as smoke. These particles reflect solar radiation. This reduces the amount of energy reaching the surface of Earth. Whether CO_2 increases world temperature or waste particles in the atmosphere decrease it is less important than the fact that wastes from fuels do have widespread effects on the biosphere.

Fossil fuels are not entirely compounds of carbon, oxygen, and hydrogen; they contain other elements. And burning is not always complete. Therefore, in addition to the particles just mentioned, many kinds of gases besides CO_2 and water vapor are produced. Some of these are particularly noticeable in the waste gases from automobile engines. Among them are carbon monoxide and oxides of sulfur and nitrogen—all of which are harmful to most kinds of living things. Under certain atmospheric conditions these gases, together with solid particles and water vapor, accumulate in air. Called *smog,* such an accumulation is especially likely to occur near large cities,

How does carbon monoxide
affect a person?

Figure 20 • 26
Effects of sulfur dioxide, an air pollutant derived from fuels, on parts of a rhubarb plant. Plants are sensitive detectors of such pollution.

USDA Photo

where automobile traffic is heavy and wastes from burning other fuels are added to those from gasoline.

Hominids have a history of fuel-burning that goes back beyond the origin of *Homo sapiens*. We humans of the present have problems of fuel wastes—just as we have sewage and garbage problems—because there are so many of us and because we depend upon a technology that uses such a vast amount of resources. This same technology, based on science, can also contribute to reducing these problems.

In what ways has air pollution been reduced in your region during recent years?

Figure 20 • 27

In March, 1967, the oil tanker *Torrey Canyon* broke up in the English Channel. Oil ruined miles of beaches and killed thousands of seabirds such as these. Even without wrecks, oil pollution is a continuing problem in marine waters.

Radioactive wastes. Figure 20 • 23 shows that the percentage—not the *amount*—of power obtained from fossil fuels is declining. The percentage obtained from nuclear energy is increasing both in the United States and in other parts of the world.

Nuclear energy is usually put to use by being changed to electrical energy in power plants. Nuclear-power plants produce neither smoke nor injurious gases, but they do produce radioactive wastes. Each year such plants produce wastes with a radioactivity of 2 curies for each kilowatt of electrical-generating capacity. The plants now (1972) operating or being built will produce, each year, wastes carrying about 76,000,000 curies of deadly radioactivity. And many more new plants will be built in coming years.

The radioactive half-life of many of these wastes is thousands of years. Therefore, they must be kept out of the vicinity of living things for many generations. Where can they be put? At present the

In what other way may nuclear energy be used?

curie. See Appendix 1, page 702. A substance giving off 1 curie, if placed in the middle of a football field, would make the whole field unsafe for a person—even for a few seconds.

Figure 20 • 28

Radiation damage to a forest
ecosystem (Brookhaven, New
York). Organisms in an experimental forest are exposed
to radioactive cesium-137
for 20 hours each day. A
nearby unirradiated forest is
used as a control.

Can you suggest any other
ways to dispose of these
wastes?

best plan seems to be to pack them away in abandoned salt mines.
This plan is less than perfect, because there is always a possibility
that they may contaminate underground water. And there is further
possibility that they may escape during railroad or highway accidents
as they are transported from the power plants.

Toxic metals. Solid metals make up a large percentage of junk.
But many metallic elements are discarded as ions or as parts of complex molecules that are carried in air and water. Some of these
substances—forms of such elements as mercury, lead, zinc, and
cadmium—are toxic to living things.

Elemental mercury is sometimes discarded into rivers and lakes
by industries that find it easier to get new supplies than to reuse it.
Certain bacteria are able to change elemental mercury into toxic
organic mercury compounds that are soluble in water. Taken in by
aquatic producers, the toxic substances then move through food
webs. Other toxic mercury substances that are used to prevent the
destruction of seeds by fungi enter food webs through water runoff
from agricultural fields.

Lead compounds are used to improve the burning qualities of
gasoline. They get into air in automobile-exhaust gases. Lead also
enters the biosphere from industrial processes and from some kinds
of paint. In experimental animals, lead compounds have effects on
brain development. There is also direct evidence that similar effects
occur in children.

Suggest ways pollution by
toxic metals might be reduced.
Do not forget trade-offs.

Other toxic substances. One of the greatest sources of pollution is
substances that are designed to poison living things. Their names
are derived from their targets—insecticides, nematocides, herbicides,
fungicides, for example. But in general they may be called *pesticides*
—that is, substances used for killing organisms that for one reason
or another are considered pests. Because of the basic similarity in

pesticide [pĕs′tə sīd′; Latin:
pestis, any injurious thing, +
caedere, to kill]

Arthur D. Hasler, Dir., Lab. of Limnology, Univ. of Wisconsin

Figure 20 • 29
Peter and Paul, twin lakes
that are used in experimental
studies of water pollution
(Michigan). Many ecological
problems cannot be com-
pletely understood by means
of small-scale laboratory
experiments.

metabolism of all living things, it is difficult to find substances that are
poisonous to one organism and not to another, particularly another
closely related one. For example, a substance poisonous to wasps
(which might be considered pests) is also very likely to be poisonous
to honeybees (which seldom are considered pests).

To produce enough food for the growing human population,
poisons against crop pests are considered necessary by agriculturists.
Poisons are also important for controlling vectors of disease microorganisms. About 30 years ago a poison that killed arthropods without
noticeable bad effects on warm-blooded animals came into use for
both of these purposes. This substance, DDT, has been especially
important in controlling the mosquitoes of malaria. Nearly everyone
concerned with food production and malaria control had unlimited
praise for DDT and the chemically related poisons that were later
developed.

As use of these substances increased, difficulties began to
appear. One was the development by natural selection of pest populations that are resistant to the poisons. Another resulted from the fact
that these poisons are chemically very stable. Therefore such a poison
persists in soils and waters, from which it is taken in by producers.
Though the amount in an individual producer may be small, consumers accumulate it principally in fatty tissues. The farther along a
food chain the consumer is, the greater the accumulation. Thus the
concentration of DDT in the fat of some fishes may be 140,000 times
greater than in the surrounding water.

Eventually, it was found that DDT does have injurious effects
on non-arthropod animals, chiefly by decreasing reproduction. In
birds, for example, DDT causes eggshells to be so thin that many

Wide World

Figure 20 • 30
Rachel Carson (1907–1966),
biologist and author who
directed public attention to
problems created by the
increasingly widespread use
of poisons.

Can you find examples of bird
species in which this has
been thought to be a cause of
population decline?

break before hatching. Though direct effects of DDT on man have not been clearly demonstrated and its effectiveness in controlling malaria is still good, many governments are urging reduction in its use or banning it completely.

Chemists are now attempting to develop poisons that disintegrate in soils and waters and that do not accumulate in food chains. They are also synthesizing hormone-like substances that interfere with the metabolism of some species but do not harm others. Meanwhile biologists are improving methods of controlling pests by nonchemical means. But daily the task of these scientists becomes more difficult, for daily the human population grows and, therefore, the demand for control of populations of other organisms becomes greater.

disintegrate [dĭs ĭn'tə grāt'; Latin: *dis-*, apart, + *integer*, whole]: to break a thing apart

Heat. When we think of wastes, we usually think of substances. But energy can also be a waste and a pollutant. At every step in a food chain some biological energy is lost as heat; ultimately all of it is lost, for energy cannot be recycled.

How is some of the waste heat from an automobile engine used?

The same principle holds true for all conversions of energy. In every power plant or engine where chemical energy of a fuel is converted to mechanical or electrical energy, some energy is lost as heat. Factories are often located on river or lake shores partly because water is needed to cool boilers and other equipment—that is, to absorb heat. Power generators need large quantities of water; nuclear generators need even more water than those operated with fossil fuels. It has been estimated that by 1980 about 20 percent of the entire daily run-off of water from the streams of the United States will be used for cooling power plants, raising the temperature of this water nearly 10°C.

thermal [Greek: *therme*, heat]

This heat that is added to streams, lakes, and estuaries may be considered thermal pollution. Such pollution is a threat to many aquatic organisms, which, unlike terrestrial organisms, are not tolerant of rapid temperature changes. And in some cases, even water that is gradually warmed may rise in temperature above the maximum tolerance of some organisms. In other cases, warmed water may change an aquatic community, favoring the multiplication of formerly rare species and reducing the numbers of formerly abundant species.

Can you think of any ways to change this waste heat into a resource?

There is some possibility, of course, that heated waters might produce ecosystem changes that would be an advantage to mankind. With the limited ecological knowledge now available, however, accurate predictions of the effects of thermal pollution are difficult to make, and caution in increasing it seems desirable.

VALUES

Biology—science, in general—does not exist except in human minds. Science accomplishes nothing; science is neither good nor bad. *Scientists* investigate; *scientists* discover; *scientists* reach conclusions. And scientists may be both good and bad—as are the rest of us. But what is good and what is bad? This is not a scientific question.

The questions with which you began this course in Investigation 1.1 were not scientific questions either. They were questions of values—what each person thinks good or bad, important or unimportant, desirable or undesirable. Scientists have widely differing values and so view such questions in varying ways. So may you. But those questions concern human beings and other living things. Therefore, a biological scientist can understand many aspects of those questions better than can persons without biological knowledge. Now, after a year of study, you should understand the questions better than you did at the beginning. However, *answers* to the questions—a biologist's or yours—go far beyond biology.

Let us consider just three value questions that this course may have helped you think about.

1. How many children should each person have?

In response to a recent questionnaire, nearly 67 percent of young people said that the population of the United States should no longer increase; more than 50 percent also said they would like three or more children. These people had less understanding of biology than you have.

Figure 20 • 31 shows responses to another questionnaire regarding desired family size and a graph of the effect such desires would

Why not?

Why are the answers contradictory?

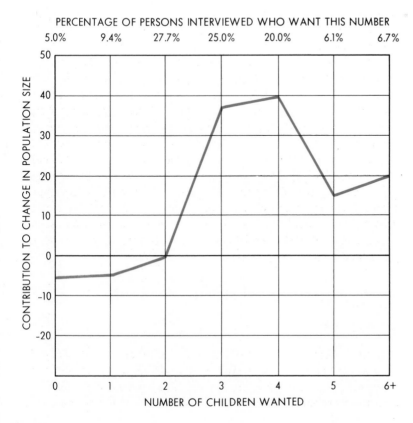

PERCENTAGE OF PERSONS INTERVIEWED WHO WANT THIS NUMBER

| 5.0% | 9.4% | 27.7% | 25.0% | 20.0% | 6.1% | 6.7% |

Figure 20 • 31

The percentage contribution to population growth made by persons wanting different numbers of children.

have on population size. Couples with two children do not affect the present size of a population (provided that both children survive), and so, regardless of the proportion of persons wanting this number, the point on the graph falls on the line representing zero growth. Who, then, contributes most to population growth? A person who desires three or four children! Persons wanting five, six, or more children are so few in number that they have a rather small effect on population size. Similarly, persons wanting one child or none are also few and have a small effect.

How many children do *you* want? For the future welfare of mankind—of which your children will be a part—how many do you think you should have? How do you think you should control the number you have?

2. How should biological knowledge contribute to human health?

Despite medical advances, large numbers of human beings do not receive much medical care—even in the countries where most of these advances have been made. Either the proper treatment is too expensive, or a doctor is not available, or hospitals or clinics are too far away. We have the capability of providing excellent health care—but it is available to only a fraction of the world's population.

Where health care is good, control of the more serious infectious diseases has lengthened the lives of most persons. Of every 1000 babies born in the United States today, more than half will still be living at age 75. Despite the best medical efforts, degenerative dis-

Eve Arnold from Magnum

Figure 20 · 32
What is the fate of the aged?

eases—cancer, heart diseases, strokes—make many of these persons unable to care for themselves for many months or years. Good care can be very costly. And much of the care is now given in ways that are physically successful but psychologically upsetting.

Do you want perfect health care or a kind that can be shared by most of the world's people? Would you want to be kept alive by a kidney machine while many others were dying for lack of it? Would you be willing to share in the care of a feeble grandparent in order to give him the happiness of dying among his family at home?

3. How can mankind live with minimum harm to environment?

This seems to be a simple question. And many persons are providing simple, but misleading, answers.

You have observed, at least in part, the cycles of matter and the flow of energy, which together make up the biosphere. You have studied the physiology of organisms and the conditions required for the complex biochemical activities within an organism and between an organism and its environment. You have come to understand that man, like every other kind of organism, is dependent upon the functioning of the biosphere. So you can appreciate the impact on Earth of man's enormous numbers, his insatiable demand for resources, and his tremendous outpouring of wastes.

insatiable [ĭn sā'shə bel; Latin: *in-*, not, + *satis*, enough]: incapable of being satisfied

Choices in a grassland ecosystem.

Figure 20 • 33

Man's powers to shape his environment may lead toward depletion and ruin or toward continuing usefulness. Consider the choices shown here and on the following page.

R. W. Cottrol from FPG

Eric G. Carle from Shostal

Choices in an urban ecosystem.

Soil Conservation Service, USDA

Haven Kolb

Choices in a forest ecosystem.

How much can your individual actions contribute to solving this problem? How many of your demands for material goods and for energy-consuming comforts can you give up? Are you willing to support laws that regulate *your* environmental actions as well as those of others?

And so we end as we began—with questions.

GUIDE QUESTIONS

1. What was the ecological niche of man in a hunting and gathering culture?

2. What change in man's method of obtaining his biological energy first greatly changed his ecological niche?

3. What further discovery greatly increased man's ability to cultivate fields?

4. Why was the rate at which culture developed probably greater in agricultural villages than in hunting camps?

5. How did specialized skill in toolmaking change the structure of early human communities?

6. How did the geographically unequal distribution of resources broaden the extent of human ecosystems?

7. Explain the statement "The industrial revolution . . . has been essentially a revolution in the human application of energy to reshaping ecosystems."

8. What is happening at present to the size of the human population in the world as a whole?

9. How is human population size related to medical knowledge?

10. What changes have occurred in the principal causes of death in the United States during the 20th century?

11. How does natural selection act as a factor in the control of infectious diseases today?

12. How is the action of human organisms in the biosphere similar to the action of cancer cells in tissues?

13. How have some human societies used mortality to control their numbers?

14. Why is the control of natality the most likely way by which the rate of human population growth may be reduced?

15. What cultural factors limit natality in some societies?

16. What would be the most effective means of reducing natality?

17. What means are available at present to prevent pregnancy even though coitus occurs?

18. Trout for sports fishing and trees for timber are both classed as renewable resources. Does "renewable" have the same meaning for both? Explain.

19. Why must resources such as coal and oil be considered nonrenewable?

20. What has happened during this century to the human food supply in the United States?

21. Why cannot human food supply be considered only in terms of Calories?

22. Why is modern agricultural knowledge difficult to apply to solving the problem of the whole world's food needs?

23. Why are the oceans probably not a sufficient answer to the food needs of the increasing human population?

24. Why is the forest resource difficult for individuals to manage?

25. What relationships exist between trees and soil in a forest ecosystem?

26. What is meant by "open space"?

27. What evidence supports the idea that open space is needed by human beings?

28. In what ways are wildlife resources related to land usage and to human population density.

29. What are the biological arguments for protecting species near extinction?

30. What shifts have occurred in power sources in the United States during the last century?

31. How is the idea expressed by the word "waste" related to the idea of "resource"?

32. Under what conditions may a waste be considered a pollutant?

33. What environmental problems arise from sewage?

34. What environmental problems arise from garbage and junk?

35. What are some effects that wastes from the burning of fossil fuels have on environment?

36. What is the major drawback of nuclear energy as a source of power?

37. In what forms may metals be toxic?

38. Why is the term "pesticide" misleading?

39. What difficulties have developed in the use of pesticides such as DDT?

40. How are scientists attempting to improve the present methods of controlling pest populations?

41. Under what conditions can heat be considered a pollutant?

PROBLEMS

1. Diagram a Stone Age food web centered on man. Be sure to include the protists.

2. The Agricultural Revolution is not as well known as the Industrial. Find out what archaeologists have been able to learn of this important turning point in man's history. You might begin with C. O. Sauer, *Agricultural Origins and Dispersals* (New York: American Geographical Society, 1952).

3. An anthropologist who has studied the Pygmies of the Congo reported this statement by a Pygmy: "When the forest dies, we die." Comment on the ecological understanding of this "savage."

4. In the 1930's antibiotics were discovered and many other important pathogen-killing drugs were developed also. Which diseases were most affected by these medical advances? Study Figure 20 • 8 to find causes of death that sharply declined after 1940. Find others that continued declining more gradually. And find still others that increased rather than declined. Show examples of each kind on a line graph. Explain the differences.

5. Demographers are concerned with more than changes in the total numbers of persons; they are also interested in the *structure* of populations—the relative numbers of individuals of various kinds. For example, two populations of the same size may have different proportions of males and females. Or two populations of the same size may have different proportions of children and adults. Such data often provide much information about a population.

    a. The total populations of the United States and Ceylon are quite different, but more important is the fact that the population of the United States has a smaller proportion of children than that of Ceylon. What hypotheses can you suggest on the strength of this information?

    b. We may divide the population of the United States into three age groups: (1) persons under 20, most of whom are not self-supporting; (2) persons 20 to 65, most of whom are working; (3) persons over 65, most of whom are retired. In recent years the first and third groups have been increas-

ing more rapidly than the second group. What hypotheses can you suggest to explain this? Can you see a future economic problem in this situation?

    c. In human females reproduction occurs mostly between the ages of 15 and 45. Suppose this age group increases more slowly than the age group over 45 but the number of children per female remains the same. What will happen to the birth rate in the population when expressed as births per 1000 of population?

    d. The average age at which a female has her first child is higher in Nation A than in Nation B; the average age of death is about the same in both nations. From this information, make a guess about the rate of population growth in the two countries. What additional information would make your guess more reliable?

6. What are the ecological and economic reasons for doubting that the seas can soon become a great food resource? What methods are now being used to increase the yield of human food from seas? What possibilities do marine ecologists see for marine farming? You can make a good start on answering these questions by reading G. B. Pinchot, "Marine Farming" (*Scientific American,* December, 1970).

7. Poisoning is not the only method used to control organisms that destroy man's agricultural crops. Find out what is meant by "biological control." Discuss methods of biological control from the viewpoint of ecological principles. What kinds of information are needed in applying biological controls? How do the effects of biological controls on ecosystems differ from those of chemical controls?

8. This book has included enough history to show something of the international character of biological science. Construct a chart or table to demonstrate this feature of biology, beginning with biologists named in the text. What nationalities can you add through your own efforts?

9. American foreign-aid policies have political, ethical, and economic aspects that

are important and often stressed. They also have biological aspects, which are not often stressed but which underlie the other three. Your year as a biology student should enable you to pick out some of the biological aspects of the American foreign-aid program and discuss them—particularly with respect to their economic implications.

10. How much land in your state has been set aside by federal, state, and local governments as parks, forests, recreational areas—open spaces? What percentage of your state's total land area is this? How does this compare with the percentage of such lands in the United States as a whole? Calculate the amount of open space per person in your state. Do you think the amount is adequate?

11. What trade-offs are involved in deciding whether or not to use a poison such as DDT? In deciding whether or not to build a nuclear power plant along a particular river? In deciding whether or not to strip-mine a forested watershed?

12. The term "ecology" has become a household word but it is often used as if it were a synonym for "pollution" or "environment" and sometimes merely as a vague indication of something good. How would you explain the scientific meaning of the word "ecology" to a person who has never studied biology?

SUGGESTED READINGS

BATES, M. *Man in Nature*. 2nd ed. Englewood Cliffs, N.J.: Prentice-Hall, Inc., 1964. (This book parallels our Chapters 19 and 20 rather closely, but it provides a much more detailed account. Fairly easy.)

BECKER, H. F. *Resources for Tomorrow*. New York: Holt, Rinehart & Winston, Inc., 1964. (A small book that surveys present United States resources and emphasizes the need for intelligent planning for future use.)

CARSON, R. *Silent Spring*. Boston: Houghton Mifflin Co., 1962. (Describes the effects of man's attempts at chemical control of undesired organisms. Some biologists disagree with a number of Miss Carson's interpretations. Rather easy.)

DOBZHANSKY, T. *Mankind Evolving: The Evolution of the Human Species*. New Haven, Conn.: Yale University Press, 1962. (A geneticist considers man's past evolution and the future possibilities for both biological and cultural evolution of man. Advanced.)

FARVER, M. T., and J. MILTON (eds.). "The Unforeseen International Ecologic Boomerang" (9 articles), *Natural History*, February, 1969. Pp. 42–74.

FRIEDMANN, T. "Pre-natal Diagnosis of Genetic Disease," *Scientific American*, November, 1971. Pp. 34–43.

GOLDWATER, L. J. "Mercury in the Environment," *Scientific American*, May, 1971. Pp. 15–21.

GRAHAM, F. *Since Silent Spring*. Boston: Houghton Mifflin Co., 1970. (An appropriate follow-up of Rachel Carson's book. Fairly easy.)

HARPSTEAD, D. D. "High-Lysine Corn," *Scientific American*, August, 1971. Pp. 34–42.

HASLER, A. D., and B. INGERSOLL. "Dwindling Lakes," *Natural History*, November, 1968. Pp. 8–19.

KORMONDY, E. J. *Concepts of Ecology*. Englewood Cliffs, N.J.: Prentice-Hall, Inc., 1969. (Chapter 6 contains a good discussion of "Ecology and Man." Moderately difficult.)

LANGER, W. L. "Checks on Population Growth: 1750–1850," *Scientific American*, February, 1972. Pp. 92–99.

LYNCH, K. "The City as Environment," *Scientific American*, September, 1965. Pp. 209–214.

MALTHUS, R., J. HUXLEY, and F. OSBORN. *On Population: Three Essays*. New York: New American Library of World Literature, Inc., 1960. (The 18th-century work of Malthus is accompanied by 20th-century essays on the same problem by two eminent biologists.)

NEWELL, R. E. "The Global Circulation of Atmospheric Pollutants," *Scientific American*, January, 1971. Pp. 32–42.

TURNBULL, C. M. "The Lesson of the Pygmies," *Scientific American*, January, 1963. Pp. 28–37.

UDALL, S. L. "The Ecology of Man and the Land Ethic," *Natural History*, June, 1965. Pp. 32–41.

WALLACE, B. *Essays in Social Biology*. 3 vols. Englewood Cliffs, N.J.: Prentice-Hall, Inc., 1972. (A collection of readings from many sources woven together with essays by a biologist. Varying difficulties.)

WEAVER, K. F. "The Search for Tomorrow's Power," *National Geographic*, November, 1972. Pp. 650–681.

WILLIAMS, C. M. "Third-Generation Pesticides," *Scientific American*, July, 1967. Pp. 13–17.

WOODWELL, G. M. "The Ecological Effects of Radiation," *Scientific American*, June, 1963. Pp. 40–49.

YOUNG, G., and J. D. BLAIR. "Pollution, Threat to Man's Only Home," *National Geographic*, December, 1970. Pp. 737–781.

It is interesting to contemplate a tangled bank, clothed with many plants of many kinds, with birds singing on the bushes, with various insects flitting about, and with worms crawling through the damp earth, and to reflect that these elaborately constructed forms, so different from each other, and dependent upon each other in so complex a manner, have all been produced by laws acting around us. These laws, taken in the largest sense, being Growth with Reproduction; Inheritance which is almost implied by reproduction; Variability from the indirect and direct action of the conditions of life, and from use and disuse; a ratio of increase so high as to lead to a Struggle for Life, and as a consequence to Natural Selection, entailing Divergence of Character and the Extinction of less-improved forms. Thus, from the war of nature, from famine and death, the most exalted object which we are capable of conceiving, namely, the production of the higher animals, directly follows. There is grandeur in this view of life . . . that, whilst this planet has gone cycling on according to the fixed laws of gravity, from so simple a beginning endless forms most beautiful and most wonderful have been, and are being, evolved.

DARWIN, *The Origin of Species*

Some General Procedures

LABORATORY

On the whole, biologists are perhaps no more orderly or cleanly than other people. But they must maintain an unusual amount of orderliness and cleanliness during their scientific work. First, their observations and experiments must be verifiable. Therefore, they must know what they have done and how they have done it. Good order helps ensure this. Second, a good many biologists work with dangerous, disease-producing microscopic organisms. The biologist who is not cleanly is not likely to survive very long.

In your classroom laboratory there is additional need for orderliness and cleanliness, because space and apparatus must be shared with other classes. How you achieve these conditions depends upon each classroom situation.

USE OF MATERIALS

Apparatus. It is still possible to do some kinds of biological work with few and simple tools. But as biologists have probed deeper, they have often found it necessary to use complex kinds of apparatus for handling and observing their materials.

There are right ways and wrong ways to use each piece of apparatus. "Right" refers to ways that will aid in obtaining scientific information, and "wrong" refers to ways that will hinder or even mislead. Therefore, you must learn how to use apparatus—from beakers and flasks to balances and microscopes.

Living materials. All biologists deal with living things; this is what marks them as biologists. Though some biologists have no need to handle living things directly in their daily work, no one in a general biology classroom or laboratory can get along without living materials. You, as a biology student, should learn how to care for living organisms.

Animals must be cared for gently and humanely. General rules are:

1. Provide an escape-proof container suitable for the animal.

2. Keep the container clean. This is necessary for the health of the animal. Cages of small birds and mammals should be cleaned daily.

3. Provide water at all times.

4. Feed regularly. The frequency of feeding depends upon the kind of animal being fed. Small birds and mammals may be provided with a continuous food supply.

5. Treat laboratory animals with kindness at all times. Cruelty has no place in biology.

6. When animals must be disposed of or released, your teacher will provide a suitable method.

Plants are just as much living things as are animals; they, too, can be injured or killed. Therefore, it is necessary to handle them carefully and gently.

Most plants must be provided with light, soil, and water. Requirements differ a great deal among different kinds of plants. Therefore, the care of your classroom plants will be the responsibility of individual students, who will learn the requirements of the particular kinds of plants in their charge.

Special methods are necessary for handling most microorganisms. Specific instructions are given when needed.

RECORD-KEEPING

Science deals with verifiable observations. No one—not even the original observer—can check an observation that is hazy, indefinite, or half-remembered. All scientists must, therefore, keep clear and accurate records of what they have observed, made *at the time of observation.*

Data books. The best method of keeping such records is to jot them down in a data book. This should be a stiff-cover book, permanently bound (not loose-leaf), preferably with unlined pages.

Records should usually be kept in a diary form, the date being the first item recorded. If observations on 2 or more investigations are made on the same day, the numbers or abbreviations of the titles can be used as subheadings.

Data are usually recorded in 1 of 3 forms. First, they may be recorded in words. In the laboratory, time is short, so you should make these notes brief but to the point. It is not necessary to write complete sentences, but single words are seldom satisfactory, either. Phrases are usually most useful.

Second, observations may be recorded in the form of sketches. A drawing often records an observation more easily, completely, and accurately than words. Remember, however, that sketches of this kind are not intended to be works of art. Their success depends upon your ability to observe, not upon your artistic talent. They should be simple, usually without shading, and drawn with a hard pencil.

Third, data may be recorded numerically as counts or measurements. It is important to give the units in which measurements are made. Often, numerical data are most easily recorded in the form of a table.

Under no circumstances should data be jotted down on other papers to be copied into the data book later. This practice might increase neatness, but it will *decrease* accuracy. Both are virtues in a scientist, but neatness is of value only when it increases accuracy. Your data book is *your* record. Your teacher may want to look at it to help you with your work, but he is interested in the accuracy of your data, not in the blots and stains that are a normal hazard of field and laboratory work.

Remember to:

1. Record immediately.
2. Record accurately.
3. Record completely.

More and more, science is becoming a cooperative enterprise—a team activity. Much of your own laboratory work must be done as a member of a team. Therefore your data book will sometimes contain data contributed by other members of your team. It is important that you know what you yourself have observed. You can keep track of this if you encircle (or record in a different color) the observations made by others. You should be able to say: "This I know because I saw it; that I believe because I have confidence in my teammates."

Laboratory reports. Discoveries become a part of science only when they are made known to others. Therefore communication is a most important part of science. In writing, a scientist must express himself so clearly that another person can repeat his procedures exactly. The reader must know what material was used (in biology, this includes the kind of organism) and be able to comprehend every detail of the work. Scientists must be free to communicate, but they can use this freedom only if they know *how* to communicate. For publication, scientific reports are usually written in a rather standard form, somewhat as follows:

1. Title
2. Introduction: usually states how the problem arose and often gives a summary of past work

3. Materials and equipment

4. Procedure: complete and exact account of what was done in gathering the data

5. Results: data obtained from the procedure, often in the form of tables and graphs

6. Discussion: relating the data to the purpose of the work

7. Conclusion: summary of the meaning of the results, often suggesting further work that might be done

8. References: published scientific reports that have been specifically mentioned

If you undertake work on an independent problem, your report should follow this form. But for the usual work in this course, you do not have to be so elaborate. You are communicating with your fellow students and your teacher, who already know a great deal about the work. Occasionally your teacher may wish you to do a rather complete job of reporting. Usually, however, he will want a much shorter report—perhaps merely the answers to the questions in an investigation. In either case, the material in your data book is the basis for your reports.

MEASUREMENT

In 1790 the government of France adopted a new system of measurement to replace the many systems that were being used there.

This system, called the *metric* system, had a decimal basis—that is, it was based on multiples of 10—just as did the money system that had recently been adopted by the young government of the United States. As years went by, almost all nations adopted decimal monetary and measurement systems. Today among the nations of the world, the United States is almost alone in the legal use of a different system of measurement. However, even in the United States scientists use the modern descendant of the metric system, called the SI ["Systeme Internationale"].

The basic unit in the metric system is the *meter.* From this unit all others are derived. The meter is the distance between 2 scratches on a platinum-iridium bar that is kept in the vaults of the International Bureau of Measures near Paris. Fractions and multiples of the meter are designated by prefixes: *milli-* (X 0.001), *centi-* (X 0.01), *deci-* (X 0.1), *deka-* (X 10), *hecto-* (X 100), and *kilo-* (X 1000).

The metric unit of volume is the *liter,* which is defined as the volume of a cube having an edge 10 centimeters long. The metric unit of surface is the *are,* which is defined as an area of 100 square meters. Volumes and areas may also be indicated by the squares and cubes of linear units. The metric unit of mass is the *gram,* which is defined as the mass of a milliliter of pure water at 4 degrees Celsius (4°C). Although it is not strictly correct to do so, the gram is commonly used as a unit of weight.

Figure A • 1

Some common units of the metric system. Abbreviations are given in parentheses.

SCALE	LENGTH	VOLUME	MASS	SURFACE
0.001	millimeter (mm)	milliliter (ml)	milligram (mg)	
0.01	centimeter (cm)			
0.1	decimeter (dm)			
1	meter (m)	liter (l)	gram (g)	are
10	dekameter (dkm)			
100	hectometer (hm)			hectare (ha)
1000	kilometer (km)		kilogram (kg)	

Following are some useful additional units:

micron (μ): a unit of length equal to one millionth of a meter; $1000\mu = 1$ mm

calorie: the quantity of heat needed to raise the temperature of 1 g of water 1°C

Calorie: equal to a kilocalorie

curie: the amount of any radioactive substance that emits the same number of alpha rays per unit of time as does 1 g of radium

Familiarity with units of the metric system is best acquired through repeated use of them. Memorizing many equivalents to another system is a waste of time.

In the United States temperature is usually expressed on a scale devised by Gabriel Daniel Fahrenheit (1686–1736). In countries using the metric system, temperature is expressed on a scale devised by Anders Celsius (1701–1744). The Celsius scale is sometimes called *centigrade*. Figure A • 2 shows why this term is used and compares the two scales.

There is only 1 system of units for measuring time, though in many parts of the world (and in the armed forces of the United States) hours are designated from midnight to midnight with 1 set of 24 numbers—thus making "A.M." and "P.M." unnecessary. For example: 16:00 hours = 4:00 P.M.

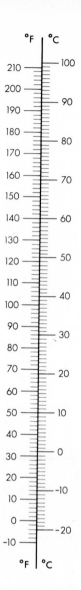

Figure A • 2

Comparison of Fahrenheit and Celsius (centigrade) temperature scales.

Appendix

2

Supplementary Investigations

Investigation A.1

USE OF A MICROSCOPE: INTRODUCTION

BACKGROUND

There are many different kinds of microscopes. A magnifying glass is the simplest kind. But usually the word "microscope" refers to an instrument made up of 2 groups of glass lenses, 1 at each end of a tube—a *compound microscope.*

One type of compound microscope frequently used in biology laboratories is the *monocular microscope.* In working with this kind of microscope you use only 1 eye, so you see an image having length and width but little apparent depth. Most objects examined under a monocular microscope must be so small or thin that light can pass through them. You are able to distinguish form and structure in such objects because some of their parts absorb more light than others. Things seen in this way are said to be observed by *transmitted* light.

MATERIALS AND EQUIPMENT

(for each student or pair of students)

monocular microscope
microscope slide
cover slip
lens paper
paper towels
strips of newspaper
scissors
forceps
medicine dropper
finger bowl or beaker
transparent plastic millimeter rule
pieces cut from magazine photograph

PROCEDURE

A. Setting up a microscope. Remove your microscope from its case or space in the storage cabinet. Grasp the *arm* of the instrument with one hand and place your other hand under the *base.* Always use two hands when carrying a microscope. Set it down gently on the laboratory table, with the arm toward you and the *stage* away from you. The base should be a safe distance from the edge of your table.

Your teacher will help you identify each part of the microscope (Figure A • 3) and explain its use. Make certain that you are familiar with each part before proceeding further.

B. Preliminary adjustments. Using the coarse-adjustment knob, raise the *body tube* so that the *objectives* do not hit the stage when the revolving nosepiece is rotated. Turn the nosepiece so that the *low-power* (shorter) objective is in line with the body tube; you will hear a click when the objective moves into position. Now adjust the substage *dia-*

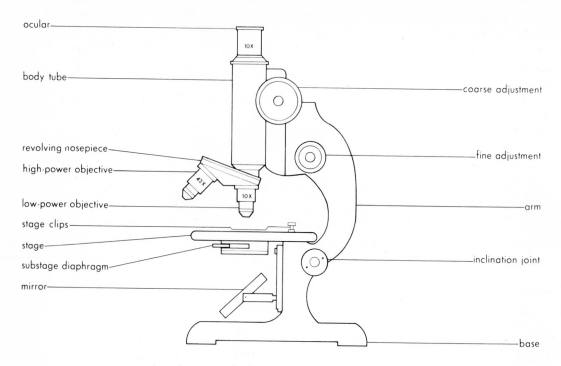

Figure A · 3

Two styles of monocular compound microscopes.

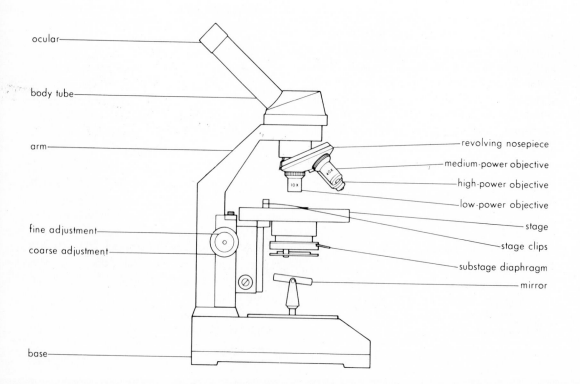

phragm to the largest possible opening. Adjust the *mirror* so that it reflects light upward through the opening in the stage. Never let direct sunlight strike the mirror. Look into the *ocular,* and make final adjustment of the mirror so that the circular *field of view* is evenly illuminated. Adjust the diaphragm to eliminate any glare.

If the lenses of the ocular or the objective appear to be cloudy or dusty, wipe them gently with a piece of *lens paper,* using a circular motion and light pressure. Never use any other kind of paper or cloth. When a piece of lens paper has been used once, discard it. If this procedure does not clean the lenses, consult your teacher.

C. Preparation of materials for examination. Material to be studied under a microscope is usually placed on a piece of glass called a *microscope slide.* In most cases the material is covered with a small, thin piece of glass called a *cover slip.* Both slide and cover slip should be as clean as possible before use. Always handle them by the edges. Avoid touching their flat surfaces with your fingers.

To clean a slide, hold it by the edges, between index finger and thumb, and dip into water. Then wipe dry, using a soft piece of clean cloth or paper towel.

Cover slips are much more fragile than slides. To clean a cover slip, hold it by the edges, using the index finger and thumb of one hand, and dip into water. A piece of thin, soft cloth or lens paper should then be folded and held between the finger and thumb of the

other hand. Next, insert the wet cover slip in the fold and apply pressure to *both* surfaces *at the same time* by bringing thumb and finger together (Figure A · 4). A gentle, circular motion is most effective.

Now prepare a *wet mount* for microscopic observation. Using scissors, cut out a piece of newspaper that includes at least one letter *e.* The piece should be not more than 3–5 mm square. If possible, find a section that has printing on only one side of the paper. Place

Figure A · 5
Making a wet mount.

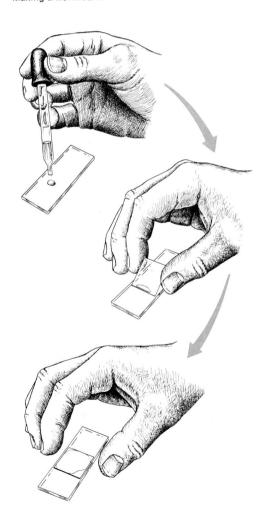

Figure A · 4
Cleaning a cover slip.

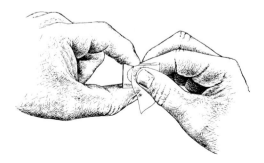

the piece of newspaper in the center of a slide, printed side up. Put a single drop of water on the piece of newspaper. Some of the water will soak into the newspaper, but some should still remain surrounding it. If necessary, add another drop of water. Place a cover slip over the newspaper. If this is done properly, the remaining water will spread out in a thin, even layer between cover slip and slide, with the newspaper sandwiched between them. It requires some skill to place the cover slip on the slide in such a way that no air bubbles are included in the mount. The best method is to hold the cover slip at an angle of about 45° to the slide; then bring the cover slip down to the slide until the lower edge touches the drop of water. Continue to lower the slip *slowly* until it is parallel to the surface of the slide (Figure A • 5). Remaining bubbles may be removed by *gently* tapping the cover slip with the tip of a forceps.

D. Focusing. Using the coarse-adjustment knob, raise the body tube until there is a space of approximately 2 cm between the low-power objective and the surface of the stage. Place the slide on the stage of the microscope. Position the slide so that a letter *e* on the newspaper is located in the center of the stage opening and faces you as it would on a newspaper page. Use the **stage clips** to hold the slide in position. Looking at the microscope from the side, and again using the coarse-adjustment knob, slowly lower the body tube until the lower end of the objective is approximately 1 mm above the upper surface of the cover slip. Never allow the objective to touch the cover slip.

Now look through the ocular and slowly raise the body tube until the print on the newspaper becomes visible. If you still see no image after you have raised the objective more than 1 cm, you have missed the position for correct focus. Refocus—look at the microscope from the side, lower the objective to its original position, and try again. *Never* lower the tube with the coarse-adjustment while you are looking into the ocular. When you see an image of the printed material, rotate the *fine-*

adjustment knob to obtain the best possible focus. Further adjustment of the diaphragm may improve clearness.

Compare the position of the *image* of the letter *e* in the ocular with the position of the printed *e* (the **object**) on the slide. • Is the image in the same position as the object seen with the unaided eye? If not, describe its position.(1)   • While looking into the ocular, slowly move the slide from right to left. Which way does the image move?(2)   • Move the slide away from you. Which way does the image move?(3)

Now rotate the revolving nosepiece so that the **high-power** (longer) objective is in line with the body tube. In doing this, make sure that the lower end of the objective does not touch the cover slip. If this happens, you will have to repeat the entire sequence of operations, beginning with focusing of the low-power objective. Now use *only* the fine-adjustment knob to bring the image into focus. Usually less than 1 full turn (in either direction) is needed.

• Is the field of view larger or smaller?(4) • Does the switch from low power to high power change the position of the image?(5)   • Is the illumination brighter or less bright than it is with low power?(6)

Using the coarse adjustment, raise the body tube. Remove the slide and save it for later use.

E. Magnification. When working with the microscope, you will find it useful to know how much the instrument is magnifying the object. If an object is magnified 50 diameters (50X), the image you see is 50 times longer and wider than if the object were viewed with the unaided eye at a distance of 25.4 cm. Engraved on each objective or ocular is a number indicating the degree of magnification it provides. The magnification of combined ocular and objective is equal to the product of these numbers. If, for example, the number on the ocular is 5X and that on the low-power objective is 12X, the combined magnification is 5 × 12, or 60, diameters. Using the same ocular and a high-power objective that magnifies

45X, a magnification of 5 X 45, or 225, diameters will be obtained. Find the magnification numbers on your microscope. • Calculate the magnifications obtained when using low power. (7) • When using high power.(8)

F. Measuring with a microscope. Because objects examined with a microscope are usually quite small, biologists find it convenient to use units of length smaller than centimeters or millimeters for microscopic measurement. One such unit is the *micron,* which is 1/1000th of an mm and for which the Greek letter μ (called "mu") is the symbol.

You can estimate the size of a microscopic object by comparing it with the size of the circular field of view. The size of the field may be determined as follows: Place a plastic millimeter rule on the stage. Following the directions already given for focusing, use the low-power objective to obtain a clear image of the divisions on the rule. Carefully move the rule until its marked edge passes through the exact center of the field of view. Now count the number of divisions that can be seen within the field of view. The marks on the rule will appear quite wide; 1 mm is the distance from the *center* of one mark to the *center* of the next. • What is the diameter of the low-power field of your microscope in millimeters?(9) • What is it in microns?(10)

To measure the diameter of the high-power field, use the following procedure: First divide the magnification number of the high-power objective by the magnification number of the low-power objective. Then divide the diameter of the low-power field of view by this quotient. The result is the diameter of the high-power field of view. For example, if the magnification of your low-power objective is 12X and of your high-power objective 48X, the quotient is 4. If the diameter of the low-power field of view is 1600 μ, the diameter of the high-power field of view is 1600 ÷ 4, or 400 μ. • Using this method of calculation, what is the diameter of your high-power field in microns?(11)

Remove the plastic rule and replace it with the wet mount of the letter *e.* (If the mount

has dried, add water.) Using low power, compare the height of the letter with the diameter of the field of view. • Estimate as accurately as possible the actual height of the letter in millimeters.(12) • In microns.(13)

G. Resolving power. Remove the slide from the stage and carefully lift off the cover slip. Discard the piece of newspaper. Dry the slide and the cover slip. Now prepare another wet mount, using a small piece of paper cut from a magazine photograph and following the procedure for preparing a wet mount outlined in *C.* Examine this mount under low power. • How does the magnified image of the picture compare with the photograph as seen with the unaided eye?(14) You have just seen an example of a microscope's *resolving power,* its ability to clearly separate details. For most people, 2 objects that are less than 0.1 mm apart cannot be seen as separate by the unaided eye. A microscope permits us to detect space between objects that are much closer together than this.

Thus a microscope actually does 2 things: it provides magnifying power, and it provides resolving power.

H. Care of a microscope. Microscopes, like all other instruments in the laboratory, must be given proper care.

At the end of the laboratory period, turn the revolving nosepiece until the low-power objective is in place. Adjust the position of the body tube so that the lower end of the objective is approximately 1 cm above the stage. If you tilted the instrument at the *inclination joint,* return it to its untilted position. Turn the stage clips so that they do not extend beyond the side of the stage. Make sure a slide does not remain on the stage. Return the microscope to its storage space. Clean and dry all slides and cover slips.

FOR FURTHER INVESTIGATION

If a stereoscopic microscope is available in your laboratory, you may explore its use. This instrument is most often used to view whole objects by *reflected* rather than by transmitted light.

Investigation A.2

USE OF A MICROSCOPE: BIOLOGICAL MATERIAL

MATERIALS AND EQUIPMENT

(for each student or pair of students)
small piece of white potato
glass slide
medicine dropper
beaker or finger bowl containing water
cover slip
monocular microscope
iodine - potassium-iodide (I$_2$KI) solution
     in dropper bottle
paper towel
yeast culture
lens paper

PROCEDURE

For setting up the microscope, cleaning slides and cover slips, and preparing wet mounts, follow the directions given in Investigation A.1 (pages 703–707).

A. Observing starch grains. Place a *small* piece of white potato in the center of a clean slide. Place the slide on your laboratory table and press the potato with a finger until some juice is forced out onto the surface of the slide. Distribute the juice evenly over the center of the slide by moving the piece of potato in a circular pattern. Discard the piece of potato. Add a drop of water and a clean cover slip to the slide, avoiding, if possible, the inclusion of air bubbles in the mount.

Examine the mount under low power. You can observe starch grains more readily if you decrease the size of the opening in the substage diaphragm. This increases contrast between the starch grains and the water surrounding them. Move the slide on the stage until you locate a field in which well-separated grains are visible. Center a group of these grains in the field and switch to high power. • Describe the shape of an individual starch grain.(1) • Can you see any internal structure in these grains? If you can, describe what you observe.(2)

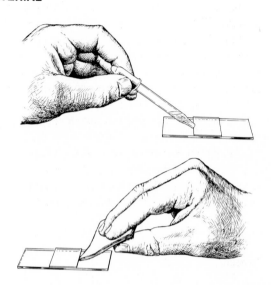

Figure A • 6
Putting a liquid under a cover slip.

Turn again to low power. Stain the starch grains by placing a small drop of the iodine - potassium-iodide (I$_2$KI) solution on the slide, at one side of the cover slip (Figure A • 6). Tear off a small piece of paper towel and place the torn edge in contact with the water at the opposite edge of the cover slip. As water is absorbed by the paper towel at one edge of the mount, I$_2$KI solution will be drawn under the cover slip at the opposite edge. Continue until the I$_2$KI solution is drawn halfway across the space under the cover slip. I$_2$KI solution will continue to spread slowly throughout the mount. By examining various regions of the mount, you can observe the effects of different concentrations of I$_2$KI solution on the starch grains. Examine under low power, then under high power. • What changes do you observe in the starch grains exposed to relatively high concentrations of I$_2$KI solution?(3) • What differences do you see between these grains and others exposed to lower concentrations of I_2KI?(4) • Can you observe internal structure in the stained grains? If so, describe what you see.(5) • Using the method given in Investigation A.1, estimate the size (in microns) of the larger starch grains.(6)

Now remove the slide from the stage, lift off the cover slip, and dip both slide and cover slip into water. Dry them. Carefully wipe off any liquid that may have run off the slide onto the microscope stage.

B. Examining yeast cultures. Place 1 drop of the culture on a clean slide, add a cover slip, and examine first under low power, then under high power. • Describe the shape of the yeast organisms.(7)

Study the arrangement of small groups of these organisms. • From your observations, can you come to any conclusions about how new yeast organisms develop?(8) • Sketch any internal structures you can observe.(9)

Using I_2KI solution, stain the yeast in the same way you stained the starch grains. • Compare the effects of the I_2KI solution on the yeast organisms with its effects on starch grains.(10) • Can you see any structures that were not visible in the unstained yeast organisms? If so, describe them.(11) • Using the method previously described, estimate the size (in microns) of an average yeast organism.(12)

Investigation A.3

STUDY OF A POND COMMUNITY

INTRODUCTION

Ponds have many advantages for the study of aquatic communities. They furnish a variety of habitats, have many relationships with the surrounding land, and are available in many places. Natural ponds usually show the most complex relationships, but man-made ponds are both simpler to study and most widely distributed geographically. If your class has studied a land community, that experience ought to increase your ability to investigate a pond.

MATERIALS AND EQUIPMENT

A. *Field study*

   (for the entire class)

glass-marking crayons, 4

jars (wide-mouth, screw-top),
   about 1000-ml, 2

jars (wide-mouth, screw-top),
   about 4000-ml, 7

jars (wide-mouth, screw-top),
   about 500-ml, 13

plankton net

can (No. 3), lid smoothly removed

sieve (No. 8 mesh)

forceps, 2

plastic bags, 6

rubber bands, 6

plant-grappling bar

trowel

dip net

seine, wire-cloth

refrigerator

B. *Laboratory study*

   (by teams: quantities depend upon
     team size)

manuals for identification

medicine droppers

microscope slides

cover slips

monocular microscopes

stereomicroscopes

hand lenses

forceps

scalpels

finger bowls

PROCEDURE

A. Field study. Organize 4 teams: the 1st to study plankton organisms, a 2nd to study the

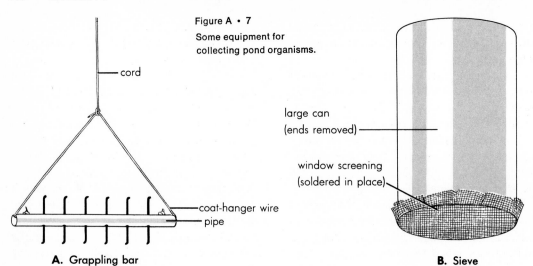

Figure A • 7
Some equipment for
collecting pond organisms.

cord

large can
(ends removed)

window screening
(soldered in place)

coat-hanger wire
pipe

A. Grappling bar

B. Sieve

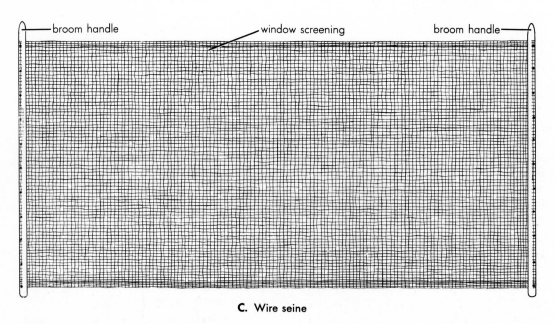

broom handle — window screening — broom handle

C. Wire seine

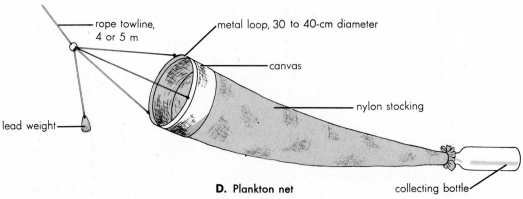

rope towline,
4 or 5 m

metal loop, 30 to 40-cm diameter

canvas

nylon stocking

lead weight

collecting bottle

D. Plankton net

organisms on the bottom, a 3rd to study the larger water plants, and a 4th to study the larger animals.

All teams must be careful not to disturb the environment more than is absolutely necessary. Remember that only a few specimens of each species are needed.

Team 1: Before leaving the laboratory, use a glass-marking crayon to label 2 wide-mouth, 1-liter jars as follows: *Surface-Water Zone* and *Deep-Water Zone.*

Take the jars and plankton net to a place from which the plankton net can be cast into the water. Place clear pond water in each jar until it is about 1/3 full.

Cast the net into the water and pull it through the open-water zone. If the net is pulled rapidly, it will stay near the surface. Pull the net through the water several times; then raise it. You may be able to see a number of tiny organisms in the bottle. Untie the bottle from the net and empty its contents into the jar labeled *Surface-Water Zone.* Repeat the surface collecting 3 or 4 times.

To collect organisms in the deep-water zone, allow the net to sink to the desired depth and then pull slowly. Place collections from the deep water in the 2nd jar. If you must wait for other teams, put the jars in the shade until you are ready to leave. If jars are left in sunlight, the temperature in them will rise and many of the organisms will die.

Team 2: Before leaving the laboratory, select 3 small (about 500-ml) jars and 3 large (about 4000-ml) jars. Use a glass-marking crayon to label one of each size as follows: *Bottom: Emergent-Plant Zone, Bottom: Submerged-Plant Zone,* and *Bottom: Open-Water Zone.*

Take the jars, a sieve, and a can to the pond. Place clear pond water in each jar, filling it about halfway. With the can, scoop up some mud from among the emergent plants. Dump this mud into the sieve; then shake the sieve in the water until the mud is washed out. Remove dead leaves and sticks by hand. Pick out whatever organisms you find and put these into the appropriate large jar. Then carefully scoop up a small sample of the mud and place it in the appropriate small jar. Repeat this procedure in the other 2 zones.

Team 3: Before leaving the laboratory, use a glass-marking crayon to label 6 large plastic bags. Label 2 *Emergent Plants,* 2 *Floating Plants,* and 2 *Submerged Plants.*

Take the labeled bags, 6 rubber bands, a trowel, and a plant-grappling bar to the pond.

In each of the 3 plant zones collect a specimen of each kind of plant found. Whenever possible the specimen should consist of a whole plant. Roots and underground stems are often important for identification. If the whole plant is too large, collect leaves and flowers or fruits. Put the plants of each zone into separate plastic bags.

Team 4: Before leaving the laboratory, select 10 jars of about 500-ml capacity. Using a glass-marking crayon, label 5 of the jars *Emergent-and-Floating-Plant Zone,* and the other 5 *Submerged-Plant Zone.* Select 4 large (about 4000-ml) jars, and label 2 *Emergent-Plant Zone* and the other 2 *Submerged-Plant Zone.*

Take all the jars, a dip net, and a seine to the pond. One member of the team should be assigned to record animals seen but not collected. This should include all animals that seem to be a part of the pond community, whether they live *in* the pond or not.

Use the dip net or the seine to collect the larger animals—for example, fish, crayfish, some of the larger insect larvae, turtles, and snakes. The smaller ones will go through the holes in the collecting equipment.

Catch the animals in the emergent-plant zone, near the edge of the pond. Put them into the labeled jars. Insects may be placed together in the same jar, with some sticks and leaves for shelter. Only a few fish should be placed together in one jar. Use the smaller jars for specimens that might injure one another. Be careful in handling animals; some of the insects as well as larger animals can inflict painful bites.

In a similar manner collect organisms in the submerged-plant zone. Do not collect more than 1 or 2 specimens of each of the larger animals.

Upon returning to the laboratory, loosen the caps and place the jars in the lower part of the refrigerator or in some other cool place. This will make the organisms less active and will help to keep the large ones from eating the smaller ones.

B. Laboratory study. Each team should study its own collections and report its findings to the class.

Most organisms should be identifiable to the phylum level; many will be identifiable to lower levels. Identification to the species level is not necessary. In addition to the manuals listed at the ends of the chapters in Section Two, the following are useful for the identification of aquatic organisms:

> Needham, P. *Guide to the Study of Freshwater Biology.* San Francisco: Holden-Day, Inc., 1962.
>
> Pennak, R. W. *Freshwater Invertebrates of the United States.* New York: The Ronald Press Co., 1953.
>
> Reid, G. K. *Pond Life.* New York: Golden Press, 1967.

This investigation is not designed as a *quantitative* study, but some idea of the relative abundance of different kinds of organisms will be useful in understanding the community. Whenever possible, record your observations with respect to numbers of identified organisms in the pond community. Listing kinds of organisms in order of abundance might be one method.

Team 1: The plankton organisms are mostly microscopic; use medicine droppers for handling the organisms, slides and cover slips for mounting them, and monocular microscopes for observing them.

Team 2: Use hand lenses or stereomicroscopes to observe organisms washed from the mud. The organisms will be more easily seen if you place them in a finger bowl over a piece of white paper. Handle the larger organisms with forceps, the smaller ones with medicine droppers. Examine samples of mud in the small jars by placing a small bit of mud in a drop of water on a microscope slide under a monocular microscope.

Teams 3 and 4: Hand lenses, forceps, and finger bowls (or porcelain pans) are the only tools you need for examining your collections.

SUMMARY

When you have received the data from all teams, write a description of the pond community, attempting to relate all the data.

Consider the niches of the various organisms. To begin with, you can assume that macroscopic green plants are producers. Microscopic organisms are more difficult to decide about; some consumers may be colored green by algae they have eaten, and the green of some producers may be obscured by other pigments. Carnivores can sometimes be separated from herbivores on the basis of structure or observed behavior. Can you see any relationship between the size of organisms and their relative abundance? If so, what is the relationship and how can you explain it? Finally, consider the relationships between the pond and surrounding communities on the land. How does energy received from the sun flow from the pond community into land communities? Is there any reverse flow of energy? If so, how does it occur?

Investigation A.4

PERCEPTUAL WORLDS

INTRODUCTION

Though biologists often use complicated and expensive apparatus in studying animal behavior, much can be learned by merely watching—noting what an animal does and under what circumstances it does it. Whether well equipped or not, a student of animal behavior needs first to know something about the stimuli that an animal under study can perceive —something about its perceptual world. You have already observed a little of the perceptual worlds of a few animals (Investigations 4.3 and 14.1). Now you will try to find out all you can, within the limits of available time, about the perceptual world of one particular kind of animal.

PROCEDURE

Organize your class into teams. Each team should choose a different animal species for study. The species must be one of which a number of living specimens can be obtained. Your teacher will provide a list of suitable species.

Your study must, of course, depend upon the nature of the species. Consider the species' size, natural habitat, and any obvious sense organs. You must become generally familiar with your animal before making plans for studying its behavior. Preliminary observations may lead you to suspect senses that were not at first obvious.

Now plan simple experiments that will provide information about your animal's perceptual world. Consider such matters as reaction to light (intensity and color), sound, gravity, touch, and chemical substances (odor and taste); ability to see and the kinds of things seen; awareness of the biotic environment (organisms of its own species and of others). Consider how you will determine whether or not an observed behavior is brought about by a particular factor in the environment. Remember that the best understanding of behavior can be gained when the animal is disturbed as little as possible.

When your team has made its plans, draw up a list of materials and equipment. Your teacher will review the list. Then assemble the materials before the laboratory periods in which the experimenting is to be done.

SUMMARY

Prepare a team report on the perceptual world of the animal studied. The report should clearly indicate how each bit of information in it was obtained.

Investigation A.5

FROG EMBRYOLOGY

BACKGROUND INFORMATION

You have learned how pituitary hormones function in the reproductive cycle of a human female. In general the pituitary glands of vertebrates influence the activity of the gonads by means of hormones called *gonadotrophins.* In female frogs the seasonal changes of spring stimulate the pituitary to secrete large quantities of gonadotrophins into the bloodstream. Reaching the ovaries, these hormones cause eggs to be released into the oviducts. After the eggs are laid, the ovaries build up a new crop of eggs during the summer. When female frogs go into hibernation in autumn, the eggs to be laid the following spring need only the stimulus of gonadotrophins to be released from the ovaries. Therefore, if gonadotrophic hormones are injected into a female frog during late fall or winter, eggs can be obtained long before the frog's own gonadotrophic hormones are secreted from its pituitary.

In male frogs, also, pituitary hormones stimulate the gonads by secreting gonadotrophins. This results in copulatory behavior and the release of sperm cells over the eggs as they are laid by the female. Gonadotrophins may be secreted by the frog's own pituitaries in spring, or they may be injected into the frog. But active sperm cells may be obtained—even in winter—by removing the gonads (testes) from a male frog and chopping them up in a little water.

MATERIALS AND EQUIPMENT

(for each team)

A. *Inducing ovulation*
   female frog, live
   hypodermic syringe, 2-ml or larger
   hypodermic needle, #25
   pituitary suspension
   battery jar with weight-screen cover

B. *Fertilizing frog eggs*
   male frog, pithed
   scissors
   scalpel
   forceps
   petri dish
   pond water
   graduated cylinder, 25-ml
   female frog (from *A*, above)
   Syracuse watch glass
   medicine dropper
   finger bowls, 3 or 4
   glass-marking crayon
   frog eggs, fertilized several hours before
      the laboratory period
   temperature-gradient box, 1 per class

C. *Observing frog embryos*
   developing frog eggs (from *B*, above)
   stereomicroscope
   thermometer ($-10°$ to $+110°C$)
   medicine dropper
   forceps
   graph paper, 1 sheet per student
   pencils, 4 or 5 colors

PROCEDURE

A. Inducing ovulation. Part A can best be done by 3 members of the team (Students A, B, and C); meanwhile, the other members can assist by keeping all materials ready for use as needed.

Student A: Grasp the frog gently in your left hand. Rest the dorsal surface of the frog against your palm. Hold the posterior legs firmly between the fingers of your right hand.

Student B: Grasp the frog's ventral skin between your thumb and forefinger and lift it away from the body wall.

Student C: Draw into the hypodermic syringe the amount of pituitary suspension recommended by your teacher. Attach the needle and insert it through the frog's skin and into the muscle of the body wall. (CAUTION: Do not insert the point of the needle *through* the body wall!) Inject the pituitary suspension.

Put the frog into a battery jar. Add water to a depth of about 2 cm and cover the mouth of the jar with a weighted screen. Place the jar where the frog will not be disturbed and will have an even room temperature (20° to 22°C). In 2 or 3 days the frog should be ready to release eggs.

B. Fertilizing frog eggs. When the female frog is ready to ovulate, open the abdominal cavity of a pithed *male* frog quickly, using the technique described in Investigation 14.1. Move the internal organs aside and locate the testes. These are 2 whitish, oval organs located on each side of the backbone and just ventral to the kidneys. Using scissors and forceps, remove both testes and put them in a petri dish containing about 2 ml of pond water at room temperature. With a scalpel cut the testes into fine pieces; use the flat side of the blade to mash the pieces against the bottom of the dish. Add 20 ml of pond water and set the dish aside for 10 minutes. During this time, sperm cells released from the testes will become active and form a sperm suspension.

While this is happening, place a few milliliters of pond water into a Syracuse watch glass. Grasp the ovulating female frog in one hand, dorsal side against your palm, and extend the hind legs with your other hand. Hold the frog in this position over the watch glass. Squeeze the frog's abdomen gently, applying pressure gradually from the anterior part of the abdomen toward the posterior part. In this manner strip a few eggs into the watch glass. When the sperms have had 10 minutes to become active, use the squeezing technique again to strip 100–150 eggs from the female frog into the petri dish containing the suspension. Using a medicine dropper, bathe the eggs with the sperm suspension; leave the eggs in the suspension for 10 minutes.

Meanwhile, observe the eggs in the Syracuse watch glass, using a stereomicroscope. Note whether the eggs are floating dark side up, light side up, or without regard to color. Note the thickness of the eggs in relation to the thickness of the jelly that surrounds them.

After the eggs have been in the sperm suspension 10 minutes, gently pour the sperm suspension from the petri dish, disturbing the eggs as little as possible. Use a medicine dropper to remove the last few milliliters of the suspension, picking up any remaining pieces of testes as you do so. Pour about 20 ml of pond water over the eggs and again allow them to stand—this time for 15 minutes.

While you are waiting, number some finger bowls (your teacher will designate the quantity needed). Label the bowls with your team symbol and pour 100 ml of pond water into each one.

Place in the watch glass a few of the frog eggs that were fertilized before your laboratory period began. Observe with the stereomicroscope. In your data book, record the time at which these eggs were fertilized (obtain this from your teacher) and the time at which you observe them. Study the stages of development shown in Figure A · 8 (page 716) and record the number of the stage that most closely resembles the eggs you are observing. Also compare these eggs with the ones that were just fertilized and with the unfertilized eggs, noting any differences.

When jelly has swelled around the eggs in the petri dish, it is safe to handle them. Use a scalpel to free any eggs that stick to the dish. With scissors, cut the ribbon of eggs into groups of 5 to 10 eggs each. (CAUTION: Be careful to avoid stretching or squeezing the eggs.) Using forceps, gently transfer 25–30 eggs into each finger bowl. Put the bowls in the temperature-gradient box or in other places designated by your teacher.

C. Observing frog embryos. On each succeeding day, for as long as your teacher directs, observe the embryos in each bowl. During the 1st few days watch for eggs that are not developing. Using a medicine dropper and forceps, remove any of these. In your data book, record the day of observation (if the eggs were fertilized on Monday, Tuesday is recorded as "Day 1," and so on). Next to this, record the number of the bowl observed. Next, record the temperature of the water in the bowl at the time you begin observation. Finally, record the number designating the stage in Figure A · 8 that most closely resembles the majority of the embryos.

In Figure A · 8 the eggs and embryos are shown without the surrounding jelly. In your own observations (through Stage 19) the jelly will look something like a halo. You will probably have particular difficulty seeing the differences among Stages 15, 16, 17, and 18, since at those stages the embryos are somewhat folded in the jelly covering. As you refer to Figure A · 8, keep these points in mind: (1) The drawings and the ages given are those of embryos developing at a *constant temperature* of 18°C. (2) The notes under the drawings will help you to identify stages in the embryos you are observing. (3) The drawings show stages at which the embryos can be clearly distinguished; the embryos, of course, gradually change from one stage to another. Many of the embryos you observe will be at intermediate stages and will not look exactly like any one of the drawings. Indicate intermediate stages by using decimals (6.5, 10.5, etc.).

After each day's observation, return each finger bowl to its place, so that its temperature may be kept as stable as possible.

STUDYING THE DATA

Plot the data from your team's bowls on a single grid, using a different color for each bowl. Show stages of development on the vertical axis and time on the horizontal axis. Compute the average temperature maintained in the water of each bowl; in the key to the graph, write each average next to the appropriate color. Finally, use another color to plot the data from Figure A · 8: write "Constant 18°C"

Figure A · 8
Stages of development of *Rana pipiens*. (From Waldo Shumway, *The Anatomical Record*, Vol. 78, pp. 143–147.)

STAGE	AGE (in hrs at 18°C)	Description
1	0	unfertilized
2	1	gray crescent
3	3.5	2-cell
4	4.5	4-cell
5	5.7	8-cell
6	6.5	16-cell
7	7.5	32-cell
8	16	mid-cleavage
9	21	late cleavage
10	26	dorsal lip
11	34	mid-gastrula
12	42	late gastrula
13	50	neural plate
14	62	neural folds
15	67	rotation
16	72	neural tube
17	84	tail bud

STAGE	AGE (in hrs at 18°C)	LENGTH (in mm)	Description
18	96	4	muscular response
19	118	5	heartbeat
20	140	6	gill circulation
21	162	7	mouth open; cornea transparent
22	192	8	tail-fin circulation
23	216	9	opercular fold; teeth
24	240	10	operculum closed on right
25	284	11	operculum complete

next to this color in the key. • Which line shows the most even development?(1) • How can you explain this?(2) • Which line shows the most rapid development?(3) • Which line shows the least rapid development?(4) • Explain.(5)

SUMMARY

• From the results, what general statement can you make about the influence of temperature on the rate of embryonic development in a frog?(6)

Investigation A.6

GERMINATION OF SEEDS

BACKGROUND INFORMATION

In mammals natality is usually calculated from birth; in many other animals it is calculated from hatching. In seed-bearing plants it is calculated from germination. Both birth and hatching are usually processes that occur during a continuous development; germination, however, is a process of renewed development in an embryo that has been dormant (see page 154). Germination is an important stage in the embryology of seed plants; it has received much study from botanists, and—because of its importance in crop production—it is of interest to agriculturists, also.

MATERIALS AND EQUIPMENT

(for each team)
seeds, all of 1 kind, 50
beaker, large enough to hold all seeds
fungicide, 300 ml
beakers, each large enough to soak
    10 seeds, 5
glass-marking crayon
waste jar for fungicide (1 per class)
paper towels, 2
petri dishes, 5
filter paper, 20 pieces
scissors
graph paper, 1 sheet per student

PROCEDURE

Read through the procedure. • Write a suitable hypothesis for the experiment.(1)

Select a kind of seed you would like to study. Place 50 seeds in a beaker and add enough fungicide solution to cover them. (Avoid getting the fungicide on your skin.) While the seeds are being treated with fungicide, mark 5 beakers with a glass-marking crayon, as follows: *0 hours, 4 hours, 24 hours, 48 hours, 72 hours*. On each beaker place your team symbol.

After 10 minutes pour off the fungicide solution into a container provided by your teacher. Rinse the seeds with water and spread them on a paper towel. Use another paper towel to dry the seeds as much as possible. Place 10 seeds in each marked beaker. Devise a schedule for soaking so that all seeds will have soaked their allotted times when you are ready to set them up for germination. At the times indicated on your schedule, add to each beaker enough water to bring the level 2 cm above the top of the seeds.

On the day scheduled for "planting," obtain 5 clean petri dishes and 20 pieces of filter paper. Cut each piece to fit snugly, without wrinkling, into the bottom half of a petri dish. Remove the top of each dish; place 4 pieces of filter paper in the bottom half. Wet the paper thoroughly. Drain off excess water; replace the top of each dish. Mark the dishes with the same labels used for the jars.

Place the seeds from each beaker in the petri dish that has the same label. Stack the petri dishes and store in a place where temperature and light will vary little.

Observe the seeds each day for 7 days and record the number of germinated seeds you see in each container. Record the data in a form like that below.

Kind of Seed _____

	HOURS SOAKED				
	0	4	24	48	72
Day 0					
Day 1					
↓	↓	↓	↓	↓	↓
Day 7					

STUDYING THE DATA

Draw 5 bar graphs, one for each petri dish. Place the number of germinated seeds on the vertical axis and the number of days on the horizontal axis. On each graph show the *total number* of seeds that have germinated up to and including the time of each daily count. Thus, for all days after Day 1, you should add the data of all previous days.

If different teams have used different kinds of seeds, you can compare the germination rates. To do this, use the seeds that received no soaking (0 hours). Each team should calculate the percentage of germinated seeds on the 3rd, 5th, and 7th days. Place these percentages for each kind of seed on a chalkboard chart.

CONCLUSIONS

• From the data on your graphs state a conclusion for your hypothesis.(2)

Examine the data on the chalkboard chart. • Did any kind of seed have 100% germination on Day 3? If so, which kind?(3) • Did any kind of seed have 0% germination on Day 7? If so, which kind?(4)   • Arrange the kinds of seeds in order, from the kind that was the quickest to germinate to the kind that was the slowest.(5)

Investigation A.7

HUMAN INHERITANCE

PROCEDURE

You are given here a number of facts and asked to answer questions based on the facts. The answers to one set of questions lead to the next set of facts, so you must move step by step through the procedure.

Percentages of male and female infants. With respect to the sex chromosomes, females can be designated XX, and males XY. • Considering only the sex chromosomes, how many kinds of gametes can females produce?(1) • How many kinds of gametes can males produce?(2)

The frequency of any particular characteristic within a group is expressed as a fraction. Thus, in a group of 100 marbles containing 20 red and 80 blue marbles, the frequency of red marbles is 20/100 = 1/5 = 20% = 0.2. The frequency of blue marbles is 80/100 = 4/5 = 80% = 0.8. It is customary to represent 2 frequencies with the letters p and q. Thus for any group of red (R) and blue (B) marbles, frequencies of the 2 kinds may be written as "$pR + qB$."

Any population of sperms, then, may be represented by the mathematical expression $pX + qY$. • Using your knowledge of meiosis, what are the values of p and q?(3)   The same kind of mathematical expression may be used to represent the population of eggs produced by a female. • What are the values of p and q for the egg population?(4)

The frequencies of males and females among human offspring may be predicted in the same way you predicted the percentages of "heads" and "tails" when tossing coins:

$$\text{sperms} \qquad \text{eggs} \qquad \text{zygotes}$$
$$(pX + qY) \times (pX + qY) = \quad ?$$

• Calculate the expected frequencies of the zygotes.(5)

On the basis of your results you might predict that equal numbers of male and female infants would be born. This expectation is based on 2 assumptions: (*a*) that X-carrying sperms and Y-carrying sperms have exactly equal chances of reaching and fertilizing an egg, and (*b*) that XX and XY zygotes have equal chances of developing to birth stage. The 2 assumptions seem natural, and they are commonly made. But available data do not support your prediction. Data on deaths of embryos and on deaths during birth show that males have a much poorer chance of developing and of surviving birth than do females. • In the light of these data which assumption must you reject?(6) • If you still accept the other assumption, how must the expected per-centages of male and female infants be changed?(7)   Data on live births show that for every 100 females born, about 105 males are born. • What do these data suggest about the other assumption?(8)

Inheritance of hemophilia. Hemophilia is a condition in which the blood platelets have great stability, so that normal clotting does not occur. It is a sex-linked trait.

Figure A • 9 shows, in part, the occurrence of hemophilia among the royal families of Europe during the 19th and 20th centuries. • List the mothers who *must* have been carriers, that is, heterozygous.(9)

The chart shows the actual occurrence of hemophilia in a pedigree. Now consider the frequencies (expressed as percentages) of hemophiliacs—persons afflicted with hemophilia—that we may *expect* among the offspring of certain marriages.

First, consider the marriage of a hemophiliac man and a woman homozygous for

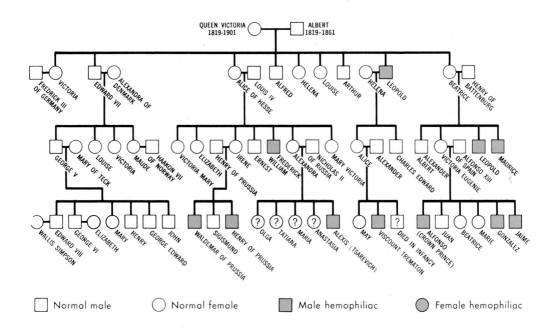

Figure A • 9
Inheritance of hemophilia in descendants of Queen Victoria of England.

normal blood clotting.   • What percentage of their male offspring do you expect to be hemophiliacs?(10)   • What percentage of their female offspring do you expect to be hemophiliacs?(11)   • What percentage of females do you expect to be carriers?(12)

Second, consider the marriage of a man whose blood clots normally and a woman who is a carrier of hemophilia.   • What percentage of their male offspring do you expect to be hemophiliacs?(13)   • What percentage of their female offspring do you expect to be hemophiliacs?(14)   • What percentage do you expect to be carriers?(15)

Investigation A.8

CHANGES IN GENE FREQUENCIES

INTRODUCTION

Many aspects of the way gene frequencies change in populations can be studied by means of models. In the model used here beans of 2 colors represent 2 alleles of a gene. We shall manipulate the beans in 2 different ways in order to discover the effects of 2 different factors in changing gene frequencies.

Part A

MATERIALS AND EQUIPMENT

(per team)
cans, 9
red beans, 450
white beans, 450

PROCEDURE

Set up the 9 cans as follows:

Can	Contents
1	10 red beans and 90 white beans
2	20 " " 80 " "
3	30 " " 70 " "
4	40 " " 60 " "
5	50 " " 50 " "
6	60 " " 40 " "
7	70 " " 30 " "
8	80 " " 20 " "
9	90 " " 10 " "

Across a page in your data book write the numbers *1* through *15*. Down the left margin write the numbers *1* through *20*. Label the horizontal row of numbers *Populations;* label the vertical row of numbers *Generations.*

Shake the contents of each can. Without looking into the can, draw 10 beans from Can 5. Record the number of red beans drawn as ''Generation 1 of Population 1.'' *Return the 10 beans to Can 5.* Go to the can that contains the same frequency of red beans as was contained in the ones you drew. For example, if you drew 4 red and 6 white beans, go to Can 4. Draw 10 beans from the new can. Record the number of red beans as ''Generation 2 of Population 1.'' *Return the 10 beans to the can from which they were drawn.* Go to the can that contains the same frequency of red beans as was contained in the ones you drew. Draw 10 beans from that can. Continue in this way until the 10 beans drawn are all reds or all whites. Then finish the generations in the column with 10, if your last draw was all red beans, or with 0, if your last draw was all white beans.

Repeat the procedure for Population 2, Population 3, and so on, until you have completed data for all 15 populations.

STUDYING THE DATA

Look across the 1st line in your data chart. • What number is most frequent?(1)   • What number is least frequent?(2)   Look across the 5th line in your data chart.   • What number is most frequent?(3)   • What number is least frequent?(4)   Look across the 10th line in your data chart.   • What number is most frequent? (5)   • Least frequent?(6)   Look across the

15th line in your data chart.   • What number is most frequent?(7)   • Least frequent?(8)

CONCLUSIONS

Now consider what the beans of the model represent (Introduction).   • What was the number of genes in each generation?(9) • What was the size of each generation?(10) • Would you consider this to represent a large or small population?(11)   • In general, what does your model show about the effect of such a population size on alleles of a gene that may exist in some starting population?(12)   • What is this effect called (Chapter 19)?(13)

Part B

MATERIALS AND EQUIPMENT

(per team)

can
beans, red, 50
beans, white, 50
graph paper, 1 sheet per student

PROCEDURE

For recording your results, list numbers from 1 to 100. Beside each number you will record, in order, the result of each draw up to 100 draws.

Shake the contents of the can thoroughly. Without looking, draw 2 beans from the can. Record the draw as *WW* (white : white); *WR* (white : red); or *RR* (red : red). If the draw is red : red, discard the 2 red beans. If the draw is white : white or white : red, replace the beans in the can. Shake the can.

Continue for 100 draws, discarding or returning the beans after each draw according to the directions in the previous paragraph.

STUDYING THE DATA

On a piece of graph paper place on the horizontal axis numbers representing the draws and on the vertical axis numbers representing the frequencies of beans—50W : 50R; 50W : 48R; 50W : 46R, etc.—from the top downward to 50W : 0R. Plot the frequencies of beans in the can at the end of each draw.   • Describe the shape of the resulting line graph.(1)   • At what stage of drawing is the rate of decline of red-bean frequency greatest?(2)   • How can you explain the change in rate of decline of red-bean frequency?(3)

CONCLUSIONS

• What process among genes does discarding the pairs of red beans represent?(4)

Assume that a red bean represents an allele that, when heterozygous, has no effect but, when homozygous, results in failure of a zygote to develop. Further assume that there are no mutations of that allele.   • Predict the change in frequency of that gene over many generations.(5)

Taxonomic Alternatives

Figure A • 10

A two-kingdom system of classification.

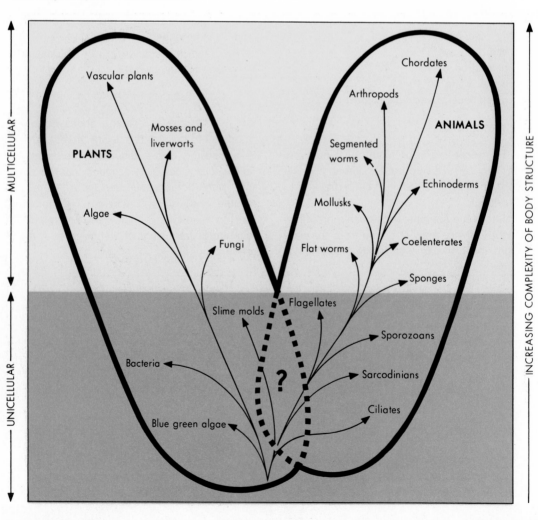

Out of the discussion of taxonomy in Section Two came two ideas that are developed somewhat further here. One is that systems of biological classification represent compromises between convenience and the attempt to show kinship relationships. The other is that such systems are subject to modification as new knowledge is discovered and as better insights into existing knowledge are obtained.

Until the middle of the 19th century, biologists found adequate a classification system that divided the living world into two kingdoms, plant and animal. Then improvements in microscopes and in methods used to prepare small organisms for study revealed that many species have both plant and animal characteristics. As a result, a modification of the two-kingdom system established an area of overlap between the kingdoms, as indicated by the question mark in Figure A · 10.

During the last third of the 19th century, information about these in-between organisms increased rapidly—partly because of man's desire to understand and control infectious diseases. Placement of these organisms in a third kingdom, the Protista, was recognized by some, but by no means all, taxonomists in the first part of the 20th century. This three-kingdom system (Figure A · 11) is the one used in this text.

Figure A · 11

A three-kingdom system of classification.

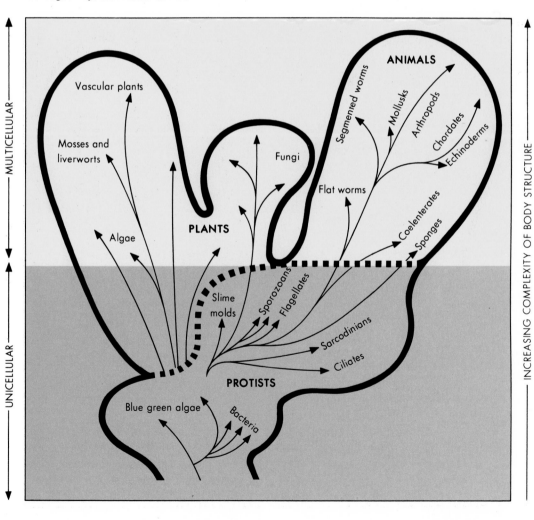

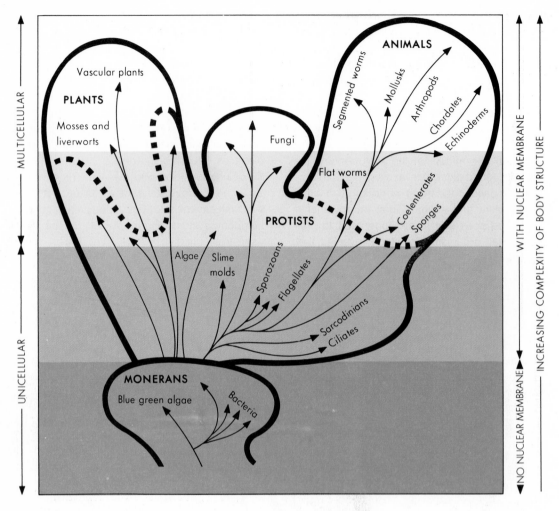

Figure 4 · 12
A four-kingdom system of classification.

Within the past 25 years, extensive use of electron microscopes plus increasingly refined methods of biochemical analysis have resulted in information that has led some taxonomists to recognize a fourth kingdom. They place in the Kingdom Monera (Figure A · 12) unicellular organisms that lack many structures—nuclear membranes, mitochondria, endoplasmic reticula, for example. These structures are present in organisms in all other kingdoms.

More recently, many distinctive features of fungi, both structural and functional, have so impressed a few taxonomists that they have proposed that a fifth kingdom (Figure A · 13) be established for this group.

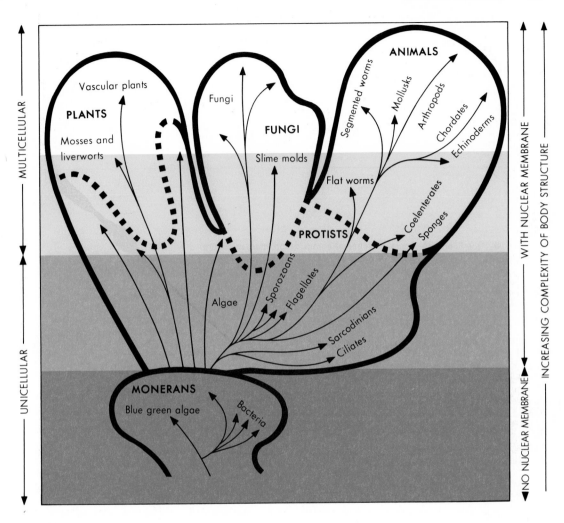

Figure A · 13

A five-kingdom system of classification.

Index

An asterisk (*) indicates an illustration (chart, diagram, graph, map, or picture). **Boldface** numbers indicate pages carrying explanations of terms.